Dairy processing

Related titles from Woodhead's food science, technology and nutrition list:

Functional dairy products (ISBN: 1 85573 584 9)
Dairy products constitute one of the most important types of functional food. Edited by two of the leading authorities in this area, this major collection first reviews how functional dairy products help to prevent such chronic diseases as cancer, osteoporosis and cardiovascular disease. Part II considers product development and such issues as clinical trials and safety evaluation. Part III reviews particular types of product from oligosaccharides to lactic acid bacteria.

Texture in food, Volume 1: Semi-solid foods (ISBN: 1 85573 673 X)
Understanding and controlling the texture of semi-solid foods such as yoghurt and ice cream is a complex process. With a distinguished international team of contributors, this important collection summarises some of the most significant research in this area. The first part of the book looks at the behaviour of gels and emulsions, how they can be measured and their textural properties improved. The second part of the collection discusses the control of texture in particular foods such as yoghurt, ice cream, soups, spreads and sauces.

Taints and off-flavours in foods (ISBN: 1 85573 449 4)
Taints and off-flavours are a major problem for the food industry. Part 1 of this important collection reviews the major causes of taints and off-flavours, from oxidative rancidity and microbiologically derived off-flavours, to packaging materials as a source of taints. The second part of the book discusses the range of techniques for detecting taints and off-flavours, from sensory analysis to instrumental techniques, including the development of new rapid, on-line sensors.

Details of these books and a complete list of Woodhead's food science, technology and nutrition titles can be obtained by:

- visiting our website at www.woodhead-publishing.com
- contacting Customer Services (e-mail: sales@woodhead-publishing.com; fax: +44 (0) 1223 893694; tel: +44 (0) 1223 891358, ext. 30; address: Woodhead Publishing Limited, Abington Hall, Abington, Cambridge CB1 6AH, England)

If you would like to receive information on forthcoming titles in this area, please send your address details to: Francis Dodds (address, telephone and fax as above; e-mail: francisd@woodhead-publishing.com). Please confirm which subject areas you are interested in.

Dairy processing

Improving quality

Edited by
Gerrit Smit

CRC Press
Boca Raton Boston New York Washington, DC

WOODHEAD PUBLISHING LIMITED
Cambridge England

Published by Woodhead Publishing Limited
Abington Hall, Abington
Cambridge CB1 6AH
England
www.woodhead-publishing.com

Published in North America by CRC Press LLC
2000 Corporate Blvd, NW
Boca Raton FL 33431
USA

First published 2003, Woodhead Publishing Limited and CRC Press LLC
© 2003, Woodhead Publishing Limited
Reprinted 2005
The authors have asserted their moral rights.

British Library Cataloguing in Publication Data
A catalogue record for this book is available from the British Library.

Library of Congress Cataloging in Publication Data
A catalog record for this book is available from the Library of Congress.

Woodhead Publishing Limited ISBN 1 85573 676 4 (book); 1 85573 707 8 (e-book)
CRC Press ISBN 0-8493-1758-4

Cover design by The ColourStudio
Project managed by Macfarlane Production Services, Markyate, Hertfordshire
(e-mail: macfarl@aol.com)
Typeset by MHL Typesetting Limited, Coventry, Warwickshire
Printed and bound by Replika Press Pvt. Ltd., India

Contents

Contributor contact details

Chapter 1

Professor Gerrit Smit
Manager of the Department of
  Flavour, Nutrition and Ingredients
NIZO Food Research
Kernhemseweg 2
PO Box 20
6710 BA Ede
The Netherlands

Tel: +31 (0) 318 659511
Fax: +31 (0) 318 650400
Direct call: +31 (0) 318 659538
E-mail: gerrit.smit@nizo.nl

Chapter 2

Professor P. F. Fox
Department of Food and Nutritional
  Sciences
University College
Cork
Ireland

Tel: +353 21 490 2362
Fax: +353 21 427 0001
E-mail: PFF@ucc.ie

Chapter 3

Dr Mike Boland
Executive Manager Science
Fonterra Research Centre
Palmerston North
New Zealand

Tel: +64 (0) 6 350 4664
Fax: +64 (0) 6 350 6320
Mobile: +64 21338049
E-mail: mike.boland@fonterra.com

Chapter 4

Dr ir Meike C. te Giffel
Department of Processing, Quality
  and Safety
NIZO Food Research
Kernhemseweg 2

6710 BA Ede
The Netherlands

Tel: +31 (0) 318 659511
Fax: +31 (0) 318 650400
Direct call: +31 (0) 318 659590
E-mail: meike.te.giffel@nizo.nl
http://www.nizo.com

Chapter 5

Dr Mike Lewis
Department of Food Science and
    Technology
The University of Reading
PO Box 226
Reading
RG6 6AP
UK

Tel: +44 (0) 1734 318700
Fax: +44 (0) 1734 310080
E-mail: m.j.lewis@reading.ac.uk
http://www.fst.rdg.ac.uk

Chapter 6

Dr R. C. McKellar
Food Research Program
Agriculture and Agri-Food Canada
93 Stone Road West
Guelph
Ontario N1G 5C9
Canada

E-mail: mckellarr@agr.gc.ca

Chapter 7

Dr A. E. M. Boelrijk
Department of Flavour, Nutrition and
    Ingredients
NIZO Food Research
Kernhemseweg 2
PO Box 20
6710 BA Ede
The Netherlands

Tel: +31 (0) 318 659511
Fax: +31 (0) 318 650400
Direct call: +31 (0) 318 659638
E-mail: Alexandra.Boelrijk@nizo.nl
http://www.nizo.com

Chapter 8

Dr D. Jaros and Professor H. Rohm
Institute of Food Technology and
    Bioprocess Engineering
Dresden University of Technology
D-01062 Dresden
Germany

E-mail:
    harald.rohm@mailbox.tu-dresden.de
    doris.jaros@mailbox.tu-dresden.de

Chapter 9

Professor Donald Muir
Hannah Research Institute
Hannah Research Park
Ayr
KA6 5HL
Scotland

Tel: +44 (0) 1292 670170
Fax: +44 (0) 1292 670180
E-mail:
    donald.muir@charisfoods.co.uk

Chapter 10

Professor Franz Ulberth
Department of Dairy Research and
   Bacteriology
University of Agricultural Sciences
Gregor Mendel Str. 33
A-1180 Vienna
Austria

E-mail: fulberth@edu1.boku.ac.at

Chapter 11

Dr Maija Saxelin
Valio Ltd
Meijerite 4 A
PO Box 30
00039 Helsinki
Finland

E-mail: maija.saxelin@valio.fi

Chapter 12

Dr J. Snel
Department of Flavour, Nutrition and
   Ingredients
NIZO Food Research
Kernhemseweg 2
PO Box 20
6710 BA Ede
The Netherlands

Tel: +31 (0) 318 659511
Fax: +31 (0) 318 650400
Direct call: +31 (0) 318 659549
E-mail: hans.snel@nizo.nl

Chapter 13

Dr Geert Ellen
NIZO Food Research
Kernhemseweg 2
PO Box 20
6710 BA Ede
The Netherlands

Tel: +31 (0) 318 659511
Fax: +31 (0) 318 650400
E-mail: Geert.Ellen@nizo.nl

Chapter 14

Dr Aziz Amine
Faculté de Sciences et Techniques
Université Hassan II-Mohammedia
20650 Mohammedia
Morocco

Tel: +212.23.314705; /315352/
   314708
Fax: +212.23.315353
E-mail: aziz-amine@uh2m.ac.ma

Dr Laura Micheli, Dr Danila Moscone
   and Professor Giuseppe Palleschi
Dipartmente di Scienze e Tecnologie
   Chimiche
Università di Roma 'Tor Vergata'
Via della Ricerca Scientifica
Rome
Italy

Tel: +39 06 7259 4423
Fax: +39 06 7259 4328
E-mail:
   Giuseppe.Palleschi@uniroma2.it

Chapter 15

Dr J. Van Camp
Department of Food Technology and
    Nutrition
Faculty of Agricultural and Applied
    Biological Sciences
Ghent University
Coupure Links 653
B-9000 Ghent
Belgium

Tel: +32 9 2646208
Fax: +32 9 2646218
E-mail: John.Vancamp@UGent.ac.be

Chapter 16

Ir R.E.M. Verdurmen
Department of Processing, Quality
    and Safety
NIZO Food Research
Kernhemseweg 2
PO Box 20
6710 BA Ede
The Netherlands

Tel: +31 (0) 318 659511
Fax: +31 (0) 318 650400
Direct call: +31 (0) 318 659563
E-mail: Ruud.Verdurmen@nizo.nl

Chapter 17

Ir Gerrald Bargeman
NIZO Food Research
Kernhemseweg 2
PO Box 20
6710 BA Ede
The Netherlands

Tel: +31 (0) 318 659511
Fax: +31 (0) 318 650400
E-mail:
    gerrald.bargeman@akznobel.com

Chapter 18

C. R. Loss and Dr J. H. Hotchkiss
Department of Food Science
Cornell University
Stocking Hall
Ithaca
NY 14853
USA

Chapter 19

Dr P. L. H. McSweeney
Department of Food and Nutritional
    Sciences
University College
Cork
Ireland

Tel: +353 21 490 2011 (direct line)
Fax: +353 21 427 0001
E-mail: p.mcsweeney@ucc.ie
http://cheese.ucc.ie

Mr V. K. Upadhyay
Department of Food and Nutritional
    Sciences
University College
Cork
Ireland

Chapter 20

Dr Tom Beresford
Dairy Products Research Centre
Moorepark
Fermoy
Co Cork
Ireland

Tel: +353 025 42222
Fax: +353 025 42340
E-mail:
    tberesford@moorepark.teagasc.ie

Chapter 21

Dr W. Bockelmann
Institut für Mikrobiologie
Bundesanstalt für Milchforschung
Postfach 6069
D-24121 Kiel
Germany

Tel: +49 (0) 431 609 2438
Fax: +49 (0) 431 609 2306
E-mail: bockelmann@bafm.de

Chapter 22

Dr W. J. M. Engels
Department of Flavour, Nutrition and
    Ingredients
NIZO Food Research
Kernhemseweg 2

PO Box 20
6710 BA Ede
The Netherlands

Tel: +31 (0) 318 659511
Fax: +31 (0) 318 650400
Direct call: +31 (0) 318 659532
E-mail: wim.engels@nizo.nl
http://www.nizo.com

Chapter 23

D. Givens and K. Shingfield
The University of Reading
Reading RG6 6AR
UK

E-mail: d.i.givens@reading.ac.uk

1

Introduction

G. Smit, NIZO Food Research, The Netherlands

Milk and the range of dairy products derived from milk have long been central to diet in both developed and developing countries. Some dairy processing technologies such as fermentation have been used for thousands of years. Building on this long lasting foundation, the dairy processing industry continues to be at the forefront of innovation in the food industry. This important new collection sums up some of the most important recent developments.

Part I considers key aspects of safety and quality. Chapter 2 provides a foundation by summarising current knowledge about the major constituents of milk. The following chapter discusses how factors such as breed and husbandry practices on the farm influence milk composition. The next three chapters focus on safety, covering hygienic practices on the farm, developments in pasteurisation and sterilisation technologies, and the growing use of modelling to improve these techniques whilst retaining milk quality. A final group of chapters in Part I consider key aspects of dairy product quality. There are discussions of the latest research on the control of flavour in milk and other dairy products, improving texture in fermented dairy products, controlling stability and shelf-life, and testing the authenticity of milk and milk products. Building on the traditional nutritional importance of milk, the final two chapters consider the new generation of functional dairy products.

The second part of the book reviews the range of new technologies that have emerged recently to improve dairy product quality. The first two chapters look at on-line techniques to monitor and control various aspects of milk safety and quality. They are then followed by chapters on extending the shelf-life of dairy products through such techniques as high pressure processing, the production of powdered dairy products and the use of carbon dioxide. There is also a chapter on developments in separation techniques to maximise returns by producing a wide range of dairy ingredients. The final part of the book considers key developments in improving flavour and other qualities in cheese manufacture.

The quality of dairy products, e.g. taste, texture, health and safety, as perceived by the consumer should be the prime and ultimate driver for the dairy industry. The new developments described in this book will certainly add to their achievement.

Part I

Dairy product safety and quality

2

The major constituents of milk

P. F. Fox, University College Cork, Ireland

2.1 Introduction

Milk and dairy products are major components of the human diet in Western countries, providing about 30% of dietary proteins and lipids and about 80% of dietary calcium. Current annual production of milk is $\approx 600 \times 10^6$ tonnes, of which $\approx$85%, 11%, 2% and 2% are bovine, buffalo, caprine and ovine, respectively. Although some raw milk is still consumed, the vast majority of milk is processed to at least some extent. Liquid (beverage) milk is a major food item in all developed dairying countries, representing $\approx$40% of total milk production. The remainder is processed into one of several thousand products – the dairy industry is probably the most diverse and flexible sector of the food industry. The flexibility of milk as a raw material resides in the chemical and physico-chemical properties of its constituents, many of which are unique. The principal constituents of milk can be modified by enzymatic, chemical and/or physical methods, permitting the production of new products. However, the concentrations and properties of milk constituents are variable and hence the processability of milk and the properties of dairy products are inconsistent, although much of this variability can be eliminated by modern technology, which exploits certain features of milk constituents. Today, most milk is processed in large, highly mechanized and automated factories, where consistency in processing properties is essential. The resulting products are distributed through large wholesale and retail outlets, where consistency is, again, paramount. Consumers expect consistency also. The consistency expected by the processor, distributor and consumer can be achieved only if the properties of milk constituents are understood at the molecular level. This chapter will describe the principal chemical and physico-chemical properties of the major constituents of milk, i.e., lactose, lipids, proteins and salts, and variations in the concentrations and properties of these constituents.

The natural function of milk is to supply the neonatal mammal, of which there are ≈4500 species, with its complete nutritional and some of its physiological requirements. Because the nutritional requirements are species-specific and change as the neonate matures, the composition of milk shows very large inter-species differences, e.g., the concentrations of fat, protein and lactose range from 1 to 50%, 1 to 20% and 0 to 10%, respectively, and the concentration of each changes during lactation. Inter-species differences in the concentrations of many of the minor constituents are even greater than those of the macro-constituents.

Milk from domesticated animals has been used by humans since at least 8000 BC. Although sheep and goats were the first domesticated dairy animals, because they are more easily managed than cattle, the latter, especially certain breeds of *Bos taurus*, are now the dominant dairy animals. Total recorded world milk production is $\approx 600 \times 10^6$ tonnes per annum, of which ≈85% is bovine, 11% is buffalo and 2% each is from sheep and goats. Small amounts of milk are produced from camels, mares, reindeer and yaks in certain regions with specific cultural and/or climatic conditions. This chapter will concentrate on the constituents and properties of bovine milk. Although the constituents of the milk of the other main dairy species are generally similar to those of bovine milk, they differ in detail and the technological properties of the milk of these species differ significantly.

Milk is a very flexible raw material from which several thousand types of dairy products are produced around the world in a great diversity of flavours and forms, including ≈1000 varieties of cheese. The proportions of total world milk production used for the principal dairy products are: liquid (beverage) milk, ≈39%; cheese, ≈33%; butter, ≈32%; whole milk powder, ≈6%; skimmed milk powder, ≈9%; concentrated milk products, ≈2%; fermented milk products, ≈2%; casein, ≈2%; and infant formulae, ≈0.3%. (The sum value exceeds 100%; this is due to 'double accounting', e.g., butter and skim milk powder, and the standardization of fat content, e.g., for liquid milk, cheese, etc.) This flexibility and diversity are a result of the properties, many of them unique, of the constituents of milk, the principal of which are easily isolated from milk, permitting the production of valuable food ingredients. Milk is free of off-flavours, pigments and toxins, which is a very important feature of milk as a raw material for food ingredients.

The processability and functionality of milk and milk products are determined by the properties and concentrations of its principal constituents: proteins, lipids, lactose and salts. Many of the principal problems encountered during the processing of milk are caused by variability in the concentrations and properties of these constituents arising from several factors, including breed, individuality of the animal, stage of lactation, health of the animal, especially mastitis, and nutritional status. Synchronized calving, as practised in New Zealand, Australia and Ireland to avail of cheap grass, has a very marked effect on the composition and properties of milk (see O'Brien *et al.*, 1999a, 1999b,

1999c; Mehra *et al.*, 1999). Much of the variability can be offset by standardizing the composition of milk or by modifying the process technology. Genetic polymorphism of milk proteins has a significant effect on the concentration and type of protein in milk. The chemical and physical properties of the principal constituents of milk are well characterized and described, including in the following textbooks: Walstra and Jenness (1984), Wong (1988), Fox (1992, 1995, 1997), Jensen (1995), Fox and McSweeney (1998, 2003) and Walstra *et al.* (1998).

2.2 Lactose

Bovine milk contains about 4.8% lactose. Because lactose is responsible for ~50% of the osmotic pressure of milk, which is equal to that of blood and is nearly constant, the concentration of lactose in milk is independent of breed, individuality and nutritional factors but decreases as lactation advances and especially during mastitic infection, in both cases due to the influx of NaCl from the blood.

Chemical and physico-chemical properties of lactose
Lactose is a reducing disaccharide comprised of glucose and galactose, linked by a β1-4-O-glycosidic bond. Among sugars, lactose has a number of distinctive characteristics, some of which cause problems in milk products during processing and storage; however, some of its characteristics are exploited to advantage.

- The aldehyde group on the C-1 of the glucose moiety exists mainly in the hemiacetal form and, consequently, C-1 is a chiral, asymmetric carbon. Therefore, like all reducing sugars, lactose exists as two anomers, α and β, which have markedly different properties. From a functional viewpoint, the most important of these are differences in solubility and crystallization characteristics: α-lactose crystallizes as a monohydrate while crystals of β-lactose are anhydrous.
- The solubility of α- and β-lactose in water at 20°C is ≈7 g and ≈50 g per 100 ml, respectively. The solubility of α-lactose is much more temperature dependent than that of β-lactose and the solubility curves intersect at ≈93.5°C.
- At equilibrium in aqueous solution, lactose exists as a mixture of α and β anomers in the approximate ratio 37:63. When an excess of α-lactose is added to water, ≈7 g per 100 ml dissolve immediately, some of which mutarotates to give an α:β ratio of 37:63, leaving the solution unsaturated with respect to both α- and β-lactose. Further α-lactose dissolves, some of which mutarotates to β-lactose. Solubilization and mutarotation continue until two conditions exist, i.e., ≈7 g of dissolved α-lactose per 100 ml and an α:β ratio of 37:63, giving a final solubility of ≈18.2 g per 100 ml.

- When β-lactose is added to water, $\approx$50 g per 100 ml dissolve initially but $\approx$18.5 g of this mutarotate to α-lactose, which exceeds its solubility and therefore some α-lactose crystallizes. This upsets the α:β ratio and more β-lactose mutarotates to α-lactose, which crystallizes. Mutarotation of β-lactose and crystallization of α-lactose continue until $\approx$7 g and $\approx$11.2 g of α- and β-lactose, respectively, are in solution.

- Although lactose has low solubility in comparison with other sugars, once dissolved, it crystallizes with difficulty and forms a supersaturated solution. α-Lactose crystallizes spontaneously from highly supersaturated solutions, but if the solution is only slightly supersaturated, it crysallizes slowly as sharp, tomahawk-shaped crystals. If the dimensions of the crystals exceed $\approx$15 μm, they are detectable on the tongue and palate. Crystals of β-lactose are smaller and monoclinical in shape. In the metastable zone, crystallization of lactose is induced by seeding with finely powdered lactose.

- Since α-lactose is less soluble than the β anomer below 93.5°C, it is the normal commercial form.

- When concentrated milk is spray-dried, there is not sufficient time for lactose to crystallize and an amorphous glass is formed. If the moisture content of the powder is kept low, the lactose glass is stable, but if the moisture content increases to about 6%, e.g., on exposure of the powder to a high humidity atmosphere, the lactose will crystallize as α-lactose monohydrate. If extensive crystallization occurs, an interlocking mass of crystals is formed, resulting in 'caking', which is a particularly serious problem in whey powders owing to their high content of lactose ($\approx$70%). The problem is avoided by extensive crystallization of lactose before drying, induced by seeding the solution with finely powdered lactose.

- Spray-dried milk powder has poor wettability because the small particles swell on contact with water, blocking the channels between particles. The wettability (often incorrectly referred to as 'solubility') of spray-dried milk powder may be improved by modifying the drying process to produce milk powder with coarser, more easily wetted particles. This is achieved by agglomerating the fine powder particles, in effect by controlling lactose-induced caking; such powders are said to be 'instantized'.

- The crystallization of lactose in frozen milk products results in destabilization of the casein, which aggregates when the product is thawed. In this case, the effect of lactose is indirect. When milk is frozen, pure water freezes and the concentration of solutes in the unfrozen water is increased. Since milk is supersaturated with respect to calcium phosphate ($\approx$66% and $\approx$57% of the Ca and PO_4, respectively, are insoluble and occur in the casein micelles as colloidal calcium phosphate; see Section 2.6), when the amount of water becomes limiting, soluble $Ca(H_2PO_4)_2$ and $CaHPO_4$ crystallize as $(Ca)_3(PO_4)_2$, with the concomitant release of H^+ and a decrease in pH to $\approx$5.8. Unless the temperature is maintained below -30°C, lactose will crystallize as α monohydrate during frozen storage, thus reducing the amount of solvent water and aggravating the problems of calcium phosphate solubility and pH decline. Thorough crystallization of lactose before freezing alleviates, but does not eliminate, the problem. Pre-heating milk prior to freezing also alleviates the problem, but pre-hydrolysis of lactose to the more soluble glucose and galactose using β-galactosidase appears to be the best solution.

- Although lactose is hygroscopic when it crystallizes, properly crystallized lactose has very low hygroscopicity and, consequently, it is a very useful component of icing sugar.
- Lactose has low sweetness (16% as sweet as sucrose as a 1% solution). This limits its usefulness as a sweetener (the principal function of sugars in foods) but makes it is a very useful diluent, e.g., for food colours, flavours, enzymes, etc., when concomitant sweetness is undesirable.
- Being a reducing sugar, lactose can participitate in the Maillard reaction, with very undesirable consequences in all dairy products, e.g., brown colour, off-flavours, reduced solubility and reduced nutritional value.

Food applications of lactose

The amount of whey produced annually as a by-product of the manufacture of cheese and casein contains $\approx 8 \times 10^6$ tonnes of lactose. About 400 000 tonnes of lactose are produced per annum. In addition, $\approx 2\,000\,000$ tonnes of whey permeate powder, which serves as a source of lactose for certain applications, e.g., infant formulae, are produced annually.

Owing to many of its properties, especially low sweetness, the market for lactose is limited; it is, therefore, often regarded as a waste product and in the past caused disposal problems. However, some of the properties of lactose make it a valuable ingredient for pharmaceutical and food applications. Lactose is most valuable when used in the pharmaceutical industry where it is widely used as a diluent in pelleting operations.

The principal application of lactose in the food industry is in the humanization of infant formulae – human milk contains $\approx 7\%$ lactose in comparison with $\approx 4.8\%$ in bovine milk. Demineralized whey powder (DWP) is very suitable for this purpose – it is cheaper than lactose and in addition to supplying lactose, DWP supplies whey proteins and adjusts the casein:whey protein ratio to a value closer to that in bovine milk (40:60 compared to 80:20 in bovine milk). It is necessary to demineralize bovine whey since it contains approximately four times as much minerals as human milk.

Lactose is also used as an agglomerating/free-flowing agent in foods, in the confectionery industry to improve the functionality of shortenings, as an anti-caking agent at high relative humidity, in icing mixtures or as a reducing sugar if Maillard browning is required. The low sweetness of lactose is an advantage in many of these applications. Lactose absorbs compounds and may be used as a diluent for food flavours or pigments or to trap food flavours.

Lactose derivatives

A number of more useful and more valuable products may be produced from lactose. The most significant are:

- Lactulose (galactose β1-4 fructose): this sugar, which does not occur in nature, is produced from lactose by heating, especially under slightly alkaline conditions. It is not hydrolysed by intestinal β-galactosidase and enters the large intestine where it promotes the growth of *Bifidobacterium* spp. It is a mild laxative and is used fairly widely for this purpose. More than 20 000 tonnes are produced annually.
- Glucose–galactose syrups, produced by acid or enzymatic (β-galactosidase) hydrolysis: the technology for the production of such hydrolysates has been developed but the product is not cost-competitive with other sugars (sucrose, glucose, glucose–fructose).
- Galactooligosaccharides: β-galactosidase has transferase as well as hydrolytic activity and under certain conditions, the former predominates, leading to the formation of galactooligosaccharides, which have bifidogenic properties and are considered to have promising food applications.
- Ethanol is produced commercially by the fermentation of lactose by *Kluyveromyces lactis*.
- Other derivatives which have limited but potentially important applications include lactitol, lactobionic acid, lactic acid, acetic acid, propionic acid, lactosyl urea and single-cell proteins.

Nutritional aspects of lactose

Lactose is involved in two enzyme-deficiency syndromes: lactose intolerance and galactosemia. The former is due to a deficiency of intestinal β-galactosidase which is rare in infants but common in adults except north-west Europeans and a few African tribes. Since humans are unable to absorb disaccharides from the small intestine, unhydrolysed lactose enters the large intestine where it is fermented by bacteria, leading to flatulence and cramp, and to the absorption of water from the intestinal mucosa, causing diarrhoea. These conditions cause discomfort and may be fatal. Individuals suffering from lactose intolerance avoid the consumption of milk and lactose-containing dairy products. Hydrolysis of lactose by β-galactosidase renders such products suitable for lactose-intolerant individuals. Hydrolysis may be performed at the dairy using soluble or immobilized β-galactosidase or by the consumer at home. Lactose-hydrolysed products enjoy limited commercial success in western countries but have not resulted in a substantial increase in the consumption of dairy products in Asia, which is a very large potential market for dairy products but where lactose intolerance is very widespread.

Galactosemia is caused by the inability to catabolize galactose owing to a deficiency of either of two enzymes, galactokinase or galactose-1P:uridyl transferase. A deficiency of galactokinase leads to the accumulation of galactose which is catabolized via alternative routes, one of which leads to the accumulation of galactitol in various tissues, including the eye, where it causes cataract. A deficiency of galactose-1P:uridyl transferase leads to abnormalities in membranes of the brain and to mental retardation unless galactose is excluded from the diet within a few weeks *post partum*. Both forms of galactosemia occur at a frequency of 1 per $\approx$50 000 births.

Lactose in fermented dairy products

The fermentation of lactose to lactic acid by lactic acid bacteria (LAB) is a critical step in the manufacture of all fermented dairy products. The fermentation pathways are well established (see Cogan and Hill, 1993). Lactose is not a limiting factor in the manufacture of fermented dairy products – only ≈20% of the lactose is fermented in the production of fermented milks. Individuals suffering from lactose intolerance may be able to consume fermented milk products without ill-effects, possibly because LAB produce β-galactosidase and emptying of the stomach is slower than for fresh milk products, thus delaying the release of lactose into the small intestine.

In the manufacture of cheese, most (96–98%) of the lactose is removed in the whey. The concentration of lactose in fresh curd depends on its concentration in the milk and on the moisture content of the curd and varies from ≈1%, w/w, in fresh Cheddar curd to ≈2.5%, w/w, in fresh Camembert. The metabolism of residual lactose in the curd to lactic acid has a major effect on the quality of mature cheese (see Fox *et al.*, 1990, 2002). The resultant lactic acid may be catabolized to other compounds, e.g., carbon dioxide and water by the surface mould in Camembert, or to propionic acid, acetic acid and carbon dioxide in Emmental-type cheeses. Excessive lactic acid in cheese curd leads to a low pH, a strong, acidic, harsh taste, and a brittle texture. In Cheddar and related varieties, the L-lactic acid produced by the starter bacteria is racemized to DL-lactic acid; Ca-D-lactate is less soluble than Ca-L-lactate and if its concentration is too high, it will crystallize on the surface of the cheese, giving it an undesirable appearance. Excess residual lactose may also be fermented by heterofermentative lactobacilli, with the production of carbon dioxide, leading to an open texture.

In the manufacture of some cheese varieties, e.g., Dutch cheeses, the curds are washed to reduce their lactose content and thereby regulate the pH of the pressed curd to ≈5.3. In most other varieties, e.g., Cheddar and Emmental, the level of lactose, and hence of lactic acid, in the curd is not controlled by washing. Hence, changes in the concentration of lactose in milk may affect the quality of such cheeses. The concentration of lactose in milk decreases throughout lactation, e.g., from ≈4.8% to <4.0%. When synchronized calving is practised, there is a marked seasonal change in the lactose content of milk and hence of cheese, which may have a significant effect on quality. To overcome seasonal variations in the lactose content of milk, the level of wash water used for Dutch-type cheeses is varied according to the concentrations of lactose and casein in the milk. Ideally, the lactose-to-protein ratio should be standardized, e.g., by washing the curds, to minimize variations in the level of lactic acid, the pH and the quality of cheese.

The curds for acid-curd cheeses are washed free of lactose to improve their keeping quality. Thus, acid-coagulated and mature rennet-coagulated cheeses may be consumed by lactose-intolerant individuals without ill-effects.

2.3   Lipids

Definition and variability

Lipids are defined as those compounds in foods and tissues that are soluble in apolar solvents (ethyl/petroleum ether or chloroform/methanol). The lipid fraction of milk is comprised mainly of triglycerides (98%), with ≈1% phospholipids and small amounts of diglycerides, monoglycerides, cholesterol, cholesteryl esters and traces of fat-soluble vitamins and other lipids. The lipids occur as globules, $0.1–20\,\mu\mathrm{m}$ in diameter, surrounded by the milk fat globule membrane (MFGM), which serves as an emulsifier. The concentration of lipids varies with species, breed, individual animal, stage of lactation, mastitic infection, plane of nutrition, interval between milkings, and point during milking when the sample is taken. Among the principal dairy breeds, Friesian/Holsteins produce milk with the lowest fat content (≈3.5%) and Jersey/Guernsey the highest (≈6%). The fat content varies considerably throughout lactation; when synchronized calving is practised, the fat content of bulk milk varies from ≈3% in early lactation to >4.5% in late lactation. Such large variations in lipid content obviously affect the economics of milk production and the composition of milk products but can be modified readily by natural creaming or centrifugal separation or addition of cream and hence need not affect product quality. Milk lipids exhibit variability in fatty acid composition and in the size and stability of the globules. These variations, especially of the fatty acid profile, are essentially impossible to standardize and hence are responsible for considerable variations in the rheological properties, colour, chemical stability and nutritional properties of fat-containing dairy products.

Fatty acid profile

Ruminant milk fat contains a wider range of fatty acids than any other lipid system – up to 400 fatty acids have been reported in bovine milk fat; the principal fatty acids are the homologous series of saturated fatty acids, $C_{4:0}$–$C_{18:0}$ and $C_{18:1}$ (see Fox, 1995). The outstanding features of the fatty acids in bovine milk fat are a high concentration of short and medium chain acids (ruminant milk fats are the only natural lipids that contain butanoic acid) and a low concentration of polyunsaturated fatty acids (PUFA).

In ruminants, the fatty acids for the synthesis of milk lipids are obtained from triglycerides in chylomicrons in the blood or synthesized *de novo* in the mammary gland from acetate or β-hydroxybutyrate produced by microorganisms in the rumen. The triglycerides in chylomicrons are derived from the animal's feed or synthesized in the liver. Butanoic acid ($C_{4:0}$) is produced by the reduction of β-hydroxybutyrate which is synthesized from dietary roughage by bacteria in the rumen and therefore varies substantially with the animal's diet. All $C_{6:0}$–$C_{14:0}$ and 50% of $C_{16:0}$ are synthesized in the mammary gland via the malonyl-CoA pathway from acetyl-CoA produced from acetate synthesized in the rumen. Essentially 100% of $C_{18:0}$, $C_{18:1}$, $C_{18:2}$ and $C_{18:3}$ and 50% of $C_{16:0}$ are derived from blood lipids (chylomicrons) and represent ≈50% of total fatty acids in ruminant milk fat. Unsaturated fatty acids in the animal's diet are hydrogenated by bacteria in the rumen unless they are protected, e.g., by encapsulation.

When milk production is seasonal, e.g., in Australia, New Zealand and Ireland, very significant changes occur in the fatty acid profile of milk fat throughout the production season (see Fox, 1995; Fox and McSweeney, 1998). These variations are reflected in the hardness of butter produced from such milk; winter butter is much harder than summer butter. Owing to the lower degree of unsaturation, winter butter should be less susceptible to lipid oxidation than the more unsaturated summer product but the reverse appears to be the case, probably owing to higher levels of pro-oxidants, e.g., Cu and Fe, in winter milk.

Although a ruminant's diet, especially if grass-based, is rich in PUFAs, these are hydrogenated by bacteria in the rumen and, consequently, ruminant milk fat contains very low levels of PUFAs, e.g., bovine milk fat contains $\approx2.4\%$ $C_{18:2}$ compared to $\approx13\%$ and $\approx12\%$ in human and porcine milk fat, respectively. PUFAs are considered to be nutritionally desirable and consequently there has been interest in increasing their concentration in bovine milk fat. This can be done by feeding encapsulated PUFA-rich lipids or crushed PUFA-rich oil seeds to the animal. Increasing the PUFA content also reduces the melting point of the fat and makes butter produced from it more spreadable. However, the lower MP fat may have undesirable effects on the rheological properties of cheese, and PUFA-rich dairy products are very susceptible to lipid oxidation. Although the technical feasibility of increasing the PUFA content of milk fat by feeding protected PUFA-rich lipids to the cow has been demonstrated, it is not economical to do so in most cases. Blending milk fat with PUFA-rich or $C_{18:1}$-rich vegetable oil appears to be much more viable and is now widely practised commercially.

Conjugated linoleic acid

Linoleic acid (*cis, cis* Δ 9,12-octadecadienoic acid) is the principal essential fatty acid and has attracted the attention of nutritionists for many years. However, conjugated isomers of linoleic acid (CLA) have attracted very considerable attention recently. CLA is a mixture of eight positional and geometric isomers of linoleic acid which have a number of health-promoting properties, including anticarcinogenic and antiatherogenic activities, reduction of the catabolic effects of immune stimulation and the ability to enhance growth promotion and reduce body fat (see Parodi, 1994, 1997a, 1999; Belury, 1995; Banni and Martin, 1998; Yurawecz *et al.*, 1999). Of the eight isomers of CLA, only the *cis* 9, *trans* 11 isomer is biologically active. This compound is effective at very low concentrations, 0.1 g per 100 g diet.

Fat-containing foods of ruminant origin, especially milk and dairy products, are the principal sources of dietary CLA which is produced as an intermediate during the biohydrogenation of linoleic acid by the rumen bacterium, *Butyrivibrio fibrisolvens*. Since CLA is formed from linoleic acid, it is not surprising that the CLA content of milk is affected by diet and season, being highest in summer when cows are on fresh pasture rich in PUFAs (Lock and

Garnsworthy, 2000; Lawless *et al.*, 2000) and higher in the fat of milk from cows on mountain than on lowland pasture (Collomb *et al.*, 2002). The concentration of CLA in milk fat can be increased 5–7 fold by increasing the level of dietary linoleic acid, e.g., by duodenal infusion (Kraft *et al.*, 2000) or by feeding a linoleic acid-rich oil, e.g., sunflower oil (Kelly *et al.*, 1998).

A number of other lipids may have anticarcinogenic activity, e.g., sphingomyelin, butanoic acid and ether lipids, but few data are available on these to date (Parodi, 1997a, 1999).

Rheological properties of milk fat

The melting characteristics of ruminant milk fat are such that at low temperatures (e.g., ex-refrigerator) it contains a high proportion of solid fat and has poor spreadability. The rheological properties of milk lipids may be modified by fractional crystallization. Best results are obtained by removing the middle fraction and blending high and low melting point fractions. Fractional crystallization is expensive and is practised to only a limited extent. Securing profitable outlets for the middle melting point fraction is a further problem.

The rheological properties of milk fat may be modified also by increasing the level of PUFAs by feeding PUFA-rich lipids, but this practice is also expensive. The melting characteristics of blends of milk fat and vegetable oils can be varied at will by changing the proportions of the different fats and oils in the blend. This procedure is economical and is widely practised commercially; blending also increases the level of nutritionally desirable PUFAs. The rheological properties of milk fat-based spreads can also be improved by increasing the moisture content of the product; obviously, this is economical and nutritionally desirable in the sense that the caloric value is reduced but the product is less microbiologically stable than butter.

Size and stability of milk fat globules

The average size of the milk fat globules decreases with advancing lactation. Consequently, the separation of fat from milk is less effective in winter than in summer, especially when milk production is seasonal, and this may mean that it is not possible to meet the upper limit for fat content in some products, e.g., casein, during certain periods.

Since lipids are incompatible with aqueous systems, phase separation will occur unless an emulsifier is used to reduce the interfacial tension. In milk, the emulsifier is a membrane, known as the milk fat globule membrane (MFGM). On the inner side of the MFGM is a layer of unstructured lipoproteins acquired within the secretory cells as the triglycerides move from the site of synthesis in the rough endoplasmic reticulum (RER) in the basal region of the cell towards the apical membrane. The fat globules are excreted from the cells by exocytis, i.c., they are pushed through and become surrounded by the apical membrane. Milk proteins and lactose are excreted from the cell by the reverse process: they also are synthesized in the RER and are transferred to the Golgi region, where they are encapsulated in Golgi membrane; the visicles move towards, and fuse with the apical cell membrane, open and discharge their contents into the alveolar lumen, leaving the visicle (Golgi) membrane as part of the apical membrane, thereby replacing the membrane lost on the excretion of fat globules. Thus, the outer layer of the MFGM is a trilaminar membrane, composed of phospholipids and proteins, with a fluid mosaic structure. The MFGM contains many enzymes which originate mainly from the Golgi apparatus; in fact, most of the indigenous enzymes in milk are concentrated in the MFGM, notable exceptions being plasmin and lipoprotein lipase (LPL), which are associated with the casein micelles. The trilaminar membrane is unstable and is shed during storage into the aqueous phase, where it forms microsomes; it becomes less stable with advancing lactation.

The stability of the MFGM is critical for many aspects of the milk fat system, notably:

- It protects the lipids in the core of the globule against lipolysis by LPL in the skim milk. The MFGM may be damaged by agitation, foaming, freezing and especially by homogenization (during which the natural membrane is replaced by a layer of skim milk proteins, mainly caseins), allowing access for LPL to the core lipids and leading to lipolysis and hydrolytic rancidity which is potentially a major problem in the dairy industry. Milking installations must be properly installed and serviced regularly if damage to the MFGM is to be avoided. Milk should be pasteurized before or immediately after homogenization to inactivate the LPL; in practice, the homogenizer is placed in a loop between the regeneration and final heating sections of an HTST pasteurizer.
- The MFGM is destabilized by freezing, e.g., on bulk tank walls, which may induce lipolysis and related problems.
- The MFGM appears to be less stable in winter/late lactation than in summer/ mid lactation; therefore, hydrolytic rancidity is more likely to be a problem in winter than in summer. An aggravating factor is that less milk is usually produced in winter than in summer, especially in seasonal milk production systems, which leads to greater agitation during milking and, consequently, greater damage to the MFGM.
- Damage to the MFGM leads to the formation of non-globular (free) fat, which may be evident as 'oiling-off' on tea or coffee and cream plug or age thickening of cream. Problems related to or arising from free fat are more serious in winter than in summer, due to the reduced stability of the MFGM. Homogenization, which replaces the natural MFGM by a layer of skim milk proteins, eliminates problems caused by free fat.

Lipid oxidation
The chemical oxidation of lipids, a major cause of instability in dairy products, is a free radical, autocatalytic process, involving principally the methylene group between a pair of double bonds in PUFAs. The process is initiated and/or catalysed by polyvalent metals, especially copper (Cu) and iron (Fe), UV light,

ionizing radiation or enzymes (in the case of milk by xanthine oxidase, which is a major component of the MFGM). Oxygen is a primary reactant. The principal end-products are unsaturated carbonyls, which cause flavour defects. Polymerization of free radicals and other species leads to the formation of pigmented products and an increase in viscosity, but polymerization is unlikely to be significant in dairy products. Lipid oxidation can be prevented or controlled by:

- Avoiding metal contamination at all stages through the use of stainless steel equipment.
- Avoiding exposure to UV light by using opaque packing (foil or paper).
- Packaging under an inert atmosphere, usually nitrogen (N_2).
- Using scavengers of oxygen (O_2) or free radicals, e.g., glucose oxidase or superoxide dismutase (an indigenous enzyme in milk), respectively.
- Using antioxidants which break the free radical chain reaction; addition of antioxidants to dairy products is not permitted but the level of natural antioxidants, e.g., tocopherols (vitamin E), in milk may be increased by supplementing the animal's feed.

Creaming

Since the specific gravity of lipids and skim milk is 0.9 and 1.036, respectively, the fat globules in milk held under quiescent conditions will rise to the surface under the influence of gravity, a process referred to as creaming. The rate of creaming, V, of fat globules is given by Stokes' equation:

$$V = \frac{2r^2(\rho_1 - \rho_2)g}{9\eta}$$

where
- r = radius of the globule
- ρ_1 = specific gravity of skim milk
- ρ_2 = specific gravity of the fat globules
- g = acceleration due to gravity
- η = viscosity of skim milk.

The values of r, ρ_1, ρ_2 and η suggest that a cream layer would form in milk after ≈ 60 h but milk creams in ≈ 30 min. The rapid rate of creaming is due to the strong tendency of the fat globules to cluster due to the effect of indigenous immunoglobulin M which precipitates onto the fat globules when milk is cooled (and, therefore, is called cryoglobulin). Large globules rise faster than smaller ones, collide with them and form aggregates, an effect promoted by cryoglobulins. The clusters of globules rise rapidly and therefore the creaming process is accelerated as the globules rise and clump. Ovine, caprine or buffalo milk does not contain cryoglobulins and therefore creams much more slowly than bovine milk.

In the past, creaming was a very important physico-chemical property of milk:

- The cream layer served as an index of fat content and hence of the quality of milk to the consumer.

- Creaming was the traditional method for preparing cream from milk for the manufacture of butter. Its significance in this respect declined with the development of the mechanical separator in 1878 but natural creaming is still used to adjust the fat content of milk for some cheese varieties, e.g., Parmigiano-Reggiano. A high proportion of the bacteria in milk becomes occluded in the clusters of fat globules and hence creaming has a sanitizing effect.

Homogenization of milk

Today, creaming is of little general significance. In most cases its effect is negative, and for most dairy products, milk is homogenized, i.e., subjected to a high shearing pressure which reduces the size of the fat globules (average diameter <1 μm), increases the fat surface area (4–6 fold), replaces the natural MFGM by a layer of skim milk proteins, denatures cryoglobulins and hence prevents the agglutination and clustering of globules. The valve homogenizer was introduced in France by Gaulin in 1902 and homogenization became widespread after about 1940 (Trout, 1950). Homogenization has several very significant effects on the properties of milk:

- If properly executed, creaming is delayed indefinitely due to the reduced size of the fat globules and the denaturation of cryoglobulins.
- Susceptibility to hydrolytic rancidity is markedly increased because LPL has ready access to the triglycerides; consequently, milk must be heated under conditions sufficiently severe to inactivate LPL before (usually) or immediately after homogenization.
- Susceptibility to oxidative rancidity is reduced because pro-oxidants in the MFGM, e.g., metals and xanthine oxidase, are distributed throughout the milk.
- The whiteness of milk is increased owing to the greater number of light-scattering particles.
- The strength and syneretic properties of renneted-coagulated milk gels for cheese manufacture are reduced; hence, cheese with a higher moisture content is obtained. Milk for cheese manufacture is not normally homogenized; an exception is reduced-fat cheese, in which a higher moisture content improves texture.
- Homogenization reduces the heat stability of whole milk, the effect increasing with fat content and homogenization pressure; homogenization has no effect on the heat stability of skimmed milk.
- The viscosity of whole milk and cream is increased by single-stage homogenization due to the clustering of newly formed fat globules; if desired, the clusters of globules are dispersed by a second homogenization at a lower pressure.

Fat-soluble vitamins

Since the fat-soluble vitamins (A, D, E and K) in milk are derived from the animal's diet, there are large seasonal variations in their concentration in milk;

the breed of cow also has a significant effect: high-fat milk (Jersey and Guernsey) has a higher content of these vitamins than Friesian or Holstein milk (see Fox, 1995). Variations in the concentrations of fat-soluble vitamins in milk have a number of consequences:

- Nutritional: milk contributes a substantial portion of the RDA for these vitamins in Western diets; it is common practice in some countries to fortify milk and butter with vitamins A and D.
- The yellow-orange colour of high-fat dairy products depends on the concentrations of carotenoids and vitamin A, and hence on the animal's diet; fresh, especially clover-rich, pasture is rich in carotenoids.
- Goats, sheep and buffalo do not transfer carotenoids to their milk and products produced therefrom are whiter than corresponding products from bovine milk. The darker colour of the latter may be unattractive to consumers accustomed to caprine or ovine milk products. If necessary, the carotenoids in bovine milk may be bleached (by benzoyl peroxide) or masked (by chlorophyll or TiO_2).
- Vitamin E (tocopherols) is a potent antioxidant and contributes to the oxidative stability of dairy products. The tocopherol content of milk and meat can be increased by supplementing the animal's diet with tocopherols, which is sometimes practised.

2.4   Proteins

Introduction
Technologically, the proteins of milk are its most important constituents (see Fox and McSweeney, 2003, for a comprehensive review of milk proteins). They play important, even essential, roles in all dairy products except butter, ghee and anhydrous milk fat. The roles played by milk proteins include:

- Nutritional: all protein-containing dairy products.
- Physiological: immunoglobulins, lactoferrin, lactoperoxidase, vitamin-binding proteins, protein-derived biologically active peptides.
- Functional:
  - gelation: enzymatically, acid or thermally induced gelation in all cheeses, fermented milks, whey protein concentrates and isolates;
  - heat stability: all thermally processed dairy products;
  - surface activity: caseinates, whey protein concentrates and isolates;
  - rheological: all protein-containing dairy products;
  - water sorption: most dairy products and in food products containing functional milk proteins.

Heterogeneity of milk proteins
It has been known since 1830 that milk contains two types of protein which can be separated by acidification to pH 4.6. The proteins insoluble at pH 4.6 are

called caseins and represent $\approx$78% of the total nitrogen in bovine milk; the soluble proteins are called whey or serum proteins. It was shown as early as 1885 that the whey proteins were of two types, globulins and albumins, and it was thought that these were transferred directly from the blood (the proteins of blood and whey have generally similar physico-chemical properties and are classified as albumins or globulins), but it was recognized at an early stage that the caseins are distinctly different milk-specific proteins. It is now known that the two principal whey proteins, β-lactoglobulin (β-Lg) and α-lactalbumin (α-La), are also milk-specific.

Evidence began to accumulate in the 1920s that the casein, albumin and globulin fractions are heterogeneous and this was confirmed in the 1930s using analytical ultracentrifugation and free-boundary electrophoresis. Methods for the isolation of the individual proteins were developed and gradually improved so that by about 1970, all the principal milk proteins had been purified to homogeneity.

Bovine milk contains six milk-specific proteins: four caseins, α_{s1}-, α_{s2}-, β- and κ-, representing approximately 38%, 10%, 36% and 15%, respectively, of whole casein, and β-Lg and α-La, which represent approximately 40% and 20%, respectively, of total whey proteins. It also contains several minor whey proteins, including bovine serum albumin (BSA) and immunoglobulins (Ig), which are transferred from the blood; each represents about 10% of the whey proteins in mature bovine milk. The remaining 10% is mainly non-protein nitrogen and trace amounts of several proteins, including approximately 60 indigenous enzymes.

The application of electrophoresis in starch or polyacrylamide gels, which were introduced about 1960, showed that the milk protein system is very heterogeneous due to:

- Genetic polymorphism, usually involving substitution of one or two amino acids
- Variations in the degree of phosphorylation of the caseins
- Variations in the degree of glycosylation of κ-casein
- Intermolecular disulphide bond formation in α_{s1}- and κ-caseins
- Limited proteolysis by plasmin, especially of β- and α_{s1}-caseins; the resulting peptides include the γ- and λ-caseins and proteose peptones.

The concentration of total protein in milk is affected by most of the same factors that affect the concentration of fat, i.e., breed, individuality, nutritional status, health and stage of lactation, but with the exception of the last, the magnitude of the effect is less than for milk fat. The concentration of protein in milk decreases very markedly during the first few days *post partum*, mainly due to the decrease in Ig from $\approx$10% in the first colostrum to 0.1% within about one week. The concentration of total protein continues to decline more slowly thereafter to a minimum after about four weeks and then increases until the end of lactation. Data on variations in the groups of proteins throughout lactation have been published (see Mehra *et al.*, 1999) but there are few data on variations in the concentrations of the principal proteins individually.

Table 2.1 Characteristics of the principal proteins in cow's milk protein

	Molecular mass	AA residues			PO_4	Concentration (g/L)	
		Total	Pro	Cys			
α_{s1}-Casein	23 164	199	17	0	8	10.0	A,B,C,D,E,F,G,H
α_{s2}-Casein	25 388	207	10	2	10–13	2.6	A,B,C,D
β-Casein	23 983	209	35	0	5	9.3	A^1,A^2,A^3,B,C,D,E,F,G
κ-Casein[a]	19 038	169	20	2	1	3.3	A,B,C,E,F^I,G^S,H,I,J
β-Lactoglobulin	18 277	162	8	5	0	3.2	A,B,C,D,E,F,H,I,J
α-Lactalbumin	14 175	123	2	8	0	1.2	A,B,C

[a] Glycosylated to variable extent.

Molecular properties of milk proteins

The principal lactoproteins are very well characterized at the molecular level; the principal properties are summarized in Table 2.1. The most notable features of the principal milk-specific proteins are:

- All milk proteins are quite small molecules, $\approx$15–25 kDa.
- All the caseins are phosphorylated but to different and variable degrees; the phosphate groups are esterified as monoesters of serine residues.
- β-Casein is the only one of the principal milk proteins that is glycosylated. The sugar moieties are galactose, galactosamine and N-acetylneuraminic acid (sialic acid), which occur as tri- or tetra-saccharides. Zero to four oligo-saccharides are attached to the polypeptide via serine residues in the C-terminal region of the molecule.
- The primary structures of the principal milk proteins and of many of their variants are known. The caseins have a rather uneven distribution of polar and apolar residues along their sequences, creating hydrophobic and hydrophilic patches; this structural feature bestows the caseins with very good surface activity, giving them very good emulsifying and foaming properties.
- The two principal caseins, α_{s1}- and β-, are devoid of cysteine or cystine residues; the two minor caseins, α_{s2}- and κ-caseins, contain two inter-molecular disulphides. β-Lg contains two intramolecular disulphides and one sulphydryl group which is buried and unreactive in the native protein but becomes exposed and reactive when the molecule is denatured; it reacts via sulphydryl–disulphide interactions with other proteins, especially κ-casein, with major consequences on many important properties of the milk protein system, especially heat stability and cheesemaking properties. α-La has four intramolecular disulphides.
- All the caseins, especially β-casein, contain a high level of proline, which disrupts α- and β-structures; consequently, the caseins are rather unstructured molecules and are readily susceptible to proteolysis. However, theoretical calculations suggest that the caseins may have a considerable level of secondary and tertiary structures; to explain the differences between the experimental and theoretical indices of higher structures, it has been suggested that the caseins have very mobile, flexible structures and are referred to as rheomorphic.
- In contrast, the whey proteins are highly structured and compact, with high levels of α-helices, β-sheets and β-turns. In β-Lg, the β-sheets are in an anti-parallel arrangement and form a β-barrel calyx. This is a member of the lipocalin family of proteins to which a Special Issue of the journal *Biochimica et Biophysica Acta* has been devoted (Akerstrom *et al.*, 2000).
- The caseins are often regarded as rather hydrophobic proteins but they are not particularly so; however, they do have a high surface hydrophobicity owing to their open structure; in globular proteins, the hydrophobic residues are buried within the molecule but they are exposed in the caseins.

- Also due to their open structure, the caseins are quite susceptible to proteolysis, which accords with their putative function as a source of amino acids for the neonate. However, their hydrophobic patches give them a high propensity to yield bitter hydrolysates, even in cheese which undergoes relatively little proteolysis. In contrast, the highly structured whey proteins are very resistant to proteolysis in the native state and may transverse the intestinal tract of the neonate intact.
- Probably because of their rather open structures, the caseins are extremely heat stable, e.g., sodium caseinate can be heated at 140°C for 1 h without obvious physical effects. The more highly structured whey proteins are comparatively heat labile, although in comparison with many other globular proteins, they are quite heat stable; they are completely denatured on heating at 90°C for 10 min.
- Under the ionic conditions in milk, α-La exists as monomers of MW ≈ 14.7 kDa. β-Lg exists as dimers (MW ~ 36 kDa) in the pH range 5.5–7.5; at pH values <3.5 or >7.5 it exists as monomers, while at pH 3.5–5.5 it exists as octamers. The caseins exist as very complex structures, known as casein micelles, which are described below.
- The function of the caseins appears to be to supply amino acids to the neonate. They have no biological function *sensu stricto* but their Ca-binding properties enable a high concentration of calcium phosphate to be carried in milk in a 'soluble' form; without the 'solubilizing' influence of casein, $Ca_3(PO_4)_2$ would precipitate in the ducts of the mammary gland and cause atopic milk stones (see Holt, 1994).
- β-Lg binds several hydrophobic molecules; it binds and protects retinol *in vitro* and perhaps functions as a retinol carrier *in vivo*. In the intestine, it may exchange retinol with a retinol-binding protein. It also binds fatty acids and thereby stimulates lipase – perhaps this is its principal biological function. All members of the lipocalin family have some form of binding function (see Akerstrom *et al.*, 2000).
- α-La is a metalloprotein – it binds one calcium atom per molecule in a peptide loop containing four Asp residues. The apoprotein is quite heat labile but the metalloprotein is rather heat stable; the difference in heat stability between the halo- and apoprotein is exploited in the isolation of α-La on a potentially industrial scale.
- α-La is a specifier protein in lactose synthesis; it makes UDP-galactose transferase highly specific for glucose as an acceptor of galactose, resulting in the synthesis of lactose.

Casein micelles

α_{s1}-, α_{s2}- and β-caseins, which together represent approximately 85% of total casein, are precipitated by calcium at concentrations above 6 mM at temperatures above 20°C. Since milk contains ≈ 30 mmol/L Ca, it would be expected that most of the caseins would precipitate in milk. However, κ-casein is soluble in

Table 2.2 Average characteristics of casein micelles

Characteristic	Value
Diameter	120 nm (range: 50–600 nm)
Surface area	$8 \times 10^{-10} \, cm^2$
Volume	$2.1 \times 10^{-15} \, cm^3$
Density (hydrated)	$1.0632 \, g/cm^{-3}$
Mass	$2.2 \times 10^{-15} \, g$
Water content	63%
Hydration	$3.7 \, g \, H_2O$ per g protein
Voluminosity	$44 \, cm^3/g$
Molecular weight (hydrated)	$1.3 \times 10^9 \, Da$
Molecular weight (dehydrated)	$5 \times 10^8 \, Da$
Number of peptide chains	5×10^3
Number of particles per ml milk	$10^{14}-10^{16}$
Surface of micelles per ml milk	$5 \times 10^4 \, cm^2$
Mean free distance between micelles	240 nm

high concentrations of calcium and it reacts with and stabilizes the Ca-sensitive caseins through the formation of casein micelles.

The micelles are spherical colloidal particles, with a mean diameter of ≈ 120 nm (range 50–600 nm). They have a mean particle mass of $\approx 10^8$ Da, i.e., there are about 5000 casein molecules (20–25 kDa) in an average micelle. On a dry weight basis, the micelles contain $\approx 94\%$ protein and $\approx 6\%$ non-protein species, mainly calcium and phosphate, with smaller amounts of magnesium (Mg) and citrate and traces of other metals; these are collectively called colloidal calcium phosphate (CCP). Under the conditions that exist in milk, the micelles are hydrated to the extent of ≈ 2 g water per g protein. There are $\approx 10^{15}$ micelles per ml milk, with a surface area of $\approx 5 \times 10^4 \, cm^2$; the micelles are about 240 nm apart (see Table 2.2). Owing to their very large surface area, the surface properties of the micelles are of major significance, and because they are quite closely packed, even in unconcentrated milk, they collide frequently due to Brownian, thermal convection and mechanical motion.

The micro-structure of the casein micelle has been the subject of considerable research, especially during the past 50 years, i.e., since the discovery and isolation of the micelle-stabilizing protein, κ-casein; however, there is still a lack of general consensus. Numerous models have been proposed, the most widely supported being the sub-micelle model first proposed by Morr in 1966 and refined several times since. Essentially, this model proposes that the micelle is built up from sub-micelles (MW $\approx 5 \times 10^6$ Da) held together by CCP and surrounded and stabilized by a surface layer rich in κ-casein but with some of the other caseins exposed also (Fig. 2.1). It is proposed that the hydrophilic C-terminal region of κ-casein protrudes from the surface, creating a hairy layer around the micelle and stabilizing it through a zeta potential of about -20 mV and steric stabilization. The principal direct experimental support for this model is provided by electron microscopy, which indicates a

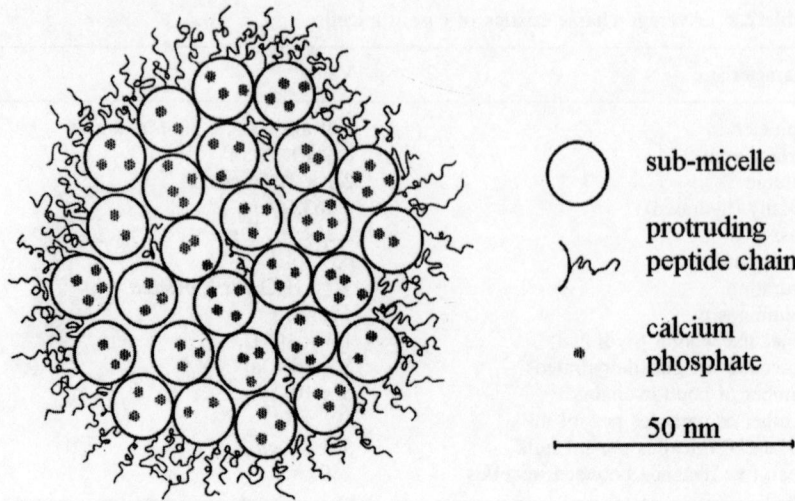

sub-micelle

protruding
peptide chain

calcium
phosphate

50 nm

Fig. 2.1   Schematic model of a cross-section through a casein micelle (from Walstra, 1999).

non-uniform electron density which has been interpreted as indicating sub-micelles.

However, several authors have expressed reservations about the sub-unit model and several alternatives have been proposed. In one of these (Holt, 1992), it is proposed that the Ca-sensitive caseins are linked by micro-crystals of CCP and surrounded by a layer of κ-casein with its C-terminal region protruding from the surface (Fig. 2.2). In the dual-binding model of Horne (2003), it is proposed that individual casein molecules interact via hydrophobic regions in their primary structures, leaving the hydrophilic regions free and with the hydrophilic C-terminal region of κ-casein protruding into the aqueous phase (Fig. 2.3). Thus, the key structural features of the sub-micelle model are retained in both alternatives, i.e., the integrating role of CCP and a surface layer consisting predominantly of κ-casein.

The micelles disintegrate when the CCP is solubilized, e.g., by acidification, citrate or oxalate, followed by dialysis; about 60% of the CCP can be removed without disintegration of the micelles. The micelles can also be dispersed by raising the pH to $\approx$9.0, which does not solubilize the CCP and presumably causes disintegration by increasing the net negative charge. Urea at >5M or sodium dodecyl sulphate (SDS) also dissociates the micelles, suggesting that hydrogen and/or hydrophobic bonds are important for micelle integrity. At 20°C, the micelles are precipitated by ethanol or other low MW alcohols at approximately 35% or over, but if the temperature is increased above about 70°C, surprisingly, the precipitated casein dissolves and the solution becomes quite clear, indicating dissociation of the micelles (O'Connell *et al.*, 2001a, 2001b). Micelle-like particles reform on cooling and these form a gel at about 4°C. It is not known whether the sub-particles

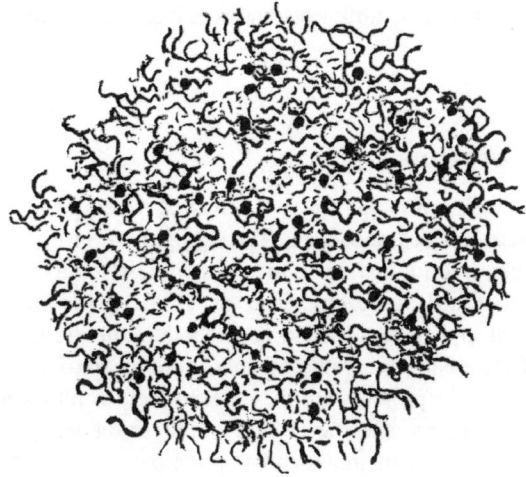

Fig. 2.2   Schematic diagram of a casein micelle showing a generally uniform protein matrix and calcium phosphate nanoclusters (from Fox and McSweeney, 1998).

formed on treating milk with acid, urea, SDS or ethanol correspond to casein sub-micelles.

There have been few studies on variations in micelle size throughout lactation and these have failed to show consistent trends. No studies on variability in the microstructure of the casein micelle have been published. There are no reported studies on the effects of the nutritional and health status of the animal on the structure of the casein micelles, although their stability and behaviour are

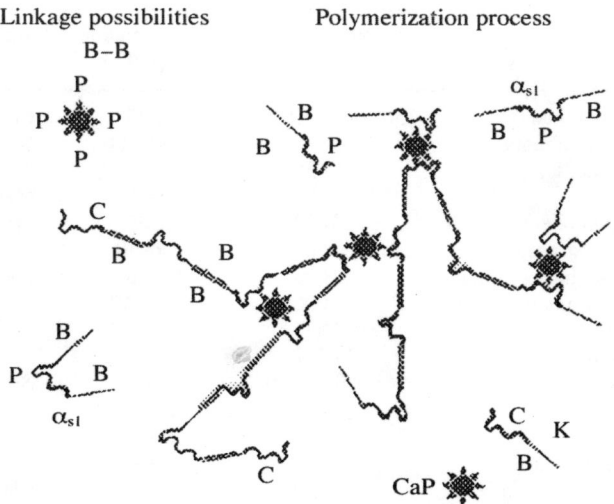

Fig. 2.3   Dual binding model of a section of the casein micelle showing interactions between α_{s1}-, β- and κ-caseins (from Horne, 2003).

strongly dependent on pH, milk salts and whey proteins, which are affected by such factors.

2.5   Minor proteins

In addition to the caseins and the two principal whey proteins, milk contains several proteins at low or trace levels. The significance of most of these proteins has been largely overlooked by dairy technologists but many of them are biologically active (see Schrezenmeir *et al.*, 2000); some are now regarded as highly significant and have attracted considerable attention as neutraceuticals. When ways of increasing the value of milk proteins are discussed, the focus is usually on these minor proteins but they are, in fact, of little economic value to the overall dairy industry. They are found mainly in the whey but some are also located in the fat globule membrane. The principal minor proteins are listed in Table 2.3 and will be described briefly; reviews of the minor proteins include Fox and Flynn (1992) and Haggarty (2003).

2.5.1   Immunoglobulins
It has long been recognized that colostrum contains a very high ($\approx$10%) concentration of immunoglobulins (Ig) and that this level declines rapidly after parturition to $\approx$0.1%. IgG1 is the principal Ig in bovine milk, with lesser amounts of IgG2, IgA and IgM. IgA is the principal Ig in human milk. The cow,

Table 2.3   Some properties of minor proteins in bovine milks

Protein	Molecular mass (daltons)	Concentration (mg/L)	Source
Immunoglobulins	150 000–1 000 000	200	Blood, mammary
Blood serum albumin	66 433	100–400	Blood
β_2-Microglobulin	11 636	9.5	Monocytes
Osteopontin	60 000	3–10	Mammary
Proteose peptone 3	28 000	300	Mammary
Folate-binding protein	30 000	6–10	—
Vitamin D-binding protein	52 000	16	Blood
Vitamin B_{12}-binding protein	43 000	0.1–0.2	—
Angiogenin-1	14 577	4–8	Mammary
Angiogenin-2	14 522	—	—
Kininogen	68 000/17 000	—	Blood
Lactoferrin	82 000	20–350	Mammary
Transferrin	77 000	—	Blood
Ceruloplasmin	132 000	—	Mammary
α_1-Acid glycoprotein	40 000	<20	Blood
Prosaposin	66 000	6.0	Mammary
Enzymes (~60)	Various	Trace	Blood, mammary

sheep, goat and some other species do not transfer Ig to the foetus *in utero*; the neonate is born devoid of serum Ig and, consequently, it is very susceptible to bacterial and viral infection, with a very high risk of mortality. The young of these species can absorb Ig from the intestine for several days after birth and thereby acquire passive immunity until they synthesize their own Igs within a few weeks. Some species, including the human, transfer Ig *in utero* and the offspring are born with a broad spectrum of antibodies. Although the young of these species cannot absorb Ig from the intestine, the ingestion of colostrum is still very important because the Igs it contains prevent intestinal infection. Some species, e.g., the horse, transfer Ig both *in utero* and via colostrum.

The modern dairy cow produces colostrum far in excess of the requirements, even the consumption capacity, of its calf. Therefore, colostrum is available surplus to the requirements of the calf and there is commercial interest in the recovery of Ig and other nutriceuticals therefrom (Pakkanen and Aalto, 1997). There is also considerable interest in hyperimmunizing cows against certain human pathogens, e.g., rota virus, for the production of antibody-rich milk for human consumption, especially by infants; the Ig could be isolated from the milk and presented as a 'pharmeutical' or consumed directly in the milk.

2.5.2 Bovine serum albumin (BSA)

About 1–2% of the protein in bovine milk is BSA which enters by leakage through intercellular junctions. BSA represents ≈50% of the protein in bovine blood in which it performs several functions. As befits its physiological import-ance, BSA is very well characterized (see Carter and Ho, 1994). It is a single polypeptide of 582 amino acid residues with a calculated MW of 66 433 Da. Its primary structure has 17 intramolecular disulphide bridges that hold the molecule in nine loops, which form three equally sized globular domains; it has one sulphydryl group. BSA has no known biological function in milk, and considering its very low concentration, it probably has no technological significance in milk.

2.5.3 Metal-binding proteins

Milk contains several metal-binding proteins, of which the caseins are quantitatively the most important. The significance of calcium in the structure of α-La has been discussed. Several enzymes are metallo-proteins, e.g., xanthine oxidase (Fe, Mo), alkaline phosphatase (Zn, Mg), lactoperoxidase (Fe), catalase (Fe) and glutathione peroxidase (Se).

The most significant metallo-protein is lactoferrin (Lf), a non-haem iron-binding glycoprotein (see Lonnerdal, 2003). It is a member of a family of iron-binding proteins, which includes transferrin and ovotransferrin (conalbumin). In spite of its name, it is not milk-specific, being present in several body fluids, including saliva, tears, sweat and semen. Bovine Lf consists of 689 amino acid residues, has a MW of 77 kDa (a glycoprotein) and three disulphide bonds; it binds two atoms of Fe per molecule. Lf has several potential biological functions, of which improving the bioavailability of Fe and a bacteriostatic effect (by sequestering Fe and making it unavailable to intestinal bacteria) are the best established, at least *in vitro*. Other possible functions include antioxidant, antibacterial, antiviral, anti-inflammatory, immunomodulatory and anticarcinogenic activity. Human milk contains a much higher level of Lf ($\approx$20% of total N) than bovine milk and this has stimulated interest in fortifying bovine milk-based infant formulae with Lf. The pI of Lf is $\approx$9.0, i.e., it is cationic at the pH of milk whereas most milk proteins are anionic. This difference in pI is the principle of an industrial-scale method for the isolation of Lf. Hydrolysis of Lf by pepsin yields peptides called lactoferricins, which are more bacteriostatic than Lf; their activity is independent of iron status.

Bovine milk also contains transferrin, which is identical to serum transferrin. It is a single polypeptide chain with a calculated MW of 75 830 Da; it has one N-linked glycan and can bind two moles of iron per mole.

A copper-binding glycoprotein, ceruloplasmin, also known as ferroxidase (EC 1.16.3.1), has been identified in the milk of several species, including cattle (see Wooten *et al.*, 1996). Serum ceruloplasmin is a single chain, copper-binding α_2-globulin with a MW of ~126 000 Da. It can bind six atoms of copper per molecule and may play a role in delivering essential copper to the neonate.

2.5.4 β_2-Microglobulin

β_2-Microglobulin occurs free in body fluids and on the surface of all nucleated cells; it is a component of the immune system (see Groves and Greenberg, 1982). β_2-Microglobulin, initially called lactollin, was first isolated from bovine acid-precipitated casein by Groves *et al.* (1963). Lactollin was reported to have a MW of 43 000 Da but was subsequently found to be a tetramer of β_2-microglobulin, which consists of 98 amino acids, with a calculated MW of 11 636 Da. Apparently, β_2-microglobulin is produced from the cellular fraction in milk, probably monocytes, by proteolysis mainly within the mammary gland. No significance has been attached to β_2-microglobulin in milk.

2.5.5   Osteopontin

Osteopontin (OPN) is a highly phosphorylated acidic glycoprotein consisting of 261 amino acid residues with a calculated MW of 29 283 (total MW of the glycoprotein, $\approx$60 000 Da). It contains 27 phosphoserine and one phospho-threonine residue and has three O-glycosylated threonines. OPN has 50 potential calcium-binding sites, about half of which are saturated under normal physiological concentrations of calcium and magnesium.

OPN occurs in bone (it is one of the major non-collagenous proteins in bone), in many other normal and malignant tissues and in milk and urine, and can bind to many cell types. It is believed to have a diverse range of functions (Denhardt and Guo, 1993; Bayless *et al.*, 1997), including:

- An adhesive and/or signalling role in injury-related events
- Mineralization and the resorption of bone matrix
- Calcium-dependent or calcium-mediated processes
- Inhibition of the growth of calcium oxalate crystals.

The role of OPN in milk is not clear. It may be important in calcium binding but, considering its low concentration in milk, its total Ca-binding capacity is small in comparison with casein. It is not known whether OPN, or peptides derived from it, are absorbed from the gastrointestinal tract and, if so, whether they retain their biological function and are transported to possible sites of activity within the body.

2.5.6   Proteose peptone 3

Bovine proteose peptone 3 (PP3) is a heat-stable phosphoglycoprotein that was first identified in the proteose peptone fraction of milk. Unlike the other peptides in this fraction, which are proteolytic products of the caseins, PP3 is an indigenous milk protein, synthesized in the mammary gland. Bovine PP3 is a single polypeptide chain of 135 amino acids with five phosphorylation and three glycosylation sites. The constituent sugars are fucose, mannose, galactose, N-acetylglucosamine, N-acetylgalactosamine and sialic acid. The calculated MW of the apoprotein is 15 304 Da. When isolated from milk, the PP3 fraction contains at least three components of MW $\approx$28, 18 and 11 kDa, the largest of which is PP3 while the smaller components are fragments thereof generated by plasmin (see Girardet and Linden, 1996). Initially, PP3 was considered to be an exclusively whey protein, but subsequent immunochemical studies showed that it is present in the MFGM also. Clearly, the term proteose peptone is a misnomer and it has been proposed to change the name to *lactophorin* or *lactoglycophorin* (Girardet and Linden, 1996).

PP3 cDNA from bovine mammary gland has 56% homology with mouse and rat glycosylation-dependent cell-adhesion molecule 1, GlyCAM-1, which is involved in the adhesion of lymphocytes to endothelial cells. However, the glycan moieties of PP3 and GlyCAM-1 differ and PP3 is unable to bind to L-selectin, which is essential for the function of murine GlyCAM-1.

PP3 has excellent foaming and emulsifying properties. Owing to its strong surfactant properties (Campagna *et al.*, 1998), it can prevent contact between milk lipase and its substrates, thus preventing spontaneous lipolysis. Although its amino acid composition suggests that PP3 is not a hydrophobic protein, it behaves hydrophobically, possibly owing to the formation of an amphiphilic α-helix, one side of which contains hydrophilic residues while the other side is hydrophobic. PP3 has been referred to as the *hydrophobic fraction of proteose peptone*.

The biological role of PP3 is unknown; proposed functions include stimulation of the growth of bifidobacteria and calcium ion binding via the phosphorylated N-terminus of the molecule.

2.5.7   Vitamin-binding proteins

Milk contains binding proteins for at least the following vitamins: retinol (vitamin A), vitamin D, folic acid, riboflavin and cobalamin (vitamin B_{12}). The precise role of these proteins is not clear but they may improve the absorption of vitamins from the intestine or act as antibacterial agents by rendering vitamins unavailable to bacteria. The concentration of these proteins varies during lactation but the influence of factors such as individuality, breed and nutritional status is not known. The activity of these proteins is reduced or destroyed on heating at temperatures slightly higher than HTST pasteurization. As discussed earlier, β-Lg binds and perhaps acts as a carrier for retinol, although this may not be its function *in vivo*.

Most of the folate and its derivatives in raw bovine milk are bound to a folate-binding protein (FBP) which is present at a level of ≈ 10 mg/L. Bovine protein milk FBP is a single chain of 222 amino acid residues with a calculated MW of 25 825 Da. It contains eight disulphide bridges and two N-linked carbohydrate moieties (Asp 49 and 141) which represent $\approx 10\%$ of the mass of the molecule. The principal sugars are N-acetylglucosamine, N-acetylgalactosamine, fucose, mannose, galactose and sialic acid; the glycoprotein has a MW of 30 000 Da. FBP tightly binds one mole of folate per mole in the pH range 5.5 to 8.0. The folate is released at acidic pH values but is rebound on neutralization. FBP increases the retention and bioavailability of folate. It may also protect folate from folate-requiring intestinal bacteria, and sequester folate synthesized by other microorganisms in the large intestine. Thus, milk FBP may contribute in several ways to the maintenance of the folate economy of the neonate (see Parodi, 1997b).

A vitamin D-binding protein (DBP) is present in the plasma of most vertebrates. It is a glycoprotein with a MW of 52 000 Da. It has high structural homology with BSA and, like BSA, can bind long-chain fatty acids. DBP has been detected in the milk of several species at ~2% of the level in blood serum. The concentration of DBP is higher in bovine colostrum and early milk than in mature milk; the protein is probably derived from serum as no synthesis of DBP has been observed in the mammary gland.

Three proteins are required for the uptake of vitamin B_{12} (cobalamin) in mammals. Gastric intrinsic factor (GIF) binds the free vitamin released from foods on digestion. The GIF–cobalamin complex enters the ileal mucosal cells by a receptor-mediated mechanism by which the vitamin is transferred to another protein, transcobalamin (TC). The TC–cobalamin complex and unsaturated TC are released into the portal plasma along with the third cobalamin-binding protein, haptocorrin (HC), the function of which is not clear but which may bind and remove from circulation cobalamin analogues that could interfere with the function of cobalamin. HC has been identified in the milk of several species (human, rat, pig and rabbit) where it exists mainly in an unsaturated form. Its function appears to be to sequester cobalamin released from food, to facilitate its absorption and prevent it being taken up by vitamin B_{12}-requiring intestinal microorganisms. It may also protect the neonate against pathogenic bacteria that require cobalamin. However, the vitamin B_{12}-binding protein found in bovine milk is TC (Fedosov *et al.*, 1996), which has been isolated in two molecular forms: a low MW protein (43 000 Da) and its aggregated form (280 000 Da) which dissociates on treatment with urea.

A riboflavin-binding protein (RfBP), with a MW of $\approx$38 000 Da, has been partially purified from raw bovine milk. The RfBP–riboflavin complex has good antioxidant properties, similar to those of the protein isolated from avian eggs where it has an important nutritional role. The RfBP in milk may be derived from serum; its physiological function has not been established.

2.5.8   Angiogenins

Angiogenins induce the growth of new blood vessels, i.e., angiogenesis. They have high sequence homology with members of the RNaseA superfamily of proteins and have ribonucleolytic activity. Angiogenesis is a complex biological process of which the ribonucleolytic activity of angiogenins is only one of a number of essential biochemical steps that lead to the formation of new blood vessels (Strydom, 1998).

Two angiogenins (angiogenin-1 and angiogenin-2) have been identified in bovine milk and blood serum. Both strongly promote the growth of new blood vessels in a chicken membrane assay. Bovine angiogenin-1 (ANG-1) is a highly basic non-glycosylated, single-polypeptide protein containing 125 amino acids and three disulphide bonds. Its calculated MW is 14 577 Da. ANG-1 has 64% sequence identity with human angiogenin and 34% identity with bovine RNase A.

ANG-2 is a single polypeptide chain of 123 amino acids, with three disulphide bonds and a calculated MW of 14 522 Da. Unlike ANG-1, ANG-2 has one *N*-linked glycosylation site (Asp 33). Glycosylation may have a major effect on the function of ANG-2. The amino acid sequence of bovine ANG-2 has 57% identity with that of bovine ANG-1 and it has lower RNase activity than ANG-1.

The function(s) of the angiogenins in milk is unknown. They may be part of a repair system to protect either the mammary gland or the intestine of the neonate and/or part of the host-defence system, due to their high transfer RNase activity.

2.5.9   Kininogen

Two forms of kininogen have been identified in bovine milk, a high MW form (>68 000 Da) and a low MW form (16 000–17 000 Da) (Wilson *et al.*, 1989). Bradykinin, a biologically active peptide containing nine amino acids released from the high MW kininogen by the action of the enzyme kallikrein, has been detected in the mammary gland, and is secreted into milk, from which has been isolated. The forms of kininogen in milk are apparently different from those in bovine plasma.

Plasma kininogen is an inhibitor of thiol proteases and has an important role in blood coagulation. Bradykinin has several functions: it affects smooth muscle contraction, induces hypertension and is involved in natriuresis and diuresis. The biological significance of bradykinin and kininogen in milk is unknown, although a fragment of bovine milk kininogen promotes the proliferation of osteoblastic MC3T3-E1 cells and may play a role in bone formation.

2.5.10   Glycoproteins
Many of the minor proteins discussed above are glycoproteins; in addition, several other minor glycoproteins have been found in milk and colostrum but their identity and function have not been elucidated fully. Some of these glycoproteins, which have been isolated, belong to a family of closely related, highly acidic glycoproteins called M-1 glycoproteins. Their average MW is 10 000 Da and they contain galactose, glucosamine, galactosamine, sialic acid and other sugars. Some glycoproteins stimulate the growth of bifidobacteria, presumably via their aminosugars.

One of the M-1 glycoproteins in colostrum, but which has not been detected in milk, is orosomucoid (α_1-acid glycoprotein), a member of the lipocalin family. It has a MW of $\approx 40\,000$ Da and contains five N-linked glycan groups. α_1-Acid glycoprotein is thought to modulate the immune system; its concentration in blood increases during inflammatory diseases, malignancy and pregnancy.

One of the high molecular weight glycoproteins in bovine milk is prosaposin, a neurotrophic factor which plays an important role in the development, repair and maintenance of the nervous system (Patton *et al.*, 1997). It is a precursor of saposins A, B, C and D, which are sphingolipid activator proteins, but saposins are not detected in milk. Prosaposin is present in whey as a monomer of about 66 000 Da. The amino acid sequence, determined from cDNA, consists of 525 amino acids with a calculated MW of 58 051 Da. The physiological role of milk prosaposin in the neonate or the mammary gland is not known, although the potent biological activity of saposin C, released by digestion, could be important for the growth and development of the young.

2.5.11   Growth factors
A great diversity of protein growth factors (hormones), including epidermal growth factor, insulin, insulin-like growth factors 1 and 2, three human milk growth factors ($\alpha 1$, $\alpha 2$ and β), two mammary-derived growth factors (I and II), colony stimulating factor, nerve growth factor, platelet-derived growth factor and bombasin, are present in milk (see Fox and Flynn, 1992). It is not clear whether these factors play a role in the development of the neonate or in the development and functioning of the mammary gland or both. There is little information on the variability of these hormones or the effect of animal or husbandry factors. Studies on such variability appear warranted.

2.5.12   Indigenous milk enzymes

Milk contains about 60 indigenous enzymes, which represent a minor but very important part of the milk protein system. The principal indigenous enzymes in milk have been isolated and well characterized; the extensive literature has been reviewed (see Fox *et al.*, 2003). The enzymes originate from the secretory cells or the blood and enter milk as a result of the mechanisms by which the constituents of milk, especially the fat globules, are exported from the mammocytes. With the possible exception of bile salts-activated lipase in human milk and that of a few other species, the indigenous enzymes probably have no direct function in milk. Many of the indigenous enzymes are concentrated in the MFGM and originate in the Golgi membranes of the cell or the cell cytoplasm, some of which may becomes entrapped as crescents inside the encircling membrane during exocytosis. A few enzymes, notably plasmin and lipoprotein lipase, are associated with the casein micelles and several are present in the milk serum; many of the latter are derived from the MFGM which is shed as the milk ages. The indigenous enzymes are significant for the following reasons.

Technological
- Plasmin causes proteolysis in milk and some dairy products; it may be responsible for age gelation in UHT milk and contributes to proteolysis in cheese during ripening, especially in varieties that are cooked at a high temperature and in which the coagulant is extensively or completely denatured, e.g., Emmental, Parmesan and Mozzarella.
- Lipoprotein lipase may cause hydrolytic rancidity in milk and butter but contributes positively to the ripening of raw milk cheese.
- Acid phosphatase can dephosphorylate casein and modify its functional properties; it may contribute to cheese ripening.
- Xanthine oxidase is a very potent prooxidant and may cause oxidative rancidity in milk; it reduces nitrate to nitrite, which prevents the growth of clostridia in cheese.
- Lactoperoxidase is a very effective bacteriocidal agent in the presence of a low level of H_2O_2 and SCN^- and is exploited for the cold-sterilization of milk.

Indices of milk quality and history
The standard assay for the adequacy of HTST pasteurization of milk is the inactivation of alkaline phosphatase. Proposed assays for super-pasteurization of milk are based on the inactivation of γ-glutamyltranspeptidase or lactoperoxidase.

The concentration/activity of several enzymes in milk increases during, and may be used as an index of, mastitic infection, e.g., catalase, acid phosphatase and especially *N*-acetylglucosaminidase. These increases reflect the breakdown of mammary tissue during infection and the increase in the number of leucocytes (somatic cells) in milk.

Antibacterial
Milk contains several bactericidal agents, two of which are the enzymes, lysozyme and lactoperoxidase.

Considering the routes through which enzymes enter milk, it is not surprising that there is considerable variation in the activity of all enzymes in milk for which data are available. However, the data are limited to the most significant enzymes and even for these, only a few causes of variation have been investigated. For those enzymes for which data are available, e.g., plasmin, lipoprotein lipase, xanthine oxidase and superoxide dismutase, there is considerable inter-breed and inter-cow variability, although the consistency of this variability is not certain; usually, the data are from one-off analysis. The activity of most enzymes increases markedly during a mastitic infection and with advancing lactation. Physiological and nutritional stress cause an increase in LPL activity in milk and probably of other enzymes also.

The indigenous enzymes in milk have the potential to cause considerable changes in milk lipids and proteins and hence in the processability of milk and in the quality of dairy products. Some of the enzymes are inactivated by HTST pasteurization but most are quite stable; although most are present at quite low levels, they can cause considerable change during a prolonged storage period. Plasmin activity in milk is actually increased by HTST pasteurization, probably due to inactivation of indigenous inhibitors.

The activity of some indigenous enzymes is strongly suppressed in milk but full activity may be realized under certain circumstances. For example, the triglycerides in milk are protected from LPL, which is associated mainly with the casein micelles, by the MFGM, and very little lipolysis normally occurs. However, if the MFGM is damaged by agitation, foaming, etc., lipolysis will occur rapidly. Some plasmin activity occurs in all milk but it is relatively low because most (80%) of the potential activity occurs as plasminogen, the activation of which by indigenous activators is inhibited by indigenous inhibitors of the activators; inhibitors of plasmin are also present in milk. Both sets of inhibitors are in the serum phase whereas plasmin, plasminogen and plasminogen activators are associated with the casein micelles. If the micelles are separated from the serum and redispersed in buffer, very rapid and extensive proteolysis occurs.

2.5.13   Biologically active peptides
One of the most exciting recent developments in milk proteins is the discovery that all milk proteins contain sequences that possess biological/physiological activities following specific proteolysis (see Gobbetti *et al.*, 2002, Pihlento-Leppala, 2003; FitzGerald and Meisel, 2003). The best studied and perhaps the most important of these peptides are:

• Phosphopeptides
• Angiotensin-converting enzyme inhibitory peptides

- Platelet-modifying peptides
- Opiate peptides
- Immunomodulating peptides.

The rennet coagulation of milk involves the specific hydrolysis of the Phe_{105}–Met_{106} bond of the micelle-stabilizing protein, κ-casein. The C-terminal part of κ-CN (residues 106–169), known as the caseinomacropeptide (CMP) or glycomacropeptide (GMP) or caseinoglycomacropeptide, diffuses into the whey while the N-terminal part (*para*-κ-CN; κ-CNf1-105) remains in the cheese curd. The CMPs represent $\approx$30% of κ-CN ($\approx$4% of total casein) and 15–20% of the total N in cheese whey. Thus, large quantities of CMP are readily available from whey from which it can be isolated fairly readily (see Brody, 2000).

The CMP has a number of interesting biological properties (see Brody, 2000):

- It contains no aromatic amino acids and therefore is suitable for the nutrition of individuals suffering from phenylketonuria; unfortunately, it lacks other essential amino acids, i.e., Cys, His, Trp and Tyr as well as Phe.
- It inhibits the binding of cholera toxin and *E. coli* enterotoxins.
- It inhibits bacterial and viral adhesion.
- It suppresses gastric secretions.
- It promotes the growth of bifidobacteria.
- It modulates immune system responses.

Smaller peptides derived from the CMP by proteolysis also have interesting properties, e.g.:

- Antithrombotic (κ-CN f106–116 and especially 113–116) (Maubois *et al.*, 1991)
- Growth-promoting activity for *Lc. lactis* ssp. *lactis* (Bouhallab *et al.*, 1993).

2.5.14 Protein-related aspects of quality

With the exception of butter, ghee and anhydrous milk fat, the properties and functionality of the proteins have major effects on the quality, even the existence, of dairy products. The most significant protein-rich dairy products are liquid (beverage) milk (HTST pasteurized and UHT sterilized), cheese (rennet- or acid-coagulated), milk powders, concentrated-sterilized milk, functional milk protein products (caseins, caseinates, whey protein concentrates, whey protein isolates), fermented milk products, ice cream and infant foods. Many of these products will be considered in some detail in the following chapters. The importance of protein functionality depends on the product, e.g.:

- Rennet coagulability
- Acid coagulability
- Heat stability

- Thermal gelation
- Surface activity
- Water binding.

For comprehensive discussions of these subjects, the reader is referred to Fox and McSweeney (2003). The significance of milk proteins as food ingredients was discussed by Fox (2001). The functionality of the milk proteins, especially the caseins, is strongly affected by the ions in milk, especially H^+ and Ca^{2+}. The salts in milk are discussed below.

2.6   Salts

When milk is heated in a muffle furnace at 500°C for ≈5 h, a residue, ash, derived mainly from the inorganic salts of milk and representing ≈0.7%, w/w, of the milk, remains. However, the elements are changed from their original forms to oxides or carbonates and the ash contains P and S derived from caseins, lipids, sugar phosphates or high-energy phosphates. The organic salts, the most important of which is citrate, are oxidized and lost during ashing; some volatile metals, e.g., sodium, are also partially lost. Thus, ash does not accurately represent the salts of milk. However, the principal inorganic and organic ions in milk can be determined directly by potentiometric, spectrophotometric or other methods. The typical concentrations of the principal elements, often referred to as macro-elements, are shown in Table 2.4. There is considerable variability in reported values, due, in part, to poor analytical methods and/or to samples from cows in very early or late lactation or suffering from mastitis. Milk also contains 20–25 elements at very low or trace levels (Table 2.5). These micro-elements are very important from a nutritional viewpoint and some, e.g., Fe and Cu, are very potent lipid prooxidants (see Fox and McSweeney, 1998).

Some of the salts in milk are fully soluble but others, especially calcium phosphate, exceed their solubility under the conditions in milk and occur partly in the colloidal state, associated with the casein micelles; these salts are referred to as colloidal calcium phosphate (CCP), although some magnesium, citrate and traces of other elements are present also. The typical distribution of the principal organic and inorganic ions between the soluble and colloidal phases is summarized in Table 2.4. The actual form of the principal species can be either determined or calculated, after making certain assumptions; typical values are shown in Table 2.4.

The solubility and ionization status of many of the principal ionic species are interrelated, especially H^+, Ca^{2+}, PO_4^{3-} and citrate^{3-}. These relationships have major effects on the stability of the caseinate system and consequently on the processing properties of milk. The status of various species in milk can be modified by adding certain salts to milk, e.g., $[Ca^{2+}]$ by PO_4^{3-} or citrate^{3-}; addition of $CaCl_2$ to milk affects the distribution and ionization status of calcium, phosphate and the pH of milk.

Table 2.4   Concentration and distribution of the principal ions in bovine milk (modified from Fox and McSweeney, 1998)

Species	Concentration (mg/L)	Soluble		Colloidal
		%	Form	%
Sodium	500	92	Ionized	8
Potassium	1450	92	Ionized	8
Chloride	1200	100	Ionized	—
Sulphate	100	100	Ionized	—
Phosphate	750	43	10% bound to Ca and Mg 51% H_2PO^- 39% HPO_4^{2-}	57
Citrate	1750	94	85% bound to Ca and Mg 14% $Citr^{3-}$ 1% $HCitr^{2-}$	
Calcium	1200	34	35% Ca^{2+} 55% bound to citrate 10% bound to phosphate	66
Magnesium	130	67	Probably similar to calcium	33

The precise nature and structure of CCP are uncertain. It is associated with the caseins, probably via the organic phosphate residues; it probably exists as microcrystals which include PO_4 residues of casein. The simplest stoichiometry is $Ca_3(PO_4)_2$ but spectroscopic data suggest that $CaHPO_4$ is the most likely form.

The distribution of species between the soluble and colloidal phases is strongly affected by pH and temperature. As the pH is reduced, CCP dissolves and is completely soluble below approximately pH 4.9; the reverse occurs when the pH is increased. These pH-dependent shifts mean that some acid-precipitated products, e.g., acid casein and acid-coagulated cheeses, have a very low concentration of Ca, which has nutritional significance.

The solubility of calcium phosphate decreases as the temperature is increased. Consequently, soluble $CaPO_4$ is transferred to the colloidal phase, with the release of H^+ and a decrease in pH:

$$CaHPO_4/Ca(H_2PO_4)_2 \leftrightarrow Ca_3(PO_4)_2 + 3H^+$$

These changes are quite substantial but are at least partially reversible on cooling. Since milk is supersaturated with calcium phosphate, concentration of milk by evaporation of water increases the degree of supersaturation and the transfer of soluble calcium phosphate to the colloidal state, with the concomitant release of H^+. Dilution has the opposite effect.

Milk salts equilibria are also shifted on freezing. Since pure water freezes, the concentrations of solutes in the unfrozen liquid are increased. Soluble calcium phosphate precipitates as $Ca_3(PO_4)_2$, releasing H^+ (the pH of the liquid phase may decrease to 5.8). The crystallization of lactose as a monohydrate aggravates the situation by reducing the amount of solvent water.

Table 2.5 Mineral composition (mg/L or µg/L) in mature human or bovine milk (modified from Flynn and Power, 1985)

Constituent	Mature human milk		Bovine milk	
	Mean	Range	Mean	Range
Sodium (mg)	150	110–200	500	350–900
Potassium (mg)	600	570–620	1500	1100–1700
Chloride (mg)	430	350–550	950	900–1100
Calcium (mg)	350	320–360	1200	1100–1300
Magnesium (mg)	28	26–30	120	90–140
Phosphorus (mg)	145	140–150	950	900–1000
Iron (µg)	760	620–930	500	300–600
Zinc (µg)	2950	2600–3300	3500	2000–6000
Copper (µg)	390	370–430	200	100–600
Manganese (µg)	12	7–15	30	20–50
Iodine (µg)	70	20–120	260	—
Fluoride (µg)	77	21–155		30–220
Selenium (µg)	14	8–19	—	5–67
Cobalt (µg)	12	1–27	1	0.5–1.3
Chromium (µg)	40	6–100	10	8–13
Molybdenum (µg)	8	4–16	73	18–120
Nickel (µg)	25	8–85	25	0–50
Silicon (µg)	700	150–1200	2600	750–7000

The concentration of macro-elements, their distribution between the soluble and colloidal phases and their ionization status have been investigated extensively, e.g., White and Davies (1958), Keogh *et al.* (1982) and O'Brien *et al.* (1999c). The changes are the consequence of stage of lactation, nutrition, genetic effects and perhaps other factors. The distribution and ionization status are strongly affected by pH, which increases during lactation. Changes in salts equilibria have major effects on the stability of milk proteins, and to a lesser extent of milk lipids, and consequently on the processability of milk. The changes are particularly significant for the production, yield and quality of cheese, of heat-sterilized products (UHT and in-container sterilized) and of milk powders.

2.7   References

AKERSTROM, B., FLOWER, D.R. and SALIER, J.-P. 2000. Lipocalins 2000. *Biochim. Biophys. Acta* **1482**: 1–356.

BANNI, S. and MARTIN, J.-C. 1998. Conjugated linoleic acid and metabolites, in *Trans Fatty Acids in Human Nutrition*, J.L. Sebedio and W.W. Christie, eds, The Oily Press, Dundee, pp 261–302.

BAYLESS, K.J., DAVIS, G.E. and MEININGER, G.A. 1997. Isolation and biological properties of osteopontin from bovine milk. *Prot. Expr. Purif.* **9**: 309–314.

BELURY, M.A. 1995. Conjugated dienoic linoleic acid: a polyunsaturated fatty acid with unique chemoprotective properties. *Nutr. Rev.* **53**: 83–89.

BOUHALLAB, S., FAVROT, C. and MAUBOIS, J.-L. 1993. Growth-promoting activity of tryptic digests of caseinomacropeptide for *Lactococcus lactis* subsp *lactis*. *Lait* **73**: 73–77.

BRODY, E.P. 2000. Biological activities of bovine glycopeptide. *Brit. J. Nutr.* **84**: Suppl. 1, S39–S46.

CAMPAGNA, S., VITOUX, B., HUMBERT, G., GIRARDET, J.M., LINDEN, G., HAERTLE, T. and GAILLARD, J.L. 1998. Conformational studies of a synthetic peptide from the putative lipid-binding domain of bovine milk component PP3. *J. Dairy Sci.* **81**: 3139–3148.

CARTER, D.C. and HO, J.X. 1994. Structure of serum albumin. *Adv. Protein Chem.* **45**: 153–203.

COGAN, T.M. and HILL, C. 1993. Cheese starter cultures, in *Cheese: Chemistry, Physics and Microbiology*, Volume 1, 2nd edition, P.F. Fox, ed., Chapman & Hall, London, pp 193–255.

COLLOMB, M., BUTIKOFER, U., SIEBER, R., JEANGROS, B. and BOSSET, J.-O. 2002. Composition of fatty acids in cow's milk fat produced in the lowlands, mountains and highlands of Switzerland using high-resolution gas chromatography. *Int. Dairy J.* **12**: 649–659.

DENHARDT, D.T. and GUO, X. 1993. Osteopontin: a protein with diverse functions. *FASEB J.* **7**: 1475–1482.

FEDOSOV, S.N., PETERSEN, T.E. and NEXØ, E. 1996. Transcobalamin from cow milk: isolation and physico-chemical properties. *Biochim. Biophys. Acta* **1292**: 113–119.

FITZGERALD, R. and MEISEL, H. 2003. Milk protein hydrolyzates and bioactive peptides, in *Advanced Dairy Chemistry*, Volume 1, *Proteins*, 3rd edition, P.F. Fox and P.L.H. McSweeney, eds, Kluwer Academic – Plenum Publishers, New York, pp 675–698.

FLYNN, A. and POWER, P. 1985. Nutritional aspects on minerals in bovine milk, in *Developments in Dairy Chemistry 3: Lactose and Minor Constituents*, P.F. Fox, ed., Elsevier Science Publishers, London, pp 183–215.

FOX, P.F. 1992. *Advanced Dairy Chemistry*, Volume 1, *Proteins*, 2nd edition, Elsevier Applied Science, London.

FOX, P.F. 1995. *Advanced Dairy Chemistry*, Volume 2, *Lipids*, 2nd edition, Chapman & Hall, London.

FOX, P.F. 1997. *Advanced Dairy Chemistry*, Volume 3, *Lactose, Salts, Water and Vitamins*, 2nd edition, Chapman & Hall, London.

FOX, P.F. 2001. Milk proteins as food ingredients. *Int. J. Dairy Technol.* **54**: 41–55.

FOX, P.F. and FLYNN A. 1992. Biological properties of milk proteins, in *Advanced Dairy Chemistry*, Volume 1, *Proteins*, 2nd edition, P.F. Fox, ed., Elsevier Applied Science, London, pp 255–284.

FOX, P.F. and MCSWEENEY, P.L.H. 1998. *Dairy Chemistry and Biochemistry*, Chapman & Hall, London.

FOX, P.F. and MCSWEENEY, P.L.H. 2003. *Advanced Dairy Chemistry*, Volume 1, *Proteins*, 3rd edition, Kluwer Academic – Plenum Publishers, New York.

FOX, P.F., LUCEY, J.A. and COGAN, T.M. 1990. Glycolysis and related reactions during cheese manufacture and ripening. *Crit. Rev. Food Sci. Nutr.* **29**: 237–253.

FOX, P.F., OLIVECRONA, T., VILARO, S., OLIVECRONA, S., KELLY, A.L., MCSWEENEY, P.L.H., SHAKEEL-UR-REHMAN, FLEMING, C.M., STEPANIAK, L., GOBBETTI, M., CORSETTI, A., PRUITT, K. and FARKYE, N.Y. 2003. Indigenous enzymes of milk, in *Advanced Dairy Chemistry*, Volume 1, *Proteins*, 3rd edition, P.F. Fox and P.L.H. McSweeney, eds,

Kluwer Academic – Plenum Publishers, New York, pp 467–604.

GIRARDET, J.-M. and LINDEN, G. 1996. PP3 component of bovine milk: a phosphorylated whey glycoprotein. *J. Dairy Res.* **63**: 333–350.

GOBBETTI, M., STEPANIAK, L., DE ANGELIS, M., CORSETTI, A. and DI CAGNO, R. 2002. Latent bioactive peptides in milk proteins: proteolytic activation and significance in dairy products. *Crit. Rev. Food Sci. Nutr.* **42**: 223–239.

GROVES, M.L. and GREENBERG, R. 1982. β_2-Microglobulin and its relationship to the immune system. *J. Dairy Sci.* **65**: 317–325.

GROVES, M.L., BASCH, J.J. and GORDON, W.G. 1963. Isolation, characterization, and amino acid composition of a new crystalline protein, lactollin, from milk. *Biochemistry* **2**: 814–817.

HAGGARTY, N.W. 2003. Milk proteins: minor proteins, bovine serum albumin and vitamin-binding proteins, in *Encyclopedia of Dairy Sciences*, H. Roginski, J. Fuquay and P.F. Fox, eds, Academic Press, London, pp 1939–1946.

HOLT, C. 1992. Structure and properties of bovine casein micelles. *Adv. Protein Chem.* **43**: 63–151.

HOLT, C. 1994. The biological function of casein, in *Yearbook 1994*, The Hannah Institute, Ayr, Scotland, pp 60–68.

HORNE, D. 2003. Caseins – micellar structure, in *Encyclopedia of Dairy Sciences*, H. Roginski, J. Fuquay and P.F. Fox, eds, Academic Press, London, pp 1902–1909.

JENSEN, R.G. 1995. *Handbook of Milk Composition*, Academic Press, San Diego, CA.

KELLY, M.L., BERRY, J.R., DWYER, D.A., GRIINARI, J.M., CHOUINARD, P.Y., VAN AMBURG, M.E. and BAUMAN, D.E. 1998. Dietary fatty acid sources affect conjugated linoleic acid concentrations in milk from lactating dairy cows. *J. Nutr.* **128**: 881–885.

KEOGH, M.K, KELLY, P.M., O'KEEFFE, A.M. and PHELAN, J.A. 1982. Studies on milk composition and its relationship to some processing criteria. II. Seasonal variation in the mineral levels of milk. *Irish J. Food Sci. Technol.* **6**: 13–27.

KRAFT, J., LEBZIEN, P., FLACHOWSKI, G., MOCKEL, P. and JAHREIS, G. 2000. Duodenal infusion of conjugated linoleic acid mixture influences milk fat synthesis and milk CLA content in dairy cows, in *Milk Composition*, British Society of Animal Science, Occasional Publication No 25, pp 143–147.

LAWLESS, F., MURPHY, J.J., FITZGERALD, S., O'BRIEN, B., DEVERY, R. and STAUNTON, C. 2000. Dietary effect on bovine milk fat conjugated linoleic acid content, in *Milk Composition*, British Society of Animal Science, Occasional Publication No 25, pp 283–293.

LOCK, A.L. and GARNSWORTHY, P.C. 2000. Changes in the conjugated linoleic acid content of milk from dairy cows throughout the year, in *Milk Composition*, British Society of Animal Science, Occasional Publication No 25, pp 125–129.

LONNERDAL, B. 2003. Lactoferrin, in *Advanced Dairy Chemistry*, Volume 1, *Proteins*, 3rd edition, P.F. Fox, and P.L.H. McSweeney, eds, Kluwer Academic – Plenum Press, New York, pp 449–466.

MAUBOIS, J.-L., LEONIL, J., TROUVE, R. and BOUHALLAB, S. 1991. Les peptides du lait a activité physiologique. III. Peptides du lait a effet cardiovasculaire: activités antithrombotique et antihypertensive. *Lait* **71**: 249–255.

MEHRA, R., O'BRIEN, B., CONNOLLY, J.F. and HARRINGTON, D. 1999. Seasonal variation in the composition of Irish manufacturing and retail milk. 2. Nitrogen fractions. *Irish J. Agric. Food Res.* **38**: 65–74.

O'BRIEN, B., MEHRA, R., CONNOLLY, J.F. and HARRINGTON, D. 1999a. Seasonal variation in the composition of Irish manufacturing and retail milk. 1. Chemical composition and renneting properties. *Irish J. Agric. Food Res*. **38**: 53–64.

O'BRIEN, B., LENNARTSSON, T., MEHRA, R., COGAN, T.M., CONNOLLY, J.F., MORRISSEY, P.A. and HARRINGTON, D. 1999b. Seasonal variation in the composition of Irish manufacturing and retail milk. 3. Vitamins. *Irish J. Agric. Food Res*. **38**: 75–85.

O'BRIEN, B., MEHRA, R., CONNOLLY, J.F. and HARRINGTON, D. 1999c. Seasonal variation in the composition of Irish manufacturing and retail milk. 4. Minerals and trace elements. *Irish J. Agric. Food Res*. **38**: 87–99.

O'CONNELL, J.E., KELLY, A.L., AUTY, M.A.E., FOX, P.F. and DE KRUIF, K.G. 2001a. Ethanol-dependent heat-induced dissociation of casein micelles. *J. Agr. Food Chem*. **49**: 4420–4423.

O'CONNELL, J.E., KELLY, A.L., FOX, P.F. and DE KRUIF, K.G. 2001b. Mechanism for the ethanol-dependent heat-induced dissociation of casein micelles. *J. Agr. Food Chem*. **49**: 4424–4428.

PAKKANEN, R. and AALTO, J. 1997. Growth factors and antimicrobial factors of bovine colostrum. *Int. Dairy J*. **7**: 285–297.

PARODI, P.W. 1994. Conjugated linoleic acid: an anticarcinogenic fatty acid present in milk fat. *Aust. J. Dairy Technol*. **49**: 93–97.

PARODI, P.W. 1997a. Cows' milk fat components as potential anticarcinogenic agents. *J. Nutr*. **127**: 1055–1060.

PARODI, P.W. 1997b. Cow's milk folate binding protein: its role in folate nutrition. *Aust. J. Dairy Technol*. **52**: 109–118.

PARODI, P.W. 1999. Conjugated linoleic acid and other anticarcinogenic agents in bovine milk fat. *J. Dairy Sci*. **82**: 1399–1349.

PATTON, S., CARSON, G.S., HIRAIWA, M., O'BRIEN, J.S. and SANO, A. 1997. Prosaposin, a neurotrophic factor: presence and properties in milk. *J. Dairy Sci*. **80**: 264–272.

PIHLENTO-LEPPALA, A. 2003. Milk proteins: bioactive peptides, in *Encyclopedia of Dairy Sciences*, H. Roginski, J. Fuquay and P.F. Fox, eds, Academic Press, London, pp 1960–1967.

SCHREZENMEIR, J., KORHONEN, H., WILLIAMS, C.M., GILL, H.S. and SHAJH, N.P. 2000. Beneficial natural bioactive substances in milk and colostrum. *Brit. J. Nutr*. **84**: Suppl. 1, S1–S166.

STRYDOM, D.J. 1998. The angiogenins. *Cell. Mol. Life Sci*. **54**: 811–824.

TROUT, G.M. 1950. *Homogenized Milk: A Review and Guide*, Michigan State College Press, East Lansing, MI.

WALSTRA, P. and JENNESS, R. 1984. *Dairy Chemistry and Physics*, John Wiley & Sons, New York.

WALSTRA, P. 1999. Casein sub-micelles: do they exist? *Int. Dairy J*. **9**: 189–192.

WHITE, J.C.D. and DAVIES, D.T. 1958. The relationship between the chemical composition of milk and the stability of the caseinate system. I. General introduction, description of samples, methods and chemical composition of samples. *J. Dairy Res*. **25**: 236–255.

WILSON, W.E., LAZARUS, L.H. and TOMER, K.B. 1989. Bradykinin and kininogens in bovine milk. *J. Biol. Chem*. **264**: 17777–17783.

WONG, N.P. (ed.) 1988. *Fundamentals of Dairy Chemistry*, 3rd edition, AVI Publishing, Westport, CT.

WOOTEN, L., SHULZE, R.A., LANCEY, R.W., LIETZOW, M. and LINDER, M.C. 1996. Ceruloplasmin is found in milk and amniotic fluid and may have a nutritional role. *Nutr. Biochem*. **7**: 632–639.

YURAWECZ, M.P., KRAMER, J.K.G. and PARIZA, M.W. 1999. *Advances in Conjugated Linoleic Acid Research*, American Oil Chemists Society, Minneapolis, MN.

3

Influences on raw milk quality

M. Boland, Fonterra Research Centre, New Zealand

3.1 Introduction

Milk is produced by all mammalian species for feeding their young, and there is a very large range of milk properties across all the species. Some mammals, such as the Tamar wallaby, can even produce milk of different compositions from adjacent mammary glands of the same individual at the same time (Nicholas, 1988). This chapter focuses exclusively on the range of quality (i.e. composition and related milk characteristics) of raw milk from dairying breeds of cattle (*Bos taurus*).

Although many people are persuaded that 'milk is milk' and that is the end of the matter, not all milks are created equal. There is significant variation in milk composition, which creates both problems and opportunities for the dairy industry. At the simplest level, differences in milk produced by different breeds are well recognised and have been used as a market position by some companies (Canada – Jersey Farm; USA – Promised Land Dairy; UK – 'Gold Top' – see Internet URLs at the end of this chapter). Despite thousands of years of domestication and selective breeding of dairy cattle, there is still a wide variation in milk composition from cow to cow. Table 3.1 gives an indication of the scope of variation within the herd of just one country (New Zealand). Much of this variation is evened out by a combination of milk from many animals at the farm level, with further evening out as collections from various farms are accumulated in the milk tanker, and in the silo at the factory, as shown in Fig. 3.1. A major survey of the protein composition of milk at the national level was carried out by the International Dairy Federation in the early 1990s (Higgins *et al.*, 1995). The survey covered 25 milk-producing countries. Annual average protein in the milk varied between countries from 3.00% to 3.55%, with monthly

Table 3.1 Range of composition in milks from individual cows in New Zealand. Data were collected from milk samples from 16 000 Friesian cows, 5800 Jersey cows and 340 Ayrshire cows and were analysed using Fourier Transform infrared spectrometry (S. Petch, unpublished, personal communication)

Component	Breed	Low	High
Milkfat %	Friesian	1.4	8.6
	Jersey	2.0	10.9
	Ayrshire	2.4	6.7
Protein %	Friesian	2.4	5.2
	Jersey	2.8	5.7
	Ayrshire	2.7	5.0
Lactose %	Friesian	3.7	5.7
	Jersey	4.2	5.6
	Ayrshire	4.3	5.4

values ranging from 2.75% to 4.09%. Protein as a percentage of the SNF (solids, non-fat) ranged from 32.7% to 46%, and the ratio of casein to whey protein varied from 3.24 to 5.87. Thus, even with national averages, there is considerable variation.

Variability in milk composition (and hence quality) extends considerably beyond simple breed characteristics. In this chapter, milk characteristics are addressed according to the source of variation, although they could equally well be divided according to where they impact and have economic or other effect. Milk characteristics have an effect at the processing level, on processability and yield, at the product level, in terms of the overt characteristics of the product, and on the consumer, in terms of nutrition and other physiological activity.

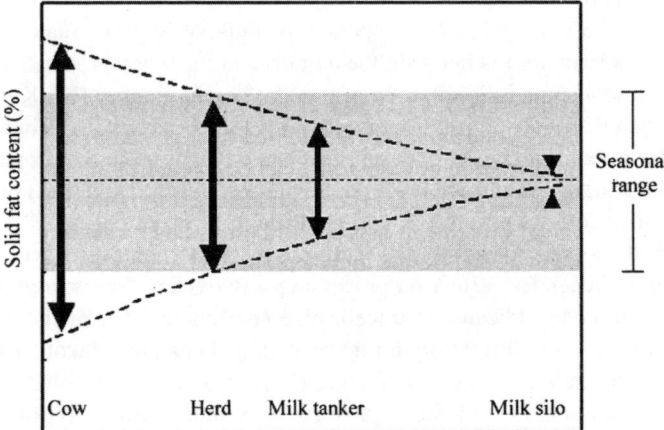

Fig. 3.1 Variation in milk characteristics. Although the example shown relates to butter hardness as measured by solid fat content, the principle is generally applicable. The seasonal range is the variation in milkfat in the silo during a season. Figure courtesy of A.K.H. MacGibbon, Fonterra Research Centre.

Genetic variations, many of which are breed linked, are the predominant source of variation in milk protein (Ng-Kwai-Hang and Grosclaude, 1992) and have a significant effect on milkfat composition and the amount of water in the milk. These are covered in Section 3.2. The second major influence on milk characteristics is the diet of the cow. This has a much greater effect on milkfat than on protein. It is covered in Section 3.3. In Section 3.4, the effects of other aspects of animal husbandry are dealt with. Section 3.5 gives a speculative view of what might happen in the future of milk production.

3.1.1   Economic importance of milk composition

Before discussing variations in milk composition in detail, it is worth considering the importance to the dairy industry of some of the compositional variables. This area has recently been reviewed by Williams (2002) and Hillbrick and Augustin (2002).

The first component of importance is water. Water is not usually directly cited as a compositional variable, but is implicit in the way other components are expressed, as water makes up the bulk volume of milk. Water is important in milk for consumption in its liquid form, as it affects the nutritional value per unit volume; however, in milk for processing, it has other important consequences. In dried products such as milk powders, water must be removed, and there is an energy cost for that removal; in the manufacture of cheese, water creates the bulk of the whey and has either a disposal cost, or a removal cost when other products are created from the whey. Further, water has a cost in transport, storage prior to processing, and size of processing plants in manufacturing. Thus, the ideal milk for most manufacturing purposes would have the highest possible solids content consistent with being able to be expressed from the mammary gland.

Protein is the most valuable component of milk. Within the major proteins, the most important split is between the caseins and the whey proteins. The ratio of casein to total protein is often known as the casein number (Ng-Kwai-Hang and Grosclaude, 1992) and is usually expressed as a percentage. This number defines the amount of cheese or casein that can be made from the protein in the milk, and is usually around 80. If the casein number gets too low (i.e. not enough casein relative to total protein), it can be difficult to make cheese.

Within the casein proteins, the only casein that seems to have a major concentration-dependent effect on processing is κ-casein. The ratio of κ-casein to total casein is an indicator of micelle size (Anema and Creamer, 1993) and relates in turn to curd formation during renneting (Puhan and Jakob, 1994) and stability during milk powder manufacture (Singh and Creamer, 1992).

The composition of milkfat is a very important variable (Hillbrick and Augustin, 2002). In today's consumer environment, low fat products are valued, and milkfat is often the component that must be removed, for example, in producing half fat and low fat drinking milks. However, fat has a value in its own right, being an essential component in cheese, butter and a range of milkfat-based ingredients. As well as the amount of fat in milk being important, the properties of the fat need consideration. Proper functional behaviour of butter, and to some extent of cheese, depends on the appropriate melting behaviour of the fat. Butter needs sufficient solid fat to maintain shape at room temperature, but sufficient liquid phase to allow it to spread from the refrigerator. In all fats, the consumer requirement is for low levels of saturated fats and higher levels of mono- and polyunsaturated fatty acids. Finally, some specific fat components, such as omega-3 fatty acids and conjugated linoleic acid (CLA), are becoming recognised for their possible health benefits (Gurr, 1995; Hillbrick and Augustin, 2002). CLA is of particular interest because milkfat is one of the main dietary sources of this fatty acid.

Lactose has importance as the bulk phase of milk powders. In most countries, lactose is not considered to be a valued component of milk, although recent changes in the Codex Alimentarius of FAO/WHO, allowing standardisation of the level of protein in milk powders by adding lactose, may change this.

Minerals are not generally considered to be valuable components in milk, with the possible exception of calcium. Milk is an important dietary source of calcium, which is important for bone health and the prevention of osteoporosis. In practice, milk calcium is tightly regulated and the calcium level does not vary greatly, with a calcium to protein ratio in the range from 0.7 to 1.0 mmol/g (Davis et al., 2001). It is a relatively simple matter to fortify drinking milks with calcium from other sources.

3.2   Breed, genetics and milk quality

Differences in composition between milks from different breeds are apparent even at the simplest levels of analysis, and are well known to dairy farmers and the processing industry alike. The Jersey breed, once dominant for commercial milk production in some countries, is known for high levels of fat and protein, and higher overall levels of solids in the milk (i.e. less water); however, it produces more fat relative to the amount of protein. It has been observed that Jersey milk performs better in cheesemaking, but recent work has shown that, if milk is standardised for both fat content and protein content, the cheesemaking properties are indistinguishable between the Jersey and Friesian–Holstein breeds (Auldist et al., 2001). Sensory analysis of ripened Cheddar cheese showed only minor differences, all attributable to slight differences in mineral composition due to the standardisation process (Greenwood et al., 2002).

In New Zealand, the majority of herds are tested at one central laboratory, the National Milk Analysis Centre in Hamilton. Because of a relatively uniform regime of pastoral farming across New Zealand, their results allow a good breed comparison. Compositional data for each of the main dairy breeds in New Zealand are given in Table 3.2.

Recently, it has been noticed that the Friesian breed, the main dairy breed farmed in New Zealand and Australia, has diverged noticeably from the Holstein

Table 3.2 Breed differences in New Zealand milk composition (calculated from Livestock Improvement Corporation, 2001)

Breed	Milk solids %	Protein %	Protein:fat %
Jersey	9.8	4.1	71
Friesian–Jersey cross (F1, F2)	8.7	3.7	75
Friesian	7.9	3.5	79
Ayrshire	7.9	3.6	81

breed of Europe and North America in terms of size of animal, milk volume yield per animal and milk composition, although both had a common origin a little over 100 years ago. The two strains were compared in an extended trial, and first lactation results suggest that the milk from Holsteins is lower in fat, protein and casein concentrations, although the lactation milk yield is higher (Auldist *et al.*, 2000a; Kolver *et al.*, 2002 – see Table 3.6 below for data).

3.2.1   The relationship between breed and genetic polymorphisms
Apart from obvious breed differences, there is a range of well-known genetic polymorphisms of milk proteins. Genetic polymorphism occurs when there is a change to the protein structure, usually as a result of a point mutation in the coding DNA. The resulting proteins are referred to as variants, and are designated by a letter, usually in the order of discovery.

Genetic polymorphism in milk proteins was first described by Aschaffenburg and Drewry (1955), and polymorphic forms, or genetic variants, have been described in the common dairy breeds for all major milk proteins excepting α_{s2}-casein and α-lactalbumin. The distribution of the main genetic variants in the major dairy breeds is given in Table 3.3. Of particular note is the higher level of κ-casein B in the Jersey breed. The β-lactoglobulin A and B variants are more or less evenly distributed in most breeds.

3.2.2   Genetic effects on gross composition
Heritability is a term that describes the proportion of natural variation that can be explained by genetic differences. Heritabilities of milk characteristics have been reported by a number of different authors. Some of these are given in Table 3.4. The values generally explain about half the within-breed variation; however, many of the genes responsible for this variation have yet to be identified. The heritabilities for concentrations of milk components are notably higher than those for production of milk components, reflecting a larger environmental impact on the volume of milk produced.

Fat and protein content in milk are often assumed to be quite tightly linked genetically. The results of a breeding programme over three generations in the Netherlands challenge this assumption. The fixed effect for protein to fat ratio

Table 3.3 Gene frequency of the major genetic variants of the major milk proteins in selected dairy breeds (data from Buchberger, 1995)

Protein/breed	Variant frequency (%)			
α_{s1}-**Casein**	**A**	**B**	**C**	
Holstein–Friesian, Ayrshire, Brown	Rare	90–99	1–9	
Jersey	Rare	71–89	·10–19	
Guernsey	Rare	71–80	20–29	
α_{s2}-**Casein**	**A**	**D**		
All breeds	100	Rare		
β-**Casein**	**A1**	**A2**	**A3**	**B**
Holstein–Friesian	46–71	46–70	Rare	1–14
Jersey	3–24	46–70	Rare	30–46
Ayrshire	46–71	20–45	Rare	1–14
Guernsey	3–24	>70	Rare	1–14
Brown	3–24	46–70	Rare	15–29
κ-**Casein**	**A**	**B**		
Holstein–Friesian, Ayrshire	70–93	7–29		
Jersey	32–49	50–66		
Guernsey, Brown	50–69	30–49		
β-**Lactoglobulin**	**A**	**B**	**C**	
Most breeds	38–58	42–69	<5	
Ayrshire	5–20	70–88	<5	
α-**Lactalbumin**	**A**	**B**		
All breeds	Rare	100		

Table 3.4 Heritabilities of milk characteristics

Characteristic	Heritability	Breed	Reference
Protein concentration	0.37	Holstein	Wilcox *et al.*, 1971
	0.56	Jersey	Wilcox *et al.*, 1971
	0.59	Holstein	de Jaeger and Kennedy, 1987
Fat concentration	0.57	Holstein	Wilcox *et al.*, 1971
	0.71	Jersey	Wilcox *et al.*, 1971
	0.61	Holstein	de Jaeger and Kennedy, 1987
Carrier[a]	0.61	Holstein	de Jaeger and Kennedy, 1987
Lactose	0.36	Ayrshire	Robertson *et al.*, 1956
Minerals	0.50	Ayrshire	Robertson *et al.*, 1956
Colour	0.40–0.49	Friesian	Winkelman *et al.*, 1999
	0.17–0.31	Jersey	Winkelman *et al.*, 1999

[a] Carrier is defined by these authors as the sum of all components other than protein and fat.

between selected high fat and low fat lines differed by 5.4%, 8.8% and 12.6% over the three successive generations of selection (Vos and Groen, 1998). This indicates clear potential to breed for changed ratios of protein to fat.

Genetic polymorphisms of the major milk proteins have in many cases been tied to changes in milk composition (Ng-Kwai-Hang *et al.*, 1987; Ng-Kwai-Hang and Grosclaude, 1992; Hill, 1993; Puhan and Jakob, 1994; Hill *et al.*, 1995a, 1995b; Ng-Kwai-Hang, 1997; Ojala *et al.*, 1997; Coulon *et al.*, 1998; Bobe *et al.*, 1999). The clearest example of this is the difference in milk composition between milks containing only the A variant of β-lactoglobulin and milks containing only the B variant. This difference was explored by Hill *et al.* (1995a, 1995b). Briefly, a farm was set up with 200 β-lactoglobulin AA phenotype cows, and 200 β-lactoglobulin BB phenotype cows. The two herds were matched for age, breeding worth and breed composition. The two groups were run as one herd, and milked in a milking shed equipped with dual milk lines and collection vats, so that the milk from each phenotype could be collected separately without disruption to milking practices. The herd was managed as a seasonal supply herd: cows were calved in July/August and were milked through to March/April. The herd was managed in this way for two years, and a variety of experiments was carried out using the milk. Composition data for the milk collected monthly over the two-year period are summarised in Fig. 3.2. The genetic basis for the difference observed in this trial has since been defined, and is a mutation within a consensus binding site for activator protein-2, at position -430 bp upstream from the transcription initiation site for β-lactoglobulin (Lum *et al.*, 1997).

Polymorphism of κ-casein has also been linked to changes in composition. This usually appears as a higher concentration of κ-casein in the milk of BB

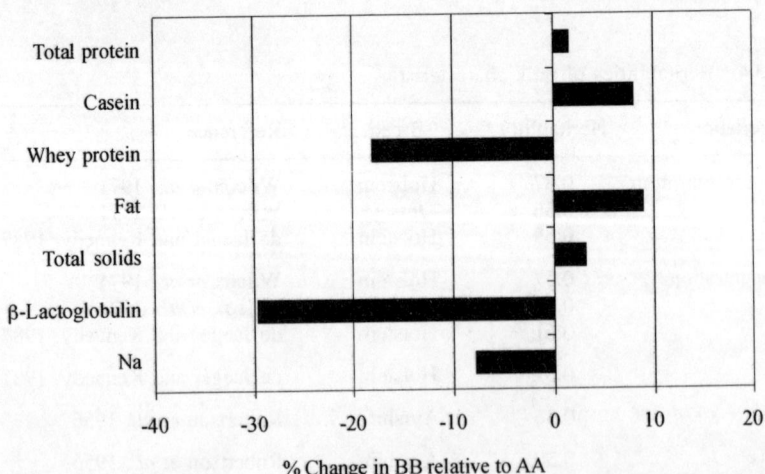

Fig. 3.2   Effect of β-lactoglobulin polymorphism on milk composition. Bars refer to the percentage difference in the composition of the BB milk relative to the AA milk. Results are based on 40 samples of each milk taken over two years. Each herd comprised 200 cows.

phenotype cows, with a consequent overall increase in total casein and cheese yield (Puhan and Jakob, 1994). The consequence of higher levels of κ-casein is a smaller micelle size, leading to better coagulation properties and firmer curd in cheesemaking. The κ-casein variant effect observed in our work was about half the effect seen for β-lactoglobulin. Because κ-casein B is only a small proportion of the gene pool in Holstein cattle, any value of breeding for this variant would probably be offset by the overall loss of genetic gain. The genetic basis for the difference in expression between the A and B forms is unclear: a study of expression in AB animals showed only a modest increase in expressed sequences of mRNA (13%), and no polymorphisms were found in the promoter region. Allele-specific differences in the length of mRNAs suggest that the level of κ-casein may be under a post-translational control (Debeljak *et al.*, 2000). As not all studies have found differential expression of protein or casein between the variants (Dikkeboom *et al.*, 2000), caution is advised concerning breeding specifically for this variant.

A study comparing both β-lactoglobulin and κ-casein polymorphisms with natural variation (Bobe *et al.*, 1999) has concluded that the κ-casein phenotype explains 25% of the phenotypic variation of the κ-casein content and 11% of the variation of α_{s1}-casein, that β-lactoglobulin polymorphism explains 26% of the variation of β-lactoglobulin composition, 4% of the variation of α_{s1}-casein and 6% of the variation of β-casein, and that neither polymorphism explains any variation in total protein. The last observation is consistent with results reported by other authors (Hill, 1993). All other effects were at the 1% level or less. This means that, for practical purposes, these polymorphisms primarily affect the ratio of casein to whey protein (casein number).

3.2.3   Genetic effects on milkfat composition

Although there are undoubtedly important genetic effects on milkfat composition, evidence to date is relatively sparse. The most obvious genetic effects are seen in the differences between butters made from Jersey and Holstein milkfats. Jersey butter is consistently seen to be harder (i.e. higher solid fat content – MacGibbon, 1996) and Jersey milkfat is more yellow than its Friesian or Ayrshire counterpart (Winkelman *et al.*, 1999). The Friesian–Jersey comparison was analysed further by MacGibbon (1996) to identify differences in the fatty acids making up the triglycerides (Table 3.5).

A recently discovered polymorphism of the gene coding for acyl CoA – diacylglycerol acyl transferase (DGAT), an essential enzyme in milkfat synthesis – explains some of the variability in milkfat composition (Grisart *et al.*, 2002). The gene for this has been found on the centromeric end of bovine chromosome 14 and the polymorphism results in a structural change from the highly conserved lysine 232 to alanine in the enzyme. This change has been linked to a change of 0.4% in milkfat proportion. No doubt further genetic polymorphisms that can explain differences in milkfat composition will soon be described.

Table 3.5 Mean solid fat content and fatty acid composition for milkfat from Friesian and Jersey factory supply herds on the same day (MacGibbon, 1996); fatty acids are expressed as g per 100 g fat

Fatty acid	Friesian ($n = 11$)	Jersey ($n = 8$)
C4:0	3.8	3.8
C6:0	2.4	2.5
C8:0	1.3	1.5[***]
C10:0	2.8	3.4[***]
C12:0	3.2	3.9[***]
C14:0	10.7	11.2[**]
C16:0	29.8	28.7[*]
C18:0	10.5	12.1[***]
C18:1	22.1	20.6[*]
C18:2	1.2	1.3[*]
C18:2c	1.3	0.9[***]
C18:3	0.8	1.0[**]
SFC10	54%	57%

Significance levels are [*]$p < 0.05$; [**]$p < 0.01$; [***]$p < 0.001$.

3.2.4   Composition effects on cheese yield and casein yield

The difference in composition between milks from different phenotypes can be used to economic advantage. The difference in composition between β-lactoglobulin AA and BB milks, shown in Fig. 3.2, leads to increased yields of casein and cheese from the same amount of milk protein (Puhan and Jakob, 1994; van den Berg, 1994; Tong et al., 1994; Hill et al., 1995a, 1995b). When milk is paid for on the basis of protein, and used for making cheese or casein, unless there is a very profitable parallel production of a specialised whey protein product, there is considerable economic benefit in using BB milk. This was piloted at the Kaikoura Dairy Co-operative in New Zealand, where the group of farmers supplying the company (which made only cheese) selectively bred for the B variant of β-lactoglobulin (Boland et al., 2000; Boland and Hill, 2001). This company was amalgamated with a larger company before the second cohort of 'BB' cows was in full production, so the final benefits could not be captured.

3.2.5   Chemistry effects – UHT fouling, pre-heater fouling

One of the more dramatic effects attributable to the chemistry of the genetic variants is the impact on heat exchanger fouling in UHT plants (Hill et al., 1997, 2000). In many warm-climate countries, recombined or reconstituted UHT milk is produced using imported milk powders. Following recombining or reconstitution, the milk is UHT treated at 140°C. Fouling of UHT heat exchangers causes decreased efficiency of operation of the plant and increased

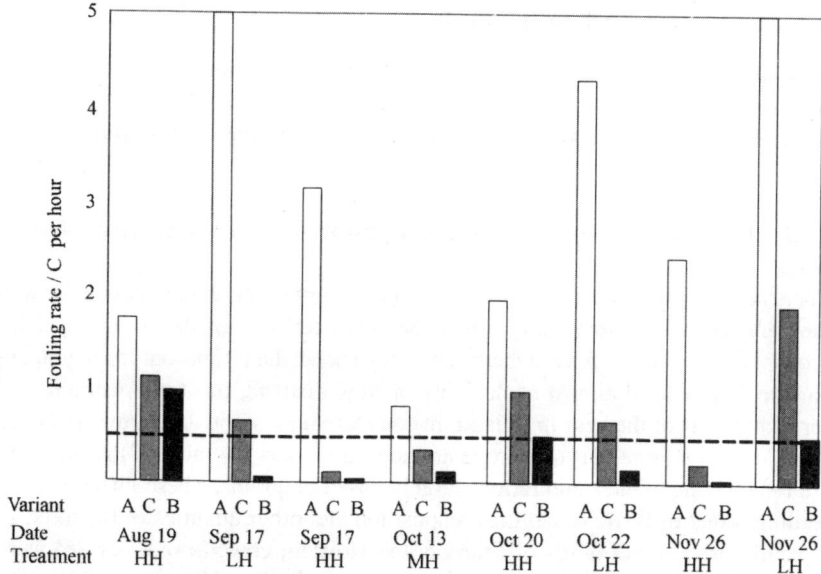

Fig. 3.3 Effect of genetic variant on fouling of UHT plants by reconstituted whole milks. Legend: A, milks containing only β-lactoglobulin AA variant; B, milks containing only β-lactoglobulin BB variant; C, control milk (mixed variants). Treatments during powder manufacture were: HH, 120°C, 180 s; MH, 95°C, 20 s; LH, 72°C, 15 s. Data from Hill *et al.* (1997).

back-pressure through the heat exchanger, and can at worst require premature plant shutdown for cleaning. Milk was collected from the β-lactoglobulin AA and BB cows in the herd described earlier in this chapter, and used to make milk powder. A range of powders was made during the peak of the production season, with different preheat treatments. These powders were then tested for UHT fouling. Typical results are presented in Fig. 3.3. This shows a dramatic difference between the A and B variants in their fouling properties. These results were seen over both years of the trial, for both skim and whole milk powders, and in pre-heater fouling in milk powder manufacture (although to a lesser degree).

Further analysis of the data from these trials shows no relationship between fouling and any compositional differences between the milks (data not shown – see Hill *et al.*, 1997, for details). Thus the difference in fouling behaviour must be attributable to differences in the chemistry of heat effects on the different β-lactoglobulin variants.

A similar genetic-variant-dependent difference in fouling was seen for κ-casein AA and BB, with the BB milk fouling at about twice the rate of the AA milk. A semi-factorial trial with both κ-casein and β-lactoglobulin variants showed the two variant effects to be independent and additive (Hill *et al.*, 2000).

3.3   Cow diet and milk quality

Cow nutrition can have important effects on milk composition. Proteins are relatively unaffected provided the cow has an adequate level of nutrition; however, the milkfat is very considerably affected by diet composition.

3.3.1   Differences between milks from pasture-fed and concentrate-fed cows

There are two quite distinct ways of managing dairy cows, which dictate the way they are fed and consequently affect the characteristics of the milk and dairy products. Pastoral farming, where the cows spend their time outdoors grazing pasture, is practised almost exclusively in New Zealand, most of Australia, and for a large part of the year in Ireland. In contrast, most of the dairy cows in North America and a large part of Europe are housed indoors for most of the time and are fed on concentrates and rations largely based on grains. These differences in feeding affect milk yield and the composition and other qualities of the milk. In a parallel trial, small herds of Friesian and Holstein cows ($n = 27$ or 26) were fed either on pasture or on total mixed rations (TMR). The pasture-fed cows produced milk with higher concentrations of milkfat, whereas the cows fed on TMR produced greater volumes of milk and higher concentrations of lactose (Auldist et al., 2000a; Kolver et al., 2000, 2002). Some data are given in Table 3.6. Milks from pasture-fed and ration-fed cows also show significant differences in fatty acid composition (Palmquist et al., 1993; White et al., 2001; Taylor and MacGibbon, 2002), though these differences are confounded with seasonal effects on milkfat from pasture-fed cows (Taylor and MacGibbon, 2002); they are discussed in Section 3.4.2.

3.3.2   Effect of diet on milkfat composition

Cow diet can have a considerable effect on milkfat composition. Milkfat is composed mostly of triglycerides. The physical properties of milkfat products are largely governed by the chain length and degree of unsaturation of the fatty acids that make up the triglyceride. Nutritional and health benefits are also affected by the positioning of double bonds and regioisomerism (i.e. position in

Table 3.6 Differences in milk composition between cows fed on pasture and total mixed rations (TMR) (data from Kolver et al., 2002)

	NZ Friesian		Holstein	
	Pasture	TMR	Pasture	TMR
Milk yield (kg per cow, full lactation)	5300	7304	5882	10 097
Fat (%)	5.03	4.60	4.28	3.62
Protein (%)	3.74	3.65	3.50	3.54

Table 3.7 Effect of pasture species and season on milkfat composition (20-day rotation) (data from Thomson *et al.*, 2002)

	Ryegrass	Timothy	Standard error of difference (between means) – s.e.d.	Significance
Spring				
Milkfat yield (kg/cow/d)	0.85	0.94	0.05	***
Monounsaturates (%)	22.8	24.9	0.51	***
Polyunsaturates (%)	3.9	4.6	0.17	***
Total unsaturates (%)	26.7	29.5	0.61	***
Autumn				
Milkfat yield (kg/cow/d)	0.52	0.48	0.04	
Monounsaturates (%)	30.8	28.9	0.54	***
Polyunsaturates (%)	6.9	6.1	0.36	*
Total unsaturates (%)	37.7	35.1	0.63	***

Significance levels are $*p < 0.05$; $**p < 0.01$; $***p < 0.001$.

the triglyceride) of the fatty acids. In the cow, the fatty acids come from two sources: fatty acids of less than C16 are synthesised *de novo* in the mammary gland, but fatty acids of C18 or longer chain length come from dietary sources. Fatty acids of C16 are derived from both sources (Hawke and Taylor, 1995). Dietary fat is extensively modified by microorganisms in the rumen, so that the fatty acid profile that is received by the cow is the product of diet composition and rumen modification. The most important modification in the rumen is the saturation of polyunsaturated fatty acids. High concentrations of polyunsaturated fatty acids are toxic to some microbial species in the rumen, which carry out desaturation as a detoxifying mechanism.

Feeding of pasture species with different lipid content results in milkfat with different composition. In a comparison between milk from cows grazing ryegrass/white clover pasture and cows grazing timothy/white clover pasture, at two different times of year, the milkfat showed species and season-dependent differences in levels of unsaturated fatty acids (Thomson *et al.*, 2002) as shown in Table 3.7. The changes in milkfat composition are as much a consequence of the amount of plant lipid as of the composition of that lipid. When the rumen is presented with a high level of polyunsaturated fat, its capacity to desaturate is limited so that more unsaturated fatty acids, particularly C18:1, are available to the cow for milkfat synthesis.

CLA has been identified as an important health-promoting component of milkfat with anti-cancer properties (Parodi, 1994, 2001; Gurr, 1995). Milkfat from pasture-fed cows contains relatively high levels of this fatty acid, of the order of 1% (MacGibbon *et al.*, 2001), in contrast to milkfat from grain-fed animals which typically contains about 0.4–0.5% (Chin *et al.*, 1992; White *et al.*, 2001). At least one company in the US has converted to pasture feeding and makes a marketing position based on the (relatively) high level of CLA in its cheese ('Northern Meadows' cheese from Full Circle Farms – see the URL at the end of this chapter). There is a wide variation in the level of CLA from milk of individual pasture-fed cows and between herds. A recent New Zealand study across 44 herds found a herd-to-herd range from 0.8% to 2.2% on a single day, and a seasonal variation from 0.8% in early spring to 1.4% in autumn for the overall average (MacGibbon *et al.*, 2001). It is now recognised that some of the CLA comes directly from production in the rumen, but that the majority arises from desaturation of trans-11 linoleic acid (vaccenic acid) in the mammary gland (Palmquist, 2001). Thus, the level of CLA in the milkfat will be a function of the availability of substrate and the activity of stearoyl-CoA Δ-9 desaturase.

3.3.3   Modification of composition by dietary supplements

Both the relative amount and the composition of milkfat can be modified by dietary supplements. A full discussion of this area is beyond the scope of this chapter, and the reader is referred to the recent reviews of Bauman and Griinari (2001) and Chilliard *et al.* (2000).

Nutritional manipulation of milkfat concentration has been reviewed by a number of authors, including Sutton (1989), Kennelly (1993), Murphy (2000) and Bauman and Griinari (2001). Milkfat concentration is depressed to a small extent when grazing cows are fed concentrates; however, an excess of readily fermentable carbohydrate in the diet, leading to an acidic condition in the rumen, will give a more dramatic decrease in milkfat concentration, so-called 'low milkfat syndrome' (Sutton, 1989; Stockdale *et al.*, 2001). This condition has been known for over 100 years. It is probably not sustainable and may impact adversely on the cow's health. Under acidic conditions, the rumen metabolism changes to produce higher concentrations of propionic acid and *trans* C18:1 (Holmes *et al.*, 2002, pp. 356–357). It has recently been proposed that low milkfat syndrome is largely due to the formation of *trans*-10, *cis*-12 CLA in the rumen (Bauman and Griinari, 2001).

Reductions in milkfat concentration have been achieved by feeding a wide range of supplements, including fat (Palmquist *et al.*, 1993; Beaulieu and Palmquist, 1995), fish oils (Chilliard and Doreau, 1997; Keady and Mayne, 2000), and oleamide (Jenkins, 1999). Many of these act in a similar way, reducing the level of short- and medium-chain fatty acids and increasing C18:1 fatty acid, suggesting a suppression of *de novo* fatty acid synthesis.

A more dramatic reduction in milkfat production can be achieved by feeding CLA (Loor and Herbein, 1998). To be effective, rumen desaturation must be avoided, so ruminal protection or rumen bypass must be used. A reduction of milkfat percentage by up to half has been demonstrated by direct infusion of CLA into the abomasum (Chouinard *et al.*, 1999; Kraft *et al.*, 2000). CLA exists as a number of isomeric forms. The common form in animal fat is the *cis*-9, *trans*-11 isomer. It has recently been identified that the other most common isomer in synthetic CLA, the *trans*-10, *cis*-12 isomer, is responsible for milkfat

Table 3.8   Yield and characteristics of fatty acids in milkfat produced by cows fed 2 kg oilseed per cow per day that was unprotected crushed seed (Canola 1) or protected against ruminal biohydrogenation by two different processes (Canola 2 and Canola 3). The control sample was from grass-fed cows (data from Thomson *et al.*, 2002)

	Control	Canola 1	Canola 2	Canola 3
Milkfat yield (kg/cow/d)	0.53[a]	0.56[a]	0.50[a]	0.58[a]
Monounsaturates (%)	32.4[a]	38.4[b]	42.0[c]	39.5b[b]
Polyunsaturates (%)	6.3[a]	6.1[a]	6.8[a]	10.6b[b]
Total unsaturates (%)	38.7[a]	44.5[b]	49.0[c]	50.0[c]

[abc] Means within fatty acid groups having superscripts with common letters are not significantly different ($p < 0.001$).

reduction (Baumgard *et al.*, 1999). It has been suggested that this isomer operates through down-regulation of expression of the stearoyl CoA Δ-9 desaturase gene (Choi *et al.*, 2000), although the mechanism is unclear.

Milkfat composition can be modified by feeding a wide variety of supplements. For a comprehensive review of this area, see Chilliard *et al.* (2000). Of particular interest is the feeding of oilseed, or ruminally protected oilseed (Ashes *et al.*, 1992, 1997; Murphy *et al.*, 1995; Chilliard *et al.*, 2000; Murphy, 2000). Feeding ruminally protected Canola can modify the level of unsaturation of milkfat and hence the perceived healthiness (Ashes *et al.*, 1992, 1997), and the level of solid fat content and thus the spreadability of butter (Thomson *et al.*, 2002). Data from some recent trials are shown in Table 3.8.

3.4   Other aspects of animal husbandry and milk quality

3.4.1   Colostrum

Colostrum is the secretion produced over the first few days after parturition. The components of colostrum are synthesised in the mammary gland over several days prior to parturition. Colostrum is rich in special nutrients for the newborn calf, in particular a high level of immunoglobulins, believed to confer significant passive immunity against gut pathogens, and a range of growth factors. In addition, the milk has a higher level of β-carotene, imparting an intense yellow colour, and a high level of somatic cells. A summary of the main differences in composition is given in Table 3.9.

Recently there has been a lot of commercial interest in colostrum because of its elevated levels of bioactives, especially growth factors, and there is a wide range of literature supporting the health benefits of colostrum (Scammell, 2001). At least nine companies are known to be producing specialist colostrum products in Europe, the US, Australia and New Zealand, with production in 2001 estimated at 600 tonnes. The price for colostrum powder is estimated to be about $25 000/tonne, more than 10 times that of normal milk powders (Scammell, 2001).

Table 3.9 Comparison of bulk components and bioactive protein components of normal milk and colostrum (data from Holmes *et al.*, 2002, p. 350 and papers cited therein for bulk components, and from Scammell, 2001, for bioactives)

Component	Colostrum	Normal milk
Total protein (%)	8–21	3–4.8
Casein (%)	3–6	2.6–3.8
Fat (%)	3–11	3–6
Carotene (ppm)	50–300	1
Somatic cells (per ml)	1–2×10^6	2–30×10^4
Total immunoglobulins (%)	3–15	0.02–0.1
IgA (%)	0.32–0.62	0.01
IgG1 (%)	4.8–8.7	0.04
IgG2 (%)	0.16–0.29	0.005
IgM (%)	0.37–0.61	0.005
IGF-1 (ppm)[a]	0.1–2	0.025
IGF-2 (ppm)[a]	0.1–2	0.002
TGF-B (ppm)[a]	20–40	0.002
EGF (ppm)[a]	4–8	0.002
Lactoferrin (g/l)	1.5–2	0.1
Lysozyme (ppm)	0.1–0.7	0.1–0.3
Lactoperoxidase (ppm)	30	20

[a] Abbreviations for growth factors: IGF: insulin-like growth factor; TGF: transforming growth factor; EGF: epidermal growth factor.

3.4.2   Seasonal effects in pastoral farming

Variations in milk characteristics during the season are well known for cows that are farmed in seasonally calving, pasture-based dairying systems. This is due largely to the combined effects of the lactation cycle of the cow and seasonal effects on the composition of the pasture, which in turn impact on milk composition. Similar variation is not normally seen to such an extent in herds housed indoors and fed concentrate, because their feed supply is constant and calving is usually staggered throughout the year. Typical seasonal variation in milk composition is shown in Fig. 3.4.

Seasonal variation was studied by Auldist *et al.* (1998) by running parallel small herds (about 20 cows each) that were calved at three-monthly intervals. Concentrations of major milk components, including total protein, casein and fat, increased as a function of the stage of lactation; however, other factors of importance for the processor, including protein to fat ratio, casein to whey protein ratio and solid fat content, were all affected primarily by the time of year.

Seasonal effects are seen in the composition of milkfat from pasture-fed cows. These are manifest in the changes in solid fat content shown in Fig. 3.4. The lush spring-growth grass is rich in C18:3 fatty acid, which is only partially desaturated in the rumen, giving rise to higher levels of C18:1 as well as C18:0 fatty acids in the milkfat triglycerides. Summer grass gives rise to lower levels

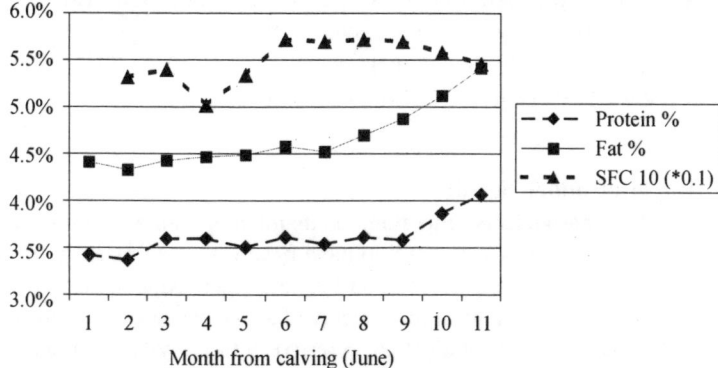

Fig. 3.4 Seasonal variation in milk composition for New Zealand milk (all breeds). Data from Livestock Improvement Corporation (2001) and MacGibbon and McLennan (1987).

of C18:0 and C18:1, but more C16:0 fatty acids in the milkfat (Taylor and MacGibbon, 2002).

3.4.3   Effects of plane of nutrition

Restriction of nutrition is well known to have the effect of reducing milk production; however, there are also impacts on the composition of the milk that is produced. Much of the work that has been done in this area relates to pasture feeding, in order to understand the impact of pasture shortages on milk (for example, in times of drought). Most authors are agreed that restricted feeding results in a lower concentration of milk protein and, importantly, casein (Macheboeuf *et al.*, 1993; O'Brien *et al.*, 1997, 1999; Petch *et al.*, 1997; Mackle *et al.*, 1999; Auldist *et al.*, 2000b). This is particularly important for making cheese (O'Brien *et al.*, 1997, 1999) and, when coupled with genetic variant effects on milk composition, can be particularly important for cheesemaking quality (Macheboeuf *et al.*, 1993; Mackle *et al.*, 1999; Auldist *et al.*, 2000b).

Many experiments concerning the plane of nutrition are complicated by genetic effects, use of supplements to top up the diet of fully fed cows, and seasonal effects. For this reason, the study by Petch *et al.* (1997) is possibly the most definitive. This study used 18 identical twin pairs, fully fed on pasture or fed at 65% of the fully fed rate on pasture (with a third leg based on supplements, not considered here). The study showed that, on the restricted diet, both casein and whey protein were significantly reduced by similar amounts (4–8%), giving no significant effect on casein number. Fat and lactose concentrations were not significantly affected. The experiments of Macheboeuf *et al,* (1993) and Auldist *et al.* (2000b) similarly showed no effect on fat or lactose; however, other studies, including those of O'Brien *et al.* (1997, 1999) and Mackle *et al.* (1999), observed differences in lactose and fat concentrations. Mackle *et al.*

(1999) also recorded differences in fat composition. The significant difference between the two types of result appears to be the use of supplementary feeding of concentrates in the fully fed animals, which can introduce differences due to nutritional quality as distinct from plane of nutrition.

3.4.4 Effect of udder health

Udder health is particularly important in maintaining milk composition. The effects of mastitis on milk composition have been reviewed recently by Auldist and Hubble (1998). A strong correlation between decreasing somatic cell count and increasing casein content in milk received at the factory has been observed (Bob Franks, personal communication, referred to in Lacy-Hulbert and Auldist, 2002). Mastitis has three important adverse effects on milk production, even at sub-clinical levels (Lacy-Hulbert and Auldist, 2002). First, bacterial toxins and the inflammatory response cause damage to mammary epithelial cells, leading to a reduction in mammary-synthesised components. Second, the inflammation of the mammary gland leads to leakiness of the tight junctions, leading to higher leakage of serum proteins, particularly serum albumin, immunoglobulins and, importantly, plasminogen, which can be activated to the proteolytic enzyme plasmin. Third, the bacteria causing the infection produce extracellular proteases and lipases that break down milk proteins and fats, particularly casein, which is more susceptible to enzyme action than globular proteins, because of its extended structure. Plasminogen can also be activated to plasmin by bacterial enzymes, causing further protein hydrolysis. The net result of all this is to produce milk with a lower casein number and poorer cheesemaking properties (Barbano, 1994). Lipolysis can also lead to flavour defects from release of short-chain fatty acids.

Milkfat is affected by increased lipolysis in some mastitic milks, leading to increased levels of free fatty acids which can have adverse flavour effects. Whether this is due to bacterial lipases or animal origin lipases may vary depending on the species of bacterial infection. It is also likely that many mastitic infections lead to fragility of the milkfat globule membrane, making the fat more susceptible to release and hydrolysis by endogenous lipases (Deeth and FitzGerald, 1995).

The degree of mastitis is generally indicated by the somatic cell count (SCC) in milk, and the SCC has been correlated in a number of cases with product deterioration on storage. It seems likely that the storage problems are caused by proteolytic and lipolytic activities resulting from the mastitic condition, rather than the SCC as such. Recent work showed that milk with low SCC (<100 000/ml) when pasteurised had superior keeping qualities, with no reduction in organoleptic properties after 21 days of refrigerated storage. A corresponding milk with higher SCC (>800 000/ml) had significantly deteriorated in this time (Ma et al., 2000). Other work has identified adverse effects of a high SCC on the storage stability of UHT milks and on whole milk powders (Auldist et al., 1996a, 1996b).

3.4.4 Effects of milk handling

This area has been reviewed by Deeth (1993) and Deeth and FitzGerald (1995). Briefly, milk contains powerful endogenous lipases. Milkfat triglycerides are protected from hydrolysis by encapsulation in the milkfat globule, surrounded by the milkfat globule membrane. Severe mechanical shear can break a proportion of the milkfat globule membrane, releasing triglyceride and allowing lipolysis to occur. The sensitivity of the milkfat globule membrane to shear can vary according to cow genetics and environmental factors such as cow nutrition and health, and stage of lactation. There is also evidence for endogenous activators and inhibitors of lipolysis in milk (Deeth and FitzGerald, 1995). Milk from late lactation, and from cows on a low plane of nutrition, is thought to be more susceptible to lipolysis, though understanding of the factors affecting lipolysis is far from clear. Typical sources of shear include some types of milking machine, and some pumps, especially if air is entrained in the milk during pumping. This can be a particular problem with poorly maintained equipment, especially milking machines with overhead milk lines. Homogenisation will induce lipolysis, though it is usually carried out on milks for drinking following an extended pasteurisation step that inactivates most of the lipase activity.

Lipolysis causes off-flavours due to the released short-chain free fatty acids (hydrolytic rancidity), and changes in functionality, which affect manufacturing and product performance. Changes in functionality can be due to free fatty acids, but are more often due to the formation of mono- and diglycerides, which have surface-active properties. One well-known example is a decrease in foam formation, for example in cappuccino coffees.

3.5   Future trends

3.5.1   Impact of genetic engineering

Leaving aside genetic modification for the production of pharmaceuticals in milk, it seems unlikely that genetic modification of cows to change the milk composition for functional or nutritional purposes will be commercially viable for the foreseeable future. There are several reasons for this.

- Consumer acceptance of genetically modified (GM) foods is still variable throughout the world, with some countries having strict labelling requirements and negative public attitudes to GM foods. Because milk is a liquid product handled in large bulk quantities during processing, maintenance of batch identity and keeping GM milk separate are more difficult than with discrete products.
- Milk is an animal product, and is strongly targeted at the health of babies and young people. This has been identified in consumer surveys as a very sensitive area (e.g. compared with the acceptability of GM fruit and vegetables), and for this reason milk will probably be one of the last foods in which genetic modification is accepted.

- The production of commercial-sized herds of GM cows will be very costly and very slow, even if expensive cloning and embryo transfer methods are used. This cannot be justified by a small premium for improved nutrition or functionality arising from genetic modification.
- Finally, and probably most importantly, a switch to genetic modification will severely limit genetic gain, because the ongoing gene pool will be restricted to the genetics of the donor animals for the original GM parents. This segregation from the wider global bovine gene pool will prevent participation in the ongoing genetic improvement of the species, which is currently occurring at about 2% per annum and worth billions of dollars a year in global herd improvement.

3.5.2 Novel forages and feeding regimes

Although it is unlikely that cows will be genetically engineered for altered milk composition in the near future, it is probable that some cows are already consuming GM crop plants such as maize, canola and cotton seeds and oils. There is considerable scope to extend the range and viability of pastoral dairy farming into now marginal areas, by developing GM plants better capable of withstanding drought or extremes of temperature. Plants capable of producing oils and proteins that are protected against rumen breakdown may also be developed, making these components available for gut absorption. Any or all of these changes have the potential to modify milk characteristics, although the significance remains to be seen.

3.5.3 Relative amounts of protein and fat in milk

If the consumer desire for low-fat diets continues, the decreasing demand for fat is likely to drive breeding in the direction of lower fat, higher protein milk. Some of the ways in which this might occur have already been indicated earlier in this chapter. Examples of cows that already produce milk with only 2% fat and normal protein levels, and with elevated levels of unsaturated fatty acids, are known; however, these are rare, and the present valuation of milkfat makes their widespread propagation unlikely. Even against a decreased breeding value for milkfat, optimum breeding means that milkfat production is almost certain to exceed demand, assuming that the current decrease in consumer demand continues (Gibson, 2000). It is perfectly feasible that we may eventually have herds producing milk with 2% fat, relatively rich in unsaturated fatty acids and with high levels of CLA, but that time is well in the future.

3.5.4 Sustainability issues

There is an increasing focus on long-term sustainability in farming and particularly dairying and its effect on greenhouse gases. The principal issue is methane production. Domestic livestock account for about 26% of all methane production (Environmental Protection Agency estimate, see http://www.epa.gov/ ghginfo/topics/topic2.htm for more detail), and cattle make up the major proportion of this. Solutions are likely to involve modification of rumen function to minimise methanogenesis, which will also change the overall energy balance of the rumen and possibly alter the fatty acid profile received by the cow. This can be expected to impact on milkfat composition, although the extent is not clear.

3.6   Sources of further information and advice

For general information on pastoral dairy farming and cow lactation, the reader is referred to the excellent *Milk Production from Pasture* by Holmes *et al.* (2002).

There are two recent periodical issues that relate specifically to milk composition and its variability and suitability for various purposes: the British Society of Animal Science Occasional Publication No. 25 (2000) entitled *Milk Composition*, edited by R.E. Agnew, K.W. Agnew and A.M. Fearon, and the *Australian Journal of Dairy Technology*, Volume 56, No. 2 (2001), a special issue on 'Farm to Fork 2001'. For further information about milk protein polymorphism, the reader is referred to 'Milk Protein Polymorphism', IDF Special Issue 9702 (International Dairy Federation, Brussels). For more information about factors relating to cheese manufacture, 'Cheese Yield and Factors Affecting its Control', IDF Special Issue 9402 (International Dairy Federation, Brussels) is recommended, particularly Topics 3 and 4.

For recent reviews on the relationship between milk composition and the properties of dairy products, the reader is referred to papers by Williams (2002) and Hillbrick and Augustin (2002) in the *Australian Journal of Dairy Technology*. These report on a major Australian initiative, the 'Milk for Manufacturing' project commissioned by the Victorian Department for Natural Resources and Environment.

The following Internet URLs describe some claimed benefits of breed-specific milk. Note that these are unsupported producers' claims and should be treated with caution:

- http://www.jerseyfarm.com/
- http://www.promisedlanddairy.com/index.html
- http://www.meistercheese.com/gmidwest.html
- http://www.gold-top.co.uk/ (under construction)
- https://www3.quik.com/texasjersey/
- http://www.springhillcheese.com/

The following URL advertises CLA-rich cheese from pasture-fed cows, and describes some background to CLA cheese, including some literature references:

- http://fullcirclefarm.net/Default.htm

3.7   Acknowledgements

I would like to thank Martin Auldist and Sue Petch for allowing me to use their unpublished results. Thanks are due to Alastair MacGibbon and Jeremy Hill (Fonterra Research Centre), Professor Jim Harper (Ohio State University) and Martin Auldist (Ellinbank Research Centre, DNRE, Victoria, Australia) for assistance with the preparation of this chapter. This work was supported by the New Zealand Foundation for Research, Science and Technology (FRST) under Contract DRIX0001, and by the Fonterra Research Centre.

3.8   References

ANEMA, S.G. and CREAMER, L.K. (1993) Effect of the A and B variants of both alpha (s1)- and kappa-casein on bovine casein micelle solvation and kappa-casein content. *J. Dairy Res.* 60: 505–516.

ASCHAFFENBURG, R. and DREWRY, J. (1955) Occurrence of different beta-lactoglobulins in cow's milk. *Nature* 176: 218–219.

ASHES, J.R., ST VINCENT WELCH, P., GULATI, S.K., SCOTT, T.W. and BROWN, G.H. (1992) Manipulation of the fatty acid composition of milk by feeding protected canola seeds. *J. Dairy Sci.* 75: 1090–1096.

ASHES, J.R., GULATI, S.K. and SCOTT, T.W. (1997) Potential to alter the content and composition of milk fat through nutrition. *J. Dairy Sci.* 80: 2204–2212.

AULDIST, M.J. and HUBBLE, I.B. (1998) Effects of mastitis on raw milk and dairy products. *Aust. J. Dairy Technol.* 53: 28–36.

AULDIST, M.J., COATS, S., SUTHERLAND, B.J., CLARKE, P.T., MCDOWELL, G.H. and ROGERS, G.L. (1996a) Effects of somatic cell count and stage of lactation on the quality and storage life of ultra high temperature milk. *J. Dairy Sci.* 63: 377–386.

AULDIST, M.J., COATS, S., SUTHERLAND, B.J., CLARKE, P.T., MCDOWELL, G.H. and ROGERS, G.L. (1996b) Effect of somatic cell count and stage of lactation on the quality of full cream milk powder. *Aust. J. Dairy Technol.* 51: 94–98.

AULDIST, M.J., WALSH, B.J. and THOMSON, N.A. (1998) Seasonal and lactational influences on bovine milk composition in New Zealand. *J. Dairy Res.* 65: 401–411.

AULDIST, M.J., NAPPER, A.R. and KOLVER, E.S. (2000a) *Asian-Aust. J. Anim. Sci.* 13 Supplement July 2000 A: 513–517..

AULDIST, M.J., THOMSON, N.A., MACKLE, T.R., HILL, J.P. and PROSSER, C.G. (2000b) Effects of pasture allowance on the yield and composition of milk from cows of different β-lactoglobulin phenotypes. *J. Dairy Sci.* 83: 2069–2074.

AULDIST, M.J., JOHNSTON, K., FITZSIMONS, P. and BOLAND, M. (2001) Effect of cow breed on cheese yield. *Aust. J. Dairy Technol.* 56: 178.

BARBANO, D.M. (1994) Overview – influence of mastitis on cheese yield. In *Cheese Yield and Factors Affecting its Control*. IDF Special Issue 9402, pp. 48–54. International Dairy Federation, Brussels.

BAUMAN, D.E. and GRIINARI, J.M. (2001) Regulation and nutritional manipulation of milk fat: low fat milk syndrome. *Livestock Prod. Sci.* 70: 15–29.

BAUMGARD, L., CORL, B., DWYER, D., SAEBO, A. and BAUMAN, D.E. (1999) Identification of CLA isomer responsible for milkfat depression. *J. Anim. Sci.* 77 (Suppl.): 117.

BEAULIEU, A.D. and PALMQUIST, D. (1995) Differential effects of high fat diets on fatty acid composition in milk of Jersey and Holstein cows. *J. Dairy Sci.* 78: 1336–1344.

BOBE, G., BEITZ, D.C., FREEMAN, A.E. and LINDBERG, G.L. (1999) Effect of milk protein genotypes on milk protein composition and its genetic parameter estimates. *J. Dairy Sci.* 82: 2797–2804.

BOLAND, M.J. and HILL, J.P. (2001) Genetic selection to increase cheese yield – the Kaikoura experience. *Aust. J. Dairy Technol.* 56: 171–176.

BOLAND, M.J., HILL, J.P. and O'CONNOR, P. (2000) Changing the milk supply to increase cheese yield: the Kaikoura experience. In *British Society of Animal Science Occasional Publication No. 25* (Agnew, R.E., Agnew, K.W. and Fearon, A.M., eds), pp. 305–316. British Society of Animal Science, Edinburgh.

BUCHBERGER, J. (1995) Genetic polymorphism of milk proteins: differences between breeds. *Int. Dairy Fed. Bull.* 304: 5–6.

CHILLIARD, Y. and DOREAU, M. (1997) Influence of supplementary fish oil and rumen protected methionine on milk yield and composition in dairy cows. *J. Dairy Sci.* 47: 1213–1216.

CHILLIARD, Y., FERLAY, A., MANSBRIDGE, R.M. and DOREAU, M. (2000) Ruminant milk fat plasticity: nutritional control of saturated, polyunsaturated *trans* and conjugated fatty acids. *Ann. Zootech.* 49: 181–205.

CHIN, S.F., LIU, W., STORKSON, J.M., HA, Y.L. and PARIZA, M.W. (1992) Dietary sources of conjugated dienoic isomers of linoleic acid, a newly recognised class of anticarcinogens. *J. Food Composition Anal.* 5: 185–197.

CHOI, Y., KIM, Y.-C., HAN, Y.-B., PARK, Y., PARIZA, M.W. and NTAMBI, J.M. (2000) The *trans*-10, *cis*-12 isomer of conjugated linoleic acid down-regulates stearoyl-CoA desaturase 1 gene expression in 3T3-L1 adipocytes. *J. Nutr.* 130: 1920–1924.

CHOUINARD, P.Y., CORNEAU, L., SAEBO, A. and BAUMAN, D.E. (1999) Milk yield and composition during abomasal infusion of conjugated linoleic acids in dairy cows. *J. Dairy Sci.* 82: 2737–2745.

COULON, J.-B., HURTAUD, C., REMOND, B. and VERITE, R. (1998) Factors contributing to variation in the proportion of casein in cows' milk true protein: a review of recent INRA experiments. *J. Dairy Sci.* 65: 375–387.

DAVIS, S.R., FARR, V.C., KNOWLES, S.O., LEE, J., KOLVER, E. and AULDIST, M. (2001) Sources of variation in milk calcium content. *Aust. J. Dairy Technol.* 56: 156.

DEBELJAK, M., SUSNIK, S., MARINSEK-LOGAR, R., MEDRANO, J.F. and DOVC, P. (2000) Allelic differences in bovine kappa-CN gene which may regulate gene expression. *Pflugers Arch.* 2000; 439 (3 Suppl): R4–6.

DEETH, H.C. (1993) Lipase activity and its effect on milk quality. *Aust. J. Dairy Technol.* 48: 96–98.

DEETH, H.C. and FITZGERALD, C.H. (1995) Lipolytic enzymes and hydrolytic rancidity in milk and milk products. In *Advanced Dairy Chemistry*, Volume 2: *Lipids*, 2nd edn (Fox, P.F., ed.), pp. 247–308. Chapman & Hall, London.

DE JAEGER, D. and KENNEDY, B.W. (1987) Genetic parameters of milk yield and composition and their relationships with alternative breeding goals. *J. Dairy Sci.* 70: 1258–1266.

DIKKEBOOM, A.L., CHEN, C.M., JAEGGI, J.J., JOHNSON, M.E., TRICOMI, W.A., ZIMBRIC, M.G., BREMEL, R. and LEWANDOWSKI, J.A. (2000) Milk proteins and cheese composition – the influence of genetic variants. *Dairy Pipeline* 12: 1–6.

GIBSON, J.P. (2000) Options for genetic improvement of milk composition. In *British Society of Animal Science Occasional Publication No. 25* (Agnew, R.E., Agnew, K.W. and Fearon, A.M., eds), pp. 109–117. British Society of Animal Science,

Edinburgh.

GREENWOOD, S., JOHNSTON, K., BOLAND, M. and AULDIST, M. (2002) Breed effects on the sensory properties of cheese and milk. *Aust. J. Dairy Technol.* 57: 21.

GRISART, B., COPPIETERS, W., FARNIR, F., KARIM, L., FORD, C., BERZI, P., CAMBISANO, N., MNI, M., REID, S., SIMON, P., SPELMAN, R., GEORGES, M. and SNELL, R. (2002) Positional candidate cloning of a QTL in dairy cattle: identification of a missense mutation in the bovine DGAT1 gene with major effect on milk yield and composition. *Genome Res.* 12: 222–231.

GURR, M.I. (1995) Nutritional significance of lipids. In *Advanced Dairy Chemistry*, Volume 2: *Lipids*, 2nd edn (Fox, P.F., ed.), pp. 349–402. Chapman & Hall, London.

HAWKE, J.C. and TAYLOR, M.W. (1995) Influence of nutritional factors on the yield, physical properties and composition of milkfat. In *Advanced Dairy Chemistry*, Volume 2: *Lipids*, 2nd edn (Fox, P.F., ed.), pp. 37–88. Chapman & Hall, London.

HIGGINS, J.J., LYNN, R.D., SMITH, J.F. and MARSHALL, K.R. (1995) Protein standardisation of milk and milk products. *Int. Dairy Fed. Bull.* 304: 26–49.

HILL, J.P. (1993) The relationship between β-lactoglobulin phenotypes and milk composition in New Zealand dairy cattle. *J. Dairy Sci.* 76: 281–286.

HILL, J.P., PATERSON, G.R., LOWE, R. and JOHNSTON, K.A. (1995a) Effect of β-lactoglobulin variants on curd firming rate, yield, maturation and sensory properties of cheddar cheese. *Int. Dairy Fed. Bull.* 304: 18–19.

HILL, J.P., THOMPSON, C.J. and ELSTON, P.D. (1995b) Effect of β-lactoglobulin variants on the yield and properties of rennet and lactic casein. *Int. Dairy Fed. Bull.* 304: 19–20.

HILL, J.P., BOLAND, M.J. and SMITH, A.F. (1997) Effect of β-lactoglobulin variants on milk powder manufacture and properties. In *Milk Protein Polymorphism*, IDF Special Issue 9702, pp. 372–394. International Dairy Federation, Brussels.

HILL, J.P., BOLAND, M.J., HARRIS, D.P. and PATERSON, G. (2000) Impact of genetic polymorphism on milk powder manufacturing and processing. In *British Society of Animal Science Occasional Publication No. 25* (Agnew, R.E., Agnew, K.W. and Fearon, A.M., eds), pp. 87–92. British Society of Animal Science, Edinburgh.

HILLBRICK, G. and AUGUSTIN, M.A. (2002) Milkfat characteristics and functionality: opportunities for improvement. *Aust. J. Dairy Technol.* 57: 45–51.

HOLMES, C.W., BROOKES, I.M., GARRICK, D.J., MACKENZIE, D.D.S., PARKINSON, T.J. and WILSON, G.F. (2002) *Milk Production from Pasture. Principles and Practices.* Massey University, Palmerston North, New Zealand.

JENKINS, T.C. (1999) Lactation performance and fatty acid composition of milk from Holstein cows fed from 0 to 5% oleamide. *J. Dairy Sci.* 82: 1525–1531.

KEADY, T.W.J. and MAYNE, C.S. (2000) The effect of fish oil supplementation to dairy cattle on milk fat content and composition. In *British Society of Animal Science Occasional Publication No. 25* (Agnew, R.E., Agnew, K.W. and Fearon, A.M., eds), pp. 275–282. British Society of Animal Science, Edinburgh.

KENNELLY, J.J. (1993) The untapped potential to alter the composition of milk by dietary means. *Adv. Dairy Technol.* 105–124.

KOLVER, E.S., NAPPER, A.R., COPEMAN, P.J.A. and MULLER, L.D. (2000) Comparison of Dutch and New Zealand Holstein Friesian genetics grazing pasture or fed a total mixed ration. *Proc. NZ Soc. Anim. Prod.* 60: 265–269.

KOLVER, E., ROCHE, J.R., DE VETH, M.J., THORNE, P.L. and NAPPER, A.R. (2002) Total mixed rations versus pasture diets: evidence for a genotype × diet interaction in dairy cow performance. *Proc. NZ Soc. Anim. Prod.* 62: 246–251.

KRAFT, J., LEBZIEN, P., FLACHOWSKY, G., MOCKEL, P. and JAHREIS, G. (2000) Duodenal infusion of conjugated linoleic acid mixture influences milk fat synthesis and milk CLA content in dairy cows. In *British Society of Animal Science Occasional Publication No. 25* (Agnew, R.E., Agnew, K.W. and Fearon, A.M., eds), pp. 143–147. British Society of Animal Science, Edinburgh.

LACY-HULBERT, S.J. and AULDIST, M.J. (2002) Effect of udder health on milk. *Proc. NZ Soc. Anim. Prod.* 62: 95–99.

LIVESTOCK IMPROVEMENT CORPORATION (2001) *Dairy Statistics 2000–2001*, Table 2.3. Livestock Improvement Corporation, Hamilton, New Zealand.

LOOR, J.J. and HERBEIN, J.H. (1998) Exogenous conjugated linoleic acid isomers reduce bovine milk fat concentration and yield by inhibiting *de novo* fatty acid synthesis. *J. Nutr.* 128: 2411–2419.

LUM, L.S., DOVC, P. and MEDRANO, J.F. (1997) Polymorphisms of bovine beta-lactoglobulin promoter and differences in the binding affinity of activator protein-2 transcription factor. *J. Dairy Sci.* 80: 1389–1397.

MA, Y., RYAN, C., BARBANO, D.M., GALTON, D.M., RUDAN, M.A. and BOOR, K.J. (2000) Effects of somatic cell count on quality and shelf-life of pasteurised fluid milk. *J. Dairy Sci.* 83: 262–274.

MACGIBBON, A.K.H. (1996) Herd-to-herd variations in the properties of milkfat. *Proc. NZ Soc. Anim. Prod.* 56: 224–227.

MACGIBBON, A.K.H. and MCLENNAN, W.D. (1987) Hardness of New Zealand patted butter: seasonal and regional variations. *NZ J. Dairy Sci. Technol.* 22: 143–156.

MACGIBBON, A.K.H., VAN DER DOES, Y.E., FONG, B.Y., ROBINSON, N.P. and THOMSON, N.A. (2001) Variations in the CLA content of New Zealand milkfat. *Aust. J. Dairy Technol.* 56: 158.

MACHEBOEUF, D., COULON, P.J.-B. and D'HOUR, P. (1993) Effect of breed, protein genetic variants and feeding on cows milk coagulation properties. *J. Dairy Res.* 60: 43–54.

MACKLE, T.R., BRYANT, A.M., PETCH, S.F., HILL, J.P. and AULDIST, M.J. (1999) Nutritional influences on the composition of milk from cows of different phenotypes in New Zealand. *J. Dairy Sci.* 82: 172–180.

MURPHY, J.J. (2000) Synthesis of milk fat and opportunities for nutritional manipulation. In *British Society of Animal Science Occasional Publication No. 25* (Agnew, R.E., Agnew, K.W. and Fearon, A.M., eds), pp. 201–222. British Society of Animal Science, Edinburgh.

MURPHY, J.J., CONNOLLY, J.F. and MCNEILL, G.P. (1995) Effects on cow performance and fat composition of feeding full fat soyabeans and rapeseeds to dairy cows at pasture. *Livestock Prod. Sci.* 44: 13–25.

NG-KWAI-HANG, K.F. (1997) A review of the relationship between milk protein polymorphism and milk composition/milk production. In *Milk Protein Polymorphism*, IDF Special Issue 9702, pp. 22–37. International Dairy Federation, Brussels.

NG-KWAI-HANG, K.F. and GROSCLAUDE, F. (1992) Genetic polymorphism of milk proteins. In *Advanced Dairy Chemistry*, Volume 1: *Proteins*, 2nd edn (Fox, P.F., ed.), pp. 405–455. Chapman & Hall, London.

NG-KWAI-HANG, K.F., HAYES, J.F., MOXLEY, J.E. and MONARDES, H.G. (1987) Variation in milk protein concentration associated with genetic polymorphism and environmental factors. *J. Dairy Sci.* 70: 563–570.

NICHOLAS, K.R. (1988) Asynchronous dual lactation in a marsupial, the Tamar wallaby (*Macropus eugenii*). *Biochem. Biophys. Res. Commun.* 154: 529–536.

O'BRIEN, B., MURPHY, J.J., CONNOLLY, J.F., MEHRA, R., GUINEE, T.P. and STAKELUM, G. (1997) Effect of altering the daily herbage allowance in mid lactation on the composition and processing characteristics of bovine milk. *J. Dairy Res.* 64: 621–626.

O'BRIEN, B., DILLON, P., MURPHY, J.J., MEHRA, R.K., GUINEE, T.P., CONNOLLY, J.F., KELLY, A. and JOYCE, P. (1999) Effects of stocking density and concentrate supplementation of grazing dairy cows on milk production, composition and processing characteristics. *J. Dairy Res.* 66: 165–176.

OJALA, M., FAMULA, T.R. and MEDRANO, J.F. (1997) Effects of milk protein genotypes on the variation of milk production traits of Holstein and Jersey cows in California. *J. Dairy Sci.* 80: 1776–1785.

PALMQUIST, D.L. (2001) Ruminal and endogenous synthesis of CLA in cows. *Aust. J. Dairy Technol.* 56: 134–137.

PALMQUIST, D.L., BEAULIEU, A.D. and BARBANO, D.M. (1993) Animal factors influencing milk fat composition. *J. Dairy Sci.* 76: 1753–1771.

PARODI, P.W. (1994) Conjugated linoleic acid: an anticarcinogenic fatty acid present in milk fat. *Aust. J. Dairy Technol.* 49: 93–97.

PARODI, P. (2001) Cow's milk components with anti-cancer potential. *Aust. J. Dairy Technol.* 56: 65–73.

PETCH, S.F., BRYANT, A.M. and NAPPER, A.R. (1997) Effects of pasture intake and grain supplementation on milk nitrogen fractions. *Proc. NZ Soc. Anim. Prod.* 57: 154–156.

PUHAN, Z. and JAKOB, E. (1994) Genetic variants of milk proteins and cheese yield. In *Cheese Yield and Factors Affecting its Control*. IDF Special Issue 9402, pp. 111–122. International Dairy Federation, Brussels.

ROBERTSON, A., WAITE, R. and WHITE, J.C.D. (1956) Variations in the chemical composition of milk with particular reference to the solids-not-fat. II. The effect of heredity. *J. Dairy Res.* 23: 82.

SCAMMELL, A.W. (2001) Production and uses of colostrum. *Aust. J. Dairy Technol.* 56: 74–82.

SINGH, H. AND CREAMER, L.K. (1992) Heat stability. In *Advanced Dairy Chemistry*, Volume 1: *Proteins*, 2nd edn (Fox P.F., ed.), pp. 621–656. Chapman & Hall, London.

STOCKDALE, C.R., WALKER, G.P., WALES, W.J. and DOYLE, P.T. (2001) Concentrates can reduce the milkfat concentration of grazing dairy cows. *Aust. J. Dairy Technol.* 56: 185.

SUTTON, J.D. (1989) Altering milk composition by feeding. *J. Dairy Sci.* 72: 2801–2814.

TAYLOR, M.W. and MACGIBBON, A.K.H. (2002) Lipids/fatty acids. In *Encyclopaedia of Dairy Sciences* (H. Roginski, editor in chief), in press, pp. 1550–1554. Academic Press, London and New York.

THOMSON, N.A., AULDIST, M.J., KAY, J.K., MACGIBBON, A.K.H. and MURPHY, J.J. (2002) On-farm management to modify milkfat composition – a review of experiments undertaken at Dexcel to produce a spreadable butter directly from the cow. *Proc. NZ Soc. Anim. Prod.* 62: 100–103.

TONG, P.S., VINK, S., FARKYE, N.Y. and MEDRANO, J.F. (1994) Effect of genetic variants of milk proteins on the yield of cheddar cheese. In *Cheese Yield and Factors Affecting its Control*. IDF Special Issue 9402, pp. 179–187. International Dairy Federation, Brussels.

VAN DEN BERG, G. (1994) Genetic polymorphism of κ-casein and β-lactoglobulin in relation to milk composition and cheesemaking properties. In *Cheese Yield and Factors Affecting its Control*. IDF Special Issue 9402, pp. 123–133. International Dairy Federation, Brussels.

VOS, H. and GROEN, A.F. (1998) Altering milk protein/fat ratio: results of a selection experiment in dairy cattle. *Livestock Prod. Sci.* 53: 49–55.

WHITE, S.L., BERTRAND, J.A., WADE, M.R., WASHBURN, S.P., GREEN, J.T. and JENKINS, T.C. (2001) Comparison of fatty acid content of milk from Jersey and Holstein cows consuming pasture or a total mixed ration. *J. Dairy Sci.* 84: 2295–2301.

WILCOX, C.J., GAUNT, S,N. and FARTHING, B.R. (1971) Northeast, Southeast, State Agric. Exp. Stn. Southern Coop. Series Bull. 155, as cited in: Gaunt, S.N. (1980) Genetic variation in the yields and contents of milk constituents. *IDF Bull.* 125: 73–82.

WILLIAMS, R.P.W. (2002) The relationship between the composition of milk and the properties of bulk milk products. *Aust. J. Dairy Technol.* 57: 30–44.

WINKELMAN, A.M., JOHNSON, D.L. and MACGIBBON, A.K.H. (1999) Estimation of heritabilities and correlations associated with milk color traits. *J. Dairy Sci.* 82: 215–224.

4

Good hygienic practice in milk processing

M. C. te Giffel, NIZO Food Research, The Netherlands

4.1 Introduction

Milk and dairy products are highly nutritious media, in which micro-organisms can multiply and cause spoilage. The levels and types of micro-organisms in milk and dairy products depend on the microbial quality of the raw materials, the conditions under which the products are produced and the temperature and duration of storage. The most common spoilage micro-organisms of milk and dairy products are Gram-negative rod-shaped bacteria (e.g. *Pseudomonas* spp., coliforms), Gram-positive spore-forming bacteria (e.g. *Bacillus* spp., *Clostridium* spp.), lactic acid producing bacteria (e.g. *Streptococcus* spp.) and yeasts and moulds.

Milk and milk products are also, to a limited extent, associated with foodborne illness. In the USA milk was involved in 0.2−0.5% of the foodborne disease outbreaks with known vehicle in the period 1993–1997, i.e. 3–105 reported cases per year. In the Netherlands, investigations of foodborne diseases in 1991–1994 showed that dairy products were involved in about 3% of reported cases with known etiological agent. More than 90% of all reported cases of dairy-related illness are of bacterial origin. Disease is mainly due to consumption of unpasteurized milk containing pathogenic micro-organisms (e.g. *Salmonella*, *Listeria monocytogenes* or *Campylobacter*).

In this chapter, the principal microbial hazards concerning milk and milk products, focused on heat-treated liquid milk products, will be described. The importance of good hygienic practice measures and dairy product safety systems at farm, processing plant and consumer level will be discussed. Finally, some future trends in dairy processing are presented.

4.2   The principal hazards

4.2.1   Raw milk

Raw milk, as secreted by healthy cows, is free of micro-organisms. However, micro-organisms associated with the teat move up the teat canal and into the interior of the udder. Most of the bacteria present in raw milk are contaminants of the outside and gain entrance into the milk from various sources including soil, bedding, manure, feed and milking equipment. Therefore, raw milk contains levels of a few to several thousands of bacteria. The microbial quality and the composition of the microflora of raw milk vary with seasons. Improvement of handling and processing of milk such as developments in closed milking systems, use of bulk tanks to store and transport raw milk and changes in refrigeration systems have resulted in shifts in the microflora from predominantly Gram-positive, acid-producing bacteria to Gram-negative, psychrotrophic micro-organisms, mainly *Pseudomonas* species. They grow rapidly at refrigeration temperatures and produce heat-resistant extracellular proteolytic and lipolytic enzymes that survive heat processing. Enzyme activity during storage will result in defects in flavour, texture and stability in milk and dairy products.

A variety of pathogenic bacteria have been isolated from raw milk including *Mycobacterium* spp., *Salmonella*, *Listeria monocytogenes*, *Bacillus cereus*, *Campylobacter jejuni*, *Yersinia enterocolitica*, *Escherichia coli* and *Staphylococcus aureus*. Depending on the country of origin, species, climate and sanitary conditions, raw milk can contain one or more of the pathogens listed.

4.2.2   Pasteurized milk

The health rules for the production and placing on the market of raw milk, heat-treated milk and milk-based products are described in Council Directive 92/46/EEC. Pasteurization is applied to destroy heat-sensitive spoilage and pathogenic bacteria present in the raw milk. The minimum requirements to destroy potential pathogenic micro-organisms are pasteurization for 15 s at 71.7°C or for 30 min at 62.7°C. In Fig. 4.1, the inactivation of vegetative (pathogenic) micro-organisms (i.e. *Listeria monocytogenes* and *Salmonella*) and bacterial spores (*Clostridium tyrobutyricum* and *Bacillus stearothermophilus*) by various heat treatments is shown. The figures demonstrate that the spores are much more resistant to heat than the vegetative micro-organisms. As can be observed, thermization and pasteurization are not sufficient to inactivate bacterial spores.

Further processing steps (pH reduction through the addition of starter, drying, addition of salt and cooling) are designed to limit the growth of the thermoduric bacteria that survive the heat treatment. Spoilage of pasteurized milk products is caused by:

• Growth and enzyme production by psychrotrophs before pasteurization
• Activity of thermoresistant enzymes

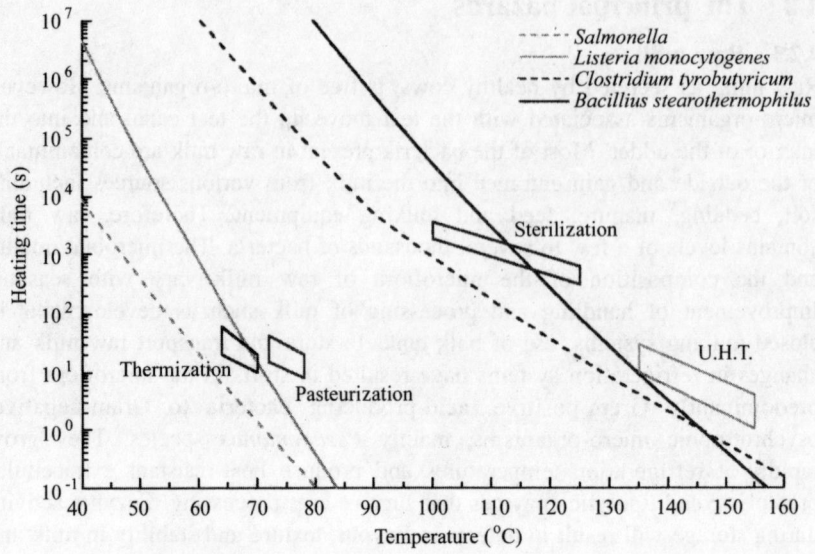

Fig. 4.1 Inactivation of micro-organisms in raw milk by various heat treatments applied in the processing of milk and dairy products.

- Growth of thermoresistant psychrotrophs
- Post-pasteurization contamination via equipment (pumps, valves, pipes, pasteurizers, storage tanks, filling equipment).

The effectiveness of cleaning and sanitizing procedures greatly influences the level of contamination and the types of micro-organisms introduced via equipment.

Trends in the dairy industry such as the extended refrigerated storage of raw milk prior to processing, the application of higher pasteurization temperatures and the more effective control of post-pasteurization contamination have enhanced the importance of thermoduric psychrotrophs. Spore-forming bacteria, predominantly *Bacillus* species, limit the shelf-life of pasteurized milk and milk products. Especially *B. cereus* is associated with defects such as off-flavours, sweet curdling and bitty cream caused by proteinase, lipase and phospholipases produced by the bacteria. Several studies have shown that *B. cereus* was present in pasteurized milk after storage.

In properly processed dairy products, most pathogens are not considered a problem, since pasteurization is effective in destroying these organisms. However, several cases of foodborne illness have been reported for, e.g., *Salmonella*, *Listeria*, *E. coli* and *Yersinia*, due to post-pasteurization contamination. Production of heat-stable enterotoxins by *St. aureus* in raw milk may also cause disease via various dairy products including pasteurized milk, cheese, ice cream, butter and non-fat dry milk.

4.2.3   UHT-milk

Sterilization is intended to destroy all the micro-organisms present, both vegetative forms and spores, or at least make them incapable of growth in the product, so that a long keeping quality is obtained without refrigerated storage.

The Milk Hygiene Directive 92/46/EEC demands that the minimum heating temperature for the manufacture of UHT-milk should be 135°C with a minimum holding time of 1 s. Typical time–temperature combinations applied in the dairy industry are holding times of the order of a few seconds at temperatures ranging from 135 to 150°C.

There are many different types of UHT-sterilizing equipment. The principles of operation and construction of the main types of equipment are summarized in Fig. 4.2.

Microbial spoilage of UHT-milk may occur by outgrowth of spores, surviving the heat processing, or by post-process contamination after heat processing (e.g. via packaging material or cooling water) or a failure in the thermal process. Typical spoilage organisms include thermoduric and spore-forming bacteria such as *Bacillus* species, *Streptococcus* and *Micrococcus* and occasionally some Gram-negative bacteria. Spores of *Bacillus* spp., e.g. *B. subtilis*, *B. megaterium*, *B. coagulans* and *B. stearothermophilus*, survive UHT-processing and can affect products such as canned or UHT-products. Defects include gas production, acid coagulation, thinning, bitterness and off-odours.

Since 1985, the occurrence of highly heat-resistant mesophilic spores (HRS) or *B. sporothermodurans*, causing non-sterility in UHT-sterilized dairy products, e.g. milk, chocolate milk, evaporated milk, reconstituted milk and cream, has been reported. The stability or sensoric quality is not altered by growth of these spore-formers. Coagulation and a pinkish colouration were only found after extended storage. All investigated *B. sporothermodurans* isolates show high resistance in the UHT-region, with D_{140} values ranging from 3.4 to 7.9 s, compared with *B. stearothermophilus* with a D_{140} value of 0.9 s. In the range 110–120°C, the spores of *B. sporothermodurans* are just as heat resistant (or less) as those of *B. stearothermophilus*. This is shown in Fig. 4.3.

Bacillus sporothermodurans is not a risk to the health of consumers. However, dairies are forced to manage the problem due to legal requirements

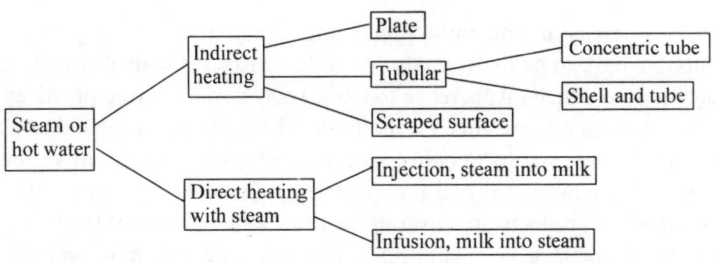

Fig. 4.2   Types of UHT-processing equipment

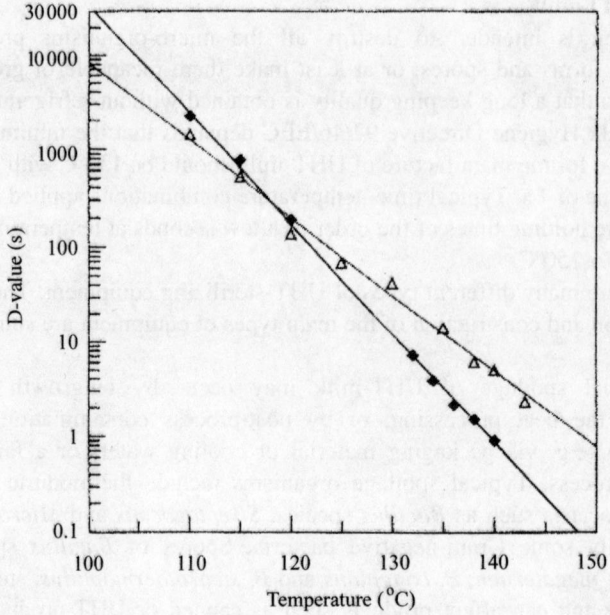

Fig. 4.3   Thermal death time curves of *B. stearothermophilus* spores (■) and *B. sporothermodurans* J16 (▲); best fit lines through experimental data.

and to avoid trade restrictions. To control *B. sporothermodurans*, direct or indirect/direct heating processes reaching F_0 values of >50 are necessary.

In addition to microbial spoilage of UHT-milk, gelation and coagulation of milk proteins and off-flavour formation may also occur as a result of heat-resistant proteolytic or lipolytic enzymes produced in the raw milk during storage. Proteolytic enzymes, naturally present in milk, probably originating from blood, are heat resistant. Studies have shown that these proteinases could survive UHT-processing.

4.3   Good hygienic practice

The various stages in the milk processing chain, from milking the cow to consumption, have to be under control in order to assure the quality and safety of milk and dairy products. Adherence to basic good manufacturing practices is one of the first steps to achieve this. Furthermore, HACCP can be applied as a tool to assess hazards and establish control systems that focus on preventive measures rather than relying mainly on end-product testing. Critical key aspects with respect to milk and dairy products are ensuring that raw materials are of the best quality, elimination of spoilage and pathogenic bacteria from raw milk and other raw materials by heat treatment, prevention of subsequent contamination, and growth limitation of undesirable micro-organisms during storage prior to consumption.

4.3.1 Farm

Micro-organisms and spores are widespread in the natural environment, with soil, water, plants and animals serving as reservoirs. Some degree of contamination of raw milk during production is inevitable, milking and milk storage equipment being the major sources of contamination. If milk is produced under sanitary conditions, the typical bacteria of the udder surface, mainly Micrococcaceae, predominate and less than 10% of the total flora are psychrotrophs. Under unsanitary conditions of production, milk can contain more than 75% psychrotrophs.

The occurrence of various bacterial species adhering to rubber and stainless steel in a milking installation has been reported. Gram-negative organisms predominated (96–100%), the majority being *Acinetobacter* spp., followed by *Pseudomonas* spp. and *Flavobacterium* spp.

The numbers and types of micro-organisms that develop subsequently during refrigerated storage are determined by the temperature and duration of the storage.

It is unlikely that all bacteria can be eliminated from the raw milk supply. Most important is to minimize contamination at the farm and keep the levels as low as possible by good hygienic practices. These include proper cleaning and sanitizing of milking equipment and rapid cooling to temperatures of 4°C or less.

The raw milk must be transported to the dairy under such conditions that the microbiological quality of the milk is not reduced. Milk collection tankers should be designed and constructed according to the IDF Code of Practice for Design and Construction of Milk Collection Tankers (IDF Document 128). During transport, the temperature of the milk should not exceed 7°C. Insulation and refrigeration of milk tankers may be necessary under some climatic conditions. The milk tanker should be cleaned and disinfected at least daily and whenever there is a gap of 4 hours or greater between collections. The sufficiency of cleaning and disinfection should be checked regularly.

4.3.2 Processing

At all stages in processing, good hygiene of the manufacturing plant is essential to ensure that the product stream is not (re)contaminated after heat treatment of raw milk (pasteurization or UHT-sterilization). Sources of post-pasteurization include equipment, packaging materials, air, aerosols, (condensed) water, lubricants, etc. Pasteurization equipment should be properly designed, installed, maintained and operated to ensure that the milk is heated to at least the specified temperature for at least the specified time.

Requirements for good hygiene design of food processing equipment, including dairy equipment, are described in various directives of the European Commission, the Hygiene of Foodstuffs' Directive and the Machinery Safety Directive (89/392/EEC). In addition, CEN/TC 153 has produced a European Standard on the hygienic requirements for food processing machinery to support 89/392/EEC.

Various organizations such as the European Hygienic Equipment Design Group (EHEDG), the International Dairy Federation (IDF), the 3-A organization and the International Standardization Organization (ISO, Technical Committee 199) have formulated and published (voluntary) principles of hygienic and aseptic design, requirements for hygienic and aseptic equipment and methods to test whether equipment fulfils these requirements. Guidance on design, construction and installation of equipment, cleaning-in-place (CIP) systems and plant is given in various IDF documents, e.g. IDF Docs 117, 123, 218, 292. Summaries of EHEDG guideline documents are published by Elsevier in *Trends in Food Science and Technology*. 3-A sanitary standards are available for many types of equipment, from fittings to silo tanks. Documents are published in *Dairy, Food and Environmental Sanitation* (*DFES*) magazine.

To maintain the factory environment in a hygienic condition, cleaning programmes should be established. Most of the equipment used for handling milk and milk products is cleaned and disinfected by CIP systems at least daily. Start-up of closed processing lines in the dairy industry is usually done by circulating hot water in order to have additional decontamination of the equipment. Monitoring CIP systems, i.e. concentrations of the cleaning agents, temperatures, flow, pressure and circulation time, is necessary to ensure the efficiency of cleaning.

Biofilms present on the surface of milk processing equipment threaten the quality and safety of dairy products. Dead ends, corners, cracks, crevices, gaskets, valves and joints are vulnerable points for biofilm accumulation. Development of biofilms in a dairy manufacturing plant depends on the type of micro-organism, the type of product being processed, the operating conditions of the plant (temperatures, length of production runs) and the type of surface. The hygienic design of processing equipment is of great importance in avoiding biofilm formation. Biofilm control also relies on well-defined cleaning and sanitizing procedures and the effectiveness of these procedures. Bacteria within biofilms are more difficult to eliminate than free-living cells and once established can act as a source of contamination. Contamination attributed to biofilm development has been reported in general milk processing (e.g. pasteurization and milk transfer line) and the manufacture of cheese, whey and milk powder. Pathogenic micro-organisms, including *Listeria monocytogenes*, *Salmonella typhimurium* and *Yersinia enterocolitica*, will also attach to surfaces in dairy processing environments, e.g. stainless steel. Subsequently, dairy products may be contaminated.

Attachment of micro-organisms may be promoted or inhibited in dairy fluids depending on the composition of the dairy fluid and the type of bacteria. The inhibition of attachment has been reported in the presence of whole milk but enhanced by the presence of lactose and non-casein protein solutions. An association of the bacteria with milk fat globules and the effect of natural antibodies have been suggested as possible reasons for this.

The pasteurizer can be a source of contamination of *Bacillus* spp., especially after non-production days such as at weekends. In addition, the growth of bacteria, e.g. *Streptococcus thermophilus*, on the surface in the regeneration section of plate heat exchangers can contaminate milk with <100 to $>10^6$ bacteria per ml and/or their metabolic products (Figs 4.4 and 4.5). This affects the quality of products manufactured from this milk, but fouling also leads to an increased use of energy, resulting in a decrease in production time, obstruction and corrosion and causing considerable economic loss. The filling machine is a

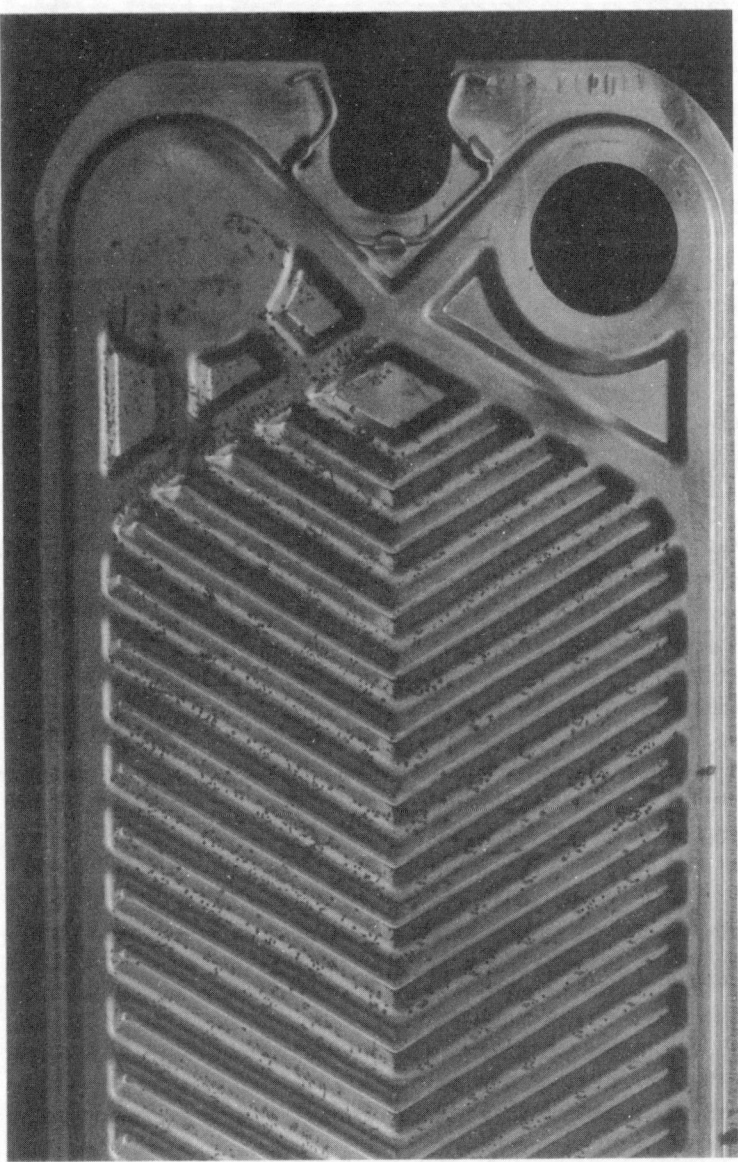

Fig. 4.4 *Streptococcus thermophilus* bacteria adhered to a plate of a heat exchanger.

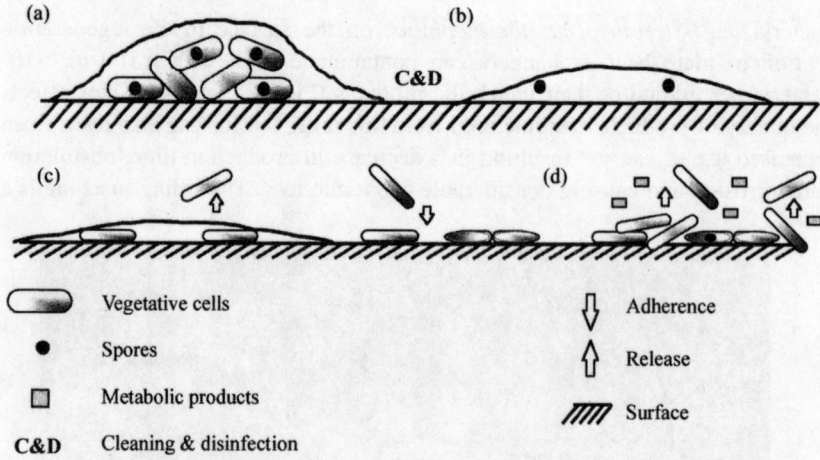

Fig. 4.5   Adherence of bacterial spores on equipment surfaces: (a) vegetative bacteria and spore-forming bacteria adhered to a surface; (b) spores survive cleaning and disinfection; (c) outgrowth of spores and release of vegetative cells into the bulk-phase, i.e. the food product; (d) adherence of bacteria, release of bacteria and metabolic products into the bulk-phase.

significant source of post-pasteurization contamination. The presence of spoilage psychrotrophs (*Acinetobacter*, *Pseudomonas* and *Flavobacterium* spp.) in pasteurized milk is considered to occur after pasteurization and indicates inadequate cleaning.

Packaging material, carton-forming mandrels, filling heads and airborne micro-organisms were identified as major contamination sources. Food-grade paper and board used in the dairy industry are usually of high hygienic quality and microbial counts are well below the limits set by the FDA, $\leq 1\,\text{cfu/cm}^2$ or $250\,\text{cfu/g}$. In a study it was demonstrated that the contamination of the inner surface of cartons intended for liquid foods rarely exceeded 10 cfu per package of one litre capacity. Re-usable milk bottles have been shown to be contaminated by spore-forming organisms such as *B. cereus* in concentrations of <10 to 250 per 100 ml rinsing water.

4.3.3   End-products
Five factors limit the shelf-life of refrigerated pasteurized milk:

- The microbiological quality of the raw milk
- Time and temperature of pasteurization
- Presence and activity of post-pasteurization contaminants
- Types and activity of pasteurization-resistant micro-organisms
- The storage temperature of milk after pasteurization.

The relation between storage temperature and shelf-life of pasteurized milk is well recognized. Low temperatures retard the growth of bacteria and conversely

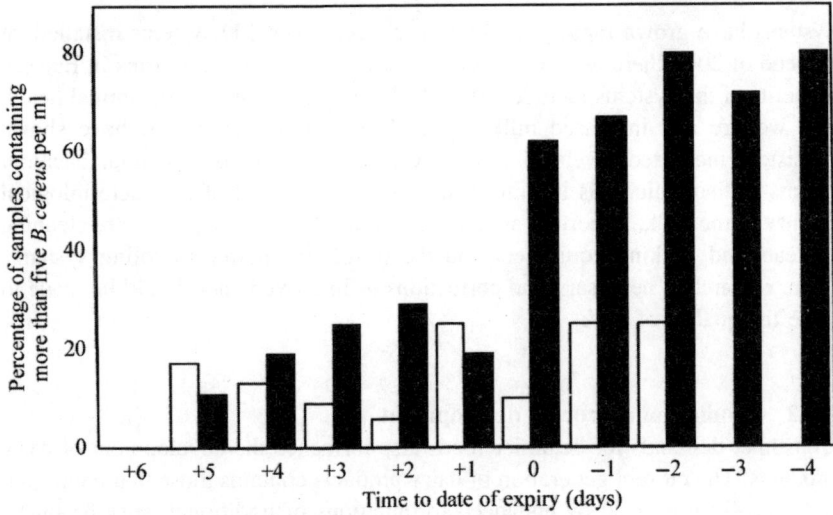

Fig. 4.6   Incidence of *B. cereus* in pasteurized milk (100 ml samples) in households in relation to storage time and temperature of the refrigerator (□ <7°C; ■ >7°C).

increase shelf-life. In Fig. 4.6 the percentage of samples containing more than five *B. cereus* per ml in household refrigerators is shown as a function of the temperature measured in the refrigerator and the time to expiry date of the milk. As expected, the level of *B. cereus* present in milk increased with storage time and temperature. The temperature should be maintained at less than 4°C in the distribution chain to reduce growth of psychrotrophs. Monitoring of the temperatures and information on temperature history can be used to identify problem areas and allow improvements to be made.

Training programmes could ensure that all people involved in processing, distribution and handling of milk and dairy products understand the principles of personal hygiene, milk spoilage and the need to keep milk cold constantly. Consumers also have to be educated as to the importance of keeping milk cold. Label information on packages may help to achieve improved quality control of milk and dairy products.

4.4   Future trends

4.4.1   Farm

In order to assure high quality standards for dairy products, it is necessary to manage the whole production chain from farm to consumer. In the whole process, the chains at the beginning of the process, especially the feed, become more and more important.

The automation of raw milk production on farms is increasing. Automatic milking systems have been commercially available since 1992 and sales of such systems have grown rapidly. In 1999 there were over 300 systems installed; at the end of 2000 there were over 1000 systems in operation on farms in Europe. Benefits of the systems include reduced labour demand, improved animal health and welfare and increased milk yields. However, investigations have shown persistent increased levels of free fatty acids, freezing points, total bacterial counts and somatic cells in milk. With respect to control of the bacteriological quality of the milk, important aspects of automatic milking systems are cleaning of teats and milking equipment and the (direct or indirect) cooling systems. More research is necessary and corrections or improvements should be made to raise the quality of milk.

4.4.2   Product and process development

Consumer demands for healthier foods also influence the development of dairy products. The current generation of dairy products contains those that have been nutritionally improved by enhanced formulations of traditional dairy products. Modifications of dairy products include modifications or reductions in fat, cholesterol, sodium or calories and addition of beneficial components such as calcium.

The dairy industry can meet the needs of consumers and expand the dairy product market by undertaking new approaches to processing and product development. Target areas that have potential are, e.g., traditional products that indulge but balance nutrition, new product concepts utilizing dairy components, food service products, processing and formulation technologies to extend shelf-life to 20–45 days, new packaging strategies, convenience, excellent sensory characteristics and safety. Innovative new technologies (e.g. high-pressure processing, separation technologies) or alternative uses of existing technologies (e.g. steam infusion) can be applied for the development of new products. Biotechnological and separation technologies can provide ingredients, isolated dairy components and bacterial cultures that are important for developing new dairy formulations. Many of the technologies are still capital intensive. Furthermore, safety issues relevant to new formulations and processing conditions for extended shelf-life products will continue to challenge the food and dairy industries.

4.4.3   Monitoring, control and optimization of production processes

The food industry has concentrated on examination of end products for controlling production processes. The accent shifted from analysis at the end of the process to control of the process, by the introduction of Good Manufacturing Practice (GMP) and the Hazard Analysis of Critical Control Points (HACCP) system. In HACCP systems, microbiological methods are needed for, among other things, assessing the quality of the raw materials, detecting microorganisms in process lines and the environment, and validation and verification. A measuring system (control measure) is necessary to make sure that the critical control points (CCPs) are controlled indeed.

Most ideal is a continuous registration system by means of physical and chemical analyses. Developments in the area of sensors will continue and lead to applications within the food industry within the next 10 years. Classical microbiological tests are unsuitable for quickly obtaining current measuring data and readjusting processes. Therefore, much research has been carried out to improve and develop rapid detection methods for micro-organisms and/or metabolites. Developments in the areas of immunology, molecular biology, automation and computer technology occur at a rapid pace, and can contribute to more rapid, more sensitive and user-friendly methods for the food industry. In a recent study, various microbiological methods were used to monitor the development of micro-organisms during thermization and pasteurization of milk. The results show that some of the methods currently available offer possibilities for application as an 'emergency brake'. The main problem is the sensitivity of the techniques. Levels of $10^4 - 10^5$ micro-organisms per ml can be measured, but this is not sufficient to adjust a production process. To permit routine in-process measurements in a production setting, the operation of the equipment will have to be simplified. Monitoring metabolites of micro-organisms is not yet an alternative because the moment anything could be measured, (too) high concentrations of bacteria are already present in the food matrix.

Control and optimization of production processes are of great importance to the food industry as this may lead to improvement of products and processes, and to cost savings. Integrated process and product development by applying rapid detection methods for critical process parameters and predictive models, therefore, is a challenge to the food industry.

In the future (objective) process control systems can be developed by integrating results of (microbiological) analyses and predictive models into process control software. In this way it is possible to adjust processes more efficiently and to respond to deviations more quickly. Computer control, neural networks and fuzzy logic may also be useful to this end.

4.5   Sources of further information and advice

http://www.nsf.org/
http://www.ehedg.org/
http://www.3-a.org/
http://www.fil-idf.org/
http://www.europa.eu.int/eur-lex/

4.6   Bibliography

3-A SANITARY STANDARDS COMMITTEES (1995) Model document for preparing 3-A Sanitary Standards and 3-A Accepted Practices, 2nd edn. 3-A Sanitary Standards Committees, Dairy and Food Industries Supply Association, McLean, VA.

ANONYMOUS (1992) *Bacillus cereus* in milk and milk products. *Bulletin of the International Dairy Federation* 275, 46 pp.

AUSTIN JW and BERGERON G (1995) Development of bacterial biofilms in dairy processing lines. *J. Dairy Res.* 62: 509–519.

BOUMAN S, LUND DB, DRIESSEN FM and SCHMIDT DG (1982) Growth of thermoresistant streptococci and deposition of milk constituents on plates of heat exchangers during long operating times. *J. of Food Prot.* 45: 806–812.

BURGESS K, HEGGUM C, WALKER S and VAN SCHOTHORST M (1994) Recommendations for the hygienic manufacture of milk and milk based products. *Bulletin of the International Dairy Federation* 292, 32 pp.

CHAMPAGNE CP, LAING RR, ROY D, MAFU AA and GRIFFITHS MW (1994) Psychrotrophs in dairy products: their effects and their control. *Crit. Rev. Food Sci. Nutr.* 34: 1–30.

FLINT SH, BREMER PJ and BROOKS JD (1997) Biofilms in dairy manufacturing plant – description, current concerns and methods of control. *Biofouling* 11: 81–97.

GOOSEN ESM, NOTERMANS SHW and BORGDORFF MW (1997) Investigations of foodborne diseases by food inspection services in the Netherlands, 1991–1994. *J. Food Prot.* 60: 442–446.

GRUETZMACHER TJ and BRADLEY RL (1999) Identification and control of processing variables that affect the quality and safety of fluid milk. *J. Food Prot.* 62: 625–631.

HOGEVEEN H and MEIJERING A (EDS) (2000) *Robotic Milking* – Proceedings of the International Symposium held in Lelystad, The Netherlands, 17–19 August 2000.

KNEIFEL W and KASER A (1994) Microbiological quality parameters of packaging materials used in the dairy industry. *Archiv für Lebensmittelhygiene* 45: 25–48.

LANGEVELD LPM, VAN MONTFORT-QUASIG RMGE, WEERKAMP AH, WAALEWIJN R and WEVER JS (1995) Adherence, growth and release of bacteria in a tube heat exchanger for milk. *Neth. Milk Dairy J.* 49: 207–220.

LEWIS SJ and GILMOUR A (1987) Microflora associated with the internal surfaces of rubber and stainless steel milk transfer pipeline. *J. Appl. Bacteriol.* 62: 327–333.

MARTH EH and STEELE JL (1998) *Applied Dairy Microbiology*. Marcel Dekker, New York.

OLSEN PJ, MACKINON LC, GOULDING JS, BEAN NH and SLUTSKER L (2000) Surveillance for foodborne disease outbreaks – United States, 1993–1997. *MMWR* 49 (SS01): 1–51.

PIRTTIJÄRVI TSM, GRAEFFE TH and SALKINOJA-SALONEN MS (1996) Bacterial contaminants in liquid packaging boards: assessment of potential for food spoilage. *J. Appl. Bacteriol.* 81: 445–458.

TE GIFFEL MC, BEUMER RR, LANGEVELD LPM and ROMBOUTS FM (1997) The role of heat exchangers in the contamination of milk with *Bacillus cereus* in dairy processing plants. *Int. J. Dairy Technol.* 50: 43–48.

5

Improvements in the pasteurisation and sterilisation of milk

M. J. Lewis, The University of Reading, UK

5.1 Introduction

Liquid milk for consumption is mostly either pasteurised or sterilised. Pasteurisation is a mild process, designed to inactivate the major pathogenic and spoilage bacteria found in raw milk. It should produce minimal chemical, physical and organoleptic changes in the product. If pasteurised milk is then cooled and packaged hygienically and stored under refrigerated conditions, it should have a shelf-life of over 10 days. Further improvements in shelf-life can be obtained by careful control of post-pasteurisation contamination (PPC), by use of good quality raw milk and manipulations of the processing conditions. Eventually, however, such milks will spoil due to survival and growth of thermoduric bacteria or any post-pasteurisation contaminants. Heat treatment regulations require pasteurised milk to show a negative alkaline phosphatase activity and a positive lactoperoxidase activity.

To keep milk for longer than a few days at ambient temperature, it needs to be sterilised. The traditional process involves heating milk in a sealed container in the temperature range 114–120°C for 20–30 min. The product would be subject to considerable changes in its nutritional value and its sensory characteristics, such as a cooked or caramelised flavour and brown colour. Originally it was heated in glass bottles and sealed with a crown cork, but now it is sterilised in plastic bottles with a foil cap.

More recently UHT processes have been introduced. These are continuous sterilisation processes and involve temperatures in excess of 135°C for times of greater than 1s, followed by aseptic packaging. UHT milks are subjected to much less chemical change compared to sterilised milk, in terms of colour development, thiamine inactivation, lactulose formation and whey protein denaturation. However, the resulting cooked flavour (cabbagy or boiled) is generally not liked by the UK consumer. Use of direct processes involving steam injection or infusion allow further improvement in cooked flavour and further reduce other chemical changes, due to the combination of the rapid heating and the flash cooling, which is quick and also removes volatiles. Both sterilised and UHT milks have a shelf-life of up to 6 months, but chemical reactions and physical changes will take place during storage which will alter the sensory characteristics of the milks. These usually result in a deterioration in product quality and take place more quickly at elevated temperatures.

Raw milk is extremely complex. Although water is the main component, milk also contains proteins, fat, lactose, a wide range of vitamins and minerals and many other trace elements and minor components. In addition, there are numerous active enzymes including acid and alkaline phosphatases, lactoperoxidase and lactoferrin. Raw milk from healthy animals has a very low microbial count, but it easily becomes contaminated with spoilage and perhaps some pathogenic micro-organisms. These need to be inactivated and this is readily achieved by heat treatment. From a milk processor's standpoint, raw milk composition and its microbial loading will vary from day to day. Milk is also available from other animals such as goats, sheep, buffalo and camels, to name but a few.

Milk composition can also be easily modified and milk is now available as a wide variety of products: skim, semi-skim, full cream, lactose-reduced, calcium or vitamin fortified and flavoured, as well as a range of creams with different fat contents. It is also concentrated, in the form of evaporated (31% TS) or sweetened condensed (72% TS). It is also produced as powders, which may be subsequently reconstituted to drinking milk or converted into a wide range of other milk products. Heat treatment is a critical step in the production of safe, high-quality liquid milk, cream and milk-based products. The main treatments for milk for consumption are pasteurisation and sterilisation and currently 91.5% of milk for drinking is pasteurised, 0.7% sterilised and 7.8% UHT treated in the UK (*Dairy Facts and Figures*, 2001). This balance is different in other European countries and in some, such as France and Germany, UHT milk is the main product. After both these heat treatments it is also crucial to reduce as far as possible post-processing contamination (PPC). This chapter will consider some of these issues.

5.2   Kinetic parameters in heat inactivation

One of the main purposes of heat treatment is to reduce the microbial population in raw milk. Also, when milk is heated enzymes are inactivated, chemical reactions take place and there are changes in its physical properties. An overview of the changes taking place when milk is heated is given by Walstra and Jenness (1984). Some important ones are a decrease in pH, precipitation of calcium phosphate, denaturation of whey proteins and interaction with casein,

Maillard browning and modifications to the casein micelle. The overall effect is to alter the sensory characteristics, i.e. overall appearance, colour, flavour and texture, and the nutritional value, as well as to improve the keeping quality.

The two most important kinetic parameters are the rate of reaction or inactivation at a constant temperature (e.g. D and k values), and the effect of temperature change on reaction rate (z and E values). The heat resistance of vegetative bacteria and microbial spores at a constant temperature is characterised by their decimal reduction time (D value); this is the time required to reduce the population by 90% or one decimal reduction (one log cycle). D values for vegetative organisms are quoted in the range 60–80°C and for spores in the range 100–140°C. Generally heat inactivation follows first-order reaction kinetics. The number of decimal reductions ($\log N_0/N$) can be evaluated from:

$$\log (N_0/N) = \frac{\text{heating time}}{D}$$

where $N_0 =$ initial population, $N =$ final population.

Two important points follow from this. Firstly, it is not possible to achieve 100% reduction; for example, four decimal reductions is equivalent to a 99.99% reduction. Secondly, for a specified heat treatment, the final population will increase as the initial population increases. Therefore sterilisation by heat is not regarded as an absolute form of sterilisation and the microbial quality of the raw material will have a big effect on the final population and hence the keeping quality of pasteurised milk and the spoilage rate for sterilised milk.

The temperature dependence of a reaction is measured by its z value, i.e. the temperature change that brings about a tenfold change in the D value. Inactivation of vegetative bacteria is very temperature sensitive ($z = 4$–8°C), whereas most heat-resistant spores are found to have a z value in the region of 10°C. Thus, one can also say for spores that a temperature rise of 10°C will result in a tenfold reduction in the processing time to achieve the same lethality. Chemical reaction rates are less temperature sensitive than spore inactivation. Thus using higher temperatures for shorter times will result in less chemical damage occurring for an equivalent level of microbial inactivation. Table 5.1 gives a summary of heat resistance data for some important spores, enzymes and chemical reactions that occur when milk is heated. It should be appreciated that chemical reactions, physical changes and reactions catalysed by any residual enzyme activity will continue to take place during storage.

5.3   Thermisation and tyndallisation

The mildest of the heating processes is known as thermisation. This can be used to extend the keeping quality of raw milk, when it is known that raw milk may be held for some time under chilled conditions, prior to it being further processed into other products. The aim is to reduce the growth of psychrotrophic

Table 5.1 Values of D and z for microbial inactivation, enzyme inactivation and chemical reactions (from Lewis, 1999b, with permission)

	D_{121} (s)	z (°C)
Bacillus stearothermophilus NCDO 1096, milk	181	9.43
B. stearothermophilus FS 1518, conc. milk	117	9.35
B. stearothermophilus FS 1518, milk	324	6.7
B. stearothermophilus NCDO 1096, milk	372	9.3
B. subtilis 786, milk	20	6.66
B. coagulans 604, milk	60	5.98
B. cereus, milk	3.8	35.9
Clostridium sporogenes PA 3679, conc. milk	43	11.3
C. botulinum NCTC 7272	3.2	36.1
C. botulinum (canning data)	13	10.0
Proteases inactivation	0.5–27 min at 150°C	32.5–28.5
Lipases inactivation	0.5–1.7 min at 150°C	42–25
Browning	–	28.2; 21.3
Total whey protein denaturation, 130–150°C	–	30
Available lysine	–	30.1
Thiamin (B$_1$) loss	–	31.4–29.4
Lactulose formation	–	27.7–21.0

bacteria, which may release heat-resistant protease and lipase enzymes into the milk. These enzymes will not be totally inactivated during pasteurisation and may give rise to off-flavours if the milk is used for cheese or milk powders. Conditions used for thermisation are 57–68°C for 15 s, followed by refrigeration. Raw milk thus treated can be stored at a maximum of 8°C for up to 3 days (IDF, 1984). The milk should also be phosphatase negative in order to distinguish it from pasteurised milk. It is usually followed later by pasteurisation or a more severe heat treatment.

Another thermal process which has been considered is tyndallisation, which involves successive heat treatments in order to inactivate spores. According to Wilbey (2002), Tyndall in 1877 suggested that if a medium was heated at 100°C for 3 min on three successive days, first the vegetative cells would be killed and the spores would germinate and then be killed on either the second or third day. In general, such double heat treatments are rarely encountered and the process is not successful in totally inactivating spores because of the unpredictability of the spore germination process.

5.4   Pasteurisation

The history of pasteurisation is documented in Cronshaw (1947) and this makes interesting reading. In fact the first stage in the history of pasteurisation between 1857 and the end of the nineteenth century might well be called the medical stage, as the main history in heat-treating milk came chiefly from the medical profession interested in infant feeding. The first positive Holder pasteurisation system was introduced in Germany in 1895 and in the USA in 1907. Thus by 1895 what was required for an effective pasteurisation process was well recognised: 'we know that this process (pasteurisation) if properly carried out will destroy all disease germs' and 'a thoroughly satisfactory product can only be secured where a definite quantity of milk is heated for a definite period of time at a definite temperature. Then too, an apparatus to be efficient must be arranged so that the milk will be uniformly heated throughout the whole mass. Only when all particles of milk are actually raised to the proper temperature for the requisite length of time is the pasteurisation process complete.'

In 1927, North and Park established a wide range of temperature–time conditions to inactivate tubercle bacillus (Cronshaw, 1947). These experiments were performed by heating milk heavily infected with tubercle bacilli under different conditions and injecting them into guinea pigs. A selection of conditions where negative results were found, i.e. where the animals survived, were 212°F (100°C) for 10 s, 160°F (71.1°C) for 20 s, 140°F (60°C) for 10 min, and 130°F (54.4°C) for 60 min.

HTST (high temperature–short time) continuous processes were developed between 1920 and 1927 and for some time the ability of the HTST process to produce safe milk was questioned. In answer to the question whether HTST pasteurisation results in as good a bottle of milk as does the Holder process, Yale in 1933 concluded that one method of pasteurisation produces as good a bottle of pasteurised milk as does the other when good methods are used and when conditions are comparable. Further developments were made in the classification of tests for evaluating the pasteurisation process. These included tests for the following:

- Raw milk quality (platform test)
- Pasteurisability (survival of thermodurics)
- Efficiency of pasteurisation (pathogens and phosphatase)
- Recontamination (thermophilic and coliform bacteria and the methylene blue test)
- General bacterial quality, including organisms surviving pasteurisation plus contaminating organisms (plate count).

The methylene blue test is now little used, but the detection of alkaline phosphatase activity is still used as a statutory test in many countries.

Pasteurisation is now defined by the International Dairy Federation (IDF, 1986) as a process applied with the aim of avoiding public health hazards arising from pathogenic micro-organisms associated with milk, by heat treatment which is consistent with minimal chemical, physical and organoleptic changes in the product. Pasteurised products should last for up to 48 hours without refrigeration and for several days when stored refrigerated. However, UK retailers of pasteurised milk are how demanding keeping qualities of 12 days. Traditionally, milk was pasteurised batchwise in the Holder process at 63°C for 30 min but, as discussed earlier, the high temperature–short time (HTST) process was introduced later. Typical conditions are 72°C for 15 s but these vary from country to country. Originally pasteurisation was introduced to destroy the pathogen *Mycobacterium tuberculosis*. It was established that the conditions required to achieve this corresponded to those required for inactivation of alkaline phosphatase, and since this was easier to measure, this was adopted as one of the procedures for establishing that milk had been adequately pasteurised. More recently, it has been required that pasteurised milk should show a positive lactoperoxidase activity, to prevent the milk being overprocessed (Statutory Instruments, 1995). Milks which showed a negative lactoperoxidase activity would be designated high pasteurised. Freshly pasteurised milk should be deemed to pass the coliform test and the plate count tests if its coliform count is less than one per ml and its plate count is less than 30 000 per ml.

Pasteurisation is a mild form of heat treatment, causing minimum whey protein denaturation, little loss of heat-sensitive vitamins and, for the majority of consumers, no change in its colour, flavour and texture.

5.5   Factors affecting the effectiveness of pasteurisation

The main control points for ensuring good quality pasteurised products are:

- Raw milk quality
- Processing conditions: temperature and time
- Post-processing contamination (PPC)
- Storage temperature.

These will be discussed in turn.

5.5.1   Raw material quality

Raw milk may contain pathogenic micro-organisms from the farmyard environment, including vegetative bacteria such as *Staphylococcus aureus, Campylobacter jejuni, Salmonella.* spp, *Escherichia coli, Yersinia enterocolitica*, and spore formers such as *Bacillus cereus* and *Clostridium* spp. It is considered that these major vegetative pathogens can be effectively controlled by pasteurisation and that they are not a major determinant of keeping quality. Pasteurisation achieves in the order of 5–8 decimal reductions of *Campylobacter* and *Salmonella*, both of which have been reported to cause food poisoning outbreaks in milk. *Listeria* is also inactivated. Pasteurisation also reduces the population of acid-producing spoilage bacteria and coliform bacteria, including *E. coli* O157. The main interest is in what survives pasteurisation or mild heat treatments. Thermoduric bacteria are defined as those which survive 63°C for 30 min, whereas spore-forming bacteria are those which survive 80°C for 10 min. *Bacillus cereus* spores are relevant here, being the main pathogen which will survive pasteurisation and grow at low temperature. It will certainly cause spoilage in heat-treated milk, for example bitty cream, and produce an intense bitter flavour, but it rarely causes food poisoning because infected products are so unacceptable.

Spore counts in raw milk have been rarely reported to exceed 10^3 per ml, although Bramley and McKinnon (1990) reported that they may reach 5000 per ml. They are higher in winter than in summer; however, the proportion of psychrotrophic spores is higher in summer. The main psychrotrophic types are *B. cereus*, *B. circulans* and *B. mycoides*. Spores are mainly derived from surfaces of teats in contact with bedding materials. Very heat-resistant spores, e.g. *B. stearothermophilus*, form only a small proportion of the total. These are also more prevalent in winter. The most common sources of *Bacillus* spores from teat surfaces are *B. licheniformis*, *B. subtilis* and *B. pumilis*; there are lower numbers of *B. cereus*, *B. firmus* and *B. circulans*. Most common in raw milk are *B. licheniformis*, *B. stearothermophilus* and *B. cereus*. *Clostridium* spores are commonest in winter: they are derived from feed silage and bedding material (fewer than one spore per ml for cows on grass). In general they do not grow well in heat-treated milks because of the high redox potential, but they may cause problems in some cheeses made from both raw and pasteurised milk. In a more recent survey on spore-forming bacteria, mesophilic spore formers were found to be predominant, with a mean value of 7600 spores per ml but occasional counts of over 2.4×10^5 per ml. Psychrotrophic spore counts were very low, with a maximum of 3.5 spores per ml; thermophilic spore counts were slightly higher, with a maximum of 54 spores per ml (McGuiggan *et al.*, 2002). Suggested reasons for the higher results included the improved recovery techniques used.

Enzymes in raw milk may give rise to problems in pasteurised milk. For example, indigenous lipases may give rise to soapy off-flavours, especially if raw milk is subjected to excessive agitation at temperatures of about 50°C, e.g. when mixing flavoured milks or other similar products. However, it is unlikely that bacterial lipases and proteases, which are very heat resistant, will cause problems in pasteurised milks because of their relatively short shelf-life and refrigerated storage conditions. Excellent reviews on the heat resistance of indigenous milk enzymes between 60 and 80°C are given by Andrews *et al.* (1987) and Griffiths (1986).

5.5.2 Processing times and temperatures

Normal HTST conditions for milk are 72°C for 15 s. One interesting question relates to the use of higher temperatures for pasteurisation. Gomez Barroso (1997) and Barrett *et al.* (1999) both showed that milk heated at 80°C for 15 s in general had a reduced keeping quality compared to milk heated at 72°C for 15 s.

Although this is not a new finding and has been identified previously by Kessler and Horak (1984), Schroder and Bland (1984) and Schmidt *et al.* (1989), it is one that should often be revisited, since it would be logical to expect a more severe heating process to result in an improved keeping quality. The usual explanation for this unexpected observation is that the more severe conditions cause heat shocking of the spores and that their activity then reduces the keeping quality, but recent evidence suggests that the lactoperoxidase system (LPS) also plays a role. The LPS involves the enzyme lactoperoxidase (LP), hydrogen peroxide and thiocyanate, all of which are present in raw milk. The oxidation products, e.g. hypothiocyanite, exhibit strong anti-microbial activity by oxidising sulphydryl groups of bacterial cell walls (Reiter and Harnulv, 1982). The LPS can be further activated in raw milk by small additions of thiocyanate and hydrogen peroxide and can be used to keep raw milk longer in countries where refrigeration is not widespread (IDF, 1988). Lactoperoxidase inactivation is shown in Fig. 5.1 and, in contrast to many enzymes, is very temperature sensitive, with z values of about 4°C. Heat treatment regulations now require that pasteurised milk should show a positive lactoperoxidase activity.

Marks *et al.* (2001) showed that pasteurisation conditions of 72°C for 15 s, resulting in an active lactoperoxidase system, were found to greatly increase the

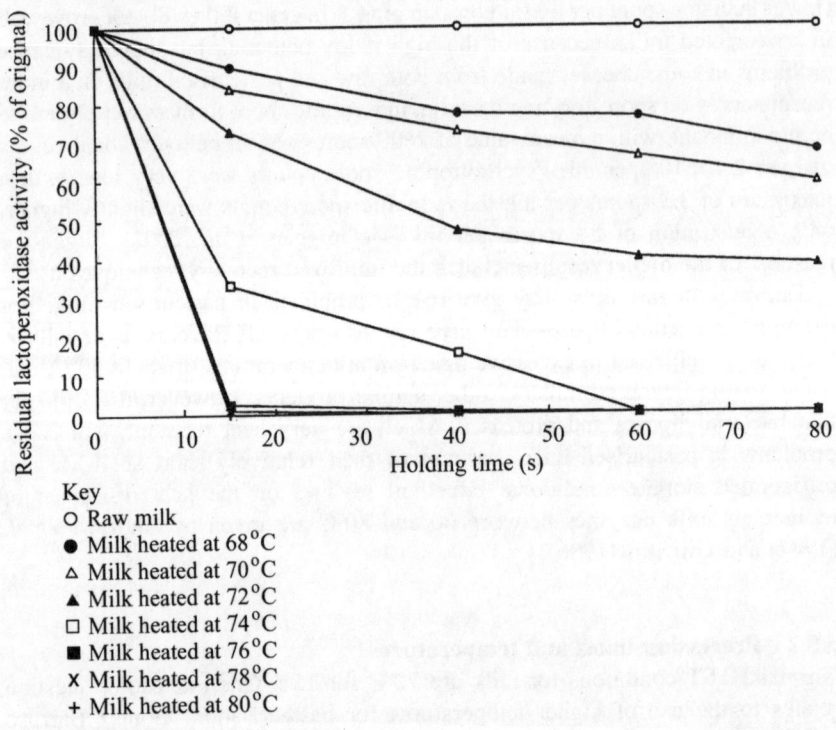

Key
○ Raw milk
● Milk heated at 68°C
△ Milk heated at 70°C
▲ Milk heated at 72°C
□ Milk heated at 74°C
■ Milk heated at 76°C
✕ Milk heated at 78°C
+ Milk heated at 80°C

Fig. 5.1 Variation in lactoperoxidase activity with holding times and temperatures (from Barrett *et al.*, 1999, with permission).

keeping quality of milks inoculated with *Pseudomonas aeruginosa*, *Staphylococcus aureus* and *Streptococcus thermophilus*, when compared to heating at 80°C for 15 s. However, pasteurisation temperature had no effect on the keeping quality of milks challenged with *Bacillus cereus* spores. Later experiments confirmed that pasteurised milk produced from high quality raw milk could be stored for up to 20 days at 8°C and for between 30 and 40 days at 4°C. However, it must be emphasised that these experiments were performed with good quality raw milk, i.e. the counts immediately after pasteurisation were never above 10^3 per ml, even after the raw milk had been stored for 8 days at 4°C prior to pasteurisation. These results also illustrate that good keeping quality can be achieved by eliminating PPC and can be further enhanced by using low storage temperatures.

In HTST pasteurisation, the holding time is controlled either by using a positive displacement pump or by a centrifugal pump linked to a flow controller, the temperature usually being controlled and recorded. A flow diversion valve diverts under processed fluid back to the feed tank. In continuous processing operations there is a distribution of residence times, and it is vital to ensure that the minimum residence time, i.e. the time for the fastest element of the fluid to pass through the holding tube, is greater than the stipulated time, to avoid under-processing. In a fully developed turbulent flow situation, the minimum residence time is about 0.83 times the average residence time.

Problems arising from a build-up of thermophilic bacteria in the heating and cooling sections associated with long operating times in continuous heat exchangers have long been recognised (Cronshaw, 1947). It may be possible to exploit some other natural anti-microbial systems in raw milk. These have been described in more detail by the IDF (1994). Double pasteurisation processes have been found to be ineffective (Brown *et al.*, 1979) and as such are rarely used.

There has been recent interest in *Mycobacterium avium* ssp. *paratuberculosis* (MAP) and whether it would survive pasteurisation. MAP levels found in raw milk appear to be low, but there is no real indication of true levels because of the decontamination procedures used to remove the other bacteria in raw milk and its extremely slow growth rate. MAP levels found in milks subjected to pasteurisation are also low but there are many inconsistencies in the experimental results (Grant *et al.*, 2001; Hammer *et al.*, 1998).

Using the Holder process (63°C for 30 min), most investigators found some survivors after pasteurisation, but inoculum levels were much higher than would be found in raw milk. The D_{63} values quoted were 2.7–2.9 min, which would give a high level of inactivation (12.4 log reductions) and would provide a more than adequate process. Most other results suggested that the Holder process was not so efficient as this. Tails were also found in the survivor curves, which implied the presence of a more heat-resistant sub-population, though this could be an artefact. Results from HTST studies are also inconsistent and suggest great variability in the heat resistance data. One report suggested a D_{72} value of 11.7 s. According to this, normal HTST conditions would only achieve about 1.3 log reductions, which would mean that all samples inoculated with 100 cfu/ml MAP would show surviving MAP after pasteurisation. However, results from milks inoculated with 10^7 and 10^4 cfu/ml indicated that about 20% and 40% of samples contained no viable MAP after HTST treatment, which suggested at least 7 and 4 decimal reductions (respectively) in some of these samples. This is inconsistent with a D_{72} value of 11.7 s.

Experiments also suggested that MAP inactivation is not temperature sensitive, although conclusions were based on the percentage of surviving bacteria rather than the numbers of decimal reductions achieved. There was a 55% survival at 72°C for 15 s and experiments at 75, 78, 80, 85 and 90°C also showed measurable survivor rates. The survival rates appeared to be higher after heat treatments at 80°C than at 75°C and 78°C. At first sight this is unexpected but it could demonstrate that MAP is inhibited by an active lactoperoxidase system, which would be inactivated at 80°C. This apparent lack of temperature dependence is unusual in a bacterium and is worthy of further investigation, as is any protective effect that may be conferred by the lactoperoxidase system (Marks et al., 2001).

Results from surveys on raw milks and pasteurised milks are also inconclusive in that MAP was found in 2% of both raw and pasteurised milk samples tested. This again would suggest that pasteurisation is having no significant effect. Clearly, the heat resistance data generated to date for MAP is inconclusive and does not permit an accurate assessment of the efficacy of the pasteurisation process with regard to MAP. Information has been recently published by the IDF (1998). In the UK it has been recommended that HTST pasteurisation conditions should be increased to 72°C for 25 s as part of a strategy for controlling MAP in cows' milk (Food Standards Agency, 2002).

Kessler (1981, 1989) has introduced a parameter (p^*) for characterising and comparing pasteurisation processes. According to him, 72°C for 15s corresponds to $p^* = 1$. However, pasteurisation conditions vary from one country to another. In the USA a wide range of conditions are used, including 63°C for 30 min, 77°C for 15 s, 90°C for 0.5 s, and 100°C for 0.01 s. Other products pasteurised are creams and ice-cream mix. In the UK minimum temperature–time conditions for these products are 72°C for 15 s and 79°C for 15 s respectively, although conditions for them are more severe in some other countries.

5.5.3 Post-pasteurisation contamination (PPC)

PPC is now considered to be a very important determinant of keeping quality, and Muir (1996a, 1996b) describes how this was recognised both for milk and for cream in the early 1980s. PPC encompasses the recontamination of the product anywhere downstream of the end of the holding tube. It can occur in the regeneration or cooling sections, in storage tanks and in the final packaging of the product, due to poor hygienic practices. It can be greatly reduced by ensuring that all internal plant surfaces in contact with the product are heated at 95°C for 30 min. It can only be completely eliminated by employing aseptic techniques down-

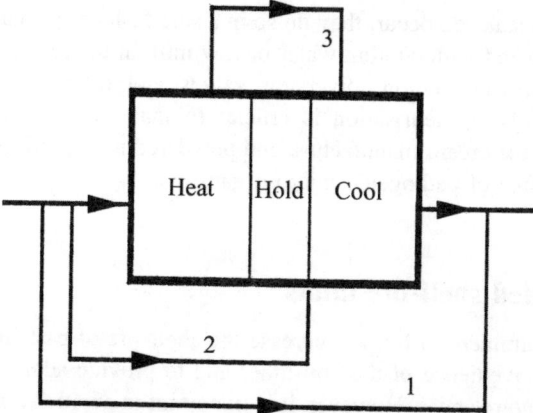

Fig. 5.2 Bypass routes in a commercial pasteuriser: 1, via cleaning routes; 2, via flow diversion route; 3, via regeneration section (e.g. pinhole leak in plate) (from Lewis, 1999a, with permission).

stream of the holding tube. One of the main safety concerns is recontamination of the product with pathogens from raw milk, which could occur due to bypassing of the holding tube by a number of possible routes (see Fig. 5.2), including pinhole leaks in plates. In terms of reducing keeping quality, recontamination with Gram-negative psychrotrophic bacteria is likely to be very important.

The presence in a pasteurised product of high counts of micro-organisms (e.g. coliform bacteria) which should be inactivated by pasteurisation is indicative of PPC, and the IDF (1993) have catalogued a large number of tests which can be used to determine the extent of the problem. In practical situations where the keeping quality of milk starts to deteriorate or is below expectations, the most likely explanation would be an increase in PPC and this should be the first factor to be investigated.

5.5.4   Storage temperature

In general the lower the storage temperature, the better is the keeping quality, bearing in mind the costs and practical problems of ensuring low temperatures throughout the cold chain and in domestic refrigerators. Before domestic refrigeration was commonplace, Cronshaw (1947) reported that the keeping time of pasteurised milk was about 24 h. Domestic refrigeration helped to improve this considerably; in the UK 10% of households had a refrigerator by 1957, increasing to 30% by 1962 and up to 90% by 1979. Raw milk is typically stored at 4°C; temperatures in the cold chain are slightly higher and they are likely to be higher still in domestic refrigerators. Some results on the effects of temperature on keeping quality were given earlier in the chapter.

HTST pasteurisation permits the use of continuous processing and regeneration of energy. Most HTST pasteurisers are of the plate type and these should be periodically tested for leaks. Consideration should be given to ensuring that if leaks do occur, they do so in a safe fashion, i.e. pasteurised milk is not contaminated with cooling water or raw milk in the regeneration section. The control instrumentation, diversion valves and other valves should be checked regularly. Pasteurisation is crucial to many processes, for example cheesemaking, ice-cream manufacture and powdered milk production, to ensure that these are free of pathogenic micro-organisms.

5.6   Extended shelf-life milks

There is a requirement to further increase the shelf-life of pasteurised products, both for the convenience of the consumer and to provide additional protection against temperature abuse. However, it is important to avoid the onset of cooked flavour, which would result from more severe pasteurisation temperatures. It is the author's experience that this occurs at a temperature of about 85–90°C for 15 seconds. Therefore one approach is to use temperatures above 100°C for very short times. Wirjantoro and Lewis (1996) showed that milk heated to 115°C for 2 s had a much better keeping quality than milks heated at both 72°C for 15 s and 90°C for 15 s. There is no doubt that temperatures in the range 115–120°C for 1–5 s are more effective than temperatures below 100 °C for extending the shelf-life of refrigerated products.

A second approach is to use small amounts of a bacteriocin. The addition of small amounts of nisin (40 IU/ml) was also effective in reducing microbial growth following heat treatment, at 72°C for 15 s and more so at 90°C for 15 s. It was particularly effective at inhibiting *Lactobacillus* at both temperatures. Results for milk heat treated at 117°C for 2 s with 150 IU/ml nisin were even more spectacular. Such milks have been successfully stored for over 150 days at 30°C with only very low levels of spoilage (Wirjantoro *et al.*, 2001). Local regulations would need to be checked to establish where nisin is a permitted additive in milk and milk-based beverages.

In general UK consumers do not like the taste associated with UHT milk, so it is important to reduce cooked flavour intensity. Direct processes (injection or infusion) offer one solution to this problem and milks processed by this method at 138°C for 2–4 s are known in the USA as ultrapasteurised. A further strategy is to store pasteurised products at 2°C, rather than 5–7°C. This would further increase keeping quality but may not be practicable.

5.7   Sterilisation

Sterilisation of milk became a commercial proposition in 1894. Milk can be sterilised either in bottles or other sealed containers or by using ultra-high temperature (UHT) processing, which involves continuous sterilisation followed by aseptic packaging.

5.7.1   Safety and spoilage considerations

From a safety standpoint, the primary objective is the production of commercially sterile products with an extended shelf-life. The main concern is inactivation of the most heat-resistant pathogenic spore, namely *Clostridium botulinum*. Since milk is a low-acid food (pH > 4.5), the main aim is to achieve 12 decimal reductions for *C. botulinum*. This involves heating the product at 121°C for 3 min, at its slowest heating point (IFST, 1991). The microbial severity of a process is traditionally expressed in terms of its F_0 value. This takes into account the contributions of the heating, holding and cooling periods to the total lethality and is expressed in terms of minutes at 121°C. It provides a useful means of comparing processes. The minimum F_0 value for any low-acid food should be 3. The minimum *botulinum* cook will produce a product which is safe but not necessarily commercially sterile. Thus although *C. botulinum* is rarely found in raw milk, there are more heat-resistant spores which may cause spoilage but are not pathogenic, such as *B. stearothermophilus* and more recently *Bacillus sporothermodurans* (Hammer *et al.*, 1996). For foods which may contain such spores, a heat treatment achieving two or more decimal reductions is recommended, corresponding to an F_0 value of 8. Target spoilage rates should be less than one in every 10 000 containers.

5.7.2   In-container methods

Foods have been sterilised in sealed containers, such as cans, for over 200 years. Milk was originally sterilised in glass bottles sealed with a crown cork but more recently plastic bottles are used. The main aim is to inactivate heat-resistant spores, thereby producing a product which is 'commercially sterile', with an extended shelf-life. Practical drawbacks of in-container sterilisation processes are that the product heats and cools relatively slowly and that temperatures are limited by the internal pressure generated. However, many dairy products are still produced this way worldwide, including sterilised milk, evaporated milk, custards, and canned puddings and desserts.

Sterilised milk is still produced in many countries and in essence the manufacturing procedure is not too far removed from that used over 50 years ago. However, the legal requirement then was that it would be expected to remain fit for human consumption for at least 7 days (Davis, 1955), though as a general rule it would keep sweet for several weeks at ordinary temperatures and there were examples of it being in usable condition after 15 years' storage. Milk sterilisation really developed after 1930 with the advent of the crown cork, which helped with the mechanisation of the bottle filling process and the reuse of bottles. In general the basic principles have remained the same. For more details of the process refer to Ashton and Romney (1981).

Milk is clarified using a centrifuge or by bactofugation, with claimed spore removal. It is heated using similar equipment to that used for pasteurisation. It is then homogenised at 63–82°C, for example at a single-stage pressure of 206 bar or at double-stage pressures of 34 and 172 bar. Glass bottles are then filled at

74–80°C in conditions which give minimal frothing and sealed using a crown cork. Plastic bottles are sealed at a lower temperature, 54–55°C. Care should be taken to avoid conditions in balance tanks which may be conducive to growth of thermophiles. Ashton and Romney (1981) cite sterilisation processing conditions of 110–116°C for 20–30 min, depending upon the extent of cooked flavour required. Batch or continuous retorting processes may be used (Davis, 1955). Other processing details are outlined by Ashton and Romney; these include more detail on continuous retorts such as hydrostatic or rotary valve sealed sterilisers which are capable of higher temperatures and shorter times (132–140°C for 12 min) and the use of steam for glass bottles or steam/air mixtures for plastic bottles.

The test for ensuring adequate sterilisation is the turbidity test, developed by Aschaffenburg in 1950. This test measures whey protein denaturation and is an indirect test (similar to phosphatase), as complete denaturation would indicate that the milk was adequately sterilised. Milk (20 ml) is mixed with 4 g of ammonium sulphate, which causes casein and any associated denatured whey protein to precipitate. The mixture is filtered, producing a clear filtrate which contains any undenatured whey protein present in the milk sample. The filtrate is then boiled, which causes any undenatured whey protein to be denatured, thereby producing a turbid solution, the amount of turbidity being proportional to the amount of undenatured whey protein in the milk. Thus properly sterilised milk should produce a negative turbidity result. It is interesting that the phosphatase test is not suitable, as heat-induced compounds increase the intensity of the blue colour used in the conventional test and hence erroneously indicate under-processing.

Some developments in the process have included the introduction of retortable plastic bottles and a combined process that involves the production of milk under UHT conditions (e.g. 137°C for 4 s), which is filled into bottles that are then sealed and passed through a conventional retorting process, although the retorting is much reduced, generally just sufficient to ensure that a negative turbidity is produced. In terms of determining the sterilisation effect, if this is to be treated as a single process, the critical point is to ensure that the milk does not become recontaminated in the intermediate filling process, especially with bacterial spores. This process was found to reduce the incidence of spoilage due to spore survivors (Ashton and Romney, 1981). There is also plenty of opportunity to promote spore production due to high temperatures being maintained for some considerable time.

Sterilised milk has a rich creamy appearance, perhaps helped by Maillard browning components, and a distinct cooked flavour (rich, nutty, caramelised) which once acquired makes other heat-treated products taste insipid. It is considerably browner than raw milk, the extent of browning depending upon the severity of the heat treatment. Davis (1955) recognised the need for ensuring that raw milk to be used for sterilisation was not heavily contaminated with spore-forming bacteria. Today this remains an important control variable. Sweet curdling was the chief bacterial fault, due to highly resistant spores of *B. subtilis* and *B. cereus*. Bacterial growth was found to produce other taints such as carbolic, bad egg, oxidised or cardboard taints. Ashton and Romney (1981) reported that the failure level of well-produced sterilised milks is of the order of 1 in 1000 units, although it may be as high as 5–10% in situations where there are large numbers of thermotolerant spores in the raw material or other contamination arising in the process. There is some loss of nutrients (Kessler, 1981, 1989). Sterilised milk cannot be coagulated with rennet unless calcium chloride is added. It should now comply with the colony count for UHT milk (see next section).

5.8   Ultra-high temperature (UHT) sterilisation

More recently, continuous processes have been introduced. Although aseptically canned milk was produced in 1921 and a steam injection system was developed in 1927 in the United States, regulations permitting the use of indirect UHT treatment came into force not until 1965 in the UK and direct processes were permitted in 1972. Ultra-high temperature (UHT) or aseptic processing involves the production of a commercially sterile product by pumping the product through a heat exchanger. To ensure a long shelf-life the sterile product is packed into pre-sterilised containers in a sterile environment and an airtight seal is formed. It has also been known for a long time that the use of higher temperatures for shorter times will result in less chemical damage to important nutrients and functional ingredients within foods, thereby leading to an improvement in product quality. This has been illustrated for reactions such as whey protein denaturation, thiamine loss, Maillard browning and HMF formation by Kessler (1981, 1989). Thus UHT sterilisation of milk is achieved by rapid heating to temperatures of about 140°C, holding for several seconds followed by rapid cooling. Ideally, heating and cooling should be as quick as possible. Both indirect and direct heating methods are available.

At a temperature of 141°C, a time of 1.8 seconds would be required to inactivate *C. botulinum*, but longer times would be required to achieve two decimal reductions (2D) for *Bacillus stearothermophilus*. For UHT products, an approximate value of F_0 can be obtained from the holding temperature (T, °C) and minimum residence time (t, s):

$$F_0 = 10^{(T-121.1)/10} \times t/60$$

In practice the real value will be higher than this estimated value because of the lethality contributions from the end of the heating period and the beginning of the cooling period as well as some additional lethality from the distribution of residence times.

In the UK, there are statutory heat-treatment regulations for some UHT products:

- Milk: 135°C for 1 s

- Cream: 140°C for 2 s
- Milk-based products: 140°C for 2 s
- Ice-cream mix: 148.9°C for 2 s.

In some cases lower temperatures and longer times can be used, provided it can be demonstrated that the process renders the product free from viable micro-organisms and their spores.

5.8.1 Process characterisation

To some extent, requirements for safety and quality conflict, as a certain amount of chemical change will occur during adequate sterilisation of the food. Therefore it is important to ask what is meant by quality and what is the scope for improving the quality. One very important aspect is minimising chemical damage and reducing nutrient loss. In this aspect, UHT processing offers some distinct advantages over in-container sterilisation. Chemical reactions are less temperature sensitive so the use of higher temperatures, combined with more rapid heating and cooling rates, helps to reduce the amount of chemical reaction. There is also a choice of indirect heat exchangers for milk, such as plate or tubular types, as well as direct steam injection or infusion plants, all of which heat products at different rates and shear conditions.

For a better understanding of the UHT process, it is required to know the temperature–time profile for the product. Some examples of such profiles are shown for a number of different UHT process plants in Fig. 5.3. Considerable differences arise in the heating and cooling rates for indirect processes and

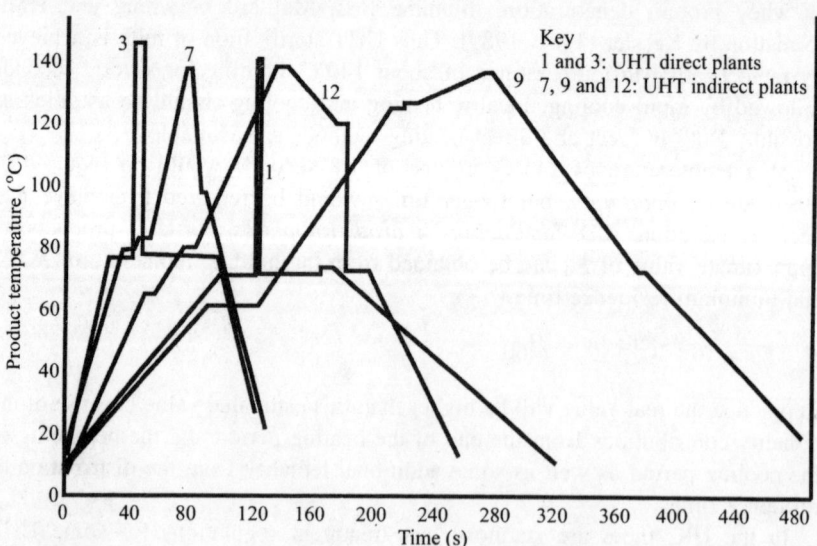

Fig. 5.3 Temperature–time profile for different UHT plants (from Lewis and Heppell, 2000, with permission).

between the direct and indirect processes due to steam injection and flash cooling. Because of these differences, similar products processed on different plants may well be different in quality. A more detailed discussion is given by Burton (1988) and Lewis and Heppell (2000).

Two other parameters introduced for UHT processing of dairy products are the B^* and C^* values (Kessler, 1981). The reference temperature used (135°C) is much closer to UHT processing temperatures than that used for F_0 (121°C) or cooking value (100°C) value estimations. B^* is a microbial parameter used to measure the total integrated lethal effect of a process. A process given a B^* value of 1 would be sufficient to produce nine decimal reductions of mesophilic spores and would be equivalent to 10.1 s at 135°C. C^* is a parameter to measure the amount of chemical damage taking place during the process. A process given a C^* value of 1 would cause 3% destruction of thiamine and would be equivalent to 30.5 s at 135°C.

Again, the criteria in most cases are to obtain a high B^* and a low C^* value. Some effects of increasing heating and cooling periods on F_0, B^* and C^* have recently been shown by Browning et al. (2001) (Table 5.2). These results are based on heating the product from 80°C to 140°C, holding it for 2 s and cooling it to 80°C. Heating and cooling times from 1 s (almost instantaneous) through to 120 s are shown. Increasing these periods increases both the chemical and the microbial parameters, with the ratio of C^*/B^* increasing with increasing heating time. At a heating time of about 8 s, the amount of chemical damage done during the heating and cooling periods exceeds that in the holding tube. It is this considerable increase in chemical reaction that is more noticeable in terms of decreasing the quality of the product. Lactulose is one useful indicator to assess the amount of chemical change taking place during sterilisation, as it is not found in raw milk (Andrews, 1986). Tentative proposals now being discussed include lactulose in UHT milk, being greater than 10 mg per 100 ml and for sterilised milk being greater than 60 mg per 100 ml.

High C^* values may be beneficial in those circumstances where a greater extent of chemical damage may be required, i.e. for inactivating heat-resistant proteases or lipases or for inactivation of natural toxic components, e.g. trypsin

Table 5.2   Comparison of heating and cooling rates (1 to 120 s) for UHT milk heated at 140°C for 2 s (from Browning et al., 2001, with permission)

Time (s)	F_0	B^*	C^*	Browning[a]
1	2.81	0.64	0.12	12.8
10	4.62	1.07	0.31	31.3
30	8.63	2.04	0.75	72.4
60	14.66	3.48	1.39	134.0
90	20.68	4.92	2.05	196.0
120	26.70	6.36	2.70	257.0

[a] Denotes equivalent time (s) at 121°C ($z = 26.3$°C) (Browning et al., 2001)

inhibitor in soy milk. Chemical damage could be further reduced by using temperatures in excess of 145°C and very short times. The best solution would be the direct process, with its accompanying rapid heating and cooling. Steam is mixed with the product, pre-heated to about 75°C, by injection or infusion. The steam condenses and becomes an ingredient in the product. Steam utilisation is about 10–15% (mass/mass). There are special requirements for the removal from the steam of impurities such as water droplets, oil and rust. Heating is almost instantaneous. The condensed steam is removed by flash cooling, which is also very quick. This process also removes volatiles and dissolved oxygen. Advantages of the process are reduced chemical damage and a less intense cooked flavour for many products. There are claims that products produced by direct UHT are indistinguishable from pasteurised products. One problem would be the very short holding times required, and their control. In theory it should be possible to obtain products with very high B^* and low C^* values at holding times of about 1 s. However, direct processes are more expensive in terms of both capital and running costs than indirect processes.

5.8.2 Controlling the process

It is recognised that UHT processing is more complex than conventional thermal processing (IFST, 1991). The philosophy of UHT processing should be based upon preventing and reducing microbial spoilage by understanding and controlling the process. One way of achieving this is by using the principles of hazard analysis critical control points (HACCP) (ICMSF, 1988). The hazards of the process are identified and procedures adopted to control them. An acceptable initial target spoilage rate of less than 1 in 10^4 should be aimed for. Such low spoilage rates require very large numbers of samples to be taken to verify that the process is being performed and controlled at the desired level. Initially a new process should be verified by 100% sampling. Once it is established that the process is under control, sampling frequency can be reduced and sampling plans can be designed to detect any spasmodic failures. More success will result from targeting high-risk occurrences, such as start-up, shut-down and product changes. Thus holding time and temperature are perhaps the two most critical parameters. Recording thermometers should be checked and calibrated regularly, and accurate flow control is crucial (as for pasteurisation). For Newtonian fluids the minimum residence time will be half the average residence time. Turbulent flow will result in a narrower distribution of residence times, with a minimum residence time of 0.83 times the average residence time. In both cases, the minimum residence time should be greater than the stipulated residence time, to avoid under-processing. Residence time distributions and their implications for UHT processing are discussed in more detail by Burton (1988).

Microbial counts in sound UHT milk should not exceed 100 per ml after 15 days' storage at 30°C. The main concern has been *Bacillus stearothermophilus*, which is very heat resistant and thermophilic and causes flat-sour spoilage.

More recently another heat-resistant spore (HRS) has been identified in UHT products in continental Europe (Hammer *et al.*, 1996). This has recently been classified as *Bacillus sporothermodurans* (Pettersson *et al.*, 1996). It is a mesophilic bacteria which has been found in some European countries and is causing UHT milk to fail the microbiological test which has been specified. However, it is a puzzle since it is not easy to grow in culture and counts in milk very rarely exceed 10^5 per ml. Furthermore it does not cause any changes in the sensory characteristics of the product, neither is it reported to be pathogenic. The question arises as to whether milks containing this micro-organism are acceptable and safe to drink.

5.8.3 Raw material quality and other processing conditions

In terms of controlling the process, the following areas will also merit some attention. All aspects of raw material are important, from an understanding of the physical properties described earlier, through to spore loadings and chemical composition. Of particular concern would be high levels of heat-resistant spores and enzymes in the raw materials, as these could lead to increased spoilage and stability problems during storage; dried products such as milk, other dairy powders, cocoa, other functional powders, and spices (if used) are ones to be particularly cautious about. Quality assurance programmes must ensure that such poor quality raw materials are avoided. The product formulation is also important, including the nature of the principal ingredients, the levels of sugar, starch and salt, and the pH of the product, particularly if there are appreciable amounts of protein. Some thought should be given to water quality, particularly the mineral content. Reproducibility in metering and weighing ingredients is also important, as is ensuring that powdered materials are properly dissolved or dispersed and that there are no clumps, which may protect heat-resistant spores. Homogenisation conditions may be important; is it necessary to homogenise and if so at what pressures? Should the homogeniser be positioned upstream or downstream of the holding tube? Will two-stage homogenisation offer any advantages? Homogenisation upstream offers the advantage of breaking down any particulate matter to facilitate heat transfer, as well as avoiding the need to keep the homogeniser sterile during processing. All of these aspects will influence both the safety and the quality of the products. For indirect processes, the use of higher temperatures may be limited by fouling considerations and it is important to ensure that the heat stability of the formulation is optimised. Heat stability and susceptibility are not easy to assess or measure quickly in a commercial situation and it may be worth developing simple tests to assess heat stability. The alcohol stability test has proved useful for milk products. Generally direct systems give longer processing runs than indirect processes.

5.9   Aseptic packaging and storage

Clean packaging systems are used for pasteurised products, where the main aim is to reduce the levels of PPC. For extended shelf-life and UHT products, aseptic packaging systems should be used of which a number are available. They all involve putting a sterile product into a sterile container in an aseptic environment. Pack sizes range from individual portions (14 ml), retail packs (125 ml to 1 litre), through to bag-in-the box systems up to 1000 litres. The sterilising agent is usually hydrogen peroxide (35% at about 75–80°C); the contact time is short and the residual hydrogen peroxide is decomposed using hot air. The aim is to achieve four decimal reductions (4D) process for spores. Superheated steam has been used for sterilisation of cans in the Dole process. Irradiation may be used for plastic bags.

Since aseptic packaging systems are complex, there is considerable scope for packaging faults to occur, which will lead to spoiled products. Where faults occur, the spoilage micro-organisms would be more random and would include those micro-organisms which would be expected to be inactivated by UHT processing; these often result in blown packages.

Packages should be inspected regularly to ensure that they are airtight, again focusing upon those more critical parts of the process, such as start-up, shut-down, product changeovers and, for carton systems, reel splices and paper splices. Sterilisation procedures should be verified. The seal integrity of the package should be monitored as well as the overall microbial quality of packaging material itself. Care should be taken to minimise contamination during subsequent handling All these could result in an increase in spoilage rate. Rinsing, cleaning and disinfecting procedures are also very important, especially the removal of fouling deposits, which may provide a breeding ground for the growth of micro-organisms, especially thermophiles.

UHT products are commonly stored at room (ambient) temperature and good quality products should be microbiologically stable. Nevertheless, chemical reactions and physical changes will take place which will change the quality of the product. These include oxidation reactions, Maillard browning and chemical and physical changes which may give rise to age-thickening and gelation. These have been discussed in more detail by Burton (1988) and Lewis and Heppell (2000).

5.10   References

ANDREWS A T, ANDERSON M and GOODENOUGH P W (1987) A study of the heat stabilities of a number of indigenous milk enzymes, *Journal of Dairy Research*, 54, 237–246.

ANDREWS G R (1986) Formation and occurrence of lactulose in heated milk, *Journal of Dairy Research*, 53, 665–680.

ASHTON T R and ROMNEY A J D (1981) In-container sterilization, in *Factors Affecting the Keeping Quality of Heat Treated Milk, IDF Bulletin,* No. 130, pp. 55–70.

BARRETT N, GRANDISON A S and LEWIS M J (1999) Contribution of lactoperoxidase to the keeping quality of pasteurized milk, *Journal of Dairy Research*, 66, 73–80.

BRAMLEY A J and MCKINNON C H (1990) The microbiology of raw milk, in *Dairy Microbiology, Volume 1, The Microbiology of Milk*, Robinson R K (ed.), Elsevier Applied Science, London, pp. 163–208.

BROWN J V, WILES R and PRENTICE G A (1979) The effect of a modified Tyndallization process upon the sporeforming bacteria of milk and cream, *Journal of the Society of Dairy Technology*, 32, 109–112.

BROWNING E, LEWIS M J and MACDOUGALL D (2001) Predicting safety and quality parameters for UHT-processed milks, *International Journal of Dairy Technology*, 54, 111–120.

BURTON H (1988) *UHT Processing of Milk and Milk Products*, Elsevier Applied Science, London.

CRONSHAW H B (1947) *Dairy Information*, Dairy Industries Ltd, London.

DAIRY FACTS AND FIGURES, 2001 edition, The Dairy Council, London.

DAVIS J G (1955) *A Dictionary of Dairying*, 2nd edn, Leonard Hill, London.

EARLY R (ed.) (1998) *The Technology of Dairy Products*, Blackie Academic and Professional, London.

FOOD STANDARDS AGENCY (2002) Consultations, *Draft strategy for the control of Mycobacterium avium subsp. paratuberculosis (MAP) in cows' milk*, London.

GAZE J E and BROWN K L (1988) The heat resistance of spores of *Clostridium botulinum* 213B over the temperature range 120 to 140°C, *International Journal of Food Science and Technology*, 23, 373–378.

GOMEZ BARROSO (1997) *Effect of raw milk quality on keeping quality of pasteurized milk*, MSc dissertation, Department of Food Science and Technology, University of Reading.

GRANT I R, ROWE M T, DUNDEE L and HITCHINGS E (2001) *Mycobacterium avium* ssp. *paratuberculosis*: its incidence, heat resistance and detection in raw milk and diary products, *International Journal of Dairy Technology*, 54(1), 2–13.

GRIFFITHS M W (1986) Use of milk enzymes and indices of heat treatments, *Journal of Food Protection*, 49, 696–705.

HAMMER P, LEMBKE F, SUHREN G and HEESCHEN W (1996) Characterisation of heat resistant mesophilic *Bacillus* species affecting the quality of UHT milk, in IDF (1996) *Heat Treatments and Alternative Methods*, IDF/FIL No. 9602, Brussels.

HAMMER P, KNAPPSTEIN K and HAHN G (1998) *Significance of Mycobacterium Paratuberculosis in Milk*, IDF Bulletin No. 330, International Dairy Federation, Brussels, pp. 12–16.

HASTING A P M (1992) Practical considerations in the design, operation and control of food pasteurisation processes, in *Food Control*, 3, *Heat Treatments and Alternative Methods*, IDF/FIL No. 9602, pp. 27–32.

ICMSF (1988) *Micro-organisms in Foods 4, Application of the Hazard Analysis Critical Control Point (HACCP) System to Ensure Microbiological Safety*, Blackwell Scientific Publications, Oxford.

IDF (1984) *The Thermization of Milk*, IDF Bulletin No. 182, International Dairy Federation, Brussels.

IDF (1986) *Monograph on Pasteurised Milk*, IDF Bulletin No. 200, International Dairy Federation, Brussels.

IDF (1988) *Code of Practice for the Preservation of Milk by the Lactoperoxidase System*, *IDF Bulletin* No. 234, International Dairy Federation, Brussels.

IDF (1993) *Catalogue of Tests for the Detection of PPC of Milk*, *IDF Bulletin* No. 281,

International Dairy Federation, Brussels.

IDF (1994) *Indigenous Antimicrobial Agents of Milk – Recent Developments*, IDF Ref. SI 9404, International Dairy Federation, Brussels.

IDF (1998) *Significance of Mycobacterium Paratuberculosis in Milk, IDF Bulletin* No. 330, International Dairy Federation, Brussels.

IFST (1991) *Food and Drink – Good Manufacturing Practice: A Guide to its Responsible Management*, 3rd edn, IFST, London.

KESSLER H G (1981) *Food Engineering and Dairy Technology*, Verlag A Kessler, Freising, Germany.

KESSLER H G (1989) Effect of thermal processing of milk, in *Developments of Food Preservation – 5*, Thorne S (ed.), Elsevier Applied Science, London, pp. 91–130.

KESSLER H G and HORAK F P (1984) Effect of heat treatment and storage conditions on keeping quality of pasteurized milk, *Milchwissenschaft*, 39, 451–454.

LEWIS M J (1999a), Microbiological issues associated with heat-treated milks, *International Journal of Dairy Technology*, 52(4), 121–125.

LEWIS M J (1999b) Ultra-high temperature treatments, *Encyclopedia of Food Microbiology*, Robinson, R K, Batt C A and Patel P D (eds), Academic Press, London, pp. 1023–1030.

LEWIS M J and HEPPELL N (2000) *Continuous Thermal Processing of Foods: Pasteurization and UHT Sterilization*, Aspen Publishers, Gaitersburg.

MCGUIGGAN J T M, MCCLEEREY D R, HANNAN A and GILMOUR A (2002) Aerobic spore-forming bacteria in bulk raw milk: factors influencing the numbers of psychrotrophic, mesophilic and thermophilic *Bacillus* spores, *International Journal of Dairy Research*, 55, 100–107.

MARKS N E, GRANDISON A S and LEWIS M J (2001) Challenge testing of the lactoperoxidase system in pasteurized milk, *Journal of Applied Microbiology*, 91, 735–741.

MILLER JONES J (1992) *Food Safety*, Egan Press, St Paul, MN.

MUIR D D (1996a) The shelf life of dairy products: 1 Factors influencing raw milk and fresh products, *Journal of the Society of Dairy Technology*, 49(1), 24–32.

MUIR D D (1996b) The shelf life of dairy products: 2 Raw milk and fresh products, *Journal of the Society of Dairy Technology*, 49(2), 44–48.

PETTERSSON B, LEMBKE F, HAMMER P, STACKEBRANDT E and PRIEST F G (1996) *Bacillus sporothermodurans*, a new species producing highly heat-resistant endospores, *International Journal of Systematic Bacteriology*, 46(3), 759–764.

REITER B and HARNULV B G (1982) The preservation of refrigerated and uncooled milk by its natural lactoperoxidase system, *Dairy Industries International*, 47, 13–19.

SATIN M (1996), *Food Irradiation – A Guidebook*, Technomic Publishing, Lancaster.

SCHMIDT D, CROMIE S J and DOMMETT T W (1989) Effects of pasteurisation and storage conditions on the shelf life and sensory quality of aseptically packaged milk, *Australian Journal of Dairy Technology*, 44(1), 19–24.

SCHRODER M A and BLAND M A (1984) Effect of pasteurisation temperature on keeping quality of whole milk, *Journal of Dairy Research*, 51, 569–578.

STATUTORY INSTRUMENTS (1995) *Food Milk and Dairies, The Dairy Products (Hygiene) Regulations*.

WALSTRA P and JENNESS R (1984) *Dairy Chemistry and Physics*, John Wiley, New York.

WALSTRA P, GUERTS T J, NOOMEN A, JELLEMA A and VAN BOEKEL M A J S (1999) *Dairy Technology: Principles of Milk Properties and Processes*, Marcel Dekker, New York.

WILBEY R A (2002) Microbiology of cream and butter, in *Dairy Microbiology Handbook –*

The Microbiology of Milk and Milk Products, Robinson R K (ed.), John Wiley & Sons, New York.

WIRJANTORO T I and LEWIS M J (1996) Effect of nisin and high temperature pasteurisation on the shelf-life of whole milk, *Journal of the Society of Dairy Technology*, 4, 99–102.

WIRJANTORO T I, LEWIS M J, GRANDISON A S, WILLIAMS G C and DELVES-BROUGHTON J (2001) The effect of nisin on the keeping quality of reduced heat treated (RHT) milks, *Journal of Food Protection*, 64, 213–219.

6

Modelling the effectiveness of pasteurisation

R. C. McKellar, Agriculture and Agri-Food Canada

6.1 Introduction: the role of predictive modelling

Processing of food products is designed in part to reduce or eliminate potentially pathogenic microorganisms which may cause serious illness if ingested. Consumers are now demanding fresher, less processed foods, and there is a move towards the development of minimally processed foods, which are protected by a series of intervention steps (or 'hurdles') (Leistner and Gorris, 1995). It is essential that the efficacy of these hurdles be assessed for each food product; however, the traditional approach of challenge testing is time consuming and labour intensive. Mathematical modelling of microbial survival and growth in foods provides a structured approach to ensure the safety of the food supply.

Thermal inactivation of microorganisms in static systems is usually described by the D- and z-value concepts as discussed below, with temperature generally held constant. The situation in canning operations or continuous flow systems such as high-temperature short-time (HTST) pasteurisation, ultra high temperature (UHT) and sterilisation processes is somewhat more complex, due to non-isothermal conditions, thus an integrated lethal effect approach is required (Kessler, 1986). In addition, the kinetics of inactivation in continuous systems differ from those of batch systems, since in the former systems there are additional factors such as pressure and shear forces which can influence microbial survival (Mackey and Bratchell, 1989; Fairchild et al., 1994). As most modern food processes are continuous, it is necessary to have additional information on survival of microorganisms in these processes; however, few studies have been published on laboratory or pilot plant continuous flow systems (for review, see Fairchild et al., 1994). Development of databases and models for microbial behaviour in foods during processing and storage is an important part of predictive modelling, thus we initiated studies to develop models for the survival of selected food-borne microorganisms and milk enzymes during HTST pasteurisation. This chapter will present some of the basic concepts of modelling thermal inactivation. It will then describe how pasteurisation models have been developed using a pilot plant pasteuriser, followed by a summary of the models developed to date. Finally, a brief review of risk assessment will be presented, with details relating to the incorporation of pasteurisation models into the risk assessment framework.

6.2   The development of thermal models

The classical approach to thermal destruction of microorganisms assumes simple first-order reaction kinetics under isothermal conditions:

$$\frac{dS_t}{dt} = -k'S_t \qquad\qquad 6.1$$

where S_t is the survival ratio (N_t/N_0, where N_t is the number of cells at time t and N_0 the number of cells at time 0), and k' is the rate constant. Thus the number of surviving cells decreases exponentially:

$$S_t = e^{-k't} \qquad\qquad 6.2$$

and when expressed as $\log_{10}$ gives:

$$\log S_t = -kt \qquad\qquad 6.3$$

where $k = k'/\ln 10$. The well-known D-value (time required for a 1-log reduction) is thus equal to $1/k$, where k is the slope (Fig. 6.1). The D-values can also be expressed as:

$$D\text{-value} = \frac{t}{\log N_0 - \log N_t} \qquad\qquad 6.4$$

When log D-values are plotted against the corresponding temperatures, the reciprocal of the slope is equal to the z-value, which is the increase in temperature required for a 1-log decrease in D-value (Fig. 6.1 inset). The rate constant can also be related to the temperature by the Arrhenius equation:

$$k = N_0 e^{-E_a/RT} \qquad\qquad 6.5$$

where E_a is the activation energy, R is the universal gas constant, and T is the temperature in K.

The food processing industry has enjoyed an enviable record of safety, thus the concept of exponential death of microorganisms has persisted, and is now considered accepted dogma. In spite of this, non-linear survival curves were reported for some bacteria almost 100 years ago (Moats et al., 1971). The theoretical basis for assuming logarithmic behaviour for bacteria is based on the assumption that bacterial populations are homogeneous with respect to thermal

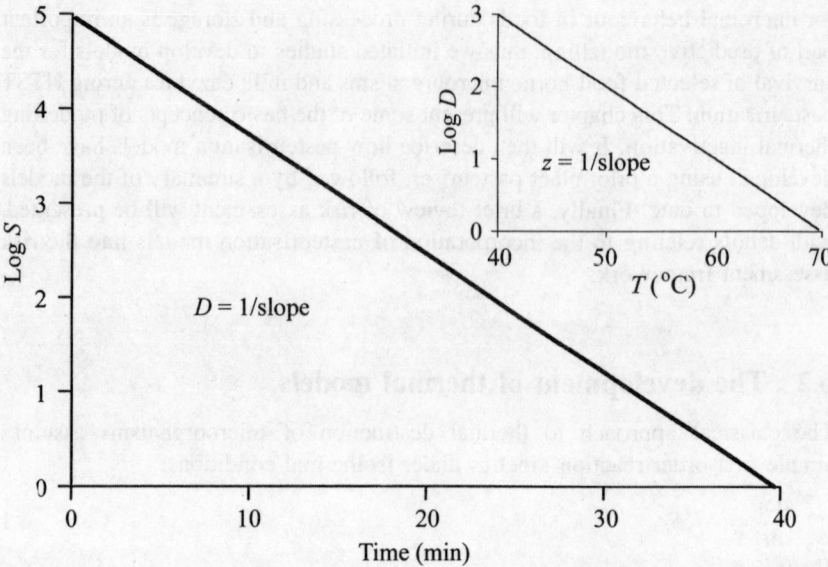

Fig. 6.1 Definition of the D- and z-values describing thermal inactivation kinetics.

tolerance, and that inactivation is due to a single critical site per cell (Moats *et al.*, 1971). Both of these assumptions have been questioned, and thus concerns have been raised regarding the validity of extrapolation of linear inactivation curves (Campanella and Peleg, 2001; Cerf, 1977). In general, there are two classes of non-linear curves: those with a 'shoulder' or lag prior to inactivation, and those which exhibit tailing. These two phenomena may be present together, or with other observed kinetics such as biphasic inactivation. A wide variety of complex inactivation kinetics have been reported, and several of these are shown in Fig. 6.2, which include shoulder (a), biphasic (b), sigmoidal (c), and concave (d).

Stringer *et al.* (2000) have assigned the possible explanations for non-linear kinetics into two classes: those due to artifacts and limitations in experimental procedure, and those due to normal features of the inactivation process. The first class encompasses such limitations as

- Variability in heating procedure
- Use of mixed cultures or populations
- Clumping
- Protective effect of dead cells
- Method of enumeration
- Poor statistical design.

The second class includes such situations as

- Possible multiple hit mechanisms
- Natural distribution of heat sensitivity
- Heat adaptation.

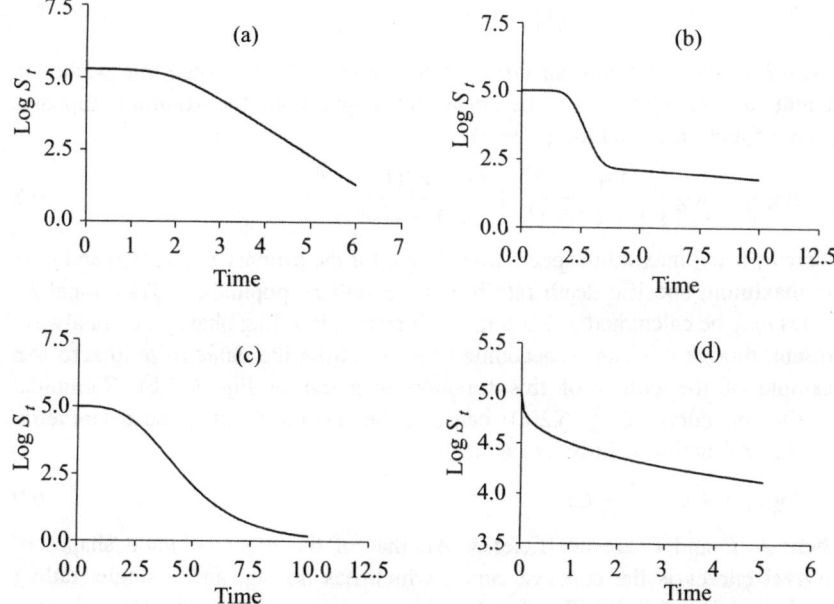

Fig. 6.2 Examples of non-linear thermal inactivation curves: (a) shoulder; (b) biphasic logistic; (c) sigmoidal; (d) concave.

These two classes roughly parallel two concepts reviewed by Cerf (1977) to explain tailing in bacterial survival curves. The first of these (the 'mechanistic' approach) also makes the assumption of homogeneity of cell resistance and proposes that thermal destruction follows a process analogous to a chemical reaction. In this approach, deviations from linearity are attributed mainly to artifacts; however, tailing is also related to the mechanism of inactivation or resistance. In the second (the 'vitalistic' approach) it is assumed that the cells possess a normal heterogeneity of heat resistance, thus survival curves should be sigmoidal or concave upward (Cerf, 1977).

Inactivation curves which deviate from simple exponential often have a lag or shoulder region prior to the exponential phase. This shape of inactivation curve is probably the one most commonly experienced by researchers. A simple linear model to account for this behaviour was developed by Whiting (1993):

$$\log N_t = \begin{cases} \log N_0 & \text{when } 0 < t < t_L \\ \log N_0 - \left(\dfrac{1}{D}\right)(t - t_L) & \text{when } t > t_L \end{cases} \qquad 6.6$$

where t_L is the lag phase prior to inactivation. The Fermi equation, which is the 'mirror image' of the common logistic growth function, is also used for death curves which exhibit a shoulder (Pruitt and Kamau, 1993):

$$\log S_t = \log \left[\frac{1 + e^{-bt_L}}{1 + e^{b(t-t_L)}} \right]$$ 6.7

where b is the maximum specific death rate (Fig. 6.2a). When one wishes to include a secondary, more heat-resistant population, the resulting biphasic logistic function is (Whiting, 1993):

$$\log S_t = \log \left[\frac{F(1 + e^{-b_1 t_L})}{1 + e^{b_1(t-t_L)}} + \frac{(1 - F)(1 + e^{-b_2 t_L})}{1 + e^{b_2(t-t_L)}} \right]$$ 6.8

where b_1 is the maximum specific death rate for the primary population and b_2 is the maximum specific death rate for the secondary population. Traditional D-values may be calculated as $2.3/b$ for each population. Lag phases are not always present, though this can be accounted for by setting the value of t_L to zero. An example of the output of this function is given in Fig. 6.2(b). Sigmoidal inactivation curves (Fig. 6.2(c)) can also be modelled using the asymmetric Gompertz function (Linton *et al.*, 1995):

$$\log S_t = Ce^{-e^{A+Bt}} - Ce^{-e^A}$$ 6.9

where A, B and C are coefficients. Another of the more common shapes of survival curves is the concave curve, which has no lag, and a single, tailing population (Fig. 6.2(d)). This function is best represented by the power law:

$$\log S_t = -\frac{t^p}{D}$$ 6.10

where p is the power. A concave curve is produced when $p < 1$.

One recent development in the modelling of bacterial survival is the use of distributions. This is based on the assumption that lethal events are probabilistic rather than deterministic, and that individual cells vary in their apparent thermal stability. The Weibull distribution is used in engineering to model time to failure, so it is appropriate for modelling bacterial inactivation. The distribution of survival times would then follow the probability density function (PDF) for the Weibull (solid line in Fig. 6.3):

$$\text{PDF} = \frac{\beta}{\alpha} \left(\frac{t}{\alpha} \right)^{\beta-1} e^{-(t/\beta)^\beta}$$ 6.11

where α and β are parameters relating to the scale and shape of the distribution, respectively (vanBoekel, 2002). The survival curve is then the cumulative distribution function (CDF) (dotted line in Fig. 6.3):

$$\text{CDF} = e^{-(t/\alpha)^\beta}$$ 6.12

It can be easily seen that the CDF of the Weibull distribution is essentially a reparameterisation of the power law function (equation 6.10).

As mentioned earlier, non-isothermal conditions predominate in continuous food processes. Bigelow's (1921) model has been the non-isothermal standard model for the low-acid canned food industry for many decades. In this approach, the processing time F is determined by integrating the exposure time at various

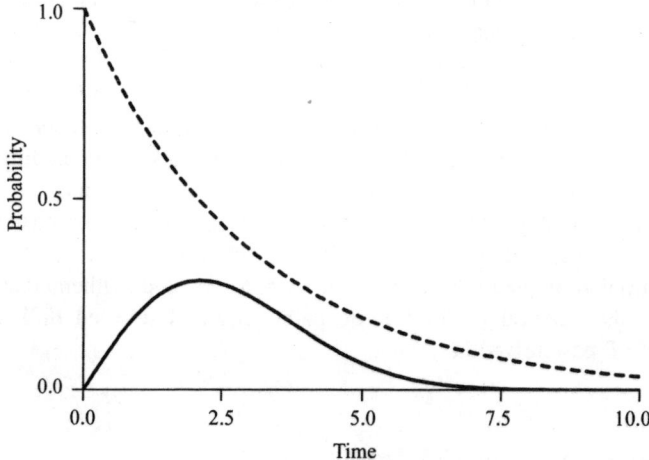

Fig. 6.3 Examples of the probability distribution function (solid line) and the cumulative distribution function (broken line) for a Weibull distribution.

temperatures $T(t)$ to time at a reference temperature T_{Ref} (Nunes *et al.*, 1993):

$$F = \int 10^{(T(t)-T_{Ref})/z} \, dt \qquad 6.13$$

This model is considered to be an approximation of the Arrhenius model which is valid over a wide range (4–160°C) of temperatures (Nunes *et al.*, 1993):

$$PE = \frac{1}{t_0} \int_0^t e^{-(E_a/R)[(1/T)-(1/T_0)]} \, dt \qquad 6.14$$

where

    PE = integrated lethal effect, or pasteurisation effect
    E_a = energy of activation (J mol^{-1})
    R = 8.314 (J mol^{-1} K^{-1})
    T = temperature (K)
    T_0 = reference temperature (345 K)
    t = time (s)
    t_0 = reference time (15 s).

The reference temperature (345 K or 72°C) and time (15 s) correspond to the International Dairy Federation standard for pasteurisation (Kessler, 1986).

It is often necessary for milk processors to demonstrate that the process they wish to use is effective in delivering the required lethal effect for the product and microorganism of concern. The integrated lethal effect is a useful concept, as it allows two or more processes which use different time/temperature combinations to be compared for efficacy against food-borne pathogens; however, there are few data available relating microbial survival to processing conditions. This is of particular concern in the case of pasteurisation of milk, where the only accepted test for proper pasteurisation is the alkaline phosphatase (AP) test (Staal, 1986; International Dairy Federation, 1991). The relationship between AP inactivation and survival of food-borne pathogens is largely unknown, as is the response of AP to processing under alternative time/temperature combinations. In addition, data are lacking on the influence of continuous thermal processing on other milk enzymes which may be useful in monitoring thermal process above or below that required for pasteurisation (Griffiths, 1986; Andrews *et al.*, 1987; Zehetner *et al.*, 1996). These considerations prompted the initiation of work to develop mathematical models describing the survival of food-borne pathogens and selected milk enzymes during HTST pasteurisation.

6.3   Key steps in model development

6.3.1   Strains and culture conditions
Bacterial strains used in the various studies were maintained in glycerol at −20°C and propagated on Tryptic Soy Broth containing 0.6% (w/v) Yeast Extract (TSBYE). Strains were transferred twice into TSBYE at 30°C for 24 h, then inoculated into 20 litres of TSBYE at 30°C for 24 h. The cultures were concentrated to approximately 800 ml using a Pellicon filtration system with an HVMP000C5 0.45 μm filter and stored overnight at 4°C.

6.3.2   Pasteuriser design
The pasteuriser (Fig. 6.4) was designed to heat milk at a rate of 363 kg h^{-1} from 2°C to temperatures as high as 80°C, and cool back to 4.5°C with 90% regeneration. Pressure on the milk leaving the regeneration section was boosted by means of a positive displacement pump to obtain a mean pressure differential of 41.4 kPa over the raw or feed side of the regeneration unit. The temperature of the milk in the pasteuriser was controlled using a Yokogawa YS170 process variable air-activated controller with three proportional settings in degrees Celsius.

6.3.3   Holding tubes
Holding tubes were constructed of 304 stainless steel with an internal diameter of 2.2 cm. The length of the holding tubes varied from 0.62 m (5.42 s) to as long as 17.23 m (63.93 s) depending on the residence time desired: a summary of holding times and lengths appears in Table 6.1.

Previous work of D'Aoust *et al.* (1987) estimated a Reynolds number of 10 500 for milk at 72°C in a 16.2 s holding tube, which is well above the critical minimum of 4000 required for turbulent flow. The minimum holding time was determined using a conductivity meter with the salt testing procedure set forth

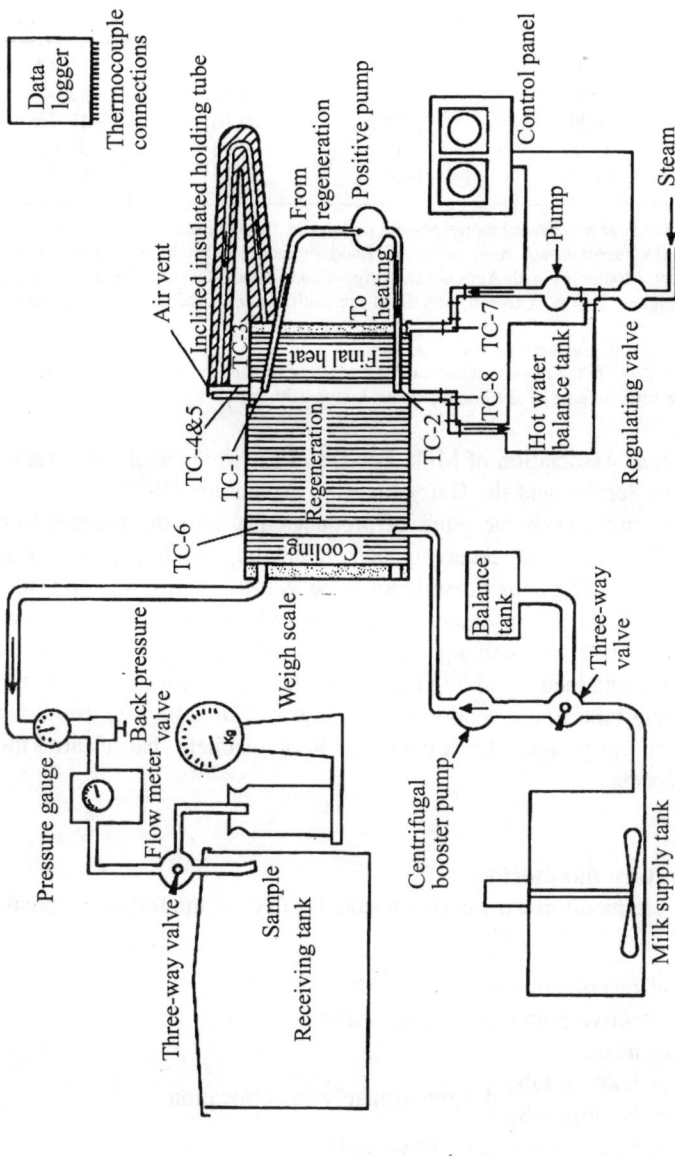

Fig. 6.4 Schematic diagram of the pilot-scale high-temperature short-time (HTST) pasteuriser from McKellar *et al.* (1994b) reprinted with permission from *Journal of Food Protection*. Copyright held by the International Association for Food Protection, Des Moines, Iowa, USA. Authors McKellar and Modler are with Agriculture & Agri-Food Canada, Guelph, Canada; authors Couture, Hughes, Mayers, Gleeson, and Ross are with Health Canada, Ottawa, Ontario, Canada.

Table 6.1   Holding times in APV-Crepaco Junior Paraflow Pasteuriser[a]

Holding tube length (m)	Measured[b] minimum holding time (s)	Standard deviation	Maximum deviation	Corrected[c] holding time (s)
0.62	2.49	0.02	0.06	5.42
2.78	9.97	0.03	0.14	12.90
4.33	14.80	0.04	0.16	17.73
8.71	31.09	0.14	0.38	34.02
17.23	61.00	0.07	0.25	63.93

[a] Data are from McKellar *et al.* (1994b) reprinted with permission from *Journal of Food Protection*. Copyright held by the International Association for Food Protection, Des Moines, Iowa, USA. Authors McKellar and Modler are with Agriculture & Agri-Food Canada, Guelph, Ontario, Canada; authors Couture, Hughes, Payers, Gleeson, and Ross are with Health Canada, Ottawa, Ontario, Canada.
[b] Determined using the salt conductivity test ($n = 5$).
[c] Obtained by adding 2.93 s to the minimum holding time to allow for feed and return port connectors (calculated from the total volume of the connectors assuming 80% efficiency).

by the International Association of Milk, Food, and Environmental Sanitarians, the Public Health Service and the Dairy Industry Committee (1992).

The minimum time, from the point of product entry into the regeneration section until collection at the receiving tank (excluding holding tubes), was estimated to be 57.8 s. The component times were as follows: regeneration (raw side) 5.00 s; heating, 4.63 s; regeneration (pasteurised side) to sampling valve 14.98 s; sampling valve to receiving tank 29.87 s; timing pump 3.28 s. Total residence time was obtained by adding the sum of the above times (57.8 s) to the 'corrected' holding tube times, reported in Table 6.1. This time was useful for determining when the product, for a particular heat treatment, had cleared the pasteurisation system.

6.3.4   Temperature monitoring

Temperatures were monitored using thermocouples (TC) at the following points (Fig. 6.4):

- TC 1 – end of regeneration (raw milk side)
- TC 2 – after positive pump and before seating
- TC 3 – end of heating
- TC 4 – end of holding tube $\Big\}$ approximately same location
- TC 5 – end of holding tube
- TC 6 – end of regeneration (pasteuriser side).

Thermocouples were inserted at the geometric centre of the product stream with the exterior stainless steel sheath being insulated with Imcolok Thermo Cel.

The thermocouples were connected to a Digistrip II recorder set to read at 2-s intervals and to print out all measurements at 1-min intervals. Data were simultaneously collected with a portable computer using Telix V3.11 communications software. The thermocouples were calibrated at the Heat and Thermometry Laboratory, Physics Division, National Research Council of Canada, and were accurate within $\pm 0.2°C$ when tested at $1°C$ intervals between 0 and $120°C$. Prior to each run the thermocouples were also checked for error against ice-water.

6.3.5 Milk processing

Milk (3.5% milkfat) was obtained from the Greenbelt Farm of Agriculture Canada one day prior to experimentation. Approximately 1200–1600 litres of Holstein milk were pumped from the delivery truck to a 1670-litre Cherry-Burrell tank. When pathogen inactivation was being studied, milk was added also to two Mueller tanks each containing 200 litres of whole milk which had been previously heated to $80°C$ for 1 h, then cooled to $4°C$. Each tank was then inoculated with 400 ml of culture concentrate (to approx. 10^8 cfu ml^{-1}), and 100 ml of the dye Fast Green FCF in distilled H_2O (1% w/v) was added as a marker for inoculated milk.

Processing consisted of starting at the highest temperature for a given holding tube, e.g. $80°C$, and working down in $0.5–1.0°C$ increments until the lowest temperature had been achieved. This normally spanned the range of $5°C$ for a total of 6–10 samples per holding tube. Samples were taken only after the desired temperature had been achieved and maintained for a minimum of 3 min. When milk containing pathogens was being processed, temperatures were set using uninoculated milk from a bulk tank. Once a constant temperature had been established, flow was switched to the Mueller tank, and milk was sampled after the green dye had become apparent in the outflow. The flow rate was monitored using a mass flow meter, and was adjusted to $6.3 \, kg \, min^{-1}$ by manually controlling the variable speed drives of the feed and booster pumps.

6.3.6 Program development

The program to calculate PE was written in VisualBasic. PE for each section of the pasteuriser was determined by converting time at the indicated temperature to the equivalent time at the reference temperature using the empirical kinetic equation described by Kessler (equation 6.14). For each section of the pasteuriser, the cumulative lethal effect was determined using the trapezoidal rule (Gibaldi and Perrier, 1975), and expressed as PE. Total PE was calculated by adding the individual PE values for each section.

The stages in the HTST modelling program are given in Fig. 6.5. When a model was being derived, data from the TCs with the corresponding holding tube and residual enzyme activity or viable counts were input for each sample. Equipment calibration factors and residence times in the various parts of the system were input from separate configuration files. Lethal temperature was arbitrarily set at $60°C$. A range for E_a/R was defined (usually 60 000 to 80 000)

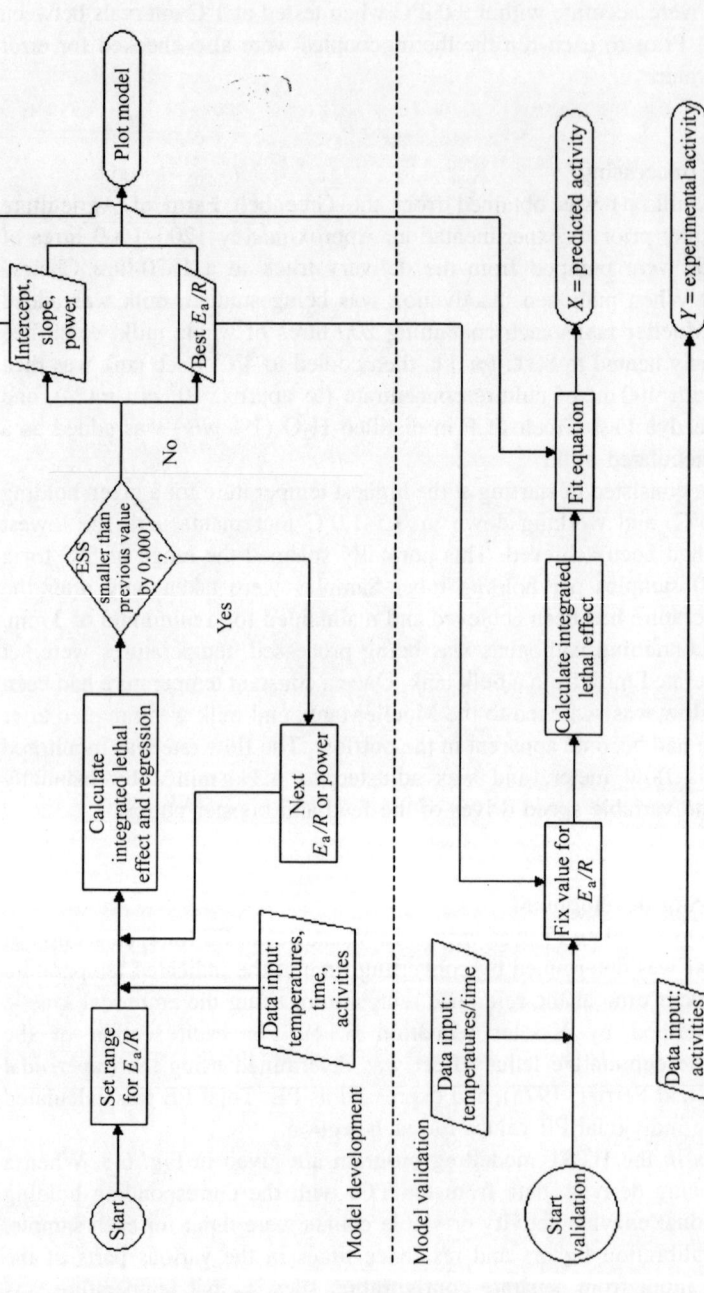

Fig. 6.5 Flow chart describing the development and validation of HTST models from McKellar *et al.* (1994b) reprinted with permission from *Journal of Food Protection*. Copyright held by the International Association for Food Protection, Des Moines, Iowa, USA. Authors McKellar and Modler are with Agriculture & Agri-Food Canada, Guelph, Canada; authors Couture, Hughes, Mayers, Gleeson, and Ross are with Health Canada, Ottawa, Ontario, Canada.

and the lowest value was selected. For each E_a/R, a total PE was calculated for each sample, and least-squares regression was performed between PE and $\log_{10}$ % initial activity or initial cfu ml^{-1}. In order to improve the fit, a power law transformation (equation 6.10) of PE was incorporated in which a range of PE^c values were calculated ($c = 0.2$ to 1.0). The method of least squares was used (PE^c vs. $\log_{10}$ % initial activity or initial cfu ml^{-1}) to obtain the best value of c by minimising the error sum of squares (ESS) for each value of E_a/R. ESS is defined as $(1 - r^2) \times$ TSS, where TSS is the total sum of squares.

Values of E_a/R were incremented by 500, and the iteration was repeated as described above. The iterations were terminated when the new ESS value did not improve on the previous value by more than 0.0001. The final model consisted of the best E_a/R, slope, intercept and power (c). Output for each sample for further plotting was in the form $x = $ PE^c, $y = $ experimental data ($\log_{10}$ % initial activity or initial cfu ml^{-1}).

When an enzyme model was being validated, TC data, $\log_{10}$ % initial activity values, and equipment configuration were input as described above (Fig. 6.5). The optimum E_a/R and c values were fixed, and PE^c was calculated for each data point. Intercept (a) and slope (b) values from the model were used to calculate predicted activity using the following equation:

$$\text{Predicted activity} = a + b \cdot \text{PE}^c \qquad\qquad 6.15$$

and output was in the form $x = $ predicted activity, $y = $ experimental activity.

6.4   Models for key enzymes and pathogens

In model development, the parameter estimates for at least three trials were pooled for each milk enzyme or pathogen studied, and the mean parameter values are given in Table 6.2. Due to the importance of pasteurisation in milk processing, the first model was developed for AP (McKellar *et al.*, 1994b). There was also a need to develop models for milk enzymes which might be used to confirm processing at temperatures above or below pasteurisation. Higher

Table 6.2   Model parameters for inactivation of various milk enzymes and food-borne pathogens during HTST pasteurisation

Target	Trials	Intercept	Slope	Power	E_a/R ($\times$ 1000)
Alkaline phosphatase	3	2.05	−4.05	0.50	66.5
γ-Glutamyl transpeptidase	3	2.00	−0.281	0.75	66.5
Lactoperoxidase	3	2.12	−0.096	0.75	59.0
Catalase	3	1.94	−2.65	0.50	82.0
α-L-fucosidase	3	1.87	−17.6	1.00	39.8
Listeria innocua	5	1.86	−24.9	0.80	59.5
Listeria monocytogenes	3	1.68	−18.4	0.80	48.5
Enterobacter sakazakii	3	2.31	−24.4	0.65	59.5

temperatures (at least 75°C) are appropriate for processing of more viscous dairy products such as ice-cream mix. Lactoperoxidase (LP) and γ-glutamyl trans-peptidase (TP) are two naturally occurring milk enzymes which are inactivated at higher temperatures, and models were developed for these enzymes (McKellar et al., 1996). Temperatures below pasteurisation of 63–65°C (termed sub-pasteurisation or thermisation) are used to extend the storage life of bulk milk. Models have also been developed for catalase (CA) (Hirvi et al., 1996) and α-L-fucosidase (FC) (McKellar and Piyasena, 2000) which are appropriate for sub-pasteurisation temperatures. Parameter values for all enzyme models are found in Table 6.2.

Validation experiments were done for AP, LP, TP and CA using data from trials not used to develop the original models (procedure in Fig. 6.5). Since there was generally close agreement among the three trials for all these enzymes, a good relationship was obtained between predicted and experimental activities, with r^2 values ranging from 0.735 to 0.993 (McKellar et al., 1994b, 1996; Hirvi et al., 1996).

Survival models for several food-borne pathogens have also been derived. *Listeria innocua*, a non-pathogen, is often used as a substitute for *L. monocytogenes* in situations (such as food processing environments) where it would be undesirable to introduce pathogens (Fairchild and Foegeding, 1993). A model developed for *L. innocua* (Table 6.2) was shown to underpredict inactivation of *L. monocytogenes*, thus predictions are 'fail-safe' (Piyasena et al., 1998). *Enterococcus faecium*, a non-pathogen, is also used as a model organism for pathogens, particularly in Europe (Gagnon, 1989). The inactivation curve for this microorganism deviated strongly from linearity, and there were large inter-trial variations. Thus a random coefficient model using the biphasic logistic function (equation 6.8) was used to fit the data (Ross et al., 1998). The average ln D-values for the two populations were 0.825 and 2.856.

One of the more interesting target microorganisms examined in these studies was *Enterobacter sakazakii*, an 'emerging' pathogen found to contaminate infant formula. It was reported by Nazarowec-White and Farber (1997b) that 0–12% infant formula samples found on the Canadian retail market (from five different companies) contained *E. sakazakii*. Taxonomy and microbiology of this microorganism were described by Nazarowec-White and Farber (1997a) in their review on *E. sakazakii*. Model parameter values (Table 6.2) were generated for this pathogen from three independent trials, and the resulting regression lines are shown in Fig. 6.6 (Nazarowec-White et al., 1999).

The power values listed for the various enzymes and pathogens (Table 6.2) give an indication of the extent of non-linearity of the inactivation curves. As described above, fitting with the power law function is appropriate for concave (tailing) inactivation curves when the power value is less than 1.0. In all cases except one, power values were less than 1.0, suggesting that, even in a continuous flow system, inactivation kinetics for many milk enzyme and food-borne pathogens deviate substantially from the linear. This supports the general observation made earlier that few, if any, survival curves are truly linear,

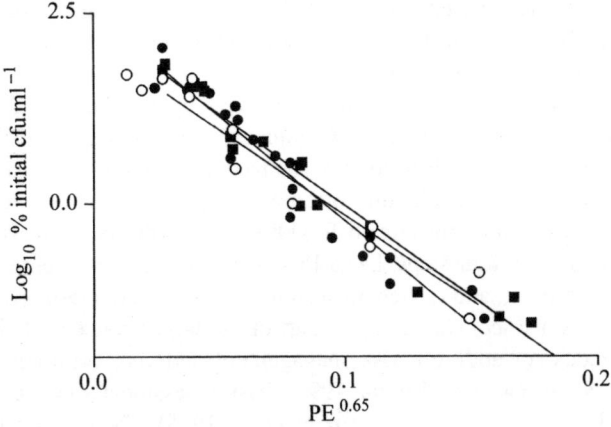

Fig. 6.6 Linear models derived from three HTST trials with *Enterobacter sakazakii*. Data are from Nazarowec-White *et al.* (1999) reprinted with permission from *Food Research International*. Copyright held by Elsevier Science Publishers.

suggesting that a first-order model for thermal inactivation is inadequate. A more mechanistic appproach is clearly required to establish standard modelling procedures for thermal inactivation of milk enzymes and pathogens in a continuous flow system.

The parameter estimates from Table 6.2 were used to develop a stand-alone software (PasTime) which was designed to provide users with a simple method for calculating log reductions of milk enzymes and pathogens achieved by time–temperature combinations specified by the user (McKellar *et al.*, 1994a). Provision was also made to allow the user to enter calibration data (i.e. holding tube times and pasteurisation efficiency). The program is available free from the author.

6.5   Modelling and risk assessment

Historically the production of safe food has been based on numerous codes of practice and regulations enforced by various governing bodies worldwide. With the increased concern regarding the existence of microbial hazards in foods, a more objective approach is warranted, which has led to the introduction of the Hazard Analysis Critical Control Point (HACCP) system. HACCP as a tool for safety management consists of two processes: building safety into the product and exerting strict process control (Notermans and Jouve, 1995). The principles of HACCP have been set out by the Codex Alimentarius Commission (CODEX, 1993) and consist of seven steps: hazard analysis, determination of Critical Control Points (CCP), specification of criteria, implementation of monitoring system, corrective action, verification, and documentation (Notermans *et al.*, 1995). HACCP processes as defined for various food products are often based on qualitative information and expert opinion. Moreover, the microbiological criteria underlying HACCP are poorly understood or defined (Buchanan, 1995).

The concept of risk assessment as defined by the Food and Agriculture Organisation and the World Health Organisation (FAO/WHO, 1995) provides a more quantitative approach to food-borne hazards. Quantitative risk assessment (QRA) is the scientific evaluation of known or potential adverse health effects resulting from human exposure to food-borne hazards (Notermans and Jouve, 1995). It consists of four steps: hazard identification, exposure assessment, dose response assessment, and risk characterisation (Fig. 6.7) (Notermans and Teunis, 1996). QRA is also considered to be part of the larger concept of risk analysis, which includes, in addition, risk management and risk communication steps (Fig. 6.7) (Notermans and Teunis, 1996). Risk assessment specifically supports step 3 of HACCP (Fig. 6.7) (Notermans *et al.*, 1995). The relationship between HACCP and risk assessment has not always been completely clear. For example, both processes start with the identification of hazards. Risk assessment is intended to provide a scientific basis for risk management, while HACCP is a systematic approach to the control of potential hazards in food operations (Foegeding, 1997). Thus, risk assessment concerns the overall product safety, while HACCP enhances overall product safety by assuring day-to-day process control (Foegeding, 1997). The view of risk assessment being associated with one step of HACCP may be a limited one. In a contrasting view, both HACCP and risk assessment are encompassed in risk analysis, with HACCP representing one management strategy (Fig. 6.7) (Foegeding, 1997).

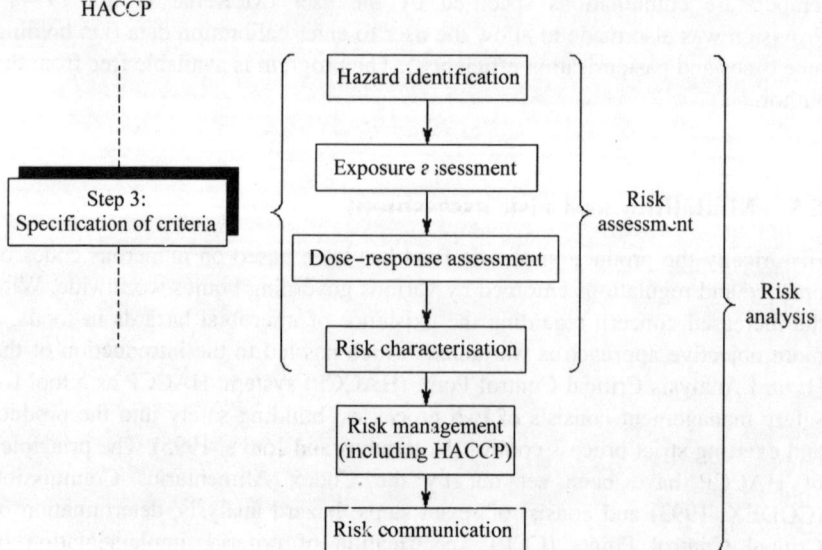

Fig. 6.7 Comparison of HACCP, risk analysis and risk assessment.

The recent ratification of the World Trade Organisation (WTO) agreement will have a major impact on the development of new approaches for the regulation of food. Countries will be encouraged to base their procedures on Codex standards and guidelines to maintain and enhance safety standards (Hathaway and Cook, 1997). This will lead to the development of harmonised risk assessment and risk management frameworks, providing input into HACCP, which is the primary vehicle for achieving enhanced food safety goals (Hathaway and Cook, 1997). As the use of HACCP increases, there will be a need for a clear understanding of the relationship among HACCP, microbiological criteria, and risk assessment (Buchanan, 1995). Regulators will be called upon to participate in all aspects of HACCP development, in particular to establish public health-based targets, elucidate microbiological criteria, develop improved techniques in microbiological risk assessment, and develop the means for evaluating the relative performance of HACCP systems (Buchanan, 1995). Harmonisation of international rules will clearly require standardised approaches (Lammerding, 1997).

In order to understand the role of predictive microbiology in risk assessment, it is necessary to further examine the various steps in more detail (Lammerding, 1997). Hazard identification involves the identification and characterisation of biological hazards that may be present in foods. Exposure assessment refers to the qualitative and/or quantitative evaluation of the likely intake of the biological agent. Dose–response assessment refers specifically to the determination of the number of microorganisms ingested, and the frequency and severity of adverse heath effects. Risk characterisation is the qualitative and/or quantitative estimation of the probability of occurrence and severity of known or potential adverse health effects in a given population.

Mathematical modelling can have the greatest influence on the exposure assessment and dose–response assessment steps. Implicit in the concept of exposure assessment is the influence of processing and environmental factors on the survival and growth of food-borne pathogens. Mathematical models can predict the extent of impact of unit operations on the numbers of microorganisms, which in turn determines the exposure (Buchanan and Whiting, 1996). Specific mathematical functions to quantitate microbial growth and death can be incorporated into risk assessments (Buchanan and Whiting, 1996; McNab, 1997; Walls and Scott, 1997; vanGerwen and Zwietering, 1998). For example, the Gompertz function is used to evaluate growth parameters:

$$\log N(t) = A + C(e^{(-e^{-B(t-M)})}) \qquad 6.16$$

where $N(t)$ is the number of cells at time t, A is the asymptotic count as t decreases to zero, C is the difference in value between the upper and lower asymptotes, B is the relative growth rate at M, and M is the time where the absolute growth rate is maximum (Buchanan and Whiting, 1996). Thermal death models can be used to establish the D-value for a microorganism (equation 6.4). Much information on microbial growth and survival has been documented, and the resulting predictive software packages such as Food MicroModel have been used to predict the influence of food composition and environmental conditions on growth and survival of potentially hazardous microorganisms (Panisello and Quantick, 1998). Models can therefore be used to develop CCPs, and show where data for risk assessments are missing (Baker, 1995). In addition, models can support regulations and optimise product formulations and support process control (Baker, 1995). Mathematical modelling can also support quantitation in dose–response assessment. The beta Poisson distribution model for dose–response is (Buchanan and Whiting, 1996):

$$P_i = 1 - \left(1 + \frac{N}{\beta}\right)^{\alpha} \qquad 6.17$$

where P_i is the probability of infection, N is the exposure, and α and β are coefficients specific to the pathogen. One is cautioned in the use of mathematical models for quantitative risk assessment; important issues to remember are the need for high quality data, extensive validation of models in foods, and avoiding extrapolation beyond the conditions used to generate the model (McNab, 1997).

In QRA, mathematical models are used to estimate the ultimate risk to the consumer as a function of input values taken from various points along the 'farm-to-fork' continuum. Due to heterogeneity of microorganisms, variability around single point estimates of risk can be significant. Thus, point estimates give limited information, describing single instances such as 'worst case' scenarios (Buchanan and Whiting, 1996; Lammerding and Fazil, 2000). Improvements in prediction can be made by incorporating uncertainty. Uncertainty is an important factor in risk analysis, since it limits our ability to make reliable predictions of risk. Uncertainty may arise from inherent variability in the biological system, or from lack of information or understanding of the mechanisms involved (McNab, 1997). Uncertainty can be minimised by obtaining more, high quality data; however, as this is not always feasible, alternatives must be sought. One approach is to describe variability using probability distributions to represent parameter values. These distributions can be built from empirical data, knowledge of underlying biological phenomena, or expert opinion (Lammerding and Fazil, 2000), and the process leads to an output where risk is expressed as a probability distribution. Risk analysis software such as @RISK™, which uses Monte Carlo analysis to simulate output distributions of risk based on variability of input data, can facilitate the risk assessment process (Buchanan and Whiting, 1996; Lammerding and Fazil, 2000).

Nauta (2000) has emphasised the need to separate true biological variability due to heterogeneity of populations from uncertainty, the lack of perfect knowledge of the parameter values. This is commonly neglected in risk assessment studies. Working with data on growth of *Bacillus cereus* in pasteurised milk, Nauta (2000) showed that prediction of outbreak size may depend on the way that uncertainty and variability are separated.

The extended application of risk assessment procedures to the survival of *E. coli* O157:H7 in ground beef hamburgers was studied by Cassin *et al.* (1998)

who defined the term Process Risk Model to predict the probability of an adverse impact as a function of multiple process parameters. This approach is based on the assumption that risk is determined by process variables, and that behaviour of the microorganism can be described mathematically. Simulations were done with the Monte Carlo approach, and rank correlations were used to find variables which were most strongly correlated with illness. This process allowed the identification of CCPs.

6.6   Risk assessment and pasteurisation

Mathematical modelling has been applied to dairy products and processes (Griffiths, 1994); however, there has been limited application of QRA. Risk assessments have been done for the growth of *B. cereus* in pasteurised milk (Zwietering *et al.*, 1996; Notermans *et al.*, 1997), survival of *L. monocytogenes* in soft cheese (Bemrah *et al.*, 1998), and survival of *L. monocytogenes* during milk processing (Peeler and Bunning, 1994). This latter study also incorporated estimates of survival with pasteurisation at several time–temperature combinations. Some of the limited number of risk assessments performed have been reviewed, and a number of weaknesses and omissions have been identified (Cassin *et al.*, 1996; Schlundt, 2000). The process of QRA is still in its infancy, however, and standards have yet to be developed. There is a clear advantage to the food industry and consumers to further develop the concepts of QRA and apply them to both common and novel food processes, and it is expected that significant advances will be made in this field over the next decade.

Returning now to the pasteurisation models, we note that mean parameter values (Table 6.2) provide single output values for each set of processing conditions, but do not take into account inter-trial variability. In order to make these models more relevant to QRA, the risk analysis software @RISK^{TM}, a Microsoft Excel add-in, was used. @RISK^{TM} expresses model parameters as distributions, and when simulations are performed, outputs are calculated as distributions. Thus, a range of probable output (e.g. survival) values for a specified set of processing conditions is obtained, and the probability of achieving a target log reduction can be estimated.

An Excel spreadsheet was prepared which contained the model and calculations of PE and $\log_{10}$ reduction for each of the target enzymes or pathogens. Model parameters (E_a/R, intercept, slope and power) were entered into the spreadsheet as normal distributions with mean and standard deviation values taken from previously published information for each target (Table 6.2). For some targets, it was discovered that parameter estimates were correlated. For example, significant correlations were observed between E_a/R and both slope ($r^2 = 0.647$) and intercept ($r^2 = 0.240$) for the five *L. innocua* trials. During simulations, @RISK^{TM} normally takes random sample values from each of the input distributions. If parameter values are correlated, it is necessary to have @RISK^{TM} adjust sampling patterns to include these correlations.

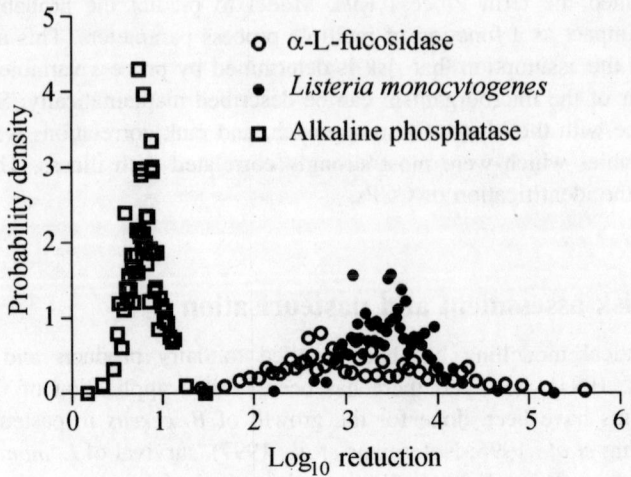

Fig. 6.8 Probability distributions for α-L-fucosidase, *Listeria monocytogenes*, and alkaline phosphatase generated from @RISK™ simulations with processing at 65°C for 15 s.

Monte Carlo is the traditional method for sampling distributions in which samples are taken randomly throughout the input distribution (Vose, 1996). Latin hypercube is a recent development in sampling technology which employs stratification of the input probability distributions, resulting in fewer iterations than the traditional Monte Carlo method. For these studies, Latin hypercube simulations were done with a total of 1500 iterations for each replicate simulation. As an example of this process, simulated log reductions were generated for AP, FC and *L. monocytogenes* using a holding time of 65°C for 15 s (corresponding to thermisation), and the probability density functions are shown in Fig. 6.8. These conditions resulted in a narrow band of probabilities for AP, with greater predicted range for both FC and *L. monocytogenes*. Thermisation does not completely inactivate AP, while FC (a potential indicator of thermisation) experiences a greater than 2 log reduction in most iterations. The mean log reduction of *L. monocytogenes* under these conditions is greater than 3.

Improvements in predictive power from @RISK™ models can be realised by the use of percentiles. Probability distributions generated by simulation are divided into equal probability increments called percentiles. Percentiles represent the percentage of generated results which are less than or equal to the associated log reduction. A failure is scored when the predicted inactivation is greater than the experimental value at that percentile (i.e., a 'fail-dangerous' prediction). The lower percentiles are associated with lower, more conservative estimates of log reduction at a particular set of processing conditions.

As an example, the results of simulations carried out with three *E. sakazakii* trials are shown in Table 6.3 (Nazarowec-White *et al.*, 1999). At the 5th percentile, the model 'failed dangerous' with Trials A and B; however, the more

Table 6.3   Validation of *E. sakazakii* model using @RISK[TM] simulations[a]

Percentile[b]	Trial A (n = 12)			Trial B (n = 24)			Trial C (n = 22)		
	1[d]	2	3	1	2	3	1	2	3
1	0	0	0	0	0	0	0	0	0
2	0	0	0	0	1	1	0	0	0
5	1	1	1	3	3	3	0	0	0
10	2	2	2	8	8	8	4	4	3
15	3	3	3	12	12	13	12	12	11
20	3	3	3	16	16	16	15	15	15
25	4	4	4	19	19	18	17	17	18
30	6	6	6	20	19	19	18	18	18
35	7	7	7	20	20	20	18	18	18
40	8	8	8	20	20	20	19	19	19

[a] Data are from Nazarowec-White *et al.* (1999) reprinted with permission from *Food Research International*. Copyright held by Elsevier Science Publishers.
[b] Probability distributions generated by simulation are divided into equal probability increments called percentiles. Percentiles represent the percentage of simulated results which are less than or equal to the associated log reduction.
[c] A failure is scored when the predicted inactivation was greater than the experimental value at that percentile (i.e., a 'fail-dangerous' situation). The lower percentiles are associated with lower, more conservative, estimates of log reduction at a particular set of processing conditions.
[d] Replicate simulations.

conservative estimated log reduction associated with the 1st percentile did not result in any failures (Table 6.3). At the higher percentiles, a greater number of failures are observed, indicating that the corresponding predicted log reductions are too ambitious, and unlikely to be achieved in practice. This approach allows the user to set the level of allowable risk, then select the processing conditions which will result in the desired degree of inactivation. The value of this approach was further examined by comparing thermal inactivation of *E. sakazakii* with that of *L. monocytogenes*. Results of the comparison (Table 6.4) show that at all temperatures simulated, *E. sakazakii* was more heat-sensitive than *L. monocytogenes*, with greater than 1-log difference at 68°C (Table 6.4). Comparison of simulated $\log_{10}$ reductions associated with the 1st and 5th percentiles revealed that *E. sakazakii* was only slightly more heat-sensitive at 68°C than *L. monocytogenes*, with differences of 0.5 and 0.25 log at the two percentiles, respectively (Table 6.4). This apparent decreased difference in heat sensitivity between the two pathogens associated with the 1st and 5th percentile predictions reflects the greater uncertainty in the slope parameter for the *E. sakazakii* model compared to that for the *L. monocytogenes* model (Nazarowec-White *et al.*, 1999).

Models which can predict the probability of achieving a desired level of safety are an important addition to risk assessment models which are still largely

Table 6.4 Comparison of $\log_{10}$ reductions for *Enterobacter sakazakii* and *Listeria monocytogenes* simulated using @RISK[TM][a]

Temperature (°C)	Simulated $\log_{10}$ reduction[b]					
	Enterobacter sakazakii			*Listeria monocytogenes*		
	Mean (S.D.)	Percentile[c]		Mean (S.D.)	Percentile[c]	
		5	1		5	1
67.0	5.46 (0.626)	4.16	3.65	4.88 (0.472)	3.89	3.47
67.5	6.51 (0.728)	5.04	4.43	5.71 (0.484)	4.67	4.23
68.0	7.75 (0.850)	6.08	5.36	6.69 (0.500)	5.59	5.13

[a] Data are from Nazarowec-White *et al.* (1999) reprinted with permission from *Food Research International*. Copyright held by Elsevier Science Publishers.
[b] 16 s holding time; 1500 iterations.
[c] Percent of the total iterations which give simulated $\log_{10}$ reductions less than the values corresponding to each temperature. For example, at 67.0°C, the *E. sakazakii* model predicted a mean $\log_{10}$ reduction of 5.46, with 5% of the 1500 iterations giving a value of <4.16. Thus, in 95% of the simulations, the model predicts >4.16 $\log_{10}$ reduction.

qualitative, and based primarily on expert opinion. To facilitate this process, the pasteurisation models described above have been incorporated into the risk analysis software, Analytica®, which is commonly used for building risk assessment models for the food industry. This software supports a modular approach, thus pasteurisation models may be easily incorporated into larger risk assessment models designed to encompass the entire 'farm-to-fork' continuum. Models for microbial survival and growth have also been incorporated into several large databases which are available to the food industry. Food MicroModel, which is based on work done by the Institute of Food Research in the UK and their collaborators (McClure *et al.*, 1994), is a commercially available software package which is continually updated, but which requires an annual licensing fee. The Pathogen Modelling Program (PMP) was designed by the United States Department of Agriculture to provide assistance to the food industry, and is available free of charge (Buchanan, 1993). Pasteurisation models discussed here will be incorporated into the PMP.

6.7   Future trends

The models described in this chapter have thus far been confined to enzymes and pathogens in whole milk. Other dairy products are also of concern, thus models will continue to be expanded to include more viscous dairy products such as ice-cream mix. For example, preliminary studies have been undertaken to assess the extent to which the thickening agent guar gum can influence HTST processing (Piyasena and McKellar, 1999). Other liquid food and beverage products may also be potential sources of risks. Apple cider is often sold unpasteurised to consumers who consider this product to be more natural; however, *E. coli* O157:H7 is often a potential risk in this product. Limited thermal treatment of this product, combined with other intervention strategies, may present a solution. To this end, preliminary HTST models have been developed for a model microorganism, *Pediococcus* sp., in simulated apple cider (Piyasena *et al.*, 2003).

Other thermal and non-thermal processing technologies are gaining in popularity. Current regulations which require specified time–temperature treatments are based on thermal processes, thus it is difficult to establish equivalent process conditions. Some of these technologies, such as radio frequency (RF) and ohmic heating, are thermal processes, and thus may be modelled by some modification of the present HTST models. In contrast, the mechanisms by which non-thermal processes such as pulse electric field (PEF) and ultraviolet light inactivate microorganisms are as yet poorly understood. It has become apparent that further work is needed to establish adequate modelling approaches for these technologies (Institute of Food Technologists, 2000).

It is now well known that thermal resistance of bacteria can be influenced by the conditions or stage of growth. Production of heat-shock proteins by bacteria renders them increasingly resistant to thermal treatment. Cross-protection with other stresses such as low pH and starvation has also been observed. Development of adequate models to describe these phenomena will require a greater knowledge of the physiological changes taking place in bacterial cells, thus there will be a move away from empirical modelling to more mechanistic models which are based on expression of key genes or synthesis of heat-shock proteins essential for survival. This molecular modelling approach is one which is being actively explored worldwide. Our research group is closely involved with a large molecular modelling project with the University of Guelph.

It is well known that bacterial survival curves are rarely first-order, yet no concerted approach to this problem has been suggested. The use of distributions, which imply heterogeneity of cells, seems like a worthwhile and most promising approach. Recent interested in the heterogeneity of bacterial cells (Booth, 2002) and an improved understanding of the factors which determine intra-cell variations in heat resistance will further strengthen our ability to provide adequate models to the food industry.

6.8   Sources of further information and advice

Important references include McMeekin *et al.* (1993), a reference book describing some of the principles of predictive food microbiology; Vose (1996), a book describing the fundamentals of risk analysis and Monte Carlo simulation; and more recently a book on food process modelling with specific chapters on modelling uncertainty (Van Impe *et al.*, 2001), food safety (Baranyi and Pin, 2001) and thermal processing (Nicolaï *et al.*, 2001 and Bakalis *et al.*, 2001).

The PMP is available from the USDA at: http://www.arserrc.gov/mfs/pathogen.htm

Food MicroModel is available from Leatherhead Food RA at: http://www.lfra.co.uk/

Other useful sites:

IDF: http://www.fil-idf.org/
National Milk Producers' Federation (US): http://www.nmpf.org/
National Dairy Council (US): http://www.nationaldairycouncil.org/
National Dairy Council of Canada: http://www.ndcc.ca
Agriculture and Agri-Food Canada: http://www.agr.gc.ca/index_e.phtml
Canadian Dairy regulations: http://www.dairyinfo.agr.ca/cdicdrcan.htm
United States Dairy regulations: http://www.dairyinfo.agr.ca/cdicdrusa.htm
International Dairy regulations: http://www.dairyinfo.agr.ca/cdicdrint.htm

6.9 References

ANDREWS A T, ANDERSON M and GOODENOUGH P W (1987), 'A study of the heat stabilities of a number of indigenous milk enzymes', *J Dairy Res*, 54, 237–246.

BAKALIS S, COX P W and FRYER P J (2001), 'Modelling thermal processes: heating', in Tijsken L M M, Hertog M L A.T M and Nicolaï B M, *Food Process Modelling*, Woodhead Publishing, Cambridge, 340–364.

BAKER D A (1995), 'Application of modelling in HACCP plan development', *Int J Food Microbiol*, 25, 251–261.

BARANYI J and PIN C (2001), 'Modelling microbiological safety', in Tijsken L M M, Hertog M L A T M and Nicolaï B M, *Food Process Modelling*, Woodhead Publishing, Cambridge, 383–401.

BEMRAH N, SANAA M, CASSIN M H, GRIFFITHS M W and CERF O (1998), 'Quantitative risk assessment of human listeriosis from consumption of soft cheese made from raw milk', *Prev Vet Med*, 37, 129–145.

BIGELOW W D (1921), 'Logarithmic nature of thermal death time curves', *J Inf Dis*, 29, 538.

BOOTH I R (2002), 'Stress and the single cell: Intrapopulation diversity is a mechanism to ensure survival upon exposure to stress', *Int J Food Microbiol*, 78, 19–30.

BUCHANAN R L (1993), 'Developing and distributing user-friendly application software', *J Ind Microbiol*, 12, 251–255.

BUCHANAN R L (1995), 'The role of microbiological criteria and risk assessment in HACCP', *Food Microbiol*, 12, 421–424.

BUCHANAN R L and WHITING R C (1996), 'Risk assessment and predictive microbiology', *J Food Protect*, Suppl, 59, 31–36.

CAMPANELLA O H and PELEG M (2001), 'Theoretical comparison of a new and the traditional method to calculate *Clostridium botulinum* survival during thermal inactivation', *J Sci Food Agric*, 81, 1069–1076.

CASSIN M H, PAOLI G M, MCCOLL R S and LAMMERDING A M (1996), 'Hazard assessment of *Listeria monocytogenes* in the processing of bovine milk – Comment', *J Food Protect*, 59, 341–342.

CASSIN M H, PAOLI G M and LAMMERDING A M (1998), 'Simulation modeling for microbial risk assessment', *J Food Protect*, 61, 1560–1566.

CERF O (1977), 'Tailing of survival curves of bacterial spores', *J Appl Bacteriol*, 42, 1–19.

CODEX (1993), 'Guidelines for the application of the Hazard Analysis Critical Control Point system. Codex Alimentarius (CCFH) Alinorm 93/13A-Appendix II'.

D'AOUST J Y, EMMONS D B, MCKELLAR R, TIMBERS G E, TODD E C D, SEWELL A M and WARBURTON D W (1987), 'Thermal inactivation of *Salmonella* species in fluid milk', *J Food Protect*, 50, 494–501.

FAIRCHILD T M and FOEGEDING P M (1993), 'A proposed nonpathogenic biological indicator for thermal inactivation of *Listeria monocytogenes*', *Appl Environ Microbiol*, 59, 1247–1250.

FAIRCHILD T M, SWARTZEL K R and FOEGEDING P M (1994), 'Inactivation kinetics of *Listeria innocua* in skim milk in a continuous flow processing system', *J Food Sci*, 59, 960–963.

FAO/WHO (1995), 'Application of risk analysis to food standards issues', in *Report of the Joint FAO/WHO Expert Consultation*, World Health Organisation, Geneva, Switzerland, 13–17.

FOEGEDING P M (1997), 'Driving predictive modelling on a risk assessment path for enhanced food safety', *Int J Food Microbiol*, 36, 87–95.

GAGNON B (1989), 'Canadian code of recommended manufacturing practices for pasteurized/modified atmosphere packed/refrigerated foods', in *Guidelines for the 'Code of Practice on Processed Refrigerated Foods'*, Agri-Food Safety Division, Agriculture Canada.

GIBALDI M and PERRIER D (1975), *Pharmacokinetics*, Marcel Dekker, New York.

GRIFFITHS M W (1986), 'Use of milk enzymes as indices of heat treatment', *J Food Protect*, 49, 696–705.

GRIFFITHS M W (1994), 'Predictive modelling: applications in the dairy industry', *Int J Food Microbiol*, 23, 305–315.

HATHAWAY S C and COOK R L (1997), 'A regulatory perspective on the potential uses of microbial risk assessment in international trade', *Int J Food Microbiol*, 36, 127–133.

HIRVI Y, GRIFFITHS M W, MCKELLAR R C and MODLER H W (1996), 'Linear-transform and non-linear modelling of bovine catalase inactivation in a high-temperature short-time pasteurizer', *Food Res Int*, 29, 89–93.

INSTITUTE OF FOOD TECHNOLOGISTS (2000), 'Kinetics of microbial inactivation for alternative food processing technologies. A report of the Institute of Food Technologists for the Food and Drug Administration', *J Food Sci*, 65, S4–S108.

INTERNATIONAL ASSOCIATION OF MILK, FOOD, AND ENVIRONMENTAL SANITARIANS, UNITED STATES PUBLIC HEALTH SERVICE AND THE DAIRY INDUSTRY COMMITTEE (1992), '3-A accepted practices for the sanitary construction, installation, testing and operation of high-temperature short-time and higher-heat shorter-time pasteurizer systems. Standard No. 603-06, revised', *Dairy Food Environ Sanit*, 12, 423–477.

INTERNATIONAL DAIRY FEDERATION (1991), *Alkaline Phosphatase Test as a Measure of Correct Pasteurization*, International Dairy Federation, Brussels.

KESSLER H G (1986), 'Considerations in relation to some technological and engineering aspects', in *Monograph on Pasteurized Milk, IDF Bulletin 200*, International Dairy Federation, Brussels, 80–86.

LAMMERDING A M (1997), 'An overview of microbial food safety risk assessment', *J Food Protect*, 60, 1420–1425.

LAMMERDING A M and FAZIL A (2000), 'Hazard identification and exposure assessment for microbial food safety risk assessment', *Int J Food Microbiol*, 58, 147–157.

LEISTNER L and GORRIS L G M (1995), 'Food preservation by hurdle technology', *Trends Food Sci Technol*, 6, 41–46.

LINTON R H, CARTER W H, PIERSON M D and HACKNEY C R (1995), 'Use of a modified Gompertz equation to model nonlinear survival curves for *Listeria monocytogenes* Scott A', *J Food Protect*, 58, 946–954.

MACKEY B M and BRATCHELL N (1989), 'The heat resistance of *Listeria monocytogenes*', *Lett Appl Microbiol*, 9, 89–94.

MCCLURE P J, BLACKBURN C D, COLE M B, CURTIS P S, JONES J E, LEGAN J D, OGDEN I D, PECK M W, ROBERTS T A, SUTHERLAND J P, WALKER S J and BLACKBURN C D W (1994), 'Modelling the growth, survival and death of microorganisms in foods: the UK food micromodel approach', *Int J Food Microbiol*, 23, 265–275.

MCKELLAR R C and PIYASENA P (2000), 'Predictive modelling of the inactivation of bovine milk α-L-fucosidase in a high-temperature short-time pasteurizer', *Int Dairy J*, 10, 1–6.

MCKELLAR R C, MODLER H W, COUTURE H, HUGHES A, MAYERS P, GLEESON T and ROSS W H (1994a), 'Pasteurisers – killing time', *Dairy Ind Intl*, 59, 49.

MCKELLAR R C, MODLER H W, COUTURE H, HUGHES A, MAYERS P, GLEESON T and ROSS W H (1994b), 'Predictive modeling of alkaline phosphatase inactivation in a high-temperature short-time pasteurizer', *J Food Protect*, 57, 424–430.

MCKELLAR R C, LIOU S and MODLER H W (1996), 'Predictive modelling of lactoperoxidase and gamma-glutamyl transpeptidase inactivation in a high-temperature short-time pasteurizer', *Int Dairy J*, 6, 295–301.

MCMEEKIN T A, OLLEY J N, ROSS T and RATKOWSKY D A (1993), *Predictive Microbiology: Theory and Application*, John Wiley & Sons, New York.

MCNAB W B (1997), 'A literature review linking microbial risk assessment, predictive microbiology, and dose–response modeling', *Dairy Food Env Sanit*, 17, 405–416.

MOATS W A, DABBAH R and EDWARDS V M (1971), 'Interpretation of nonlogarithmic survivor curves of heated bacteria', *J Food Sci*, 36, 523–526.

NAUTA M J (2000), 'Separation of uncertainty and variability in quantitative microbial risk assessment models', *Int J Food Microbiol*, 57, 9–18.

NAZAROWEC-WHITE M and FARBER J M (1997a), '*Enterobacter sakazakii*: a review', *Int J Food Microbiol*, 34, 103–113.

NAZAROWEC-WHITE M and FARBER J M (1997b), 'Thermal resistance of *Enterobacter sakazakii* in reconstituted dried-infant formula', *Lett Appl Microbiol*, 24, 9–13.

NAZAROWEC-WHITE M, MCKELLAR R C and PIYASENA P (1999), 'Predictive modelling of *Enterobacter sakazakii* inactivation in bovine milk during high-temperature short-time pasteurization', *Food Res Int*, 32, 375–379.

NICOLAÏ B M, VERBOVEN P and SCHEERLINCK N (2001), 'The modelling of heat and mass transfer', in Tijsken L M M, Hertog M L A T M and Nicolaï B M, *Food Process Modelling*, Woodhead Publishing, Cambridge, 60–86.

NOTERMANS S and JOUVE J L (1995), 'Quantitative risk analysis and HACCP: some remarks', *Food Microbiol*, 12, 425–429.

NOTERMANS S and TEUNIS P (1996), 'Quantitative risk analysis and the production of microbiologically safe food: an introduction', *Int J Food Microbiol*, 30, 3–7.

NOTERMANS S, GALLHOFF G, ZWIETERING M H and MEAD G C (1995), 'The HACCP concept: specification of criteria using quantitative risk assessment', *Food Microbiol*, 12, 81–90.

NOTERMANS S, DUFRENNE J, TEUNIS P, BEUMER R, GIFFEL M T and WEEM P P (1997), 'A risk assessment study of *Bacillus cereus* present in pasteurized milk', *Food Microbiol*,

14, 143–151.

NUNES R V, SWARTZEL K R and OLLIS D F (1993), 'Thermal evaluation of food processes: the role of a reference temperature', *J Food Eng*, 20, 1–15.

PANISELLO P J and QUANTICK P C (1998), 'Application of Food MicroModel predictive software in the development of hazard analysis critical control point (HACCP) systems', *Food Microbiol*, 15, 425–439.

PEELER J T and BUNNING V K (1994), 'Hazard assessment of *Listeria monocytogenes* in the processing of bovine milk', *J Food Protect*, 57, 689–697.

PIYASENA P and MCKELLAR R C (1999), 'Influence of guar gum on the thermal stability of *Listeria innocua, Listeria monocytogenes*, and γ-glutamyl transpeptidase during high-temperature short-time pasteurization', *J Food Protect*, 62, 861–866.

PIYASENA P, LIOU S and MCKELLAR R C (1998), 'Predictive modelling of inactivation of *Listeria* spp. in bovine milk during HTST pasteurization', *Int J Food Microbiol*, 39, 167–173.

PIYASENA P, MCKELLAR R C and BARTLETT F M (2003), 'Thermal inactivation of *Pediococcus* sp. in simulated apple cider during high-temperature short-time pasteurization', *Int J Food Microbiol*, 82, 25–31.

PRUITT K M and KAMAU D N (1993), 'Mathematical models of bacterial growth, inhibition and death under combined stress conditions', *J Ind Microbiol*, 12, 221–231.

ROSS W H, COUTURE H, HUGHES A, GLEESON T and MCKELLAR R C (1998), 'A non-linear mixed effects model for the destruction of *Enterococcus faecium* in a high-temperature short-time pasteurizer', *Food Microbiol*, 15, 567–575.

SCHLUNDT J (2000), 'Comparison of microbiological risk assessment studies published', *Int J Food Microbiol*, 58, 197–202.

STAAL P F J (1986), 'Legislation/statutory regulations applicable to pasteurized fluid milk in a selected number of countries', in *Monograph on Pasteurized Milk, IDF Bulletin 200*, International Dairy Federation, Brussels, 71–79.

STRINGER S C, GEORGE S M and PECK M W (2000), 'Thermal inactivation of *Escherichia coli* O157:H7', *J Appl Microbiol*, 88, 79S–89S.

VANBOEKEL M A J S (2002), 'On the use of the Weibull model to describe thermal inactivation of microbial vegetative cells', *Int J Food Microbiol*, 74, 139–159.

VANGERWEN S J C and ZWIETERING M H (1998), 'Growth and inactivation models to be used in quantitative risk assessments', *J Food Protect*, 61, 1541–1549.

VAN IMPE J F, BERNAERTS K, GEERAERD A H, POSCHET F and VERSYCK K J (2001), 'Modelling and prediction in an uncertain environment', in Tijsken L M M, Hertog M L A T M and Nicolaï B M, *Food Process Modelling*, Woodhead Publishing, Cambridge, 156–179.

VOSE D (1996), *Quantitative Risk Analysis: a Guide to Monte Carlo Simulation Modelling*, John Wiley & Sons, New York.

WALLS I and SCOTT V N (1997), 'Use of predictive microbiology in microbial food safety risk assessment', *Int J Food Microbiol*, 36, 97–102.

WHITING R C (1993), 'Modeling bacterial survival in unfavorable environments', *J Ind Microbiol*, 12, 240–246.

ZEHETNER G, BAREUTHER C, HENLE T and KLOSTERMEYER H (1996), 'Inactivation of endogenous enzymes during heat treatment of milk', *Neth Milk Dairy J*, 50, 215–226.

ZWIETERING M H, DEWIT J C and NOTERMANS S (1996), 'Application of predictive microbiology to estimate the number of *Bacillus cereus* in pasteurised milk at the point of consumption', *Int J Food Microbiol*, 30, 55–70.

7

Flavour generation in dairy products

A. E. M. Boelrijk, C. de Jong and G. Smit, NIZO Food Research,
The Netherlands

7.1 Introduction

In this chapter, the focus is primarily on the chemical aspects of flavour
generation in dairy products as opposed to biological flavour formation.
However, a strict separation between chemical and biological aspects of flavour
generation is rather artificial (whether you use a proton or an enzyme for a
catalytic transformation, in the end it is all chemistry!). In order to prevent
overlap with other chapters in this book which focus on the role of commercial
cultures and enzymes in flavour production as much as possible, we decided to
focus primarily on the flavour and off-flavour generation in several dairy
products caused by processing steps (such as heating and ageing). In this review
we deal with dairy products from bovine milk. Although the chapter aims to
cover the literature in this field as much as possible, the main focus is on the
literature that has been published since 1990. For the literature before 1990 we
refer to excellent reviews by Badings (1991) and Adda (1986) on the flavours in
milk.

7.1.1 Chemical pathways that are important for the generation of dairy flavours

All dairy products start from raw milk that, apart from minor ingredients such as
salts and vitamins, consists mainly of milk fat, proteins and lactose. These three
main groups can be degraded to building blocks that have a flavour of their own,
or derivatives from each group can react with each other to form new products
that have a flavour (Adda, 1986; Dumont and Adda, 1979). The possible
degradation reactions for the three main groups are summarised in Fig. 7.1(a)

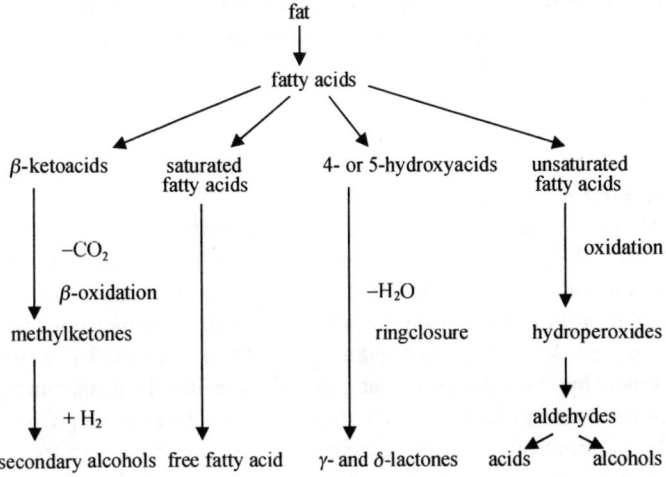

Fig. 7.1(a)   Degradation of milk fat.

Free radical:

$R_1 \diagup \underset{\bullet}{\diagup} \diagdown R_2$

Production of organic peroxides: $R^\bullet + O_2 \longrightarrow RO_2^\bullet$

$RO_2^\bullet + RH \longrightarrow ROOH + R^\bullet$

Formation of secondary products

$R_4 \diagdown \overset{OOH}{\underset{R_3}{\diagup}} \longrightarrow R_4^-CH_2^\bullet + OH^\bullet + R_3^-CHO$

$\longrightarrow R_4 \diagdown \overset{O}{\diagup}_H \;\; + OH^\bullet + R_3^\bullet$

$R_4^-CH_2^\bullet \xrightarrow{\;\; RH + O_2 \quad R^\bullet \;\;} R_4^-CH_2OOH \longrightarrow R_4^-CH_2O^\bullet + OH^\bullet$

$RH \diagup \quad \diagdown R^\bullet$

$R^\bullet \quad \diagdown RH$

$R_4^-CH_2OH \qquad R_4^-CHO$

Fig. 7.1(b)   Auto-oxidation of unsaturated fatty acids.

(degradation of milk fat) and Fig. 7.1(b) (auto-oxidation of unsaturated fatty acids), and later in the chapter in Fig. 7.2 (degradation of proteins) and Fig. 7.3 (degradation of lactose). We start this chapter by discussing these conversion pathways in more detail.

7.1.2   Degradation of milk fat

The degradation of milk fat results in a large number of different volatile flavours (Adda, 1986). Lipases (either bacterial or milk-own) degrade milk fat in C_4–C_{10} free fatty acids (Driessen, 1981). β-Keto acids are formed from saturated fatty acids and in turn result in the formation of methyl ketones after proton- or enzyme-catalysed decarboxylation (van Duin, 1965). The methyl ketones can also be formed by β-oxidation of saturated fatty acids. Hydrogenation of the methyl ketones leads to secondary alcohols. By a cyclisation step (β-oxidation followed by splitting off a water molecule), γ- and δ-lactones are formed from γ- or δ-hydroxy fatty acids. The γ- or δ-hydroxy fatty acids are present in milk fat in small quantities from the start and can also be formed from unsaturated free fatty acids by a hydration reaction (Mick *et al.*, 1982). The hydroxy acids can also lead to C_3–C_{15} esters by intramolecular esterification reactions. An important route for the formation of aldehydes and ketones from unsaturated fatty acids is auto-oxidation. An example of a general auto-oxidation scheme is given in Fig. 7.1(b). The auto-oxidation reaction cascade starts with radical formation. The resulting organic peroxide degrades in secondary products such as ketones, aldehydes and alcohols. The origin of the starting radical can be manyfold and will be discussed in more detail in section 7.2.3 on the generation of off-flavours in milk. Aldehydes are important starting products for the formation of acids (by oxidation) or for the formation of Maillard products after their reaction with amino acids. The Maillard reaction will be discussed in detail in section 7.2.2 on heated milk.

7.1.3   Degradation of proteins

A large diversity of volatile and non-volatile dairy flavours can be formed from proteins (Adda, 1986; Calvo and de la Hoz, 1992; Contarini *et al.*, 1997). Figure 7.2 summarises the different pathways. Proteinases and peptidases (bacterial or milk-own) degrade the proteins to peptides and free amino acids. Several (non-volatile) peptides have a bitter taste (Driessen, 1981) and will be discussed in detail in Chapter 22. Amino acids can be degraded to aldehydes by Strecker degradation (Nursten, 1986; Ho, 1996), which in turn can take part in the Maillard reaction or can be oxidised to form acids. Sulphur-containing amino acids, i.e. cysteine and methionine, are important sources for the generation of volatile sulphur containing compounds which have a distinct flavour. Protonation of activated sulphydryl groups leads to liberation of H_2S, while it is thought that protonation of methionine residues leads to liberation of methional (Nursten, 1986; Ho, 1996). Nitrogen-containing amino acids

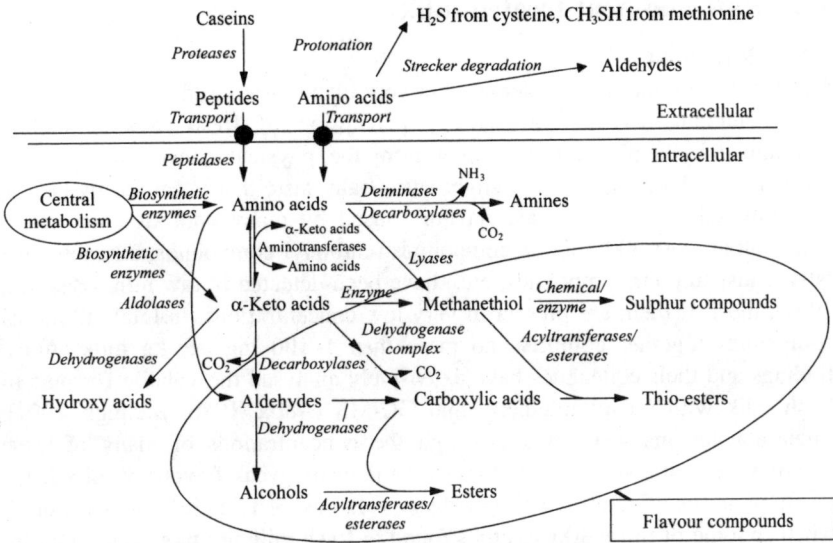

Fig. 7.2 Degradation of proteins.

eventually lead to volatile nitrogen-containing flavours such as pyrazines, pyrroles and so on. Photochemical degradation of thiamine (vitamin B1) followed by a reaction with H_2S has been reported to produce a strong aromatic volatile with a rubber taste (Buttery *et al.*, 1981), whose molecular identity has not been established yet.

7.1.4 Degradation of lactose

For the preparation of yoghurt the enzymatic degradation of lactose into lactate, acetaldehyde and diacetyl is essential. However, lactose can also react non-enzymatically with amino acids via the Maillard reaction which eventually leads to a number of volatile flavour compounds depending on the amino acids that are available and the reaction conditions that are used (van Boekel, 1998). The degradation will be discussed in more detail in the paragraph dealing with the Maillard reaction in milk in section 7.2.2.

The mixture of flavours that is eventually produced from the different milk ingredient groups (fat, protein and lactose) depends on the processing conditions and micro-organisms that are used for preparation of the dairy product. Usually a complex interaction between biological and chemical degradation pathways leads to the desired or characteristic flavour. In the next sections the pathways leading to the characteristic flavours will be discussed for different dairy products: raw milk, heated milk and fermented liquid dairy products (yoghurt and buttermilk).

7.2   Raw and heat-treated milk

7.2.1   Raw milk

Fresh, raw milk has a characteristic but very bland taste (Adda, 1986; Badings, 1991; Nursten, 1997). The sensory perception of fresh milk is mainly determined by a pleasant mouthfeel from the physical constitution of milk (Walstra and Jenness, 1988), a slight sweet/salty taste that is caused by lactose and milk salts, and a delicate flavour caused by many odorous compounds. Although at least 400 volatile compounds (carbonyl compounds, alkanols, free fatty acids, sulphur compounds, etc.) have been detected in raw milk (Badings, 1991), most of them are present in very low concentrations. In total, all aroma compounds together comprise no more than 1–100 mg per kg milk. Adda, Badings and their colleagues have extensively analysed the volatile flavours of fresh milk with GC-olfactometry and GC-MS (Adda, 1986; Badings, 1991). Their conclusions were that, although the concentrations of many of these volatiles were of a sub-threshold level, the delicate, weak flavour of milk is the result of a specific ratio between these volatiles. An interesting question is whether some of those 400 volatiles found in fresh milk are more important for sensory perception than others. Moio *et al.* (1993) tried to answer this question by doing a CHARM (Combined Hedonic Aroma Response Measurement) analysis. A CHARM analysis combines olfactometry measurements (olfactometry = using a human nose as a detector behind a gas chromatograph) with time intensity measurements and therefore gives an estimation of the flavour impact of the different volatiles (Acree *et al.*, 1984; Friedrich and Acree, 1998). Based on the CHARM analysis of fresh milk, Moio *et al.* concluded that ethylbutanoate, ethylhexanoate and dimethylsulphone have a relatively large impact on the total milk flavour.

The origin of flavours in normal fresh milk is thought to be in the metabolism of the cow. However, transfer of volatiles from the forage of the milk may also take place. A combination of certain forage and the metabolism of the cow may lead to increased concentration of certain volatiles in the raw milk such as indole, skatole, sulphides, mercaptans, nitriles, thiocyanates, etc., which lead to off-flavours in the milk (Badings, 1991; Bendall, 2001). This topic is discussed in more detail in section 7.2.3. Recently, the effects of storage conditions on lypolysis, proteolysis and sensory attributes in raw milk have been studied. Overall results showed that most of the changes in raw milk occur within the first 24 hours (Wiking *et al.*, 2002).

7.2.2   The effect of different heat treatments on the flavour profile of milk

The main reason for giving milk a heat treatment is to prolong its shelf-life. Heat treatments have a major effect on the flavour of milk. Different heat treatments lead to different flavour profiles and therefore result in different types of milk. The most widely used heat treatments and their resulting flavour profiles are discussed below.

Low-pasteurised milk
This is a very mild heat treatment (e.g. 15 s, 72°C) which eliminates pathogenic micro-organisms and gives only a modest prolongation of shelf-life. Because the effect of this treatment on the milk flavour is minimal, the milk keeps its basic taste. Only a very weak cooked flavour may be detected, which is caused by traces of H_2S. Other flavour components of LP milk were summarised by Badings (1991). Recently, hept-*cis*-4-enal was determined to make an important contribution towards the flavour of fresh homogenised/pasteurised milk at concentrations in the low to medium pg/g range (Bendall and Olney, 2001).

Medium-pasteurised milk
This heat treatment (e.g. 20 s, 75°C) is slightly more intense than the LP treatment. The result is a milk flavour that is very similar to that of LP milk but with a slightly more pronounced cooked flavour.

High-pasteurised milk
Again the heat treatment is more intense than the preceding ones (e.g. 20 s, 85°C). This milk has a distinct cooked flavour, a slight UHT/ketone flavour and sometimes a trace of caramel flavour.

Sterilised milk
When a very long shelf-life is desired, sterilisation procedures are used, either batchwise, continuously or by combining the two methods (e.g. 30 s, 145°C continuous, followed by 20 min, 115°C batchwise in a bottle). This extensive heat treatment strongly affects the flavour and colour of the product. After the heat treatment the colour turns from off-white to yellow-brownish. The sensory profile of the product is determined mainly by a strong cooked flavour, UHT/ketone type and caramelisation/sterilisation flavours. The key aroma compounds of sterilised milk have been determined based on AEDA (aroma extract dilution analysis) (Iwatsuki *et al.*, 1999) and CHARM analysis (Moio *et al.*, 1994). Key aroma compounds for sterilised milk based on AEDA have been reported to be respectively 2-pentanone, 2-heptanone, 2-nonanone, 2-undecanone, 2,6-dimethylpyrazine, 2-ethylpyrazine, 2-ethyl-3-methylpyrazine, methional, pentanoic acid, benzothiazole and vanillin (Iwatsuki *et al.*, 1999). Key aroma compounds reported for sterilised milk determined by CHARM analysis are respectively 2-nonanone, hexanal, benzothiazole and δ-decalactone (Moio *et al.*, 1994). Sulphur-containing volatiles such as H_2S, methanethiol, dimethyl-sulphide and carboxylsulphide, which are associated mainly with the cooked flavour, are produced due to the heat-induced denaturation of serum proteins (Adda, 1986; Badings, 1991; Nursten, 1997) – in particular, β-lactoglobulin starts denaturation already at 60°C – and their production is accelerated at high temperatures.

Another pathway that operates under these conditions and produces sulphur-containing and other volatiles that have a high impact on the flavour is the Maillard reaction. For the flavour of heated milk, the Maillard reaction is important because it results in the production of volatile flavours such as aldehydes, ketones, maltol, isomaltol, pyrazines, furanones and methanethiol and H_2S (when methionine and cysteine take part as the amino acids respectively). Furthermore, the Maillard reaction gives sterilised milk its characteristic yellow-brown colour and depletes the milk of some of its nutrients (vitamin C and amino acids). The extent of the Maillard reactions is proportional to the strength of the heat treatment.

The Maillard reaction is an important reaction leading to key flavours in generally all dairy products that have undergone heat treatment and/or have aged for a certain period (Ho, 1996). Therefore we discuss it in more detail. The Maillard reaction can be divided into different sub-reactions (see Fig. 7.3(a) and (b)) (van Boekel, 1998). The first step is the production of an N-substituted glycosylamine from a reducing sugar (in milk primarily lactose) and an amino acid (in milk primarily protein-bound lysine). This first step is a reversible reaction that is followed by an Amadori or Heyns rearrangement, which is irreversible and produces 1-amino-1-deoxy-2-ketoses or 1-amino-2-deoxy-2-aldoses (in milk primarily 1-amino-1-deoxylactulosyllysine). At this stage the 1-amino-1-deoxylactulosyllysine is rather stable as long as the heating conditions are not too drastic (Mauron, 1981).

From 1-amino-1-deoxy-2-ketoses and 1-amino-2-deoxy-2-aldoses, different pathways are possible. Under acidic conditions, dehydration pathways will lead to furfurals (furfural or hydroxymethyl-5-furfural). Since this route needs acidic conditions, it is not so important in milk. Products such as hydroxymethyl-furfural (HMF), furfural, furfurylalcohol and lysylpyrraline are formed in milk but indeed in very small amounts (Berg, 1993; Morales and van Boekel, 1996). Under neutral (milk) conditions the 1-deoxyosone-pathway is the most import-ant pathway leading to β-pyranone, 3-furanone, cyclopentenone, galactosyliso-maltol and (after fragmentation) to reductons and dehydroreductons. β-Pyranone is not very stable and is isomerised into cyclopentenone and subsequently converted to galactosylisomaltol (Pischetsrieder and Severin, 1996). In the presence of amino groups, β-pyranone, cyclopentenone and galactosylisomaltol are converted to nitrogen-containing products such as acetylpyrrole, pyridinium betaine and furanone-amine. The reductons and dehydroreductons can be converted to aldehydes and α-aminoketones by Strecker degradation pathways or by retro-aldolisation pathways that lead to compounds such as acetyl, diacetyl, pyruvaldehyde and other aldehydes. The reactive α-dicarbonyl com-pounds such as pyruvaldehyde and diacetyl react further with other inter-mediates to form many different potent odorants such as pyridines, pyrazines, oxazoles, thiazoles, pyrroles and imidazoles (Nursten, 1986).

In the final stage of the Maillard reaction a polymerisation takes place of the different reaction intermediates that results in different polymers called melanoidins, which are characterised by a brownish colour. This final stage is not very well characterised from a chemical point of view (van Boekel, 1998). The exact type of Maillard flavours that are formed in each product depends on the ingredients and reaction conditions. Since the Maillard reaction is very

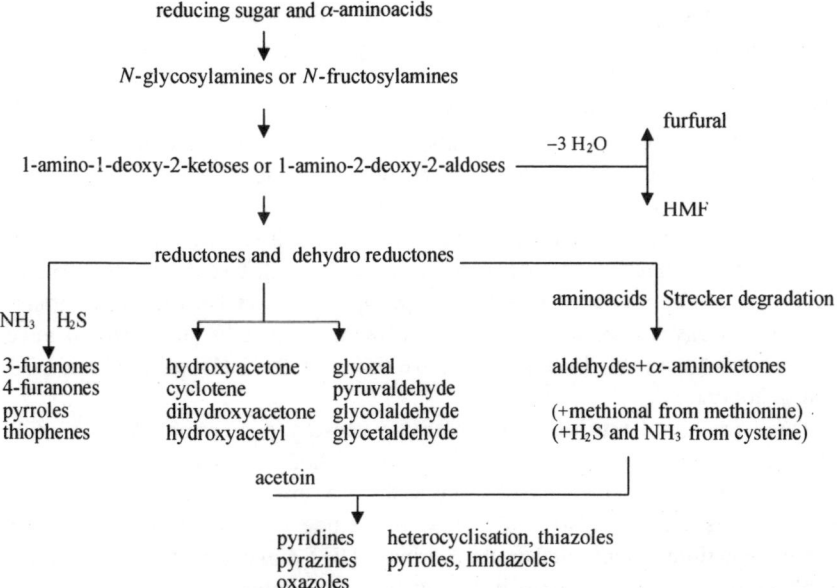

Fig. 7.3(a)   General overview of the Maillard reaction.

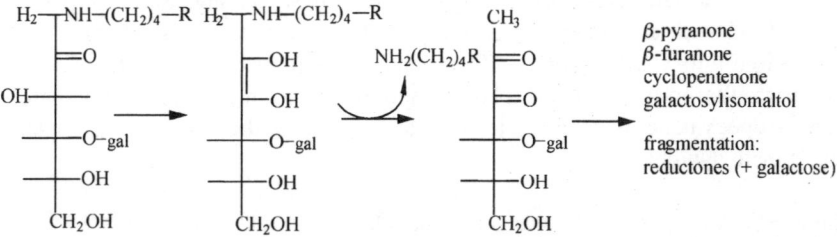

Fig. 7.3(b)   Breakdown of the Amadori product under neutral conditions in milk in the second stage of the Maillard reaction (from Vermin and Parkanyi, 1982).

complex, it is hard to obtain a kinetic model for the reaction in milk. An important complication is that lactose is not only a reactant in the Maillard reaction but also subject to isomerisation/degradation reactions (Berg, 1993; Berg and van Boekel, 1994). Van Boekel and co-workers (van Boekel, 1996, 2001) have proposed a simplified kinetic model to describe the Maillard reaction in milk.

UHT (Ultra High Temperature) milk
Over the last decade a lot of effort has been devoted to the issue of extending the shelf-life of milk as much as possible with a minimal effect on flavour. This is because in a large number of countries consumers see the flavour of pasteurised milk as the standard flavour. The process that has been most successful from a

commercial and qualitative point of view is the UHT process. In this process the milk is heated for a short time (3–15 s) at a high temperature (140–150°C). Two types of continuous flow UHT processes are common (Hinrichs and Kessler, 1995): 'direct heating' in which the milk is heated directly by a steam injection, and 'indirect heating' in which the milk is heated indirectly by tubular or plate-heat exchangers. Depending on the dispersion in residence time in the heating system and the heating temperature, UHT milk can be produced by relatively mild treatment (e.g. 4 s, 142°C, directly) or by a relatively harsh treatment (e.g. 15 s, 150°C, indirectly). As a consequence of these different heat treatments, UHT milk can be produced with flavour profiles that vary between wide limits, i.e. close to pasteurised milk with a mild treatment or close to sterilised milk with a harsh treatment. In this chapter we focus on the UHT milk with a mild heat treatment.

Three important attributes dominate the sensory perception of UHT milk (Badings, 1991): 'cooked' (sometimes also called 'sulphur' or 'cabbage'), 'sterile' (sometimes also called 'Maillard', 'caramel' or even 'gluey') and 'oxidation' (sometimes also called 'stale' or 'ketone') flavour. A fourth attribute that is sometimes mentioned is the intrinsic UHT flavour that seems to be a combination of 'ketone', 'oxidation' and 'rich' attributes.

Table 7.1 summarises the chemical volatiles that are held responsible for the different sensory attributes in UHT milk and the processes that affect the strength of the attributes (Anderson and Oste, 1995). Badings and co-workers have developed a synthetic flavour mix that can give a 'UHT taste' to pasteurised milk (Badings et al., 1981). The synthetic mix consists of a mixture of methylketones, diacetyl, H_2S, methanethiol, methylisothiocyanate, ethylisothiocyanate, benzathiazole, several lactones, maltol, isobutylmercaptan and dimethylsulphide.

Table 7.1 Aromatic volatiles that are responsible for the main attributes of UHT milk and the factors that govern them

Sensory attribute	Aromatic volatile	Factors of influence
Cooked flavour	Free SH groups Volatile sulphides H_2S Methanethiol Dimethylsulphide Carboxylsulphide	Amount of vitamin C Sulphydryl oxidase O_2 permeability of carton Volume of headspace in carton Concentration of O_2 in milk Ageing conditions
Sterile flavour	2-Alkanones Lactones Maltol Furanones	Extent of Maillard reaction Ageing conditions
Oxidation flavour (also called 'stale')	Aldehydes (C_2, C_3, C_5, C_6) Acetone Ketones (C_5, C_7, C_8, C_9)	Extent of auto-oxidation Extent of Maillard reaction Ageing conditions

The cooked flavour in UHT milk is caused by sulphur-containing flavours (e.g. H_2S, methanethiol, dimethylsulphide and carboxylsulphide) that are produced due to the denaturation of serum proteins (Calvo and de la Hoz, 1992; Anderson and Oste, 1995) or the Maillard reaction, as has been discussed above. The generation of dimethylsulphide from S-methylmethionine sulphonium salt (sometimes present in the milk due to specific forage) has also been reported (Keenan and Lindsay, 1969). In general, this cooked flavour attribute increases with increasing process temperatures. However, exemptions are reported in which an increase of heat treatment leads to a lower cooked flavour. This is thought to be due to oxidation of the free sulphur groups into disulphides or a participation of the free sulphur groups in the Maillard reaction. The threshold value for the perception of cooked flavour in milk has been reported to be a concentration of free SH groups of 20 μmol/l (Thomas et al., 1975). During the ageing process of UHT milk, the cooked flavour decreases (Mehta and Bassette, 1978; Fink and Kessler, 1986a, 1986b; Calvo and de la Hoz, 1992; Anderson and Oste, 1992, 1995). This is due to the oxidation of the free SH groups by the dioxygen that is present in milk (equation 7.1):

$$2R–SH + O_2 \rightarrow R–SS–R + H_2O_2 \qquad\qquad 7.1$$

The rate of decrease of free SH groups is affected by the dioxygen concentration in the milk during processing, and the dioxygen concentration during ageing and the ageing temperature. The dioxygen concentration during ageing is dependent on the initial dioxygen concentration in the milk and the headspace volume above the milk in the container and dioxygen permeability of the container. In general a higher dioxygen concentration and a higher temperature will result in a faster decline of the cooked flavour (Fink and Kessler, 1986a, 1986b; Adhikari and Singhal, 1992). Fink and Kessler (1986a, 1986b) studied the concentrations of free SH groups, vitamin C and dioxygen in UHT milk that was aged under different conditions. Based on these results they were able to construct a kinetic model which enabled them to predict the second-order reaction that describes the decline of the concentration of free SH groups and vitamin C. A dioxygen concentration between 3 and 5 ppm has been reported to be optimal. A higher dioxygen concentration will result in negative side-effects such as oxidation of nutrients (vitamin C) and oxidation reactions with other milk ingredients leading to off-flavours. Alternatively, the free SH groups can be transformed by other reagents than dioxygen. Examples of reported methods are:

- Reaction of free SH groups with organic thiosulphonates and thiosulphates (the so-called sulphydryl blocking agents) (Ferretti, 1973; Ferretti et al., 1974)
- Addition of L-cystine to the milk before processing (Badings et al., 1978)
- Use of immobilised sulphydryl oxidase to decrease the free SH groups (Swaisgood et al., 1980)
- Addition of cumin seeds before processing (Josephson, 1989).

However, to our knowledge none of the methods have been commercialised so far.

Once the cooked flavour has decreased to a certain extent during the ageing of UHT milk, the 'oxidation' taste will start to increase. In a way the free SH groups in UHT milk protect the milk against formation of volatiles that are responsible for the oxidation flavour. The same phenomenon is observed in another dairy product, whole milk powder (Rotkiewicz *et al.*, 1979; Baldwin *et al.*, 1991; Stapelfeldt *et al.*, 1997). In that case the high pre-heat treatment of the milk prior to the manufacture of milk powder is the major factor controlling the oxidative stability of the product. The increased anti-oxidative capacity of milk powder has been ascribed to protein unfolding which exposes thiol groups (Walstra and Jenness, 1984). The thiols can, due to the rather low binding energy of the S–H bond, act as hydrogen atom donors and quench reactive oxygen species. The resulting thiyl radicals yield inactive disulphides in chain terminating reactions.

In the literature 'oxidation' is sometimes described as 'stale'. It has been proposed that the difference between these descriptions is due to a difference in aroma concentration (the attribute 'stale' would be caused by a lower concentration of aroma than the attribute 'oxidation'), but this has not been proven. It has also been suggested that the stale attribute is mainly due to aldehydes, while the oxidation attribute is caused by ketones. Again, this hypothesis has not been proven by measurements. In this chapter we use the term oxidation. There is no clear consent in the literature about the identity of the volatiles that are responsible for the oxidation attribute. However, it is clear that aldehydes and ketones play a crucial role. Both aldehydes and ketones are produced from milk fat, but can also be derived from the Maillard reaction (see above). The C_3, C_5 and C_6 aldehydes (Mehta and Bassette, 1978), 2-heptanone and 2-nonanone (Badings *et al.*, 1981; Baldings, 1991), acetaldehyde, acetone, 2-pentanone and 2-heptanone (Nursten, 1997), acetaldehyde, propanal, pentanal, hexanal, 2-pentanone and 2-heptanone (Gaafer, 1991) and 2-heptanone and 2-octanone (Moio *et al.*, 1994) have been reported to be key flavours for the oxidation attribute. The differences between the reports might be caused by differences between the UHT processing of the analysed samples and/or the conditions (time, temperature) at which the samples are aged. However, all reports agree that the oxidation flavour in UHT milk is already present at low ageing temperatures and increases as the ageing temperature increases. Unfortunately, up to now no kinetic model has been developed to predict the level of oxidation flavour under different ageing conditions as was done before for the cooked flavour (as described above).

The 'sterile' attribute in UHT milk is caused by flavour compounds that are formed in the Maillard reaction, which has been discussed in detail above. The extent of the sterile attribute in UHT milk is dependent on the UHT processing parameters and the ageing parameters. A higher ageing temperature and time increase the sterile attribute.

Recently, mathematical models have been developed that can predict the taste of UHT milk based only on the chemical analyses of key aroma components (Boelrijk and de Jong, 2002). In order to obtain a predictive model, both the analytical and sensory data were analysed and linked using multivariate statistics. Linear discriminant analysis (LDA) proved to be most successful since it provided 'correct predicted classifications' higher than 90%.

7.2.3 Off-flavours in milk and their chemical or biological origin

Off-flavours induced by light and/or metal ions
Independent of heating processes, each oxidation process in milk has to start with a reaction of dioxygen with one of the milk ingredients. However, to be able to react with organic compounds a catalyst should activate dioxygen (e.g. change the electronic state of dioxygen from a triplet into a singlet state). A notorious oxidation off-flavour is formed in many dairy products by a combination of light, riboflavin (a photosensitiser) and dioxygen or metal ions (i.e. primarily catalytic amounts of Cu^{2+} ions) and dioxygen (Wishner, 1964; Schröder, 1983; Rysstad *et al.*, 1998). Both systems are able to generate activated dioxygen that is reactive enough to break down serum proteins and produce volatile thiols (Jung *et al.*, 1998), sulphides and disulphides or to form organic peroxides from fatty acids. The organic peroxides are able to start a cascade of reactions leading to aldehydes, ketones and acids (see Fig. 7.1(b)). Although the copper-catalysed oxidation off-flavour is well controlled these days, the light-induced oxidation off-flavour remains a topic of further investigation (Whited *et al.*, 2002). Schröder has shown that the extent of light-induced oxidation flavour is dependent on the volume of headspace above the milk in the container (Schröder, 1983). A solution for this type of off-flavour should be found in the development of improved packaging materials (Rysstad *et al.*, 1998; Simon and Hanson, 2001a, 2001b).

Off-flavours transferred from cow to milk
During lactation, the digestive tract, blood circulation and respiratory system of the cow are important organs for determining the sensory and nutritional quality of the raw milk (Fearon *et al.*, 1998; Bassette *et al.*, 1986). Compounds which have been reported to be responsible for feed-related off-flavours are dimethyl sulphide, acetone, butanone, isopropanol, ethanol and propanol (Badings, 1991; Bendall, 2001). Indole, skatole, mercaptans, sulphides, nitriles and thiocyanates have been reported to be involved in off-flavours produced by weed taints that are digested in the cow (Forss, 1979).

Off-flavours in milk caused by micro-organisms or enzymatic reactions
Lipolytic rancidity in milk is caused by the liberation of C_4–C_{12} fatty acids from milk fat by milk lipase or bacterial lipases (Badings, 1991). Terms to describe this off-flavour are soapy, rancid and butyric acid. Sometimes lipolytic rancidity is accompanied by bitterness as a result of the formation of certain mono- and diglycerides. An unclean flavour can be due to an increase of dimethylsulphide above the threshold of 14 µg/kg, which is caused by psychotrophic bacteria.

Some of these bacteria can also produce ethyl esters of butyric, isovaleric and caproic acids that will lead to a fruity off-flavour. Milk contaminated with *Streptococcus lactis* var. *maltigenes* may develop a malty flavour as a result of the formation of 3-methylbutanal, 2-methylbutanal and 2-methylpropanal. Sterile milk produced by mild UHT heating may develop a bitter off-flavour on ageing as a result of the remaining activity of thermostable bacterial proteinases, which break down milk proteins to bitter peptides.

7.3   Yoghurt and buttermilk

7.3.1   Aspects of yoghurt (off)-flavour

Yoghurt is prepared by fermentation of milk by usually two types of bacteria, namely *Streptococcus thermophilus* and *Lactobacillus bulgaricus* (Marshall, 1993; Driessen, 1988). The flavour of yoghurt is determined by a unique combination of volatile organic compounds that are mainly formed in the first couple of hours of the fermentation process. Quite a number of studies dealing with qualitative data on aromatic volatiles that are present in yoghurt have been published. More than 90 different volatiles have been identified in yoghurt including carbohydrates, alcohols, aldehydes, ketones, acids, esters, lactones, sulphur-containing compounds, pyrazines and furan derivatives (Viani and Horman, 1973; Marshall, 1982; Ott et al., 1997). However, in studies where quantitative results are reported usually only a few of these volatiles are followed, primarily a combination of ethanol, acetaldehyde, diacetyl, acetone, acetoin, butanone, formic acid, acetic acid and dimethylsulphide (Botazzi and Dellaglio, 1967; Hamden et al., 1971; Dutta et al., 1973; Marshall and Cole, 1983; Thornhill and Cogan, 1984; Scolari et al., 1985; Yuguchi et al., 1989; Hegazi and Abo-Elgena, 1990; Perez et al., 1991; Zouari and Desmazeaud, 1991; Zouari et al., 1991). From these compounds, acetaldehyde is usually thought to have the largest impact on the total yoghurt flavour. Diacetyl is thought to be important for the 'roundness' of the yoghurt flavour (Groux, 1973). A popular point of discussion in the literature is the preferred ratio between acetaldehyde and diacetyl. Too much acetaldehyde compared to diacetyl would lead to a 'green' off-flavour. A ratio between acetaldehyde and diacetyl of 1:1 would give a preferred typical taste of yoghurt (Zouari and Desmazeaud, 1991). Also the ratio of acetaldehyde to acetone (2.8:1) has been mentioned to be important for an optimal yoghurt taste. There is much discussion about the concentrations of these volatiles that are needed in order to produce an optimal yoghurt flavour. However, so far no agreement is found in the literature.

Ott and co-workers (Ott et al., 1997) have done a type of AEDA (aroma extract dilution analysis) study to determine the key aroma components of two-week-old yoghurt. AEDA is a GC-olfactometry technique, which delivers comparable information to a CHARM analysis (see section 7.2.1). The results for yoghurt are compared with an AEDA study of pasteurised milk. Some volatiles appear to be important key aroma components in both products while others appear to be specific for yoghurt. Based on this study, the key aroma components for yoghurt are acetaldehyde, diacetyl, 2,3-pentanedione, methional, 2-methyltetrahydrothiophene-3-one, (2E)-nonanal, 3-methylbutyric acid, guiacol, benzothiazole and two unidentified compounds. Imhof and co-workers (Imhof *et al.*, 1994, 1995), choose another approach to determine the key aroma components in yoghurt and use the odour activity value (OAV) concept. OAV is defined as the ratio between the concentration of the volatile in the product and its threshold concentration. The higher the OAV value, the more important the volatile is for the total flavour. Using this method, Imhof *et al.* identified six volatiles that should have a high impact (OAV > 2) on the yoghurt flavour: acetaldehyde, dimethylsulphide, diacetyl, 2,3-pentanedione, L-limonene and undecanal. It is mentioned that undecanal is a component already available in milk and is not produced by the yoghurt cultures. A critical remark concerning the OAV method is that the threshold values for the volatiles that are used in this method are usually determined in water and not in dairy products. However, it is known that the main ingredients (fat, proteins and carbohydrates) in dairy products have a major effect on the release of volatiles and subsequently on the threshold values (Fares *et al.*, 1998; Roberts and Pollien, 2000; Hansen and Heines, 1991). Therefore, the OAV data obtained by Imhof and co-workers, for which they used threshold values in water, should be interpreted with caution.

Importance of acidity
An important factor in the sensory evaluation of yoghurt is the acidity of the product. In recent years, consumers have shown a preference for milder, less acidic yoghurts (Eberhard *et al.*, 1995). However, such products were rated as less flavourful (Kneifel, 1992; Kneifel *et al.*, 1992). It appears that important differences are found in the concentrations of flavour impact compounds such as acetaldehyde, diacetyl and 2,3-pentanedione between the mild and the more acidic yoghurts (Ott *et al.*, 1999). Studies have found a decrease in acetaldehyde concentration and an increase in diacetyl and 2,3-pentanedione concentrations in mild yoghurts compared with more acidic products. Recently, Ott and co-workers (Ott *et al.*, 2000a) reported results that show a mutual influence between the key aroma compounds and the acidity of the yoghurt. In their study they characterised the sensory properties of traditional acidic and mild, less acidic yoghurts by a trained panel using descriptive analysis. Their conclusion was that there are important flavour (sensory) differences between the two classes of yoghurts but that they are mainly due to the differences in acidity and not due to different concentrations of the three flavour impact compounds (acetaldehyde, diacetyl and 2,3-pentanedione) that were analysed. Deodorisation and impact aroma compound addition had much less influence on yoghurt flavour than did pH variations. This study clearly emphasises the importance of acidity in the perception of yoghurt flavour. The same can be said for the yoghurt texture which is vital for the perception. Less viscous yoghurts are usually perceived as more acidic. However, texture–taste interactions will not be discussed here.

Origin of the key aroma components of yoghurt
The key aroma components of yoghurt are produced during fermentation. Therefore, the production routes towards these components are mainly catalysed by enzymes. In this chapter we summarise the steps for the formation of acetaldehyde in Fig. 7.4 (Ott *et al.*, 2000c) and the possible formation routes towards fatty acids in Fig. 7.5.

There are basically two routes towards the formation of acetaldehyde, one based on lactose and the other based on milk protein. Since this chapter focuses mainly on the chemical aspects of flavour generation, we refer to Chapter 6 for more details on the enzymatic steps. In the present chapter, however, we would like to mention a recent publication by Ott *et al.* (2000b) reporting the results of a study that aims to elucidate the mechanism of diacetyl and 2,3-pentanedione formation in yoghurt. Their results suggest that the addition of branched-chain amino acids (BCAA) or an inhibitor of the BCAA biochemical pathways during fermentation of milk with a lac⁻ mutant of *Lactobacillus delbrueckii* ssp. *bulgaricus* and *Streptococcus thermophilus* strongly influence the formation of diacetyl and 2,3-pentanedione as well as their precursors 2-acetolactate and 2-acetohydroxybutyrate. Based on ^{13}C incorporation studies they conclude that glucose is the major precursor via pyruvate and activated acetaldehyde for diacetyl, and L-threonine is the precursor via 2-ketobutyrate for 2,3-pentanedione. However, glucose can also be the precursor for 2,3-pentanedione via activated acetaldehyde. They also suggest an alternative route towards 2,3-pentanedione via 3-methylaspartate, an intermediate in the glutamate synthesis.

Ageing of the fresh yoghurt changes the sensory profile. However,

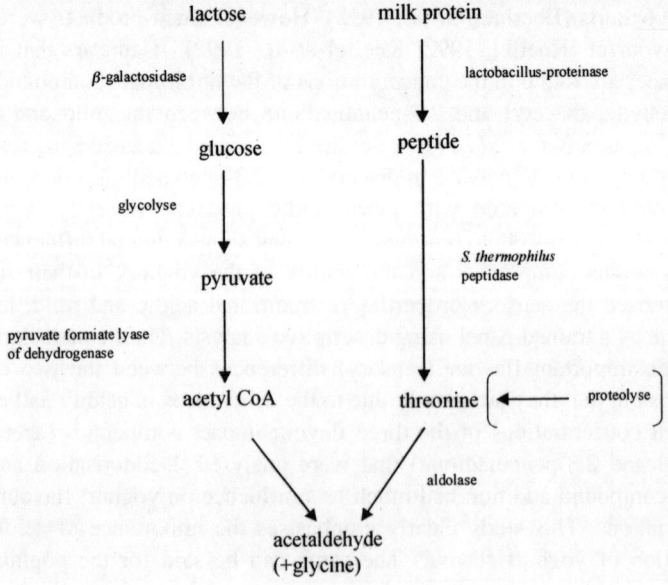

Fig. 7.4   Metabolic routes leading to acetaldehyde in yoghurt.

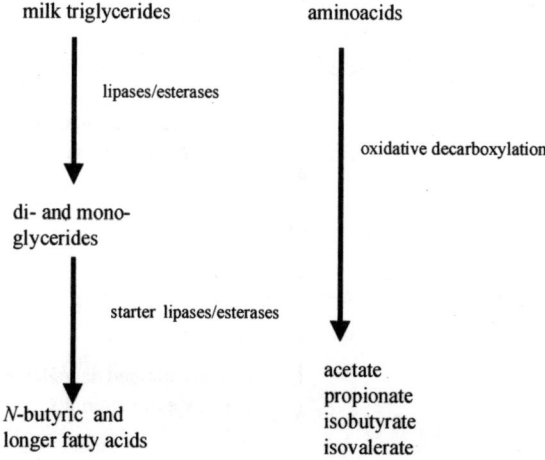

Fig. 7.5   Metabolic routes leading to volatile fatty acids.

contradictory information is published about the qualitative or quantitative change in flavour components over time (Laye *et al.*, 1993; Imhof *et al.*, 1994; McGregor and White, 1987; Kang *et al.*, 1988). Some authors find a decrease of acetaldehyde and diacetyl, while others do not detect any change or even detect an increase of certain flavour components during ageing. It is clear that the type of yoghurt (i.e. the strains that are used for fermentation), packaging material, sunlight and dioxygen levels play a role in these studies and their results.

7.3.2   Chemical aspects of buttermilk (off)-flavour

Buttermilk is obtained as a by-product of the process of making butter (Frank, 1983). There are two types of buttermilk: sweet cream buttermilk which is produced by treating the pasteurised cream with butter starter cultures after separation of the butterfat to yield so-called 'fermented buttermilk', and sour cream buttermilk which is prepared by a procedure in which the fermentation is done before separation of the butterfat. We would like to focus in this paragraph on the chemical origin of one of the main off-flavours encountered in sour cream buttermilk, namely the metallic off-flavour that becomes important during ageing of fresh buttermilk. Heiler and Schieberle (1996, 1997a, 1997b) have recently performed a detailed study to elucidate the compound responsible for this off-flavour and its metabolic and chemical origin. By using comparative AEDA of buttermilk products with and without metallic off-flavour they determined that (E,Z)-2,6-nonadienol is the key odorant responsible for the metallic off-flavour that develops during storage of sour cream buttermilk. They also showed that the flavour-quality contribution of (E,Z)-2,6-nonadienol is critically dependent on its concentration. For example, in concentrations ranging from 0.3 to 0.6 μg/l, (E,Z)-2,6-nonadienol *enhances* the buttermilk flavour, while a final concentration of 1.3 μg/l (after addition of synthetic (E,Z)-2,6-

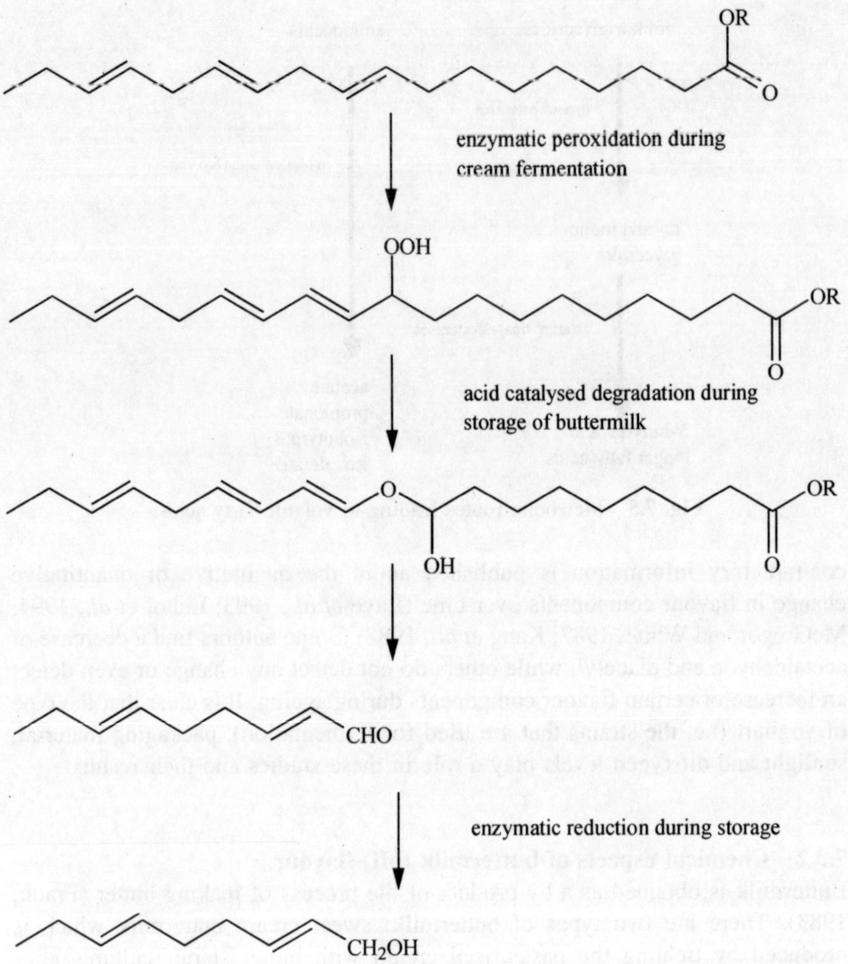

Fig. 7.6   Reaction scheme explaining the formation of (E,Z)-2,6-nonadienol in sour cream buttermilk (reproduced from Heiler and Schieberle, 1997b).

nonadienol) *decreases* the quality of the buttermilk flavour and causes the metallic off-flavour (Heiler and Schieberle, 1996, 1997a, 1997b). A detailed model study (Heiler and Schieberle, 1997b) revealed that (E,Z)-2,6-nonadienol is produced via a cascade of reactions from α-linolenic acid, as summarised in Fig. 7.6. In the first step α-linolenic acid is peroxidised by oxygenases from the starter culture, yielding glycerol-bound 9-hydroperoxy-10,12,15-octa-decatrienoate. During the preparation of butter, this polar hydroperoxide is transferred into the buttermilk and degraded into (E,Z)-2,6-nonadienal via two acid-catalysed steps. During storage of the sour cream buttermilk, the dienal is reduced to (E,Z)-2,6-nonadienol, which is the cause of the metallic off-flavour. To prevent the metallic off-flavour, the authors recommend the use of starter cultures that are low in oxygenases or creams that are low in α-linolenic acid.

Since the concentration of α-linolenic acid is usually higher in high-fat creams, the formation of (E,Z)-2,6-nonadienol is generally higher in sour cream buttermilk, which allows the starter cultures to act on cream that contains a much larger percentage of fat than in fermented sweet cream buttermilk.

7.4   Conclusion and future trends

This chapter has given a general overview of the chemical and some biochemical aspects of flavour generation in dairy products. It can be concluded that many researchers have focused their studies on determining the key flavour components that are responsible for the sensory perception of a variety of dairy products. These key flavour compounds and their origin have been reviewed for different dairy products. It is obvious that the so-called flavour balance is of great importance for sensory properties of dairy products and of milk with its bland flavour, in particular. The key flavour components that are found in dairy products originate from milk and the processing conditions (fermentation, different heat treatments and ageing conditions) that are used to produce the specific products. A disturbance of the flavour balance or the introduction of unwanted compounds may cause off-flavours.

In general, heat treatment of dairy products leads to protein and fat degradation and the Maillard reaction, leading to flavour compounds that have a large impact on sensory perception. Although already a vast amount of results on these processes have been generated in the past, more work needs to be done to be able to predict, control and optimise the processing conditions better in order to produce higher quality products for the consumer. Especially the complex Maillard reaction (important for so many dairy products) remains a subject for further study. We expect that the generation of kinetic models that are better able to predict flavour in dairy products under different processing and ageing conditions will be a major topic for future studies.

To understand the formation of flavours in dairy products, one should study the metabolic as well as the chemical pathways during production and storage. One sees in general that a certain combination of metabolic and processing steps leads to the formation of the specific flavours. The specific flavour can be a desired attribute (for example, in the formation of yoghurt flavour) or an undesired attribute or off-flavour (as is the case for the metallic off-flavour in buttermilk). In order to study the metabolic and chemical pathways in a most efficient way, it is important to have a clear view of the chemical structure of the key aroma compounds that are responsible for sensory perception. Since a large number of flavour compounds are usually produced in dairy products, it is important to separate the less important ones from the important (key) flavour components. Such methods as (comparative) AEDA, CHARM and OAV analyses have proved to be essential for this matter. Also, new techniques such as MS-Nose (Brauss et al., 1999; Weel et al., 2002) that enable the study of flavour release from the dairy product directly in vivo in the human nose while the product is being eaten, will become more important. With this technique it is possible to quantify the effect of fat, proteins and carbohydrates in the dairy matrix on the release of key aroma compounds from the dairy product into the human nose, where the flavours are perceived.

These methods, together with the development of analytical in-line control methods that enable the control of process variables earlier in the process, will result in the efficient development of high quality products that are preferred by consumers (Boelrijk and De Jong, 2002). Knowledge of the possible causes of off-flavours and the ability to control the production processes via in-line analytical measurements will also lead to a more constant quality of the end product.

7.5   Acknowledgements

The authors wish to thank Erika Schenkel and Rita Eenling for their assistance in making this manuscript ready for publication.

7.6   References

ACREE, T.E., BARNARD, J. and CUNNINGHAM, D.G. 1984. 'A procedure for the sensory analysis of GC effluents', *Food Chem.*, 14: 273.

ADDA, J. 1986. 'Flavour of dairy products', in *Developments in Food Flavours*, ed. C.G. Birch and M.G. Lindley, London: Elsevier Applied Science Publishers, pp. 151–172.

ADHIKARI, A.K. and SINGHAL, O.P. 1992. 'Effect of dissolved oxygen content on the flavour profile of UHT milk during storage', *Austr. J. Dairy Technol.*, 47: 1.

ALTING, A.C., ENGELS, W.J.M., VAN SCHALKWIJK, S. and EXTERKATE, F.A. 1995. 'Purification and characterization of cystathionine β-lyase from *Lactococcus lactis* subsp. *Cremoris* B78 and its possible role in flavor development in cheese', *Appl. Env. Microbiol.*, 61: 4037–4042.

ANDERSON, I. and OSTE, R. 1992. 'Sensory changes and free SH-groups in UHT milk', *Milchwissenschaft*, 47: 438.

ANDERSON, I. and OSTE, R. 1995. 'Sensory quality of UHT milk', in *Heat-induced Changes in Milk*, ed. P.F. Fox, Brussels: International Dairy Federation, p. 318.

ASTON, J.W. and CREAMER, L.K. 1986. 'Contribution of the components of the water-soluble fraction to the flavour of Cheddar cheese', *N.Z. J. Dairy Sci. Technol.*, 21: 229–248.

BADINGS, H.T. 1991. 'Milk', in *Volatile Compounds in Foods and Beverages*, ed. H. Maarse, New York: Marcel Dekker, pp. 91–106.

BADINGS, H.T., NEETER, R. and VAN DER POL, J.J.G. 1978. 'Reduction of cooked flavor in heated milk and milk products by L-cystine', *Lebensm.-Wiss. u.-Technol.*, 11: 237.

BADINGS, H.T., VAN DER POL, J.J.G. and NEETER, R. 1981. 'Aroma compounds which contribute to the difference in flavour between pasteurized milk and UHT milk', in *Flavour '81*, ed. P. Schreier, Berlin: Walter de Gruyter, pp. 683–692.

BALDWIN, A.J., COOPER, H.R. and PALMER, K.C. 1991. 'Effect of preheat treatment and storage on the properties of whole milk powder. Changes in sensory properties',

Neth. Milk and Dairy J., 45: 97–116.

BANKS, J.M., BRECHANY, E.Y., CHRISTIE, W.W., HUNTER, E.A. and MUIR, D.D. 1992. 'Volatile components in steam distillates of Cheddar cheese as indicator indices of cheese maturity, flavour and odour', *Food Res. Int.*, 25: 365–373.

BASSETTE, R., FUNG, D.Y.C. and MANTHA, V.R. 1986. 'Off-flavours in milk', *CRC Crit. Rev. Food Sci. Nutr.*, 24(1): 1–52.

BENDALL, J.G. 2001. 'Aroma compounds of fresh milk from New Zealand cows fed different diets', *J. Agric. Food. Chem.*, 49: 4825–4832.

BENDALL, J.G. and OLNEY S.D. 2001. 'Hept-*cis*-4-enal, analysis and flavour contribution to fresh milk', *Int. Dairy J.*, 11: 855–864

BERG, H.E. 1993. 'Reactions of lactose during heat treatment of milk: a quantitative study', PhD thesis, Wageningen Agricultural University, The Netherlands.

BERG, H.E. and VAN BOEKEL, M.A.J.S. 1994. 'Degradation of lactose during heating of milk: I-reaction pathways', *Netherlands Milk and Dairy Journal*, 48(3): 157–175.

BOELRIJK, A.E.M. and DE JONG, C. 2002. 'Relating analytical and sensory data to predict flavor quality in dairy products', in *Freshness and Shelflife of Foods*, ed. K.R. Cadwaller and H. Weenen, Washington: American Chemical Society, pp. 95–107.

BOSSET, J.O. and GAUCH, R. 1993. 'Comparison of the volatile flavour compounds of six European "AOC" cheeses by using a new dynamic headspace GC-MS method', *Int. Dairy J.*, 3: 359–377.

BOTAZZI, F. and DELLAGLIO, F. 1967. 'Acetaldehyde and diacetyl production by *S. thermophilus* and other lactic streptococci', *J. Dairy Sci.*, 34: 109–113.

BRAUSS, M.S., LINTFORD, R.S.T., CAYEUX, I., HARVEY, B. and TAYLOR, A.J. 1999. 'Altering the fat content affects flavor release in a model yogurt system', *J. Agric. Food Chem.*, 47: 2055–2059.

BRUINENBERG, P.G., DE ROO, G. and LIMSOWTIN, G.K.Y. 1997. 'Purification and characterization of cystathionine γ-lyase from *Lactococcus lactis* subsp. *cremoris* SK11: possible role in flavor compound formation during cheese maturation', *Appl. Env. Microbiol.*, 63: 561–566.

BUTTERY, R.G., SEIFERT, R.M., TURNBAUGH, J.G., GUADAGNI, D.G. and LING, L.C. 1981. 'Odour threshold of thiamin odour compound', *J. Agric. Food Chem.*, 29: 183.

CALVO, M.M. and DE LA HOZ, L. 1992. 'Flavour of heated milks, a review', *Int. Dairy J.*, 2: 69–81.

CONTARINI, G., POVOLO, M., LEARDI, R. and TOPPINO, P.M. 1997. 'Influence of heat treatment on the volatile compounds of milk', *J. Agric. Food Chem.*, 45: 3171–3177.

DRIESSEN, F.M. 1981. 'Enzymatische eiwitsplitsing in kort/hoog gesteriliseerde melkprodukten', *NIZO Nieuws*, 6: 688.

DRIESSEN, F.M. 1988. 'Bacteriën in zuursels voor gefermenteerde melk- en zuivelproducten', *Voedingsmiddelentechnologie*, 24: 22–25.

DUMONT, J.P. and ADDA, J. 1979. 'Flavour formation in dairy products', in *Progress in Flavour Research*, ed. D.G. Land and H.F. Nursten, London: Elsevier·Applied Science Publishers, pp. 245–262.

DUTTA, S.M., KUILA, R.K. and RANGANATHAN, B. 1973. 'Effect of different heat treatments of milk on acid and flavor production by five single strain cultures', *Milchwissenschaft*, 28: 231–232.

EBERHARD, P., LAVANCHY, P. and BUEHLER-MOOR, U. 1995. 'U. OLMA 1994: Sensory tests of yoghurt. Joghurtdegustation an der OLMA 1994', *Agrar. Forsch.*, 2: 439–442.

ENGELS, W.J.M. and VISSER, S. 1996. 'Development of cheese flavour from peptides and amino acids by cell-free extracts of *Lactococcus lactis* subsp. *cremoris* B78 in a model system', *Neth. Milk and Dairy J.,* 50: 3–17.

ENGELS, W.J.M., DEKKER, R., DE JONG, C., NEETER, R. and VISSER, S. 1997. 'A comparative study of volatile compounds in the water soluble fraction of various types of ripened cheese', *Int. Dairy J.,* 7: 255–263.

EXTERKATE, F.A. 1987. 'On the possibility of accelerating the ripening of Gouda cheese; a comment', *Neth. Milk and Dairy J.,* 41: 189–194.

FARES, K., LANDY, P., GUILARD, R. and VOILLEY, A. 1998. 'Physicochemical interactions between aroma compounds and milk proteins: effect of water and protein modification', *J. Dairy Sci.,* 81: 82–91.

FEARON, A.M., MAYNE, C.S. and CHARLTON, C.T. 1998. 'Effect of naked oats in the dairy cow's diet on the oxidative stability of the milk fat', *J. Sci. Food Agric.,* 76: 546–552.

FERRETTI, A. 1973. 'Inhibition of cooked flavour in heated milk by use of additives', *J. Agric. Food Chem.,* 21: 939.

FERRETTI, A., EDMONDSON, L.F. and DOUGLAS JR, F.W. 1974. 'Control of cooked flavour in HTST milk concentrates with a sulfhydryl blocking agent', *J. Agric. Food Chem.,* 22: 1130.

FINK, R. and KESSLER, H.G. 1986a. 'Reaction kinetics evaluation of the oxidative changes in stored UHT milk', *Milchwissenschaft,* 41: 90.

FINK, R. and KESSLER, H.G. 1986b. 'The effect of headspace volume on the quality of stored degassed UHT milk', *Milchwissenschaft,* 41: 152.

FORSS, D.A. 1979. 'Mechanisms of formation of aroma compounds in milk and milk products', *J. Dairy Res.,* 46: 691–706.

FOX, P.F., WALLACE, J.M., MORGAN, S., LYNCH, C.M., NILAND, E.J. and TOBIN, J. 1996. 'Acceleration of cheese ripening', *Antonie van Leeuwenhoek,* 70: 271–297.

FRANK, J.F. 1983. 'Improving the flavor of cultured buttermilk', *Cultured Dairy Products J.,* 6–9.

FRIEDRICH, J.E. and ACREE, T.E. 1998. 'Gas chromatography olfactometry of dairy products', *Int. Dairy J.,* 8: 235.

GAAFER, E.M. 1991. 'Chemical changes in UHT milk during storage', *Milchwissenschaft,* 46: 233–235.

GALLOIS, A. and LONGLOIS, D. 1990. 'New results in the volatile odorous compounds of French cheeses', *Lait,* 70: 89–106.

GROUX, M. 1973. 'Etude des components de la flaveur du yoghourt', *Le Lait,* 53: 146–153.

HAMDEN, I.Y., KUNSMAN, J.E. and DEANE, D.D. 1971. 'Acetaldehyde production by combined yoghurt cultures', *J. Dairy Sci.,* 54: 1080–1082.

HANSEN, A.P. and HEINES, J.J. 1991. 'Decrease of vanillin flavor perception in the presence of casein and whey proteins', *J. Dairy Sci.,* 74: 2936–2940.

HEGAZI, F.Z. and ABO-ELGENA, I.G. 1990. 'Growth rate, proteolysis and acid production of *Streptococcus faecalis* subsp. *liquefaciens* in skim milk with some additives', *Nahrung,* 34: 775–777.

HEILER, C. and SCHIEBERLE, P. 1996. 'Studies on the metallic off-flavour in buttermilk: identification of potent aroma compounds', *Lebensm.-Wiss. u.-Technol.,* 29: 460–464.

HEILER, C. and SCHIEBERLE, P. 1997a. 'Quantitative instrumental and sensory studies on aroma compounds contributing to a metallic flavour defect in buttermilk', *Int. Dairy J.,* 7: 659–666.

HEILER, C. and SCHIEBERLE, P. 1997b. 'Model studies on the precursors and formation of the metallic smelling (E,Z)-2,6-nonadienol during the manufacture and storage of buttermilk', *Int. Dairy J.*, 7: 667–674.

HINRICHS, J. and KESSLER, H.G. 1995. 'Thermal processing of milk – processes and equipment', in *Heat-induced Changes in Milk*, ed. P.F. Fox, Brussels: International Dairy Federation, pp. 8–21.

HO, C.-T. 1996. 'Thermal generation of Maillard aromas', in *The Maillard Reaction: Consequences for the Chemical and Life Sciences*, ed. R. Ikan, New York: John Wiley & Sons, pp. 25–53.

IMHOF, R. and BOSSET, J.O. 1994. 'Quantitative GC-MS analysis of volatile flavour compounds in pasteurized milk and fermented milk products applying standard addition method', *Lebensm.-Wiss. u.-Technol.*, 27: 265–269.

IMHOF, R., GLATTI, H. and BOSSET, J.O. 1994. 'Volatile organic aroma compounds produced by thermophilic and mesophilic mixed strain dairy starter cultures', *Lebensm.-Wiss. u.-Technol.*, 27: 442–449.

IMHOF, R., GLATTI, H. and BOSSET, J.O. 1995. 'Volatile organic aroma compounds produced by thermophilic and mesophilic single strain dairy starter cultures', *Lebensm.-Wiss. u.-Technol.*, 28: 78–86.

IWATSUKI, K., MIZOATO, Y., KUBOTA, T., NISHIMURA, O., MASUDA, H., SOTOYAMA, K. and TOMITA, M. 1999. 'Evaluation of aroma of pasteurized and UHT processed milk by aroma extract dilution analysis', *Jap. Soc. Food Sci. Technol.*, 46: 587–597.

JOSEPHSON, D.B. 1989. 'Process for masking a cooked flavor in heated milk', Mallinckrodt Inc., US Patent number 4,851,251.

JUNG, M.Y., YOON, S.H., LEE, H.O. and MIN, D.B. 1998. 'Singlet oxygen and ascorbic acid effects on dimethyl disulfide and off-flavour in skim milk exposed to light', *J. Food Sci.*, 63: 408–412.

KANG, Y., FRANK, J.F. and LILLARD, D.A. 1988. 'Gas chromatographic detection of yoghurt flavor compounds and changes during refrigerated storage', *Cultured Dairy Products J.*, 11: 6–9.

KEENAN, T.W. and LINDSAY, R.C. 1969. 'Evidence for a dimethylsulfide precursor in milk', *J. Dairy Sci.*, 51: 950.

KNEIFEL, W. 1992. 'Starter cultures for fermented milks', *Nutrition*, 16: 150–156.

KNEIFEL, W., ULBERTH, F., ERHARD, F. and JAROS, D. 1992. 'Aroma profiles and sensory properties of yoghurt and yoghurt related products. I: Screening of commercially available starter cultures', *Milchwissenschaft*, 47: 362–365.

LAYE, I., KARLESKIND, D. and MORR, C.V. 1993. 'Chemical, microbiological and sensory properties of plain nonfat yoghurt', *J. Food Sci.*, 58: 991–995.

LEMIEUX, L., PUCHADES, R. and SIMARD, R.E. 1989. 'Size-exclusion HPLC separation of bitter and astringent fractions from Cheddar cheese made with added *Lactobacillus* strains to accelerate ripening', *J. Food Sci.*, 54: 1234–1237.

LINDSAY, R.C. and RIPPE, J.K. 1986. 'Enzymic generation of methanethiol in flavor development of Cheddar cheese and other foods', in *Biogeneration of Aromas*, ed. T.H. Parliment and R. Croteau, ACS Symp. Ser., Washington DC: Am. Chem. Soc., 317: 286–308.

MARSHALL, V.M. 1982. 'Flavour compounds in fermented milks', *Perfumer and Flavorists*, 7: 27–34.

MARSHALL, V.M. 1993. 'Starter cultures for milk fermentation and their characteristics', *J. Soc. Dairy Technol.*, 46: 49–56.

MARSHALL, W.M. and COLE, W.M. 1983. 'Threonine aldolase and alcohol dehydrogenase activities in *Lactobacillus bulgaricus* and *Lactobacillus acidophilus* and their contribution to flavour production in fermented milk', *J. Dairy Res.*, 50: 375.

MAURON, J. 1981. 'The Maillard reaction in food: a critical review from a nutritional standpoint', *Prog. Food Nutr. Sci.*, 5: 5–35.

MCGREGOR, J.U. and WHITE, C.H. 1987. 'Effect of sweeteners on major volatile compounds and flavor of yogurt', *J. Dairy Sci.*, 70: 1828.

MEHTA, R.S. and BASSETTE, R. 1978. 'Organoleptic, chemical and microbiological changes in UHT sterilized milk stored at room temperature', *J. Food Prot.*, 41: 806.

MICK, S., MICK, W. and SCHREIER, P. 1982. 'The composition of neutral volatile constituents of sour cream butter', *Milchwissenschaft*, 37: 661–665.

MOIO, L., LANGLOIS, D., ETIEVANT, P. and ADDEO, F. 1993. 'Powerful odorants in bovine, ovine, caprine and water buffalo milk determined by means of GC-olfactometry', *J. Dairy Res.*, 60: 215–222.

MOIO, L., ETIEVANT, P., LANGLOIS, D., DEKIMPE, J. and ADDEO, F. 1994. 'Detection of powerful odorants in heated milk by use of extract dilution sniffing analysis', *J. Dairy Res.*, 61: 385–394.

MORALES, F.J. and VAN BOEKEL, M.A.J.S. 1996. 'Formation of lysylpyrraline in heated sugar-casein solutions', *Neth. Milk and Dairy J.*, 50: 347–370.

NEETER, R., DE JONG, C., TEISMAN, H.G.J. and ELLEN, G. 1996. 'Determination of volatile components in cheese using dynamic headspace techniques', in *Flavour Science: Recent Developments*, ed. A.J. Taylor and D.S. Mottram, Burlington House, London: Royal Society of Chemistry, pp. 293–296.

NIEROP-GROOT, M. and DE BONT, J.A.M. 1999. 'The role of manganese accumulation in benzaldehyde production in lactic acid bacteria', *Appl. Env. Microbiol.*, 65: 5590–5593.

NURSTEN, H.E. 1986. 'Aroma compounds from the Maillard reaction', in *Developments in Food Flavours*, ed. C.G. Birch and M.G. Lindley, London: Elsevier Applied Science Publishers, pp. 173–189.

NURSTEN, H.E. 1997. 'The flavour of milk and dairy products', *Int. J. Dairy Tech.*, 50: 48–55.

O'BRIEN, J. 1995. 'Heat induced changes in lactose: isomerization, degradation, Maillard browning', in *Heat-induced Changes in Milk*, ed. P.F. Fox, Brussels: International Dairy Federation, pp. 134–170.

OTT, A., FAY, L.B. and CHAINTREAU, A. 1997. 'Determination and origin of the aroma impact compounds of yogurt flavor', *J. Agric. Food Chem.*, 45: 850–858.

OTT, A., GERMOND, J.-E., BAUMGARTNER, M. and CHAINTREAU, A. 1999. 'Aroma comparison of traditional and mild yoghurt. Headspace-GC quantification of volatiles and origin of α-diketones', *J. Agric. Food Chem.*, 47: 2379–2385.

OTT, A., HUGI, A., BAUMGARTNER, M. and CHAINTREAU, A. 2000a. 'Sensory investigation of yoghurt flavor perception: Mutual influence of volatiles and acidity', *J. Agric. Food Chem.*, 48: 441–450.

OTT, A., GERMOND, J.E. and CHAINTREAU, A. 2000b. 'Vicinal diketone formation in yoghurt: 13C precursors and effect of branched-chain amino acids', *J. Agric. Food Chem.*, 48: 724–731.

OTT, A., GERMOND, J.E. and CHAINTREAU, A. 2000c. 'Origin of acetaldehyde during milk fermentation using 13C-labeled precursors', *J. Agric. Food Chem.*, 48, 1512–1517.

PEREZ, P.F., DE ANTONI, G.L. and ANON, M.C. 1991. 'Formate production by *Streptococcus thermophilus* cultures', *J. Dairy Sci.*, 74: 2850–2854.

PISCHETSRIEDER, M. and SEVERIN, T. 1996. 'Advanced Maillard products of disaccharides: analysis and relation to reaction conditions', in *Chemical Markers for Processed and Stored Foods*, ed. T.C. Lee and H.J. Kim, Washington DC: ACS Symposium

Series 631, pp. 14–23.

ROBERTS, D.D. and POLLIEN, P. 2000. 'Relative influence of milk components on flavor compound volatility', in *Flavor Release*, ed. D.D. Roberts and A.J. Taylor, Washington DC: American Chemical Society, pp. 15–27.

ROTKIEWICZ, W., HANSEN, P.S. and JENSEN, G.K. 1979. 'The effect of certain technological factors on the quality and keeping quality of instant whole milk powder', *Acta Alimentaria Polonia*, 5: 337–349.

RYSSTAD, G., EBBESEN, A. and EGGESTAD, J. 1998. 'Sensory and chemical quality of UHT-milk stored in paperboard cartons with different oxygen and light barriers', *Food Additives and Contaminants*, 15: 112–122.

SCHRÖDER, M. 1983. 'Light and copper catalysed oxidised flavours in milk', *J. Soc. Dairy Technol.*, 36: 8.

SCOLARI, G., BOTAZZI, V. and BRAMBILLA, E. 1985. 'Metabolic volatile products evaluation for the homofermentative lactic acid bacteria cultures characterisation', *Scienza, Tecnica Lattireo-Casearia*, 36: 593–602.

SIMON, M. and HANSEN, A.P. 2001a. 'Effects of various dairy packaging materials on the headspace analysis of ultrapasteurised milk', *J. Dairy Sci.*, 84: 747–783.

SIMON, M. and HANSEN, A.P. 2001b. 'Effects of various dairy packaging materials on the shelf-life and flavour of ultrapasteurised milk', *J. Dairy Sci.*, 84: 784–791.

SMIT, G., BRABER, A., VAN SPRONSEN, W., VAN DEN BERG, G. and EXTERKATE, F.A. 1995. 'Ch-easy model: a cheese-based model to study cheese ripening', in *Bioflavour '95 Dijon*, ed. P. Etievant, Paris, pp. 185–190.

STADHOUDERS, J., HUP, G., EXTERKATE, F.A. and VISSER, S. 1983. 'Bitter formation in cheese. 1. Mechanism of the formation of the bitter flavour defect in cheese', *Neth. Milk and Dairy J.*, 37: 157–167.

STAPELFELDT, H., NIELSEN, B.R. and SKIBSTED, L.H. 1997. 'Effect of heat treatment, water activity and storage temperature on the oxidative stability of whole milk powder', *Int. Dairy J.*, 7: 331–339.

SWAISGOOD, H.E., JANOLINO, V.G. and SLIWKOWSKI, M.X. 1980. In *Proc. Int. Conf. on UHT Processing and Aseptic Packaging of Milk and Milk Products*, Raleigh, NC, pp. 67–76.

THOMAS, E.L., BURTON, H., FORD, J.E. and PERKIN, A.G.J. 1975. 'The effect of oxygen content on flavour and chemical changes during aseptic storage of whole milk after UHT processing', *J. Dairy Res.*, 42: 285.

VAN BOEKEL, M.A.J.S. 1996. 'Kinetic modelling of sugar reactions in heated milk-like systems', *Neth. Milk and Dairy J.*, 50: 245–266.

VAN BOEKEL, M.A.J.S. 1998. 'Effects of heating on Maillard reactions in milk', *Food Chem.*, 62: 403–414.

VAN BOEKEL, M.A.J.S. 2001. 'Kinetic aspects of the Maillard reaction: a critical review', *Nahrung*, 45: 150–159.

VAN DUIN, H. 1965. 'The formation of methylketones during heating of butterfat', *NIZO Nieuws*, 12: 137.

VERMIN, G. and PARKANYI, C. 1982. 'Mechanisms of formation of heterocyclic compounds in Maillard and pyrolysis reactions', in *The Chemistry of Heterocyclic Flavoring and Aroma Compounds*, ed. G. Vermin, Chichester: Ellis Horwood, pp. 151–207.

VIANI, R. and HORMAN, I. 1973. 'Composition de l'arome de yoghurt', *Traveaux de Chimie Alimentaire et d'Hygiène*, 64: 66–70.

VISSER, S., SLANGEN, C.J., HUP, G. and STADHOUDERS, J. 1983. 'Bitter flavour in cheese. 3. Comparative gel-chromatographic analysis of hydrophobic peptide fractions from twelve Gouda-type cheeses and identification of bitter peptides isolated from a cheese made with *Streptococcus cremoris* strain HP', *Neth. Milk and Dairy J.*, 37: 181–192.

WALSTRA, P. and JENNESS, R. 1984. *Dairy Chemistry and Physics*. New York: John Wiley & Sons, pp. 175–176.

WALSTRA, P. and JENNESS, R. 1988. *Dairy Chemistry and Physics*. New York: Wiley Interscience.

WEEL, K.G.C., BOELRIJK, A.E.M., ALTING, A.C., VAN MIL, P.J.J.M., BURGER, J.J., GRUPPEN, H., VORAGEN, A.G.J. and SMIT, G. 2002. 'Flavor release and perception of flavored whey protein gels: perception is determined by texture rather than by release', *J. Agric. Food Chem.*, 50: 5149–5155.

WHITED, L.J., HAMMOND, B.H., CHAPMAN, K.W. and BOOR, K.J. 2002. 'Vitamin A degradation and light oxidized flavor defects in milk', *J. Dairy Sci.*, 85: 351–354.

WIKING, L., FROST, M.B., LARSEN, L.B. and NIELSEN, J.H. 2002. 'Effects of storage conditions on lipolysis, proteolysis and sensory attributes in high quality raw milk', *Milchwissenschaft*, 57: 190–194.

WISHNER, L.A. 1964. 'Light-induced oxidation in milk', *J. Dairy Sci.*, 47: 216.

WOOD, A.F., ASTON, J.W. and DOUGLAS, G.K. 1994. 'A cold-trap method for the collection and determination of headspace compounds from cheese', *Austr. J. Dairy Technol.*, 49: 42–47.

YANG, W.T. and MIN, D.B. 1994. 'Dynamic headspace analyses of volatile compounds of Cheddar and Swiss cheese during ripening', *J. of Food Sci.*, 59: 1309–1312.

ZOUARI, A. and DESMAZEAUD, M.J. 1991. 'Characterization of lactic acid bacteria isolated from Greek yoghurts II', *Lait*, 71: 463.

ZOUARI, A., ROGERS, S., CHABANET, C. and DESMAZEAUD, M.J. 1991. 'Characterization of lactic acid bacteria isolated from Greek yogurts I', *Lait*, 71: 445–461.

8

Controlling the texture of fermented dairy products: the case of yoghurt

D. Jaros and H. Rohm, Dresden University of Technology, Germany

8.1 Introduction

Starting with comments on the historical background and the economic importance of yoghurt, the first part of this chapter deals mainly with some basic biochemical and microbiological aspects of yoghurt production. An outline of different manufacturing methods resulting in various types of yoghurt is followed by a description of the main technological factors which are known to influence rheology and texture properties. These factors comprise the preparation of the base milk, including dry matter enrichment, homogenisation and pre-heat treatment, as well as incubation conditions and post-incubation treatments, which vary largely depending on whether set-style or stirred yoghurt is produced. Interrelations between technological factors and physical parameters are given and, where possible, are explained on the basis of micro-structure. The following section gives an overview of rheological methods commonly used for the testing of set-style and stirred yoghurt, and presents some tools for the numerical treatment of response data. Some empirical methods, which are the basis for simple product testing in routine laboratories or manufacturing plants, are then presented. Prior to an outline of presumable future trends and sources of additional information, a few comments deal with sensory procedures used for the evaluation of physical properties of yoghurt.

8.2 The manufacture of yoghurt

Fermentation is one of the oldest procedures for transferring raw materials of plant or animal origin into products with extended shelf-life, and it is assumed that the fermentation of milk dates back approximately 10 000 years (Stanley, 1998). The term 'fermented milk' or 'cultured milk' refers to products such as yoghurt, sour milk, cultured buttermilk and sour cream, which are usually made from cows' milk by pure lactic acid fermentation. Additionally, some products are made from milk from other species such as ewes, goats or mares, and combined fermentation (by, e.g., lactic acid bacteria and yeasts) results in products known as kefir or koumiss.

Yoghurt represents the most popular fermented milk product worldwide and originates from countries around the Balkan and the Eastern Mediterranean Sea (Staff, 1998; Walstra *et al.*, 1999). Generally, yoghurt is manufactured from pre-heated milk, with fat and dry matter content varying with respect to region and legislation, either in the plain form or with added material such as fruits or fruit premixes, sugar, cereals, or additives such as gelling agents, flavourings or colourants. Legislation and codex regulations differ widely around the world; in the one or other country, the use of additives is prohibited, or the presence of a certain number of viable starter bacteria in yoghurt is required (e.g., 10^7 bacteria per gram in the USA; Mistry, 2001). Consumption statistics for fermented milks show highest *per capita* consumptions throughout Europe and a continuous growth in nearly all major markets. Exceptions are countries with an already existing high consumption level, such as the Netherlands and Iceland (Table 8.1).

Generally speaking, cultured or fermented milk products are made by inoculation of milk with a specific combination of microorganisms, which are able to convert lactose into lactic acid. Milk is a complex fluid containing

Table 8.1 Consumption of fermented dairy products including yoghurt

Country	Consumption (kg per capita)				
	1980	1990	1993	1998[a]	2000[a]
Australia	1.8	3.5	4.8	5.6	5.7
Austria	9.8	10.4	13.0	16.4	21.4
Belgium	7.7	9.6	11.9	20.5	21.1
Canada	2.3	3.7	3.5	3.7	4.9
Czech Republic	—	—	—	10.6	13.8
Denmark	26.7	21.6	20.7	25.9	26.2
Finland	41.0	38.3	38.1	38.8	40.7
France	9.3	16.4	17.3	27.8	28.5
Germany	—	—	—	24.7	26.5
Netherlands	27.3	32.5	29.7	45.0	44.8
Norway	10.1	14.9	—	19.3	16.6
Slovakia	—	—	—	5.4	6.7
Spain	6.0	8.0	9.8	14.7	15.7
Sweden	24.0	29.1	28.6	37.9	38.0
USA	6.2	—	3.5	2.4	2.7

Compiled from various sources (Anon., 1982, 1992, 1995, 2001).
[a] Data include milk drinks and fermented milk products.

Table 8.2   Proximate composition (g/kg) of bovine, goat and ewe milks

Component	Bovine	Goat	Ewe
Protein	34	29	55
Casein	28	25	46
Fat	37	45	74
Lactose	46	41	48
Ash	7	8	10

Source: Jensen, 1995.

relatively high amounts of proteins and minerals which, as it is intended to nourish young mammals, varies in composition according to the species' needs (Table 8.2). Especially the major part of the milk proteins, the casein, which occurs in conjunction with calcium phosphate in the form of colloidal particles 100–500 nm in diameter and of MW approximately 10^8 Da (Buchheim and Welsch, 1973), is of great importance for the functional behaviour of the final acidified product. The colloidal calcium phosphate (CCP) plays an important role in maintaining the integrity of the casein micelles, which are in dynamic equilibrium with their surroundings. Therefore, a lot of structural research has been undertaken to explain the mechanisms of the stability of casein micelles and their sub-units, irrespective of whether or not these are present in the form of sub-micelles (Holt, 1993; Holt and Horne, 1996; Rollema, 1992; Schmidt and Both, 1982; Visser, 1992; Walstra, 1990; Walstra et al., 1999).

During fermentation of yoghurt, the milk sugar in the base milk is partially converted into lactic acid by the action of various enzymes, originating from the growth of thermophilic lactic acid bacteria. This causes a sufficient decrease in the pH, resulting in a dissociation of the CCP, a destabilisation of the casein micelles and even some liberation of individual casein molecules, accompanied by reaching a maximum in voluminosity (Dalgleish and Law, 1988; Lucey and Singh, 1998). Below a pH of 5.5 the casein micelles begin to swell and, as almost all CCP is dissociated, start to precipitate. This precipitation leads to a sufficient decrease in the voluminosity of casein micelles (van Hooydonk et al., 1986) and to the formation of clusters and chains that link together to form a gel, composed of a continuous three-dimensional network with the milk serum containing whey proteins, lactose and salts entrapped as liquid phase (the amount of whey proteins depends on heat treatment; see below). Electron microscopy shows the particulate character of acidified milk gels with empty spaces or pores in the network where the serum was entrapped (Kalab, 1979, 1993; McManus et al., 1993).

The classical yoghurt starter culture is a mixture of Streptococcus thermophilus and Lactobacillus delbrueckii ssp. bulgaricus, with a cocci–rods ratio of usually 1:1 (Hassan and Frank, 2001; Hutkins, 2001). These organisms grow in a protocooperative relationship, resulting in rapid acidification by stimulating each other. Depending on type and activity of the starter cultures, other metabolites such as carbon dioxide, acetic acid, diacetyl, acetaldehyde, large molecular weight exopolysaccharides or several other compounds are produced besides lactic acid, resulting in the characteristic properties of the products regarding flavour, texture and aroma. Since *Streptococcus thermophilus* is weakly proteolytic its growth is stimulated by the rods, which liberate free amino acids and small peptides from casein. The cocci in turn encourage the growth of *Lactobacillus delbrueckii* ssp. *bulgaricus* by producing formic acid and carbon dioxide (Matalon and Sandine, 1986; Rajagopal and Sandine, 1990). Nowadays, microorganisms such as *Bifidobacterium* spp. and *Lactobacillus acidophilus* are often added for therapeutic purposes (Mistry, 2001; Yucuchi *et al.*, 1992). Generally, and based on the accumulating knowledge from well-defined, randomised and placebo-controlled studies (Fondén *et al.*, 2000), health-promoting effects of some strains used for yoghurt fermentation become more and more evident. Because of their slow acid production, these bacteria are usually used in combination with classical yoghurt starters, resulting in so-called 'yoghurt-like products'; depending on local legislation, this distinction might be of great importance (Hassan and Frank, 2001; Marshall and Tamime, 1997). Lactic acid bacteria that produce high molecular weight extracellular polysaccharides (EPS) are now commonly used in the yoghurt industry to improve product texture, partly replacing the addition of stabilisers and gelling agents, by enhancing yoghurt viscosity, independent of the fat content.

Manufacturing methods vary considerably and, for example, depend on the country, the type of product manufactured, the raw materials used and the product formulation. However, a number of common principles are generally applied (Staff, 1998):

- The total solids content of the base milk is increased to enhance the water-holding capacity of the product.
- A heat treatment of the base milk, usually >80°C for some time, is applied to achieve a proper denaturation of the whey proteins, also increasing the water-binding capacity.
- Inoculation with a specific starter culture and subsequent incubation with a time-temperature profile depending on the properties of the starter, and on technical requirements.
- Cooling and addition of appropriate ingredients (fruit premixes, flavours).
- Packaging and chilled storage.

Yoghurt types are usually distinguished according to their physical state in the retail container, which results from differences in the manufacturing process. Apart from set yoghurt and stirred yoghurt (Fig. 8.1), with production figures varying from country to country, there is a generally increasing demand for yoghurt drinks consisting of yoghurt mixed with skimmed milk, whey or water, and of yoghurts with increased shelf-life such as frozen or thermised yoghurt.

Incubation of set yoghurt takes place in retail containers (plastic cups or glasses of different sizes) until the required pH (around 4.4–4.7) is reached,

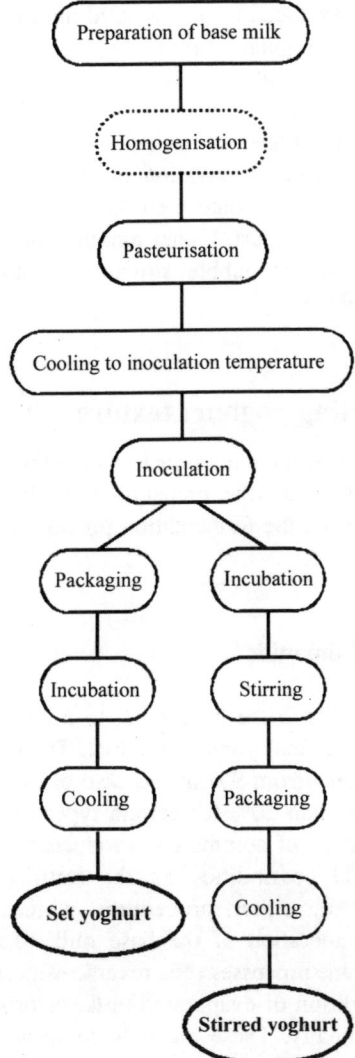

Fig. 8.1   Basic steps in the production of set and stirred yoghurt.

leading to an undisturbed gel. The viscoelastic gel network consists of aggregated spherical casein particles forming a continuous structure and enclosing fat
globules and serum. From a structural point of view, yoghurt belongs to
particulate gels with disordered structures (Horne, 1999; Walstra *et al.*, 1999).
Stirred yoghurt is inoculated and incubated in large fermentation vessels; the
formed gel is then gently stirred to obtain a smooth and viscous, but still
pourable, product, and finally packed. By breaking up the gel, a highly viscous,
non-Newtonian liquid is formed, which shows a strongly shear-rate and time-
dependent flow behaviour.

Drinking yoghurt is produced from low solid milk on the basis of the stirred manufacture process, or regular stirred yoghurt is diluted to some extent. Increased shelf-life of yoghurt may be achieved either by freezing or by thermisation of the fermented product. Whereas the thermisation process is designed to reduce the number of potential spoilage microorganisms and, therefore, results in a partial inactivation of the starter culture, the freezing procedure, provided that appropriate methods are applied, leaves the culture bacteria viable. In frozen yoghurt, higher amounts of sugar and stabilisers are required to maintain the air bubble structure during the freezing process (Tamime and Deeth, 1980).

8.3   Factors affecting yoghurt texture

It is generally accepted that three main factors determine the physical properties of yoghurt. These factors are the preparation of the base milk, comprising several possible treatments, the fermentation process and the post-fermentation treatment.

8.3.1   Preparation of the milk

Dry matter enrichment

The amount of total solids in the base milk, to a large extent, determines the physical properties of the final yoghurt product. The dry matter content of the base milk typically ranges from 9% in the case of skim milk yoghurt without fortification up to more than 20% for certain types of 'concentrated yoghurt', with the most usual values of commercial products ranging between 13% and 17%. There are several possibilities for the fortification of the base milk (Kulkarni *et al.*, 1990), either procedures which increase milk solids proportionally, e.g., evaporation of the base milk to the desired dry matter level, particular membrane processes (i.e., reverse osmosis), the addition of skim milk powder or the addition of evaporated milk, or procedures which increase milk solids disproportionally. These methods comprise the addition of certain types of protein powders, either whey protein or casein based, the addition of whey protein concentrates, or the application of several types of membrane processes such as ultrafiltration or nanofiltration. The selection of a particular method is largely determined by the availability of raw materials (e.g., whey for concentration) and the equipment of the production plant.

Independent of the type of fortification, the protein content of the base milk is the most important factor which influences rheological and physical properties of yoghurt. An increase of the protein content increases the amount of bound water and, consequently, the firmness of the resulting gel. According to Snoeren *et al.* (1982), milk casein is able to immobilise as much as 2.82 g H_2O per g protein and shows a voluminosity of 3.57 ml/g. Corresponding hydration values for undenatured and denatured whey protein are 0.32 g H_2O per g protein and

2.34 g H_2O per g protein, respectively. Data on both quantitative and qualitative effects of dry matter enrichment on physical parameters such as apparent viscosity, gel firmness or susceptibility to syneresis are available from various authors (Table 8.3).

The use of concentrated whey proteins in yoghurt manufacture is of increasing interest, both for utilisation purposes but also from a nutritional point of view; increasing the whey protein/casein ratio improves the biological value of the mixture (Meisel, 1989). Results on firmness and syneresis of yoghurt with a modified whey protein/casein ratio are somewhat contradictory. There is, however, a tendency towards less viscous, softer gels for products with an increased whey protein content, compared to products showing a similar protein content on casein basis (Buchheim et al., 1986; Jelen et al., 1987; Modler et al., 1983; Morris et al., 1995). In any case, it was suggested to limit the increase in the whey protein/casein ratio due to potential off-flavour effects (de Boer, 1996).

Homogenisation
Whole milk is homogenised at pressures of 10–20 MPa in a temperature range of 55–65°C, usually prior to heat treatment, to prevent creaming during fermentation. The process results in the disruption of the milk fat globules, which are stabilised by a specific fat globule membrane consisting mainly of proteins, phospholipids and neutral glycerides, from native size (approximate range 1–5 μm) into much smaller ones. Commonly used homogenisation techniques and the mechanism of the fat globule size reduction are described in detail by Kessler (1996) and Walstra (1995). The covering of the homogenisation-induced, enlarged fat globule surface area with fragments of milk proteins leads to the development of a secondary fat globule membrane, which is of great importance for the characteristics of fermented dairy products (Schkoda, 1999). Electron microscopic investigations (Buchheim and Dejmek, 1990) confirmed the model of the fat globule membrane of homogenised milk as proposed by Walstra and Jenness (1984), showing casein micelles and whey proteins as part of the layer: depending on the homogenisation temperature either casein micelles (at 40°C), or micelle fractions (or submicelles) and whey proteins (>60°C) represent the main part of the newly built membrane.

Large fat globules as present in unhomogenised milk may decrease firmness of fermented products by interrupting the gel network (Aguilera and Kessler, 1988). It is generally accepted that the partial replacement of the native fat globule membrane with other milk proteins allows the fat globules to be incorporated into the gel by crosslinking them to the matrix (van Vliet and Dentener-Kikkert, 1982). However, the effects of homogenisation depend on the layout of the production process. Schkoda (1999) stated that aseptic homogenisation, with the pre-heat treatment preceding the mechanical treatment, causes a higher load to the membrane due to the aggregation of denatured whey proteins to each other and to casein; on the other hand, heating after homogenisation (septic homogenisation) leads to a partial aggregation of membrane proteins to each other, resulting in the formation of aggregates of

Table 8.3 Effects of various fortification methods on physical properties of yoghurt

Reference	Fortification method[a]	Results
Becker and Puhan, 1988	SMP, UF, EV	Increase in gel firmness, less syneresis
Guirguis et al., 1987	RO (compared to milk powder addition)	Increase in gel firmness, less syneresis
Jaros et al., 2002a, 2002b	Reconstituted SMP to 10, 12 and 14% dry matter with two different starters (non-ropy, ropy)	Increase in gel firmness, viscosity and serum-holding capacity; oscillatory measurements of EPS yoghurt gels showed almost no effect of the protein content
Kulkarni et al., 1990	Whey protein concentrate	Decrease of viscosity and firmness with increasing whey protein
Lankes et al., 1998	Comparison of SMP, VEV and UF techniques	Higher firmness and viscosity for UF (higher protein content) due to membrane characteristics
Modler et al., 1983	NaC, UF-MPC, SMP, UF-WPC	Increase of firmness, decrease of syneresis; WPC less firm than casein-based products
Rohm, 1993a; Rohm and Schmid, 1993	SMP, NaC, UF	Increase in viscosity, most for NaC fortification; decrease in syneresis
Savello and Dargan, 1995, 1997	SMP, UF	UF yoghurts have higher firmness and viscosity than SMP
Schkoda et al., 2001	Increase of protein content from 3.5 to 7.0% by nanofiltration of skim milk	Increase in gel firmness, viscosity and serum-holding capacity
Tamime et al., 1984	RO (compared to milk powder addition)	Increase in firmness, less syneresis

[a] RO, reverse osmosis; SMP, skim milk powder; UF, milk protein concentrate from ultrafiltration; (V)EV, (vacuum) evaporation; NaC, sodium caseinate; UF-WPC, whey protein concentrate from ultrafiltration.

linked fat globules. Studies of physical properties of high-fat yoghurt made from whey protein-enriched base milk homogenised either aseptically or septically revealed large differences, with higher viscosity and firmness values for products where homogenisation was performed after heat treatment (Kulkarni *et al.*, 1990). The authors dedicated the different effects of heating to different mechanisms of membrane loading, enhanced by the relatively high amount of whey proteins, and concluded that casein micelles incorporated in the secondary fat globule membrane built during homogenisation will be covered with whey proteins. Their denaturation during subsequent heating might prevent the active contribution of the fat phase to the gel properties (Sharma and Dalgleish, 1994; Tamime and Marshall, 1997).

The effects of incorporating the fat globules into the gel network also depend on the globule size and, consequently, the homogenisation procedure. After homogenising whole milk at different conditions, Plock *et al.* (1992) found a linear increase in gel firmness with decreasing fat globule diameter, and achieved a higher efficiency by multiple stage homogenisation at low homogenisation pressures.

Pre-heat treatment
Heating of the base milk is essential in yoghurt manufacture, and temperature–time conditions may be varied to adjust physical properties of yoghurt products. Generally, heating conditions are much more intense than necessary for preservation purposes, causing a sufficient denaturation of whey proteins, which are then able to associate with casein micelles (Law, 1996; Pearce, 1995). Heating increases voluminosity and water-binding capacity of whey proteins (Snoeren *et al.*, 1982) and decreases their solubility. Reactive side groups of globular whey proteins, especially thiol groups, are exposed due to unfolding, resulting in an oxidation to disulphide linkages and associations between whey proteins and casein. Additionally, denatured whey proteins may associate with casein micelles via hydrophobic interactions with κ-caseins (Smits and van Brouwershaven, 1980). All possible interactions result in a significant contribution of the denatured whey proteins to the properties of the yoghurt gels.

In commercial yoghurt production temperature–time profiles usually ranging from 80–85°C for 30 min to 90–95°C for 5 min are applied (Lucey and Singh, 1998). Dannenberg and Kessler (1988a, 1988b) demonstrated the close relationship between the degree of β-lactoglobulin (β-lg) denaturation, which was linked to heating conditions by a kinetic approach (Dannenberg and Kessler, 1988c), and selected physical properties of yoghurt. Within a β-lg denaturation range of 60–99%, susceptibility to syneresis decreased linearly, whereas yoghurt gel firmness showed an optimum at a residual β-lg level of 10%. Lucey *et al.* (1997) compared acid gels made of reconstituted skim milk from powder subjected to different heat treatments during manufacture, by further subjecting reconstituted milk to several heating conditions. Increasing heating temperature and time led to higher denaturation of β-lactoglobulin and α-lactalbumin (α-la), with β-lg being more heat sensitive (i.e., 95% denaturation after heating at 90°C for 15 min). Dynamic rheological measurements showed a marked increase in the storage modulus (G') for heating conditions higher than 80°C for 15 min, indicating higher gel firmness. The authors suggested that denatured whey proteins in heated milk become susceptible to aggregation during acidification, as the isoelectric points of whey proteins are approached.

However, details on the mechanisms of the heat-induced interactions of α-lactalbumin and β-lactoglobulin with casein micelles are not yet clear. Since native whey proteins, added to the milk after heat treatment, do not contribute to the gel matrix (Lucey *et al.*, 1998a, 1999; Mahaut and Korolczuk, 1992), it appears that denatured whey proteins building associations with casein micelles during heat treatment then act as bridging material by interacting with other denatured whey proteins. Corredig and Dalgleish (1999) performed heating procedures between 70 and 90°C on skim milk after addition of different amounts of purified α-la and β-lg and reported on two main interaction mechanisms: a direct interaction of β-lactoglobulin with casein micelles, via κ-casein binding, and the formation of soluble aggregates of both types of whey proteins as an intermediate before reacting with the casein. Furthermore, the presence of β-lg was necessary for the occurrence of any association with the casein micelle, and binding sites seem to be limited.

8.3.2   Incubation conditions
Cultures
The selection of the starter culture also determines the physical properties of stirred yoghurt to a large extent. As described above, some extracellular polysaccharides (EPS) produced by lactic acid bacteria are known to cause an increase in apparent viscosity, thus leading to improved physical stability of the fermented product.

A lot of work has been done in the field of isolating and characterising the composition of EPS produced by various strains of lactic acid bacteria (e.g., Faber *et al.*, 2002; Grobben *et al.*, 2000; Petry *et al.*, 2000; van Calsteren *et al.*, 2002), but the functionality of the EPS in fermented milk is still not completely clear. It seems that not the amount of polysaccharide, but rather the type, charge and molecular mass of EPS, are important for rheological properties (Bouzar *et al.*, 1997; Laws and Marshall, 2001; Marshall and Rawson, 1999; Pleijsier *et al.*, 2000; Ruas-Madiedo *et al.*, 2002). The amount of EPS is, however, correlated to viscosity properties when a particular type of EPS is considered (Sebastiani and Zelger, 1998). Some authors suggested that the effects of EPS on yoghurt texture derive from a possible attachment to the casein matrix (e.g., Domínguez-Soberanes *et al.*, 2001; Skriver *et al.*, 1995), which has been shown in micrographs obtained by conventional SEM. From these figures, it was concluded that the junctions between polysaccharides and casein strands are responsible for increased viscosity values of yoghurt made with EPS-producing starters. However, Kalab (1993) referred to some previous work done by himself (Tamime *et al.*, 1984) and stated 'In micrographs of samples which had been dehydrated prior to electron microscopic examination, the mucus appears in the form of filaments. This appearance is an artifact; since the polysaccharides cannot be fixed chemically, they shrink on drying and form filaments.' It is more likely that EPS are either excreted outside the cell walls and remain there, thus forming a type of capsule (this was shown by confocal laser scanning microscopy by Hassan *et al.*, 1995), or are loosely attached to the cells or even excreted into the serum phase (Cerning, 1995).

Oscillatory measurements on intact yoghurt gels revealed no effects of non-charged EPS on the storage modulus of the gel network at a dry matter level of approximately 12%, whereas improved stiffness of products with lower dry matter contents was found (Jaros *et al.*, 2002a; Pleijsier *et al.*, 2000). It may be assumed that non-charged EPS are dissolved in the serum phase in the pores of the network and, therefore, do not contribute to the strength of the protein network. This might be the reason for the significant effect they show on the viscosity of stirred yoghurt, as measured either in thixotropic loops in large deformation measurements or by empirical funnel flow measurements (Jaros *et al.*, 2002b). Permeability measurements showed lower values for yoghurt gels fermented with EPS-producing cultures compared to non-EPS gels, indicating a larger resistance to capillary flow (Jaros *et al.*, 2002b; van Marle and Zoon, 1995). Van Marle *et al.* (1999) also distinguished between two different types of EPS on the basis of steady-shear viscosity measurements, with viscosities of yoghurt serum being five times higher for starter cultures producing EPS which are released into the aqueous phase.

Temperature–time regimes of fermentation
The conditions of incubation may additionally influence the properties of the final product. Generally, thermophilic lactic acid bacteria show an optimum temperature ranging around 40–43°C. In the dairy industry two different fermentation procedures are usually applied: the short incubation method and the long incubation method. By providing the microorganisms their optimum temperature range, incubation times of approximately 2.5–4 h can be achieved. When incubation should take place overnight due to technical requirements, temperature has to be reduced to 30–32°C, leading to a fermentation time of 10–12 h to reach the desired end-pH. This retarded activity of the starter organisms results in a slower rate of acidification and leads to a difference in the kinetics of protein network formation. It was generally accepted that the lower the fermentation temperature, the longer it takes to reach a certain pH and therefore firmness, but the final product is much firmer (Walstra *et al.*, 1999). However, Lankes *et al.* (1998) compared yoghurts manufactured at either 30°C or 42°C and found higher gel firmness and higher viscosity for products fermented at 42°C. Haque *et al.* (2001) found a systematic increase in gel strength for set-type yoghurt and viscosity for stirred yoghurt with increase in the temperature of fermentation from 37°C to 46°C. A possible explanation for these contradictory results was suggested by Horne (1998), who recently introduced a model of the casein micelle as a complex balance of hydrophobic attraction and electrostatic repulsion.

8.3.3   Post-incubation treatments
Set-style yoghurt
Since set-style yoghurt is fermented directly within the retail container, no treatment further than cooling is necessary after fermentation. Usually, incubation is stopped at a pH slightly above the desired pH of the product, as a sufficient period of time is necessary for cooling the cups in ventilated chambers. When using separated incubation and cooling chambers, it is essential to avoid any vibrations of the packages during transportation as the gel is still weak and susceptible to local fracture with subsequent syneresis. Generally, rapid cooling is important to diminish the continued growth of the lactobacilli, otherwise leading to excessive acid production. Furthermore, enhanced acidification to pH values below 4 may lead to body and texture defects such as gel shrinkage and syneresis.

Stirred yoghurt
After fermentation of yoghurt in large vats, the gel is broken by stirring, thus forming a viscous non-Newtonian liquid, which is strongly shear-rate thinning. Defining the stirring regime is a crucial process which induces considerable changes in the rheological properties of the final product. At a given shear rate, the apparent viscosity of stirred yoghurt depends on the firmness of the gel before stirring, giving higher viscosity with higher firmness. Additionally, higher gel firmness allows more vigorous stirring, consequently leading to smoother products which do not become too thin. Higher firmness of the gel in the vat also lowers the risk of syneresis, which might lead to less viscous and more lumpy products.

There are no generally accepted rules for the layout of the time–temperature profile during stirring and cooling, and the applied procedures vary from manufacturer to manufacturer. However, it is generally accepted that the stirred product needs some time after stirring to rebuild some structure. Typically, after reaching a particular pH, the product may be slowly stirred in the fermentation vat to achieve a homogeneous temperature distribution during cooling. Upon reaching 22–24°C, the product may then be pumped to the filling and packaging unit, where relatively high shearing forces are applied. During the subsequent cooling process of the packed product, a desired increase in viscosity will be achieved.

8.4   Measuring the rheological and textural properties of yoghurt

8.4.1   Rheological and other physical methods
Set yoghurt
It is obvious that rheological properties of intact yoghurt gels can only be accessed when the fermentation process is performed *in situ*, i.e., within a specific geometry of any rheometer. Measurements may be performed either

after the gel forming process is finalised, or even during fermentation provided that some basic requirements are fulfilled. These include, e.g., the choice of an appropriate geometry, sufficient protection against evaporation during fermentation (this can be achieved by avoiding a milk–air interface using a low viscosity oil), and an appropriate instrument setup. It is absolutely essential that the strain applied to the gelling system is kept as small as possible to minimise any disturbance of the gelation process and to achieve reliable results. This can easily be achieved by using strain-controlled rheometers but might be difficult in the case of stress-controlled instruments where the smallest applicable stress, particularly in the early stage of fermentation when almost liquid milk is within the system, will result in a sufficient angular deformation (Hemar et al., 2000). By comparing gelation profiles Haque et al. (2001) recently concluded that slippage along supporting surfaces occurs easily when using horizontal geometries (i.e., cone-and-plate and plate–plate), whereas cup-and-bob systems are much more robust towards artifacts.

Rheological studies on intact yoghurt gels fermented within a rheometer system were performed by, e.g., Fiszman et al. (1999), Haque et al. (2001), Rohm (1993b), Rohm and Kovac (1994), Rönnegard and Dejmek (1993), van Marle and Zoon (1995) and Vlahopoulou and Bell (1995). Generally, mechanical spectra obtained within the linear viscoelastic region, i.e., a strain lower than approximately 1–3%, reveal a response typical for biopolymer gels (Ross-Murphy, 1994), with the storage modulus G' (Pa) exceeding the loss modulus G'' (Pa) by a factor of about 5–7, and little dependency of either G' or G'' on angular frequency ω (rad s^{-1}), with power law slope exponents in the range 0.1–0.2 and, consequently, another power law relation between complex viscosity η^* (Pa.s) and ω (here, slope exponents are $1 - n$). As experimental conditions (base milk, heat treatment, starter, analytical conditions, etc.) vary to a large extent, a G' of 10^3 Pa can only be taken as a rough estimate of the gel firmness of set yoghurt.

Stirred yoghurt
From the rheological point of view stirred yoghurt is a complex viscoelastic fluid which exhibits shear-thinning and time-dependent properties. A complete characterisation of flow properties of yoghurt therefore requires a large set of experiments, considering both the dependency on shear rate and time effects. It is somewhat complicating that, under practical conditions and especially when using stress-controlled instruments, a stress region is observed below which no flow takes place. Recently, the existence of a yield stress has been demonstrated on the basis of several different rheological methods (Dimonte et al., 1998). However, Barnes and Walters (1985) and Barnes (1999) insisted on finite viscosity values for almost all materials, with the response at small stresses to be treated as a Newtonian plateau, and considered the yield stress as a mathematical constant for modelling purposes.

Applying constant shear rate for a specific period of time results in typical decay curves for viscosity versus time, and viscosity usually decreases at any time when the experiment is repeated with increased shear rate. Although an equilibrium viscosity was not achieved within one hour (Butler and McNulty, 1995; O'Donnell and Butler, 2002; Ramaswamy and Basak, 1991; Schellhaass and Morris, 1985), the decrease of viscosity diminishes with increased time of shear, and quasi-equilibrium values were assumed for shearing times ranging between 10 and 20 min (Benezech and Maingonnat, 1993; van Marle et al., 1999). Although these differences might not be large when expressed in figures, it is important for modelling purposes to decide whether steady-shear conditions at a specific time are met or not.

For the latter condition comprising stress decay *ad infinitum*, analytical data may be fitted to the logarithmic time model originally described by Weltman (1943):

$$\tau = A + B \ln\left(\frac{t}{t_m}\right) \qquad 8.1$$

where τ (Pa) corresponds to shear stress at time t (s), t_m (s) is the time at which maximum stress is measured, and A and B (Pa) refer to intercept and slope in the Weltman model, respectively (consequently, A corresponds to τ for $t = t_m$).

Whereas Weltman coefficients have been related linearly to the applied shear rate $\dot{\gamma}$ (s^{-1}) ranging from $100\,\text{s}^{-1}$ to $500\,\text{s}^{-1}$ by Ramaswamy and Basak (1991), O'Donnell and Butler (2002) used a power law fit and a logarithmic equation to describe the shear-rate dependency of A and B, respectively.

Assuming an approach to equilibrium viscosity η_e (Pa.s) at finite time, the model of Tiu and Boger (1974), based on the theory of Cheng and Evans (1965), may be used:

$$\tau = \lambda \tau_m \qquad 8.2$$

Here, shear stress is related to the maximum shear stress τ_m (Pa) times a dimensionless structural parameter λ ($0 < \lambda \leq 1$). Depending on the model to be used for relating shear stress to shear rate, one will find that

$$\tau_m = \lambda K \dot{\gamma}^n \qquad 8.3$$

or

$$\tau_m = \lambda(\tau_0 + K\dot{\gamma}^n) \qquad 8.4$$

for the power law equation (O'Donnell and Butler, 2002) and the Hershel Bulkley model (Butler and McNulty, 1995), respectively. In equations 8.3 and 8.4, τ_0 (Pa) corresponds to a yield stress, and K (Pa.s^n) and n (–) are fitting coefficients, with K referring to the apparent viscosity at $\dot{\gamma} = 1\,\text{s}^{-1}$, and $0 \leq n \leq 1$ as yoghurt is shear-thinning.

The time dependency of λ at constant shear rate is given by

$$\frac{1}{\lambda - \lambda_e} = \frac{1}{\lambda_m - \lambda_e} + k_1 t \qquad 8.5$$

with λ_m corresponding to λ at t_m and λ_e being the structural parameter at equilibrium conditions. Substituting equation 8.2 into $\eta = \tau/\dot{\gamma}$ yields

$$\lambda = \frac{\eta\dot{\gamma}}{\tau_m} \qquad\qquad 8.6$$

which also holds for maximum and equilibrium conditions and can be further substituted into equation 8.5 giving

$$\frac{1}{\eta - \eta_e} = \frac{1}{\eta_m - \eta_e} + \left(\frac{k_1\dot{\gamma}}{\tau_m}\right)t \qquad\qquad 8.7$$

A plot of $1/(\eta - \eta_e)$ versus time results in a straight line with a slope equal to $k_1\dot{\gamma}/\tau_m$ and, if repeated for a number of shear rates, the relation between k_1 and $\dot{\gamma}$ can be established. A similar treatment can be applied for the Hershel Bulkley model by using equation 8.4 instead of equation 8.3 to express the denominator in equation 8.6, τ_m. With the above-mentioned tools it will be possible to model initial maximum stress and equilibrium stress as well as λ_e by a power law (or whatever is intended) function of shear rate, thus completely describing shear-thinning and thixotropic behaviour.

Several authors used a more qualitative approach to study stirred yoghurt, either by increasing shear rate stepwise or by increasing shear rate linearly with time, followed by a decrease until $\dot{\gamma} = 0\,s^{-1}$. Flow curves were fitted by means of the power law (Abu-Jdayil et al., 2000; Geraghty and Butler, 1999; Keogh and O'Kennedy, 1998; Parnell-Clunies et al., 1986; Schellhaass and Morris, 1985), the Casson equation (Parnell-Clunies et al., 1986; Skriver et al., 1993) or the Hershel Bulkley equation (Hassan et al., 1996; Ramaswamy and Basak, 1991, 1992; Rohm, 1993a; Rohm and Schmid, 1993). However, it has to be noted that any equation coefficients obtained by regression analysis will depend heavily on the setup of the test, i.e., the acceleration of shear rate, due to the time-dependent viscosity decay of yoghurt (Rohm, 1992). Some additional information can be drawn from the area included between the upward and downward curves when applying the 'thixotropic loop technique'. The area is given in terms of $(N/m^2 \times s^{-1})$ or, if related to the volume of the sheared sample, can be treated in terms of the power necessary for structure degradation.

A number of studies deal with oscillatory methods applied to stirred yoghurt (Jaros et al., 2002b; Ozer et al., 1998, 1999; Rohm and Kovac, 1995; Skriver et al., 1999, Steventon et al., 1990). Qualitatively, mechanical spectra resemble those of set yoghurt, with the moduli being 8–10 times lower. Afonso and Maia (1999) and Skriver (1995) compared the results of dynamic measurements of stirred yoghurt with apparent steady shear viscosity and observed that the empirical Cox-Merz rule, which should result in identity of η^* versus ø, ω and η_{app} versus γ-curves (Cox and Merz, 1958), was only obeyed after introducing a horizontal shift factor as has been suggested by Bistany and Kokini (1983) and Rao and Cooley (1992). Most recently, Haque et al. (2001) demonstrated the importance of the sample loading procedure by showing a sufficient (approximately 25%) increase of the modulus after the first few minutes after loading, attributable to some structure recovery.

Figure 8.2 provides some interesting detail of a comparison of two samples of stirred yoghurt produced at laboratory scale under identical conditions (i.e., base

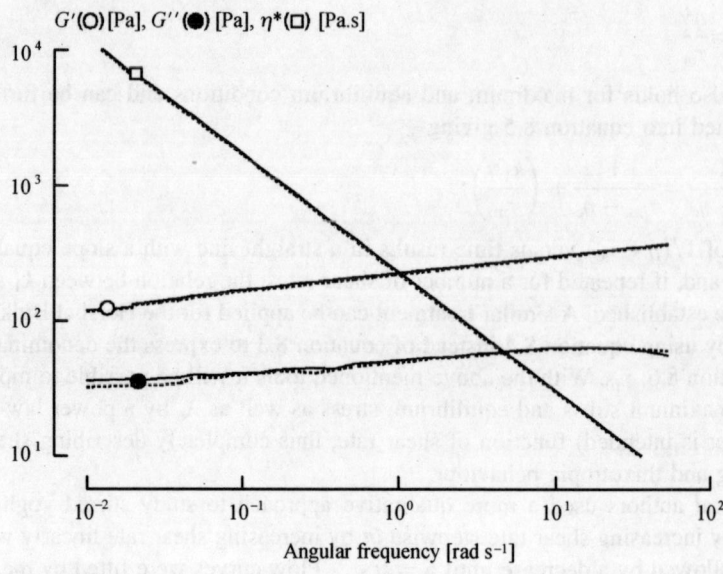

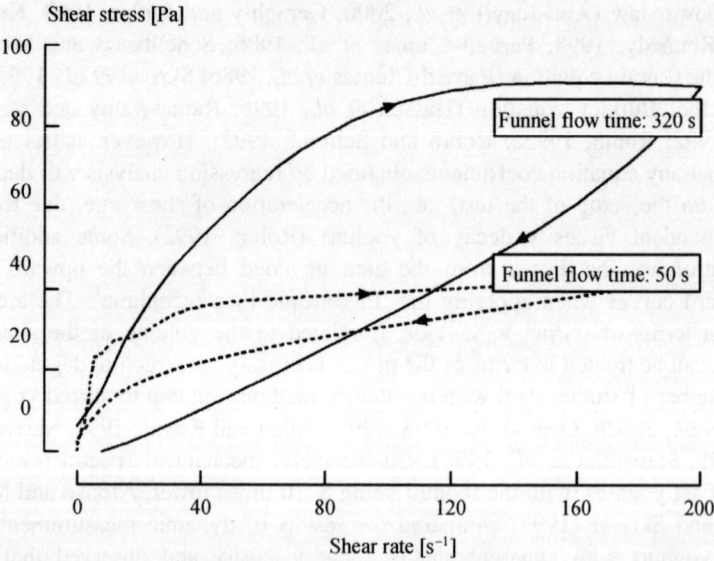

Fig. 8.2   Mechanical spectra (upper graph) and flow curves of stirred yoghurt (lower graph). Full lines, yoghurt A inoculated with a highly viscous starter; dotted lines, yoghurt B inoculated with a standard starter. For further explanations see text.

skim milk 14% total solids, pre-heat treatment 90°C for 30 min; incubation temperature 43°C, final pH 4.5). Whereas the mechanical spectra showed no noticeable differences, yoghurt A inoculated with a highly viscous starter revealed a completely different response to an up-and-down shearing cycle (shear rate acceleration $1\,s^{-2}$) than did sample B fermented with a standard starter, with a much smaller area enclosed between the upward and the downward curves. This means that, in both cases, the breakdown of structure exactly compensates for the strain rate increase that would result in a higher shear stress response if the sample remained unchanged.

Permeability

A special method, originally described for rennet milk gels but later adopted to acidified milk gels (Lucey *et al.*, 1997; van Marle and Zoon, 1995), has been introduced by van Dijk and Walstra (1986) and Roefs *et al.* (1990). Small glass tubes containing *in situ* fermented gels are placed in whey, with the gel surface below the whey level thus causing a pressure difference. The whey flux through the gel network is usually observed as a function of time and may serve as an indicator for the occurrence of microsyneresis, i.e., some rearrangement and condensation in the casein network, leading to an increase in the size of micropores, or it might be helpful in the detection of interactions between milk constituents and polysaccharides produced by starter cultures.

8.4.2   Empirical methods

Gel firmness

Gel firmness measurements of set yoghurt are usually performed by means of constant speed penetration on universal testing machines or similar instruments, using cylindrical plungers (15 mm < d < 40 mm) and crosshead speed values ranging between 10 and 100 mm/min, most likely below room temperature. With up-to-date equipment the force–response, which is affected by plunger size and penetration speed, is monitored as a function of penetration depth. Several authors (e.g., Barrantes *et al.*, 1996; Ferragut *et al.*, 2000; Hassan *et al.*, 1996; Lorenzen *et al.*, 1999; Tamime *et al.*, 1991, 1996) used force values (or force values related to plunger diameter) at a predefined penetration depth to express gel firmness.

Another way to evaluate firmness from penetration data is based on the work of Schmidt and Ahmed (1972), who proposed to express firmness as the elastic response from the undisturbed sample by calculating the initial slope of the force–penetration curve. The advantage of applying regression analysis to the response curve (Fiszman and Salvador, 1999; Fiszman *et al.*, 1999; Jaros *et al.*, 2002a; Rohm, 1995; Rohm and Kovac, 1994) is that the parameter, denoted as 'apparent firmness modulus (N/mm)', resembles mainly the elastic response of the yoghurt gel and is not influenced by upward shear forces occurring after sufficient penetration of the plunger. These shear forces along the circumference of the plunger obviously cause some fluctuations in the force–penetration curve and, finally, may result in poor repeatability (Fig. 8.3).

The use of cones with varying dimensions on constant mass penetrometers, which read penetration depth after a predefined period of time, has been described by, e.g., Davi and Shah (1998), Mistry and Hassan (1992) and Ozer and Atamer (1999).

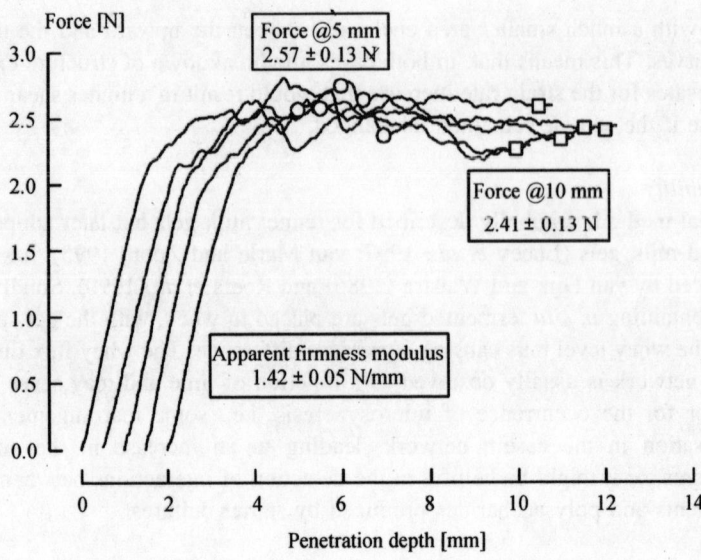

Fig. 8.3   Evaluation of different parameters from force–penetration curves applied to set yoghurt.

One-point measurements of viscosity

Although apparent viscosity of stirred yoghurt depends heavily on shear rate, shearing time (at constant rate) and shear history, single-point measurements have been performed in a number of studies to achieve appropriate indicator values. Most commonly, shear rate in the case of rotational viscometers (Abu-Jdayil *et al.*, 2000; Daubert *et al.*, 1998; Moreira *et al.*, 2000; Schkoda *et al.*, 2001) or rotations per minute in case of Brookfield-type instruments (Fernandez-Garcia and McGregor, 1997; Fernandez-Garcia *et al.*, 1998; Skriver *et al.*, 1999; Trachoo and Mistry, 1998) of the shearing device were set to a predefined value, varying to a large extent from study to study, and torque, shear stress or apparent viscosity were recorded after a predefined period of time. In some other cases, flow curves comprising a particular shear rate–time regime were recorded, and apparent viscosity was calculated from the shear stress at a predefined shear rate (Hassan *et al.*, 1996; van Marle and Zoon, 1995).

Another indicator for apparent viscosity can be obtained from the flow time necessary for a predefined amount of stirred yoghurt to pass through devices such as the Posthumus funnel, which represents a cup with a narrow efflux tube. Funnel flow can be considered as an easy-to-perform and inexpensive method for viscosity evaluation, provided that the entire sample preparation procedure (e.g., prestirring of yoghurt, transfer into the funnel) is thoroughly defined (Beal *et al.*, 1999; Martin *et al.*, 1999). Although Hellinga *et al.* (1986) showed in a theoretical approach that shear rates occurring during the flow of the product through the orifice are much higher than shear rates expected during sensory evaluation of yoghurt, Skriver *et al.* (1999) reported on a sufficient interrelation between funnel flow time and oral examination of viscosity, thus allowing one to predict sensory properties with the Posthumus device.

Syneresis

The stability of set yoghurt towards syneresis or whey drainage can be evaluated either under the influence of regular gravity or by applying additional gravitational forces by centrifugation. The afore-mentioned principle can easily be applied to both pilot plant and laboratory-scale products as well as to commercial yoghurts, whereas the procedure based on centrifugation requires the fermentation of yoghurt in special containers in the case of set yoghurt. A third method, though rarely used, which can only be applied to set yoghurt, is based on gel shrinkage after wetting.

Measurements at normal gravity

Generally, a certain amount of yoghurt supported by a container or moulded with a specific device is placed on a sieve, and the amount of separated whey is measured after a predefined period of time. Prior to measuring whey drainage, Modler *et al.* (1983) used a Cherry-Burrell knife to determine firmness of yoghurt gels. The containers were then inverted and placed on a stainless steel sieve supported by a funnel. The amount of whey was collected after 2 h of draining at 3°C and taken as a measure of syneresis. Although originally intended for enzymatic coagulation, a special device based on this principle was proposed by Pompei *et al.* (1994). Guirguis *et al.* (1987) used a container to apply this method to stirred yoghurt. Several authors have formed a hemisphere of yoghurt gel by means of an ice-cream scoop and collected the drained whey (Dannenberg and Kessler, 1988a; Hassan *et al.*, 1996; Hoffmann *et al.*, 1997; Lorenzen *et al.*, 1999).

Several authors have evaluated spontaneous whey separation in yoghurt containers after a predefined storage period (Augustin *et al.*, 1999; Fiszman and Salvador, 1999; Fiszman *et al.*, 1999; Moreira *et al.*, 2000). However, this method shows some disadvantages, especially in firm yoghurt, as the amount of spontaneously released whey is usually very small.

Centrifugation methods

Harwalkar and Kalab (1983) subjected yoghurt gels fermented in centrifuge tubes to centrifugal forces ranging between $30g$ and $2000g$ (6°C, 10 min), then observed a sigmoid relationship between separated whey and g-value, and proposed the g-value at the inflection point of the curve as a measure of susceptibility to syneresis. However, this method is laborious as it requires a number of centrifugations per sample, and several authors have used the work of Harwalkar and Kalab (1983) as a basis for a simplified procedure, covering only one centrifugation step and taking into account the relative amount of separated whey (Ferragut *et al.*, 2000; Haque *et al.*, 2001; Lucey, 2001; Rohm and Kovac, 1994; Schkoda *et al.*, 2001). Both the magnitude of the g-values as well as centrifugation time and temperature vary considerably; e.g., Lucey *et al.* (1998b) used 100*g* whereas Parnell-Clunies *et al.* (1986) applied as much as 13 500*g*.

The centrifugation method can be applied to set yoghurt (as long as the gel is fermented within the centrifugation tubes) as well as to stirred yoghurt. Generally, the amount of whey separated from the capillary space decreases with increasing dry matter content of yoghurt and is influenced by technological conditions such as pre-heat treatment of the base milk, milk homogenisation or the type of starter culture used.

Gel shrinkage measurement

Van Dijk and Walstra (1986) used the fact that milk gels in containers only start to shrink either after cutting or after wetting of the surface, and established a method for measuring the height of a defined slab of the gel after spraying whey or water onto the surface. This method was adopted for acid milk gels by Lucey *et al.* (1997).

8.4.3   Sensory assessments

Apart from simple difference testing (de Ancos *et al.*, 2000), issues related to quality perception and acceptance (Grunert *et al.*, 2000; Laye *et al.*, 1993; Muir and Hunter, 1992) as well as consumer studies using Free-Choice Profiling and Procrustes analysis (Gacula, 1997), most of the studies (e.g., Barrantes *et al.*, 1996; Biliaderis *et al.*, 1992; Faergemand *et al.*, 1999; Kneifel *et al.*, 1992; Martin *et al.*, 1999; Rohm *et al.*, 1994; Skriver *et al.*, 1999) dealing with sensory assessments of physical properties of yoghurt were performed by using the Quantitative Descriptive Analysis (QDA) originally described by Stone *et al.* (1974). Simply speaking, QDA is based on a vocabulary and sensory procedures selected by means of test products and established in a group process by subjects. In repeated measurements, data are collected by interval scales, and after applying analysis of variance, multivariate procedures (e.g., PCA, FA) may be performed to eliminate redundancy.

Descriptors for texture properties of yoghurt extracted from the literature differ to a large extent; additionally, some studies lack definitions and procedures for the assessed sensory parameters. A collection of descriptors and definitions is summarised in Table 8.4.

8.5   Future trends

Continuously increasing consumer health consciousness is responsible for the expanding worldwide interest in functional foods. Fermented dairy products such as yoghurt have long been known for their value in managing intestinal disorders such as lactose intolerance or acute gastroenteritis. Three different approaches in the dairy industry are applied to modify the intestinal microflora and thereby beneficially influence the health of the host. These include the

Table 8.4 Descriptors applied in sensory analysis of yoghurt

Reference	Texture descriptor	Sensory definition and/or procedure
Barrantes et al. (1996)	Perceived whey separation	'Not specified
	Firmness	'Not specified
	Lumpy/coarse	'Not specified
	Gummy	'Not specified
	Body and texture	'Not specified
	Creamy	'Not specified
Biliaderis et al. (1992)	Thickness	'Not specified
	Graininess	'Not specified
Faergemand et al. (1999)	Whey drainage	'Visual determination of liquid on top of yoghurt'
	Firmness	'When cutting the yoghurt gel with a spoon'
	Flakiness	'By cutting yoghurt surface with a spoon'
	Grittiness	'Oral determination'
	Creaminess	'Oral determination'
Kneifel et al. (1992)	Whey drainage	'Visual observation of gel surface after inserting a spoon into the gel'
	Texture	'Visual observation after stirring the product with a spoon'
Martin et al. (1999)	Smoothness	'Quantity of particles in the gel quantified by visual inspection of the spoon's back'
	Sliminess	'Product's ability to flow in a continuous way from the spoon'
	Thickness (non-oral)	'Product's ability to flow from the spoon'
	Thickness (oral)	'Product's flowing resistance assessed by crushing one spoonful of the product between the tongue and palate'
	Mouthcoating	'Product's ability to form a film lining the mouth'
Rohm et al. (1994)	Texture	'Gel firmness perceived by penetrating the gel with a teaspoon and removing an appropriate amount of yoghurt without exerting any shearing force'
	Mouthfeel	'Degree of smoothness perceived by squeezing yoghurt between tongue and palate'
	Viscosity	'Perceived resistance against stirring with a teaspoon'
	Ropiness	'Perceived cohesiveness of the stirred product after pouring it from a teaspoon'
Skriver et al. (1999)	Non-oral viscosity	'Penetrating the yogurt gel with a teaspoon, placing approx. 5 ml on the surface of the yoghurt gel and observing how fast it disappeared'
	Oral viscosity	'Perceived degree of thickness when eating the yogurt'

fermentation of milk with probiotics, such as various strains of lactic acid bacteria and *Bifidobacterium* spp., which inhabit the human gut; the addition of prebiotics, which are non-digestible food ingredients, supposed to stimulate the growth of various health-promoting bacteria in the human colon; and the use of synbiotics, defined as a mixture of probiotics and prebiotics. The application of each treatment potentially influences rheology and texture properties, as different starter cultures are used, or conventional starter cultures show other modified fermentation patterns.

Although technology has been applied with almost complete success to produce low-fat, low-calorie yoghurt with sufficient rheological properties, there is still a need for product optimisation. The addition of processed dairy ingredients (e.g., microparticulated whey proteins) might be a promising way to mimic fat properties and to improve physical properties and sensory characteristics. Whereas membrane processes, providing selective cut-offs of particular ingredients, may be used to enhance the quality of traditional products, new techniqes such as high pressure treatment might result in microstructural modifications, presumably leading to the development of completely new products.

8.6   Sources of further information and advice

Many different research groups around Europe and the United States are involved in studies concerning dairy products in general or yoghurt in particular. Apart from many publications in the scientific literature, a good overview of current or recently completed international projects is available on the Internet pages of the Community Research and Development Information Service of the European Union (http://www.cordis.lu). Currently, research on fermented milks is focused mainly on lactic acid bacteria, dealing with topics ranging from molecular biology and genetics to genetically engineered food products, which are supposed to improve product quality, and to consumer attitudes towards these food systems. Additionally, extensive work is being done on the isolation of new starter cultures from fermented dairy products and on human probiotics for fermented milks. The mechanisms and the controlled production of exopolysaccharides from lactic acid bacteria as natural thickeners and the improvement of the texture properties of yoghurt are still under investigation. In particular, a project finalised recently was dealing with the relationship between composition, processing conditions and gel texture of particle gel systems by means of modern technologies such as Brownian dynamics simulation of real and simulated systems.

8.7   References

ABU-JDAYIL B, SHAKER R R, JUMAH R Y (2000), 'Rheological behaviour of concentrated yogurt', *Int J Food Prop*, 3, 207–216.

AFONSO I M, MAIA J M (1999), 'Rheological monitoring of structure evolution and development in stirred yogurt', *J Food Eng*, 42, 183–190.

AGUILERA J M, KESSLER H G (1988), 'Physico-chemical and rheological properties of milk fat globules with modified membranes', *Milchwissenschaft*, 43, 411–415.

ANON. (1982), *Consumption Statistics for Milk and Milk Products 1980*, Bulletin 144, Brussels, International Dairy Federation.

ANON. (1992), *Consumption Statistics for Milk and Milk Products 1990*, Bulletin 270, Brussels, International Dairy Federation.

ANON. (1995), *Consumption Statistics for Milk and Milk Products 1993*, Bulletin 301, Brussels, International Dairy Federation.

ANON. (2001), *World Dairy Situation 2001*, Bulletin 368, Brussels, International Dairy Federation.

AUGUSTIN M A, CHENG L J, CLARKE P T (1999), 'Effects of preheat treatment of milk powder on the properties of reconstituted set skim yogurts', *Int Dairy J*, 9, 415–416.

BARNES H A (1999), 'The yield stress – a review or "παντα ρει" – everything flows?', *J Non-Newtonian Fluid Mech*, 81, 133–178.

BARNES H A, WALTERS K (1985), 'The yield stress myth?', *Rheol Acta*, 24, 323–326.

BARRANTES E, TAMIME A Y, SWORD A M, MUIR D D, KALAB M (1996), 'The manufacture of set-type natural yogurt containing different oils. II. Rheological properties and microstructure', *Int Dairy J*, 6, 827–837.

BEAL C, SKOKANOVA J, LATRILLE E, MARTIN N, CORRIEU G (1999), 'Combined effects of culture conditions and storage time on acidification and viscosity of stirred yogurt', *J Dairy Sci*, 82, 673–681.

BECKER T, PUHAN Z (1988), 'Auswirkung verschiedener Verfahren zur Erhöhung der fettfreien Trockenmasse auf die rheologischen Eigenschaften von Joghurt', *Schweiz Milchwirt Forsch*, 17, 63-68.

BENEZECH T, MAINGONNAT J F (1993), 'Flow properties of stirred yogurt: structural parameter approach in describing time-dependency', *J Texture Stud*, 24, 455–473.

BILIADERIS C G, KHAN M M, BLANK G (1992), 'Rheological and sensory properties of yogurt from skim milk and ultrafiltered retentates', *Int Dairy J*, 2, 311–323.

BISTANY K L, KOKINI J L (1983), 'Dynamic viscoelastic properties of foods in texture control', *J Rheol*, 27, 605–620.

BOUZAR F, CERNING J, DESMAZEAUD M (1997), 'Exopolysaccharide production and texture-promoting abilities of mixed-strain starter cultures in yoghurt production', *J Dairy Sci*, 80, 2310–2317.

BUCHHEIM W, DEJMEK P (1990), 'Milk and dairy-type emulsions', in Larsson K and Friberg S E, *Food Emulsions*, Marcel Dekker, New York, 203–246.

BUCHHEIM W, WELSCH U (1973), 'Evidence for the submicellar composition of casein micelles on the basis of electron microscopical studies', *Neth Milk Dairy J*, 27, 163–180.

BUCHHEIM W, PETERS K H, KAUFMANN W (1986), 'Technologische, physikalisch-chemische und sensorische Aspekte von Milch und Sauermilch mit modifiziertem Casein/ Molkenprotein-Verhältnis', *Milchwissenschaft*, 41, 139–141.

BUTLER F, MCNULTY A (1995), 'Time dependent rheological characterization of buttermilk at 5°C', *J Food Eng*, 25, 569–580.

CERNING J (1995), 'Production of exopolysaccharides by lactic acid bacteria and dairy propionibacteria', *Lait*, 75, 463–472.

CHENG D C H, EVANS F (1965), 'Phenomenological characterization of the rheological behaviour of inelastic reversible thixotropic and antithixotropic fluids', *Brit J Appl*

Phys, 16, 1599–1617.

CORREDIG M, DALGLEISH D G (1999), 'The mechanisms of the heat-induced interaction of whey proteins with casein micelles in milk', *Int Dairy J*, 9, 233–236.

COX W P, MERZ E H (1958), 'Correlation of dynamic and steady flow viscosities', *J Polymer Sci*, 28, 619–622.

DALGLEISH D G, LAW A J R (1988), 'pH-Induced dissociation of bovine casein micelles. I. Analysis of liberated caseins', *J Dairy Res*, 55, 529–538.

DANNENBERG F, KESSLER H G (1988a), 'Effect of denaturation of β-lactoglobulin on texture properties of set-style nonfat yoghurt. 1. Syneresis', *Milchwissenschaft*, 43, 632–635.

DANNENBERG F, KESSLER H G (1988b), 'Effect of denaturation of β-lactoglobulin on texture properties of set-style nonfat yoghurt. 2. Firmness and flow properties, *Milchwissenschaft*, 43, 700–704.

DANNENBERG F, KESSLER H G (1988c), 'Thermodynamic approach to kinetic studies of β-lactoglobulin denaturation in heated skim milk and sweet whey', *Milchwissenschaft*, 43, 139–142.

DAUBERT C R, TKACHUK J A, TRUONG V D (1998), 'Quantitative measurement of food spreadability using the vane method', *J Texture Stud*, 29, 427–435.

DAVI R I, SHAH N P (1998), 'The influence of ingredient supplementation on the textural characteristics of yogurt', *Aust J Dairy Technol*, 53, 180–184.

DE ANCOS B, CANO M P, GOMEZ R (2000), 'Characteristics of stirred low-fat yoghurt as affected by high pressure', *Int Dairy J*, 10, 105–111.

DE BOER R (1996), 'Yogurt and other fermented dairy products', in *Advances in Membrane Technology for Better Dairy Products*, IDF Bulletin 311, Brussels, International Dairy Federation, 21–24.

DIMONTE G, NELSON D, WEAVER S, SCHNEIDER M, FLOWER-MAUDLIN E, GORE R, BAUMGARDNER J R, SAHOTA M S (1998), 'Comparative study of viscoelastic properties using virgin yogurt', *J Rheol*, 42, 727–742.

DOMÍNGUEZ-SOBERANES J, GARCÍA-GARIBAY M, CASAS-ALENCÁSTER N B, MARTÍNEZ-PADILLA L P (2001), 'Instrumental texture of set and stirred fermented milk. Effect of a ropy strain of *Lactobacillus delbrueckii* subsp. *bulgaricus* and an enriched substrate', *J Texture Stud*, 32, 205–217.

FABER E J, VAN KUIK J A, KAMERLING J P, VLIEGENTHART J F G (2002), 'Modeling of the structure in aqueous solution of the exopolysaccharide produced by *Lactobacillus helveticus* 766', *Biopolymers*, 63, 66–76.

FAERGEMAND M, SORENSEN M V, JORGENSEN U, BUDOLFSEN G, QVIST K B (1999), 'Transglutaminase: effect on instrumental and sensory texture of set style yogurt', *Milchwissenschaft*, 54, 563–566.

FERNANDEZ-GARCIA E, MCGREGOR J U (1997), 'Fortification of sweetened plain yogurt with insoluble dietary fiber', *Food Res Technol*, 204, 433–437.

FERNANDEZ-GARCIA E, MCGREGOR J U, TRAYLOR S (1998), 'The addition of oat fiber and natural alternative sweeteners in the manufacture of plain yogurt', *J Dairy Sci*, 81, 655–663.

FERRAGUT V, MARTINEZ V M, TRUJILLO A J, GUAMIS B (2000), 'Properties of yogurts made from whole ewe's milk treated by high hydrostatic pressure', *Milchwissenschaft*, 55, 267–269.

FISZMAN S M, SALVADOR A (1999), 'Effect of gelatine on texture of yogurt and of acid-heat-induced milk gels', *Food Res Technol*, 208, 100–105.

FISZMAN S M, LLUCH M A, SALVADOR A (1999), 'Effect of addition of gelatin on microstructure of acidic milk gels and yogurt and on their rheological properties', *Int Dairy J*, 9, 895–901.

FONDÉN R, MOGENSEN G, TANAKA R, SALMINEN S (2000), *Effect of Culture-containing Dairy Products on Intestinal Microflora, Human Nutrition and Health – Current Knowledge and Future Perspectives*, IDF Bulletin 352, Brussels, International Dairy Federation.

GACULA M C (1997), 'Descriptive sensory analysis methods', in Gacula M C, *Descriptive Sensory Analysis in Practice*, Food and Nutrition Press, Trumbull, 5–13.

GERAGHTY R, BUTLER F (1999), 'Viscosity characterization of a commercial yoghurt at 5 degree C using a cup in bob and a vane geometry over a wide shear rate range $(10^{-5} \ s^{-1}–10^3 \ s^{-1})$', *J Food Proc Eng*, 22, 1–10.

GROBBEN G J, BOELS I C, SIKKEMA J, SMITH M R, DE BONT J A M (2000), 'Influence of ions on growth and production of exopolysaccharides by *Lactobacillus delbrueckii* subsp. *bulgaricus* NCFB 2772', *J Dairy Res*, 67, 131–135.

GRUNERT K G, BECH-LARSEN T, BREDAHL L (2000), 'Three issues in consumer quality perception and acceptance of dairy products', *Int Dairy J*, 10, 575–584.

GUIRGUIS N, VERSTEEG K, HICKEY M W (1987), 'The manufacture of yoghurt using reverse osmosis concentrated skim milk', *Aust J Dairy Technol*, 42, 7–10.

HAQUE A, RICHARDSON R K, MORRIS E R (2001), 'Effect of fermentation temperature on the rheology of set and stirred yogurt', *Food Hydrocoll*, 15, 593–602.

HARWALKAR V R, KALAB M (1983), 'Susceptibility of yoghurt to syneresis. Comparison of centrifugation and drainage methods', *Milchwissenschaft*, 38, 517–522.

HASSAN A N, FRANK J F (2001), 'SStarter cultures and their use', in Marth E H and Steele J L, *Applied Dairy Microbiology*, Marcel Dekker, New York, 151–206.

HASSAN A N, FRANK J F, FARMER M A, SCHMIDT K A, SHALABI S I (1995), 'Formation of yoghurt microstructure and three-dimensional visualisation as determined by confocal laser scanning microscopy', *J Dairy Sci*, 78, 2629–2636.

HASSAN A N, FRANK J F, SCHMIDT K A, SHALABI S I (1996), 'Textural properties of yogurt made with encapsulated nonropy lactic cultures', *J Dairy Sci*, 79, 2098–2103.

HELLINGA C, SOMSEN D J, KOENRADS J P J M (1986), 'Viscosity of stirred yogurt: Modern techniques useful in analysing and improving routine measurements', *Neth Milk Dairy J*, 40, 217–240.

HEMAR Y, LAW A J R, HORNE D S, LEAVER J (2000), 'Rheological investigations of alkaline-induced gelation of skimmed milk and reconstituted skimmed milk concentrates', *Food Hydrocoll*, 14, 197–201.

HOFFMANN W, SCHMIDT R, BUCHHEIM W (1997), 'Herstellung von fettreduziertem, stichfestem Joghurt mit Molkenproteinprodukten und schleimbildenden Kulturen', *Kieler Milchw Forschungsber*, 49, 113–133.

HOLT C (1993), 'Primary and secondary structures of caseins', in Dickinson E and Walstra P, *Food Colloids and Polymers: Stability and Mechanical Properties*, Royal Society of Chemistry, Cambridge, 167–172.

HOLT C, HORNE D S (1996), 'The hairy casein micelle: evolution of the concept and its implications for dairy technology', *Neth Milk Dairy J*, 50, 85–111.

HORNE D S (1998), 'Casein interactions: casting light on the black boxes, the structure in dairy products', *Int Dairy J*, 8, 171–177.

HORNE D S (1999), 'Formation and structure of acidified milk gels', *Int Dairy J*, 9, 261–268.

HUTKINS R W (2001), 'Metabolism of starter cultures', in Marth E H and Steele J L, *Applied Dairy Microbiology*, Marcel Dekker, New York, 207–241.

JAROS D, ROHM H, HAQUE A, BONAPARTE C, KNEIFEL W (2002a), 'Influence of the starter culture on the relationship between dry matter content and physical properties of set-style yogurt', *Milchwissenschaft*, 57, 325–328.

JAROS D, HAQUE A, KNEIFEL W, ROHM H (2002b), 'Influence of the starter culture on the relationship between dry matter content and physical properties of stirred yogurt', *Milchwissenschaft*, 57, 447–450.

JELEN P, BUCHHEIM W, PETERS K H (1987), 'Heat stability and use of milk with modified casein: whey protein content in yoghurt and cultured milk products', *Milchwissenschaft*, 42, 418–421.

JENSEN R G (1995), 'Introduction', in Jensen R G, *Handbook of Milk Composition*, Academic Press, San Diego, CA, 1–3.

KALAB M (1979), 'Microstructure of dairy foods. 1. Milk products based on protein', *J Dairy Sci*, 62, 1352–1364.

KALAB M (1993), 'Practical aspects of electron microscopy in dairy research', *Food Structure*, 12, 95–114.

KEOGH M K, O'KENNEDY B T (1998), 'Rheology of stirred yogurt as affected by added milk fat, protein and hydrocolloids', *J Food Sci*, 63, 108–112.

KESSLER H G (1996), *Lebensmittel- und Bioverfahrenstechnik – Molkereitechnologie*, A Kessler, München.

KNEIFEL W, ULBERTH F, ERHARD F, JAROS D (1992), 'Aroma profiles and sensory properties of yogurt and yogurt-related products. 1. Screening of commercially available starter cultures', *Milchwissenschaft*, 46, 362–365.

KULKARNI S, HUß M, KESSLER H G, PLOCK J (1990), 'Herstellung von Sahnejoghurt unter Einsatz von Molkenkonzentrat – Einflüsse von Prozeßparametern', *dmz Deutsche Molkereizeitung*, 27, 888–893.

LANKES H, OZER H B, ROBINSON R K (1998), 'The effect of elevated milk solids and incubation temperature on the physical properties of natural yoghurt', *Milchwissenschaft*, 53, 510–513.

LAW A J R (1996), 'Effect of heat treatment and acidification on the dissociation of bovine casein micelles', *J Dairy Res*, 63, 35–48.

LAWS A P, MARSHALL V M (2001), 'The relevance of exopolysaccharides to the rheological properties in milk fermented with ropy strains of lactic acid bacteria', *Int Dairy J*, 11, 709–721.

LAYE I, KARLESKIND D, MORR C V (1993), 'Chemical, microbiological and sensory properties of plain nonfat yogurt', *J Food Sci*, 58, 991–995, 1000.

LORENZEN P C, MAUTNER A, SCHLIMME E (1999), 'Effect of enzymatic crosslinking of milk proteins on the resulting properties of yogurt products', *Kieler Milchw Forschungsber*, 51, 89–97.

LUCEY J A (2001), 'The relationship between rheological parameters and whey separation in milk gels', *Food Hydrocoll*, 15, 603–608.

LUCEY J A, SINGH H (1998), 'Formation and physical properties of acid milk gels: a review', *Food Res Int*, 30, 529–542.

LUCEY J A, VAN VLIET T, GROLLE K, GEURTS T, WALSTRA P (1997), 'Properties of acid casein gels made by acidification with glucono-δ-lactone. 2. Syneresis, permeability and microstructural properties', *Int Dairy J*, 7, 389–397.

LUCEY J A, TAMEHANA M, SINGH R, MUNRO P A (1998a), 'Effect of interactions between denatured whey proteins and casein micelles on the formation and rheological properties of acid skim milk gels', *J Dairy Res*, 65, 555–567.

LUCEY J A, MUNRO P A, SINGH H (1998b), 'Whey separation in acid skim milk gels made with glucono-δ-lactone: effects of heat treatment and gelation temperature', *J Texture Stud*, 29, 413–426.

LUCEY J A, MUNRO P A, SINGH H (1999), 'Effects of heat treatment and whey protein addition on the rheological properties and structure of acid skim milk gels', *Int Dairy J*, 9, 275–279.

MAHAUT M, KOROLCZUK J (1992), 'Effect of whey protein addition and heat treatment of milk on the viscosity of UF fresh cheese', *Milchwissenschaft*, 47, 157–159.

MARSHALL V M, RAWSON H L (1999), 'Effects of exopolysaccharide-producing strains of thermophilic lactic acid bacteria on the texture of stirred yoghurt', *Int J Food Sci Technol*, 34, 137–143.

MARSHALL V M, TAMIME A Y (1997), 'Starter cultures employed in the manufacture of biofermented milks', *Int J Dairy Technol*, 50, 35–41.

MARTIN N C, SKOKANOVA J, LATRILLE E, BEAL C, CORRIEU G (1999), 'Influence of fermentation and storage conditions on the sensory properties of plain low fat stirred yogurts', *J Sensory Stud*, 14, 139–160.

MATALON M E, SANDINE W E (1986), '*Lactobacillus bulgaricus*, *Streptococcus thermophilus* and yogurt: a review', *Cult Dairy Prod J*, 21, 6–12.

MCMANUS W R, MCMAHON D J, OBERG C J (1993), 'High-resolution scanning electron microscopy of milk products: a new sample preparation procedure', *Food Structure*, 12, 475–482.

MEISEL H (1989), 'Neue Aspekte zur nutritiven Qualität von Milchprotein', *Alimenta*, 28, 3–7.

MISTRY V V (2001), 'Fermented milks and cream', in Marth E L and Steele J L, *Applied Dairy Microbiology*, Marcel Dekker, New York, 301–326.

MISTRY V V, HASSAN H N (1992), 'Manufacture of nonfat yogurt from a high milk protein powder', *J Dairy Sci*, 75, 947–957.

MODLER H W, LARMOND M E, LIN C S, FROEHLICH D, EMMONS D B (1983), 'Physical and sensory properties of yogurt stabilized with milk proteins', *J Dairy Sci*, 66, 422–429.

MOREIRA M, ABRAHAM A, DE ANTONI G (2000), 'Technological properties of milks fermented with lactic acid bacteria at suboptimal temperature', *J Dairy Sci*, 83, 395–400.

MORRIS H A, GHALEB H M, SMITH D E, BASTIAN E D (1995), 'A comparison of yogurts fortified with nonfat dry milk and whey protein concentrates', *Cult Dairy Prod J*, 30, 2–4

MUIR D D, HUNTER E A (1992), 'Sensory evaluation of fermented milks: vocabulary development and the relations between sensory properties and composition and between acceptability and sensory properties', *J Soc Dairy Technol*, 45, 73–80.

O'DONNELL H J, BUTLER F (2002), 'Time-dependent viscosity of stirred yogurt. Part I: Couette flow', *J Food Eng*, 51, 249–254.

OZER B H, ATAMER M (1999), 'Some properties of yogurts produced from milk preserved by hydrogen peroxide', *Milchwissenschaft*, 54, 628–631.

OZER B H, BELL A E, GRANDISON A S, ROBINSON R K (1998), 'Rheological properties of concentrated yogurt (labneh)', *J Texture Stud*, 29, 67–79.

OZER B H, STENNING R A, GRANDISON A S, ROBINSON R K (1999), 'Rheology and microstructure of labneh (concentrated yogurt)', *J Dairy Sci*, 82, 682–689.

PARNELL-CLUNIES E M, KAKUDA Y, MULLEN K, ARNOTT D R, DEMAN J M (1986), 'Physical properties of yogurt: a comparison of vat versus continuous heating systems of milk', *J Dairy Sci*, 69, 2593–2603.

PEARCE R J (1995), 'Food functionality: success or failure for dairy based ingredients', *Aust J Dairy Technol*, 50, 15–23.

PETRY S, FURLAN S, CREPEAU M J, CERNING J, DESMAZEAUD M (2000), 'Factors affecting exocellular polysaccharide production by *Lactobacillus delbrueckii* subsp. *bulgaricus* grown in a chemically defined medium', *Appl Env Microbiol*, 66, 3427–3431.

PLEIJSIER M T, DE BONT P W, VREEKER R, LEDEBOER A M (2000), 'Functional properties of exocellular polysaccharides in dairy based foods', in Fischer P, Marti I, Windhab E, *Proc. 2nd Int. Symp. on Food Rheology and Structure*, Zurich, Swiss Federal Institute of Technology, 326–330.

PLOCK J, HUß M, KENNEL R, KESSLER H G (1992), 'Bedeutung des Homogenisierens bei der Herstellung fetthaltiger Sauermilchprodukte', *dmz Deutsche Milchwirtschaft*, 49, 1558–1563.

POMPEI C, CASIRAGHI E, LUCISIANO M (1994), 'A method for the evaluation of curd syneresis', *Milchwissenschaft*, 49, 562–565.

RAJAGOPAL S N, SANDINE W E (1990), 'Associative growth and proteolysis of *Streptococcus thermophilus* and *Lactobacillus bulgaricus* in skim milk', *J Dairy Sci*, 73, 894.

RAMASWAMY H S, BASAK S (1991), 'Time dependent stress decay of stirred yogurt', *Int Dairy J*, 1, 17–31.

RAMASWAMY H S, BASAK S (1992), 'Pectin and raspberry concentrate effects on the rheology of stirred commercial yogurt', *J Food Sci*, 57, 357–360.

RAO M A, COOLEY H J (1992), 'Rheological behaviour of tomato pastes in steady and dynamic shear', *J Texture Stud*, 23, 415–425.

ROEFS S P F M, DE GROOT-MOSTERT A E A, VAN VLIET T (1990), 'Structure of acid casein gels. 1. Formation and model of gel network', *Colloids and Surfaces*, 50, 141–159.

ROHM H (1992), 'Viscosity determination of yogurt', *Food Sci Technol*, 25, 297–301.

ROHM H (1993a), 'Influence of dry matter fortification on flow properties of yogurt. 2. Time-dependent behaviour', *Milchwissenschaft*, 48, 614–617.

ROHM H (1993b), 'Viscoelastic properties of set-style yogurt', *Rheology*, 3, 173–182.

ROHM H (1995), 'Effect of starter cultures on rheology of yogurt', in Dickinson E, *Food Macromolecules and Colloids*, Royal Society of Chemistry, London, 492–494.

ROHM H, KOVAC A (1994), 'Effects of starter cultures on linear viscoelastic and physical properties of yogurt gels', *J Texture Stud*, 25, 311–329.

ROHM H, KOVAC A (1995), 'Effects of starter cultures on small deformation rheology of stirred yogurt', *Food Sci Technol*, 28, 319–322.

ROHM H, SCHMID W (1993), 'Influence of dry matter fortification on flow properties of yogurt. 1. Evaluation of flow curves', *Milchwissenschaft*, 48, 556–559.

ROHM H, KOVAC A, KNEIFEL W (1994), 'Effects of starter cultures on sensory properties of set-style yogurt determined by Quantitative Descriptive Analysis', *J Sensory Stud*, 9, 171–186.

ROLLEMA H S (1992), 'Casein association and micelle formation', in Fox P F (ed), *Advanced Dairy Chemistry*, Volume 1, *Proteins*, Elsevier Applied Science, London, 111–140.

RÖNNEGARD E, DEJMEK P (1993), 'Development and breakdown of structure in yogurt studied by oscillatory rheological measurements', *Lait*, 73, 371–379.

ROSS-MURPHY S B (1994), 'Rheological methods', in Ross-Murphy S B, *Physical Techniques for the Study of Food Biopolymers*, Blackie Academic, Glasgow, 343–392.

RUAS-MADIEDO P, HUGENHOLTZ J, ZOON P (2002), 'An overview of the functionality of exopolysaccharides produced by lactic acid bacteria', *Int Dairy J*, 12, 163–171.

SAVELLO P A, DARGAN R A (1995), 'Improved yogurt physical properties using ultrafiltration and very-high temperature heating', *Milchwissenschaft*, 50, 86–90.

SAVELLO P A, DARGAN R A (1997), 'Reduced yogurt syneresis using ultrafiltration and very-high temperature heating', *Milchwissenschaft*, 52, 573–577.

SCHELLHAASS S M, MORRIS H A (1985), 'Rheological and scanning electron microscopy examination of skim milk gels obtained by fermentation with ropy and non-ropy strains of lactic acid bacteria', *Food Microstructure*, 4, 279–284.

SCHKODA P (1999), *Serumbindung und Rheologie fermentierter Milchprodukte – Modellierung von Strukturparametern*, VDI-Verlag, Düsseldorf.

SCHKODA P, HECHLER A, HINRICHS J (2001), 'Influence of the protein content on structural characteristics of stirred fermented milk', *Milchwissenschaft*, 56, 19–22.

SCHMIDT T R, AHMED E M (1972), 'Textural and elastic properties of Irish potatoes. II. Elastic properties', *J Texture Stud*, 3, 18–30.

SCHMIDT D G, BOTH P (1982), 'Location of α_{s1}-, β- and κ-casein in artificial casein micelles', *Milchwissenschaft*, 37, 336–337.

SEBASTIANI H, ZELGER G (1998), 'Texture formation by thermophilic lactic acid bacteria', *Milchwissenschaft*, 53, 15–19.

SHARMA S K, DALGLEISH D G (1994), 'Effect of heat treatments on the incorporation of milk serum proteins into the fat globule membrane of homogenized milk', *J Dairy Res*, 61, 375–385.

SKRIVER A (1995), 'Characterization of stirred yogurt by rheology, microscopy and sensory analysis', PhD Thesis, The Royal Veterinary and Agricultural University, Copenhagen.

SKRIVER A, ROEMER H, QVIST K B (1993), 'Rheological characterization of stirred yogurt: viscometry', *J Texture Stud*, 24, 185–198.

SKRIVER A, BUCHHEIM W, QVIST K B (1995), 'Electron microscopy of stirred yoghurt: ability of three techniques to visualize eko-polysaccharides from ropy strains', *Milchwissenschaft*, 50, 683–686.

SKRIVER A, HOLSTBORG J, QVIST K B (1999), 'Relation between sensory texture analysis and rheological properties of stirred yogurt', *J Dairy Res*, 66, 609–618.

SMITS P, VAN BROUWERSHAVEN J H (1980), 'Heat-induced association of β-lactoglobulin and casein micelles', *J Dairy Res*, 47, 313–325.

SNOEREN T H M, DAMMAN A J, KLOK H J (1982), 'The viscosity of skim milk concentrates', *Neth Milk Dairy J*, 36, 305–316.

STAFF M C (1998), 'Cultured milk and fresh cheeses', in Early R, *The Technology of Dairy Products*, Blackie Academic, London, 123–157.

STANLEY G (1998), 'Microbiology of fermented milk products', in Early R, *The Technology of Dairy Products*, Blackie Academic, London, 50–80.

STEVENTON A J, PARKINSON C J, FRYER P J, BOTTOMLEY R C (1990), 'The rheology of yogurt', in Carter R E, *Rheology of Food, Pharmaceutical and Biological Materials with General Rheology*, Elsevier Applied Science, London, 196–210.

STONE H, SIDEL J, OLIVER S, WOOLSEY A, SINGLETON R C (1974), 'Sensory evaluation by quantitative descriptive analysis', *Food Technol*, 8, 24–32.

TAMIME A Y, DEETH H C (1980), 'Yogurt: technology and biochemistry', *J Food Prot*, 43, 939–977.

TAMIME A Y, MARSHALL V M E (1997), 'Microbiology and technology of fermented milks', in Law B A, *Microbiology and Biochemistry of Cheese and Fermented Milk*, Chapman & Hall, London, 57–152.

TAMIME A Y, KALAB M, DAVIES G (1984), 'Microstructure of set-style yoghurt manufactured from cow's milk fortified by various methods', *Food Microstructure*, 3, 83–92.

TAMIME A Y, DAVIES G, CHEHADE A S, MAHDI H A (1991), 'The effect of processing temperatures on the quality of labneh made by ultrafiltration', *J Soc Dairy Technol*, 44, 99–103.

TAMIME A Y, BARRANTES E, SWORD A M (1996), 'The effect of starch based fat substitutes on the microstructure of set-style yogurt made from reconstituted skim milk powder', *J Soc Dairy Technol*, 49, 1–10.

TIU C, BOGER D V (1974), 'Complete rheological characterization of time dependent food products', *J Texture Stud*, 5, 329–338.

TRACHOO N, MISTRY V V (1998), 'Application of ultrafiltered sweet buttermilk and sweet buttermilk powder in the manufacture of nonfat and low fat yogurts', *J Dairy Sci*, 81, 3163–3171.

VAN CALSTEREN M R, PAU-ROBLOT C, BEGIN A, ROY D (2002), 'Structure determination of the exopolysaccharide produced by *Lactobacillus rhamnosus* strains RW-9595M and R', *Biochem J*, 363, 7–17.

VAN DIJK H J M, WALSTRA P (1986), 'Syneresis of curd. 2. One-dimensional analysis of rennet curd in constant condition', *Neth Milk Dairy J*, 40, 3–30.

VAN HOOYDONK A C M, HAGEDOORN H G, BOERRITGER I J (1986), 'pH-Induced physico-chemical changes of casein micelles in milk and their effect on renneting. 1. Effect of acidification on physico-chemical properties', *Neth Milk Dairy J*, 40, 281–296.

VAN MARLE M E, ZOON P (1995), 'Permeability and rheological properties of microbially and chemically acidified skim-milk gels', *Neth Milk Dairy J*, 49, 47–65.

VAN MARLE E M, VAN DEN ENDE D, DE KRUIF C G, MELLEMA J (1999), 'Steady-shear viscosity of stirred yogurts with varying ropiness', *J Rheol*, 43, 1643–1662.

VAN VLIET T, DENTENER-KIKKERT A (1982), 'Influence of the composition of the milk fat globule membrane on the rheological properties of acid skim milk gels', *Neth Milk Dairy J*, 36, 261–265.

VISSER H (1992), 'A new casein model and its consequences for pH and temperature effects on the properties of milk', in Visser H, *Protein Interactions*, VCH, Weinheim, 135–165.

VLAHOPOULOU I, BELL A E (1995), 'Preliminary studies on the gelation processes of fermented and GDL-acidified bovine and caprine milk systems', *J Soc Dairy Technol*, 48, 112–116.

WALSTRA P (1990), 'On the stability of casein micelles', *J Dairy Sci*, 73, 1965–1979.

WALSTRA P (1995), 'Physical chemistry of milk fat globules', in Fox P F, *Advanced Dairy Chemistry*, Volume 2: *Lipids*, Chapman & Hall, London, 131–178.

WALSTRA P, JENNESS R (1984), *Dairy Chemistry and Physics*, John Wiley & Sons, New York.

WALSTRA P, GEURTS T J, NOOMEN A, JELLEMA A, VAN BOEKEL M A J S (1999), *Dairy Technology*, Marcel Dekker, New York.

WELTMAN R N (1943), 'Breakdown of thixotropic structure as a function of time', *J Appl Phys*, 14, 343–350.

YUCUCHI H, GOTO T, OKONOYI S (1992), 'The nutritional and physiological value of fermented milks and lactic drinks', in Nakazawa Y, *Functions of Fermented Milks: Challenges for the Health Sciences*, Elsevier Science, London, 217–246.

9

Factors affecting the shelf-life of milk and milk products

D. D. Muir and J. M. Banks, Hannah Research Institute, UK

9.1 Introduction

There is no straightforward objective definition of the shelf-life of milk and milk products because criteria that may be appropriate for one product may be inadequate for another. For this reason, we choose to define shelf-life as the period following manufacture during which the product meets consumer expectations. This definition is somewhat elastic, not least because the expectations of individual consumers vary. Nevertheless, its utility lies in the recognition that, in a diverse range of products, the end of shelf-life may be signalled by changes in appearance, smell or flavour. The essence of the definition is that a *change* in quality of sufficient magnitude to influence consumer opinion has taken place.

Changes imply transformations and these may be physicochemical, chemical or biochemical in nature. Examples of such processes include the following:

- *Physicochemical* – creaming of fat, gelation of protein solutions, syneresis of curds and crystallisation of minerals.
- *Chemical* – non-enzymic browning and oxidation of fat.
- *Biochemical* – growth of microorganisms, enzymic degradation, ripening of cheese and fermentation.

This chapter will highlight the various transformations that tend to limit the shelf-life of milk and milk products. As a general background, brief consideration will be given to the composition and important chemical properties of milk components. The bacterial flora of milk with reference to their potential for limiting shelf-life will then be considered and the effect of temperature on growth of spoilage bacteria discussed. Finally, examples will be given of the factors influencing the shelf-life of specific products together with comments on methods of control.

9.2　Chemical composition and principal reactions of milk

Milk was designed by nature to provide complete nourishment for the newborn and, as might be expected, is a highly complex mixture. The four main chemical classes present in milk, irrespective of species, are fat, protein, carbohydrate and mineral and each component plays a key nutritional role. In Europe, most milk is now derived from the dairy cow and the composition of typical mid-lactation milk is shown in Table 9.1. Transformation of milk protein and fat is responsible for most of the changes that govern shelf-life.

9.2.1　Milk protein

The proteins in milk are classified into two families, caseins and whey proteins. Their respective abundances are shown in Table 9.2. Casein is the most important group constituting over 80% of the protein in bovine milk in mid-lactation milk.

Casein, the major milk protein is split into five main classes, α_{s1}-, α_{s2}-, β-, γ- and κ-caseins, as shown in Table 9.3. The primary structure of every casein in bovine milk has been defined. All the caseins are modestly sized and are not

Table 9.1　Average composition of milk

Constituent	Concentration ($g\,l^{-1}$)	Proportion solids (%)
Fat	37.0	28.9
Protein: casein	27.6 } 34.0	26.6
whey protein	6.4	
Non-protein nitrogen	1.9	1.5
Lactose	48.0	37.5
Ash	7.0	5.5
Total solids	127.0	100.0

Table 9.2　Protein distribution in skim milk

Milk protein	(%)
Casein	82.2
Whey protein	
β-lactoglobulin	9.6
α-lactalbumin	3.8
bovine serum albumin	1.4
minor 'proteins'	3.0

Table 9.3 Composition and properties of casein fraction

Fraction	Molecular weight[a]	Proportion whole casein (%)	Serine phosphate residues	Calcium sensitivity	Sugar residues
α_{s1}	23 000	38.1	7–9	++	–
α_{s2}	25 000	10.2	10–13	+++	–
β	24 000	35.7	5	+	–
γ	11 600–20 500	3.2	0 or 1	–	–
κ	1 980	12.8	1	–	+

[a] Molecular weight of monomer.

Table 9.4 Minerals in milk

	Total (mmol l^{-1})	Diffusible (mmol l^{-1})
Calcium	30.1	9.5
Magnesium	5.1	3.3
Sodium	25.5	–
Potassium	36.8	–
Chloride	30.3	–
Inorganic phosphate	20.9	11.2
Citrate	9.8	9.2
Zinc, selenium, molybdenum and iodine	trace levels	

thought to possess an organised structure. As a result, the caseins cannot be denatured, for example by heating. The caseins are phosphoproteins (Table 9.3) and the extent of their reaction with multivalent ions such as calcium is very dependent on the number of serine phosphate groups present on the molecule. This ability to interact with other ions is an important aspect of the functionality of caseins, e.g. in cheese making or in the production of fermented products. In addition it plays an important role in determining the stability of in-can sterilised milk products (evaporated milk and cream) and is the primary cause of age gelation in UHT sterilised milks.

In raw milk, caseins are associated with calcium and phosphate into small particles – with an average size of approximately 100 nm – called micelles. The mineral content of milk is shown in Table 9.4. About two-thirds of the calcium and about half the phosphate are bound to the colloidal, i.e. micellar, phase. The partition of calcium (and phosphate) between the micellar and the serum phase may be manipulated by technological means. Calcium can be withdrawn from the micelle by addition of sequestrants, such as trisodium citrate, hexametaphosphate or polyphosphate. In the micellar structure there is a network of α_s-casein and calcium phosphate within which β-casein is held. The surface of the micelle is rich in κ-casein but this component is also located within the micellar structure. The 'hairy' micelle model best fits the known behaviour of casein micelles.

Another important property of caseins is derived from their primary structure.

Within the caseins, the acidic amino groups (carboxyl and ester phosphate) are unevenly distributed along the polypeptide chains. As a result, the proteins have highly charged polar regions and contrasting domains of a hydrophobic nature. Such heterogeneity confers very good emulsifying properties on the molecules because the polar regions can associate with the aqueous phase while the hydrophobic regions bind well to lipids. Thus the proteins stabilise fat droplets in solutions or in semi-solid matrices such as meat emulsions.

In contrast, the whey proteins are globular proteins with classical tertiary structures. The structure of the main whey protein, β-lactoglobulin, is stabilised by disulphide bridges. Such links are disrupted by heat treatment above 65 °C and, as a result, the proteins are denatured. On the other hand, undenatured whey proteins are not greatly affected by multivalent ions and do not readily precipitate.

Four types of reaction can influence the functional properties of milk protein:

1   Protein degradation can take place as a result of attack by milk plasmin or by bacterial enzymes.
2   The second important reaction of milk proteins occurs when they react with reducing sugars – the Maillard reaction. This reaction is characterised by browning of products but, in its early stages, there is a significant loss of nutritive value because lysine, an essential amino acid, reacts very readily with reducing sugars. The extent of loss of lysine depends on the severity of heat treatment, the pH of the product and the amount of reducing sugar present. By careful avoidance of such prejudicial conditions during manufacture, the nutritive value of milk proteins can be conserved. Nevertheless, the Maillard reaction can limit the shelf-life of dried milk products.
3   Acidification forms the basis of production of all fermented milks. The gels of fermented milks, such as yoghurt and quarg, are formed by acidification of milk. As the pH is reduced, the casein precipitates selectively. The first signs of aggregation occur around pH 5 and once the pH falls to 4.6 all the casein becomes insoluble.
4   Another property of casein is its ability to aggregate in the presence of calcium under specific conditions. As described above, casein micelles are stabilised by a κ-casein that behaves like a 'hairy' layer at the micellar surface. Chymosin, the principal enzyme in calf rennet, can selectively break down the surface κ-casein and reduce micellar stability. If the temperature of the rennet-treated milk is above 10 °C and calcium is present (as it always is in milk, viz. Table 9.4), aggregation takes place and a rennet gel is formed.

9.2.2   Milk fat

Milk fat consists almost entirely of triglycerides (triacylglycerols), i.e. esters of fatty acids with the molecule glycerol. Fatty acids in milk are derived from a number of sources and the pathways from feed to milk are not straightforward. Fat consumed by the cow is first hydrolysed to free fatty acid in the rumen or first stomach. Because of the strongly reducing conditions in the rumen, unsaturated fatty acids are hydrogenated. The saturated acid then passes to the gut where it is absorbed into the circulating blood. Some fatty acid is stored in the animal's fat reserves, after reconversion to triglyceride. Another portion is broken down to provide energy for the animal, while the remainder passes to the mammary gland where it can be re-esterified into milk triglyceride. Such pre-formed fatty acids are predominantly of chain length 16 or higher, though chain lengths of 12 and 14 can be found when the cow is fed diets rich in these acids. However, the cow also has the ability to synthesise fatty acids with chain lengths from 4 to 16 in the mammary gland. These acids can account for over a third of the total triglyceride. A further complication arises from the presence of a specific enzyme in several tissues of the cow. This enzyme is capable of taking a saturated fatty acid of chain length 18 (stearic acid) and converting it to the mono-unsaturate (oleic acid). As a result of this series of transformations the fatty acid composition of milk is fairly heterogeneous, as shown in Table 9.5. The distribution of the fatty acids in the triglycerides adds another layer of complexity, because the distribution among the three potential sites for esterification is not random. The short chain acids are preferentially linked to the hydroxyl group at one end of the molecule.

As with milk protein, fat occurs naturally as a complex structure. Milk fat globules range in size from 0.1 to 12 μm in diameter (median 3 μm). The globules are spherical droplets of triglyceride coated by a double membrane rich in phospholipid. The milk fat globule membrane (MFGM) is fragile and is damaged and disrupted by physical treatment. This reaction forms the basis of butter-making. By arranging optimum conditions for disruption of globule membrane, the droplets are induced to clump. The fat surface exposed by

Table 9.5   Fatty acid composition of April milk

Fatty acid	Mole (%)
4:0	9.6
6:0	4.0
8:0	2.0
10:0	3.5
12:0	3.6
14:0	9.9
14:1	2.1
16:0	24.7
16:1	3.2
18:0	10.5
18:1	22.6
18:2	3.0
18:3	1.4

removal of the membrane is very hydrophobic and quickly associates with exposed fat surface on other droplets. This process is called churning. The clumps of granules are first washed to remove protein, lactose and minerals (as buttermilk) then physically worked to yield a plastic mass – butter.

Milk fat is susceptible to several important reactions:

- Raw milk has an abundance of lipoprotein lipase, an enzyme that will rapidly hydrolyse milk fat to free fatty acids.
- Bacterial lipase causes serious degradation of milk fat.
- The delicate MFGM is also susceptible to enzymatic degradation.
- Another important reaction is oxidation. Reaction is initiated by free radicals of oxygen at the unsaturated bonds (especially conjugated double bonds) in fatty acids. The reaction is catalysed by light and by heavy metals such as copper. Phospholipids in milk are more prone to attack in milk than are the triglycerides which are mostly saturated. Lipid oxidation is best controlled by exclusion of oxygen, light and potential contaminants, hence packaging plays a key role.
- Milk fat droplets in raw milk are readily susceptible to creaming. The rate at which fat globules rise depends on the density difference between the fat globule and the serum, the viscosity of the serum which is influenced by temperature, the concentration of a cold agglutinin and fat globule size. In practice, creaming is inhibited by reduction of the fat globule size by homogenisation. The milk fat globules are reduced in size by pumping at very high pressure (up to 400 bar) through a small slit or orifice. The size reduction results in an increase in specific surface area and this newly-formed fat surface is immediately coated with milk protein from the serum phase. The threshold globule size below which creaming does not occur is *ca.* 0.8 μm diameter. Control of fat emulsion size is critical in products that are prone to creaming.

9.3   Bacteria in milk and related enzyme activity

9.3.1   Psychrotrophic Gram-negative bacteria

The bacteria in freshly drawn milk from a healthy cow are largely derived from the environment within which the cow is kept – the byre and milking parlour – and from the equipment through which the milk passes and in which it is stored. The majority of milk in Western Europe is cooled and refrigerated promptly after milking. As a result, conditions favour the survival and subsequent growth of organisms adapted to a low-temperature environment. Many such bacteria have an optimum growth temperature between 20 and 30 °C but also grow, albeit more slowly, at refrigeration temperature. They are known collectively as psychrotrophs.

Psychrotrophic bacteria from farm bulk tanks and from creamery silos have been extensively studied because of their potential commercial importance.

Table 9.6   Psychrotrophic Gram-negative bacteria in milk and associated enzyme activity

Bacterial genus	Isolates in genus (%)		Isolates with stated activity (%)		
	Creamery	Farm	Lipolytic	Proteolytic	Lipolytic + proteolytic
Pseudomonas					
fluorescing	33.5	50.5	5	2	71
non-fluorescing	44.1	31.5	32	1	11
Enterobacteriacea, Aeromonas,	8.5	15.8	2	2	31
Pasturella or *Vibrio*					
Acinetobacter, Moraxella or	6.2	0.0	5	9	36
Brucella					
Flavobacterium	4.0	1.3	6	6	24
Chromobacterium	2.2	0.0	25	6	41
Alcaligines	1.5	0.9	0	0	92
Number isolates	735	85			

Typical results for creamery silo milk collected in South-west Scotland and from a farm bulk tank are presented in Table 9.6. The Gram-negative bacteria, which make up over 90% of the total flora, are classified according to genus. Bacteria of the genus *Pseudomonas* were by far the most common organisms, about half being of the fluorescent type. The main species *Pseudomonas fluorescens* is characterised by the production of a diffusible fluorescent pigment during growth on an appropriate medium. Although the optimum temperature for growth lies between 25 and 30 °C, pseudomonads will also grow at temperatures just above freezing. The genera are widely distributed in water and in the soil. The second most common family of psychrotrophic bacteria in raw milk is that of the *Enterobacteriaciae*. These organisms are also small, motile, Gram-negative rods. Their optimum growth temperature tends to be higher (i.e. > 30 °C) than that of the pseudomonads but they adapt well to growth at refrigeration temperature. The usual source of coliform contamination of raw milk is from the digestive tract of the cow via faecal contamination of the bedding or udder. Some strains of *Escherichia coli* produce verotoxins and constitute a food-poisoning hazard. A number of other types of psychrotroph are also frequently found (Table 9.6), albeit at low frequency. Included in the list of common contaminants are bacteria of the genera *Flavobacterium, Chromobacterium* and *Alcaligenes*. They are all Gram-negative rods capable of low-temperature growth and, like the pseudomonads, are commonly found in soil and water.

Many of the psychrotrophic bacteria isolated from milk produce extracellular enzymes that degrade milk fat and protein (Table 9.6). Some genera have great destructive potential. For example, over 70% of isolates classified as *P. fluorescens* exhibit both proteolytic and lipolytic activity. At least 20% of all psychrotrophs isolated from raw milk can cause protein breakdown and lipolytic rancidity. It is also worth noting that all genera examined possessed some degree of extracellular degradative activity and thus pose a significant threat to milk quality and to products manufactured from milk.

9.3.2 Heat-resistant bacteria

The psychrotrophic bacteria considered above are almost all killed by modest heat treatment (e.g. pasteurisation, 72 °C/15 seconds). However, some survivors from the natural flora, given suitable conditions, are able to promote spoilage. Bacteria typical of those isolated from milk and cream are shown in Table 9.7. In general, only *Bacillus* spp. and *Corynebacteria* are found in any number, though thermoduric micrococci and lactococci are occasionally recovered. The coryneforms, microccoci and lactococci are usually incapable of further growth in pasteurised product provided the temperature is held below 6 °C. *Bacillus* spp. are the other major thermoduric group of organisms and are of greater technical significance because of their ability to grow under refrigeration conditions. Of the *Bacillus* spp. found, *B. cereus*, *B. licheniformis* and *B. coagulans* predominate. The vegetative cells of the bacilli are readily destroyed by pasteurisation and it is the spore form of the organism which is heat stable. These residual spores may – given the correct conditions – germinate after heat treatment and subsequently grow in pasteurised products. The degradative activity associated with thermoduric bacteria isolated from pasteurised cream is shown in Table 9.7. Coryneforms are largely inactive but the *Bacillus* spp. have, in general, great potential for spoilage. Almost 40% of isolates could degrade both milk fat and protein while 80% of isolates exhibited phospholipase activity. As indicated earlier, phospholipase action can destroy the native MFGM, resulting in destabilisation of the fat emulsion in milk.

In summary, the psychrotrophic thermoduric floras of milk are able to survive pasteurisation, can subsequently grow in product and also possess the

Table 9.7   Heat-resistant bacteria recovered from milk and associated enzyme activity

	Bacillus spp.	*Coryneform*
Proportion isolates, %[a]		
Heated at 63 °C/30 min	54	46
Heated at 80 °C/10 min	61	37
Enzyme activity, %		
Lipolytic only	0	0
Proteolytic only	34.1	3.3
Lipolytic + proteolytic	37.0	10.0
Phospholipase	80.4	0
Tri-butyrin hydrolase	16.8	20.0
Inactive	12.1	66.7
No. isolates	316	30

[a] No Gram-negative organisms were found.

extracellular enzyme activity necessary to induce spoilage. Thus they constitute a significant threat to the shelf-life of pasteurised product.

9.4 Raw milk enzymes

As reported above, the bacterial floras of milk are associated with extracellular enzyme activity which can lead to spoilage of milk and milk products. However, bacterial enzymes are not the only enzymes present in raw milk. Bovine milk is a biologically active product and around 50 different enzyme activities have been reported in clean, freshly drawn milk. Fortunately, only two of these native enzymes have a substantial impact on the quality or shelf-life of milk and milk products. Therefore we will consider only native enzymes with relevant activity.

9.4.1 Lipoprotein lipase

Milk lipase is a lipoprotein lipase that catalyses the breakdown of milk triglycerides to produce free fatty acids (FFAs). Some of these FFAs have low organoleptic thresholds and produce odours and flavours that are described variously as rancid, bitter, soapy or unclean. The purified enzyme is relatively unstable and can be inactivated by heat, ultraviolet light, acid or oxidising reagents. In milk, the association of the enzyme with casein affords some protection but it is generally accepted that the enzyme is almost completely inactivated by high-temperature short-time pasteurisation (i.e. heat treatment at 72 °C for 15 s). In milk, the enzyme is not normally active since the potential substrate – milk fat droplets – is encapsulated by MFGM.

Two distinct types of lipolysis by lipoprotein lipase are recognised. When freshly drawn milk is found to be rancid the condition is referred to as spontaneous lipolysis and is influenced by stage of lactation, season, diet and plane of nutrition. Nevertheless, spontaneous lipolysis is not a determinant of shelf-life because the fresh milk is unacceptable.

On the other hand, induced lipolysis can lead to spoilage of products which have not been heat treated. The key factor for expression of enzyme activity is damage to the MFGM. Two common types of damage occur – first, the membrane may be damaged by physical means such as foaming, agitation or homogenisation; and second, the integrity of the membrane may be prejudiced by temperature cycling. In all cases, the end result is similar: lipolysis proceeds. Thus products which contain active lipase must be treated with extreme care.

9.4.2 Plasmin

Although more than one proteinase has been identified in raw milk, the major proteinase is a serine proteinase with trypsin-like activity called milk plasmin. At acid and neutral pH, the enzyme is stable to pasteurisation but, at alkaline pH, it is rapidly inactivated. Some plasmin activity resists UHT processing (heat treatment at 140°C/3 s). Nevertheless, the occurrence of plasmin is associated with physiological conditions in which the tight junctions in the basal membrane of the mammary gland are 'leaky' and allow some passage of blood components into the milk. For example, in very early lactation, very late lactation and when disease is present in the udder, abnormally high concentrations of plasmin are found in milk. Provided plasmin levels are low in milk, problems will not be manifest in short shelf-life products. However, even modest levels of proteinase activity may be deleterious in long-life products. This aspect of proteinase activity will be discussed later.

9.5   Control of the quality of short shelf-life products

Short shelf-life products are those with a normal shelf-life of three weeks or less. Such products include pasteurised milk and cream, cottage cheese and yoghurt. A range of dairy desserts is also now available. The changes that occur in fresh products after manufacture are associated with physical separation of phases and with the growth of microorganisms. Chemical changes, the action of raw milk enzymes and pathogens, have no significant effect on the shelf-life of fresh dairy products. Physical separation, i.e. creaming, may be a minor consideration and is controlled by reducing the fat globule size by homogenisation. However, the main limitation on shelf-life of fresh dairy products is spoilage by bacteria, moulds and yeasts that grow at refrigeration temperature (<8°C).

9.5.1   Pasteurised milk and cream

The shelf-life of pasteurised milk and cream is governed by the same factors. Historically, shelf-life was limited by the ingress of Gram-negative spoilage bacteria after the pasteurisation process. This problem is now universally recognised and is under strict control. Nevertheless, once the Gram-negative contamination is excluded, steps must still then be taken to moderate the outgrowth, albeit slow at refrigeration temperature, of psychrotrophic spore-forming bacteria.

Post-heat treatment contamination

Gram-negative spoilage bacteria pose a risk to shelf-life. These bacteria are completely inactivated by pasteurisation but are regularly found in pasteurised products. They are post-heat treatment contaminants (PHTC). A schematic of processing sequences for pasteurised milk and cream is shown in Fig. 9.1. The most commonly used sequence relies entirely on pasteurisation to reduce the bacterial load and to inactivate enzymes with degradative potential. Provided the process downstream of the heat exchanger is aseptic, Gram-negative psychrotrophic bacteria play no part in spoilage. However, this situation is seldom realised in practice. Most problems arise in the filling line where open containers

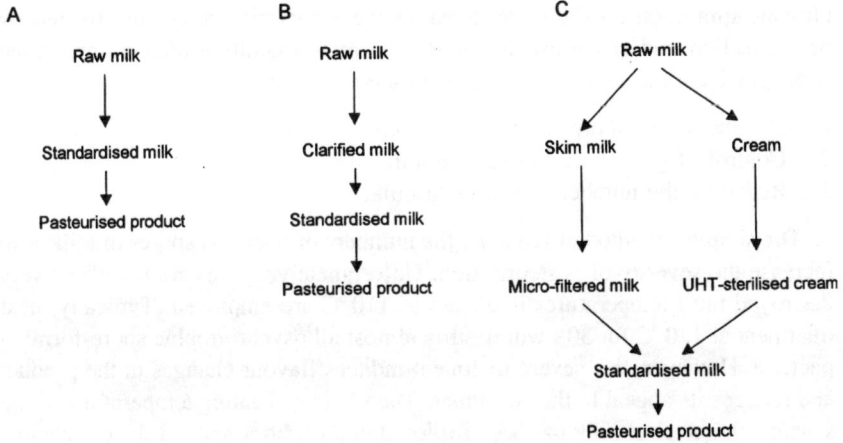

Fig. 9.1 Strategies for manufacture of pasteurised milk

permit ingress of contaminants. This can be kept to a minimum by flooding the filling line with a curtain of sterile air. Nevertheless, disruption of the high-speed packaging line by physical misalignment of containers is inevitable. When this occurs, operator intervention is inevitable and the integrity of the aseptic environment is breached. The key to limiting PHTC lies in stringent exclusion of contamination during the filling and packaging operations. In particular, it is essential to control the number of stoppages on high-speed lines.

Measurement of the extent of PHTC is not straightforward. The number of contaminating bacteria required to induce spoilage depends on the storage temperature of the product. During storage at 8 °C, ten colony-forming units (cfu) per litre of a typical pseudomonad would reduce shelf-life by several days. Because of the difficulty of enumerating low numbers of bacteria, pre-incubation techniques have been introduced to enhance the process. A necessary prerequisite for success is that the growth of Gram-positive organisms is inhibited during the pre-incubation to allow selective growth of the Gram-negative flora. Methods developed in our laboratories use a cocktail of inhibitors (penicillin, crystal violet and nisin) to inhibit the growth of Gram-positive bacteria during pre-incubation at 21 °C for 24/25 hours. After pre-incubation the extent of PHTC may be assessed by enumeration of bacterial numbers using ATP-photometry (rapid), visual counting (rapid), impedimetry (slow) or by plate-counting (slow). The pre-incubation step is rate-limiting and the overall measurement takes at least 25 hours. Nevertheless, routine estimation of the extent of PHTC is an essential tool for quality control.

Heat-resistant organisms
Provided PHTC is absent, the shelf-life of pasteurised milk and cream is anticipated to be at least eight to ten days at storage temperatures in the range 6–8 °C. Outgrowth of spore-forming bacteria (mainly *Bacillus* spp.) forms the

ultimate limitation on shelf-life. Because these bacteria are not inactivated by pasteurisation and can grow, albeit slowly, at refrigeration temperature, three strategies have been explored to control their growth:

1   Destruction of spores by heat treatment.
2   Control of growth by low-temperature storage.
3   Reducing the number of spores in milk.

The simplest method of reducing the numbers of bacterial spores in milk is to increase the severity of pasteurisation. Unfortunately, spores are not effectively destroyed until temperatures in excess of 110 °C are employed. Typically, heat treatment at 120 °C for 30 s will destroy almost all psychrotrophic spore-forming bacteria. However, this severe treatment induces flavour changes in the product and reduces its appeal to the consumer. The effect of heating temperature on the sensory character of milk has been explored in the laboratory and flavour change is detected once the heating temperature exceeds 82 °C (15 s hold). As a result, high-heat treatment is not often used for extending the shelf-life of liquid milk or cream.

Although many *Bacillus* spp. grow at refrigeration temperature, growth is slow. Significant extension of shelf-life can be achieved by storing product at or below 4 °C throughout its shelf-life. This condition is readily achieved at the dairy and in the distribution chain but is likely to be ignored by retailers and customers. Despite scientific and technological advances leading to improved milk quality, the shelf-life of the product can easily be spoiled by temperature abuse.

The best strategy to control spoilage of milk by spore-forming bacteria is to reduce the number of spores in the raw milk supply. This objective can be achieved on the farm by implementing a detailed protocol for the milking operation, e.g. washing and drying of the udder before milking and the use of teat disinfectant have significant effects. Spores can be removed from milk at the processing factory by high-speed centrifugation. The separation exploits the density difference between the spore and the milk serum. However, the process is not absolute and clarifiers and bactofuges – specially designed to remove spores – achieve an efficiency of ca. 95% in a single pass. The equipment is situated upstream of the pasteuriser (e.g. sequence B in Fig. 9.1). Inclusion of a bactofuge in the processing line might extend the shelf-life of pasteurised milk by up to three days. However, there is an inevitable increase in processing cost and the waste stream from the bactofuge or clarifier may be as high as 5% of the raw material. These costs must be offset against the further extension in shelf-life by three days.

Another method of removing bacterial spores from raw milk is to employ membrane filtration. Spores (and vegetative bacterial cells) are readily removed from skim milk using cross-flow ultrafiltration with ceramic membranes with a nominal pore size of 1.4 μm – typically a five log-cycle reduction in bacterial count is achieved. Unfortunately, a proportion of the native milk fat globules is similar in size to bacteria and must be removed by centrifugal separation before the microfiltration step. The cream portion is heat-treated independently. A typical processing sequence (c) is shown in Fig. 9.1. It is claimed that a shelf-life in excess of 21 days can be attained by application of this process. Notwithstanding this substantial increase in shelf-life, the added production cost and complexity of processing cast doubt on the viability of the method.

Although extension of the shelf-life of milk or cream is undoubtedly of benefit to the retailer, present technology has already increased the shelf-life of pasteurised products to such an extent that the consumer may safely buy fresh products on a weekly basis. A guaranteed shelf-life of two weeks blurs the concept of 'freshness' and consumer resistance may develop.

9.6   Yoghurt and fermented milk

Yoghurt and fermented milk are inherently safe. A milk base, usually fortified with protein, is severely heated to denature the whey protein and inoculated with a lactic acid starter. The starter converts lactose to lactic acid and, as a result, the pH of the mixture falls. Several concurrent changes take place – calcium phosphate is solubilised, the integrity of the casein micelles is weakened and, as the isoelectric point of the protein (pH 4.6) approaches, a gel is formed. The yoghurt is then cooled to inhibit further growth of starter. The combination of severe heat treatment, low pH and a dense population of living starter bacteria (typically 10^7–10^9 cfu ml^{-1}) inhibit growth of spoilage bacteria. Nevertheless, yeast and mould may thrive under these conditions and can spoil the product. Precautions to exclude their ingress follow the same principles as avoidance of PHTC described for milk and cream. Notwithstanding these minor problems, yoghurt may deteriorate during storage owing to fermentation continuing after the manufacturing process is complete. The product continues to develop acidity and syneresis may occur with the formation of an unsightly layer of serum. This limits shelf-life but may be avoided by prudent selection of starter bacteria that 'stop' when the product is cooled.

9.6.1   Cottage cheese

Cottage cheese is a minor dairy product but has a high added value. It is manufactured by a process in which a curd is formed, annealed and then coated with a cream dressing. The curd is made by acidification of skim milk by lactic starter bacteria (some rennet is added but this is not the primary cause of clotting). After the curd is cooked and washed, a cream dressing is added, together with fruit, herbs, or spices in some cases.

The shelf-life of the product is essentially determined by the microbiological quality of the cream dressing and microbial status of the other additives, as well as their pH. Particular attention must be paid to the quality of the water used to wash the curd. The factors which affect the shelf-life are similar to those found for other pasteurised milk products. PHTC can be enhanced if the additives –

herbs, etc. – are not properly treated before addition. The problems associated with PHTC can be ameliorated by culturing the cream dressing with lactic acid starter. The resultant drop in pH effectively inhibits growth of most commonly occurring Gram-negative rods. However, yeast and mould can grow at the acid pH values achieved and must be strictly controlled.

9.7   Factors affecting the stability of long shelf-life products

The stability of short shelf-life dairy products depends on the moderation of the growth of and subsequent degradation by spoilage microorganisms. In contrast, the shelf-life of intermediate and long-life dairy products is largely determined by enzymic degradation or by chemical deterioration. In this section, degradative enzymes in dairy products, their heat resistance, methods of detection and strategies for inactivation are considered.

9.7.1   Heat-resistant enzymes

A notable feature of the spoilage bacteria found in raw milk is their almost universal ability to produce extracellular degradative enzymes. While the bacteria – mostly Gram-negative psychrotrophs – are readily killed by pasteurisation, such heat treatment has little effect on the extracellular degradative enzymes. In this section the effect of UHT processing, a heat treatment designed for sterilisation, on proteinase, lipase and phospholipase activity will be discussed. UHT treatment represents the most severe heat treatment applied to dairy products other than those like evaporated milk and sterilised and clotted creams which are in-container sterilised.

An overwhelming proportion of the psychrotrophic floras found in milk produce heat-stable enzymes. Typical results from work conducted in our own laboratories are shown in Table 9.8 for the residual proteinase, lipase and phospholipase C activity found after treating cell-free supernatants at 140 °C for 5 s. Of the bacterial types examined, only *Acinetobacter*, *Aeromonas* and *Bacillus* spp. had residual activities below 10%. The fluorescent pseudomonads that predominate in the flora of refrigerated milk and are enzymically active had residual enzyme activities ranging between 14 and 51%. In addition, very high

Table 9.8   Residual enzyme activity after heat treatment

Type of degradation	Residual enzyme activity (%)	
	Pasteurisation	UHT treatment
Lipolysis	59	31
Proteolysis	66	41
Hydrolysis of phospholipid	30	21

residual levels of phospholipase C survived UHT treatment. When enzymes from 46 isolates exhibiting both proteolytic and lipolytic properties were compared, there was little difference in the ability of the enzyme to withstand either pasteurisation or UHT sterilisation. These results are typical of those found throughout the world for enzymes from ex-farm milk, e.g. enzymes isolated from ex-farm milk in New Zealand were equally heat-resistant.

The effect of stage of growth cycle on the thermostability of cell-free extracts from eight cultures of psychrotrophs grown for 2 to 3 days at 30 °C and at 30 °C for 14 days has been studied. At the extremes of the logarithmic phase of the growth cycle, the heat stability of the enzymes after pasteurisation or UHT treatment was the same. Furthermore, there was little difference in the thermostability of extracellular protease produced by psychrotrophic cultures grown at temperatures ranging from 2 to 30 °C. Therefore, the spoilage bacteria found in raw milk have the potential to produce extracellular degradative enzymes irrespective of the conditions of growth. Once produced, these enzymes are not destroyed by simple heat treatment. Consequently, these enzymes play a key role in the spoilage of intermediate and long shelf-life products.

9.7.2   Potential methods of reducing the effect of heat-stable enzymes

Significant inactivation of extracellular proteinase and lipase is observed above the optimum temperature for maximum activity. For example, heat treatment at 55 °C for 1 h promoted a marked reduction in proteinase activity. The most efficacious combination was UHT treatment followed by low-temperature inactivation at 55 °C for 1 h. Proteinase and lipase activity were reduced by this treatment to 17 and 7% respectively of their original value. Nevertheless, the logistics of holding large volumes of sterile milk for extended periods has precluded the application of these findings. The overwhelming conclusion to be reached is that, once extracellular enzyme activity is present in a product, it is almost impossible to inhibit its action. Attention must therefore be focused on detection of the degradative ability.

Methods of detection of extracellular enzyme activity

The simplest method of detecting extracellular enzyme activity is to use a diffusion assay. Agar or another suitable gel is cast with an indicator component and cell-free supernatant is inoculated into a well cut in the agar. Enzyme activity is then detected either as a zone of clearing or by a colour reaction with a suitable indicator compound. In our experience, skim milk agar is an effective indicator medium for proteolytic activity. Enzyme activity is detected as a zone of clearing or a zone of precipitation around the agar well. The concentration of proteinase present is directly proportional to the square of the true zone radius (that is, allowing for the diameter of the well) and there is also a relation between the area cleared and incubation time. A similar principle may be used for detecting lipase activity using tributyrin agar as the substrate. Furthermore, a high correlation exists between the ability to hydrolyse tributyrin and hydrolysis of buttcrfat. Diffusion using egg yolk emulsion in a blood agar base is also effective for detection of phospholipase activity.

Various colorimetric assay methods have also been developed based on liberation of a dye from a substrate by the enzyme action. The use of hide powder azure for proteinase detection is an apparently robust technique for use in quality control laboratories. It is reported to be sufficiently sensitive to detect the proteinase activity of 2.5×10^6 cfu ml^{-1} of an enzymically active pseudomonad grown in refrigerated whole milk. An equally robust colorimetric assay for lipase is based on the hydrolysis of colourless β-naphthol-caprylate to yield β-naphthol which is readily complexed with an azo dye.

9.8   Control of the stability of long-life milk products

In response to consumer pressure for more sophisticated and diverse food, the number of intermediate and long-life dairy products in the market place has increased significantly. As a result, it is impractical to give comprehensive details of the factors controlling the shelf-life of every product in this class. Moreover, generalisations are dangerous because of the specificity of many shelf-life problems. To illustrate the diversity of the problem, a range of specific examples has been selected and the key factors controlling shelf-life are outlined for each type of product in turn.

9.8.1   Butter and spreads

Preservation of milk fat by conversion into butter involves separation of milk into cream and skim milk. The cream is subject to phase inversion by physical disruption of the natural MFGM. When the membrane is damaged, the fat globule surfaces lose their stability in the aqueous phase and coalesce (or churn) to form fat-rich granules. After washing with clean water to remove milk solids, the granules are physically worked into a uniform mass that is called butter. Butter should comprise at least 80% fat and contain less than 16% water in the form of very small, evenly distributed water droplets.

Control of shelf-life of butter is multifactorial. Raw material quality is especially important because the droplets of aqueous phase entrained in the fat phase have the potential to support bacterial growth. Consequently, heat treatment of raw milk must be efficient and levels of heat-stable extracellular enzyme must be low. The psychrotrophic count in the raw milk should not exceed 5×10^6 cfu ml^{-1}. After heat treatment, the total bacterial count in the cream should be $<10^3$ cfu ml^{-1} with fewer than one yeast, mould or coliform organism detected per ml. Furthermore, dispersion of the water droplets within the butter must be maintained. Coalescence of droplets to form free water offers the potential for rapid spoilage even when contamination is slight.

Even under optimum production conditions the shelf-life of butter is limited at room temperature. Butter is best stored at $-25\,°C$ and sweet cream, salted butter keeps satisfactorily for several years. Oxidation is an important feature of shelf-life. The problem is not as great as might be expected because of the low temperatures employed for prolonged storage. Moreover, slightly oxidised flavours are expected by many consumers and are disguised by salt addition. Nevertheless, shelf-life can be usefully prolonged by exclusion of oxygen during packaging and during storage. Various barrier types of wrapping have been employed with success.

Dairy-based spreads are manufactured by margarine-based technology and may have fat contents from 37.5 to 76.3%. Usually the amount of butterfat present is low but, in contrast to butter, high levels of milk protein may be incorporated to stabilise the product. Because of the high water content, the water in oil emulsion may have limited stability and this limits shelf-life – especially when the product is subject to temperature cycling. A further problem, associated with the large increase in water content is the potential for bacterial growth and spoilage. As a result, the shelf-life of spreads is often limited, especially at storage temperatures above 4 °C or when preservatives are not incorporated in the blend.

9.8.2 Dried milk products

Preservation of milk by drying involves heat treatment to reduce bacterial load, concentration by evaporation to about 45–52% solids before atomisation into a stream of hot air. The milk droplets are converted into a powder within a short time (5–30 s) and are separated from the air-stream by cyclones or bag filters. The essential feature of spray drying is that the moisture content of the powder is reduced to a level at which no bacterial growth occurs and there is little damage to the functionality of the milk components.

Shelf-life is determined by three factors: quality of the raw material, the drying process itself and the conditions under which the powders are stored. The heat treatment applied during processing ensures that the final bacterial load of powder is low. For all but low-heat powders the bacterial load bears little relation to raw milk quality. Nevertheless, heat-resistant, extracellular enzymes are not destroyed. The bacterial count in the raw milk should not exceed a level at which extracellular enzymes from psychrotrophic bacteria can initiate degradation – this threshold is about 2×10^6 cfu ml^{-1}.

The second factor to influence the shelf-life of dried milk is the nature of the drying process. It has been found that the extent of heat treatment applied to the milk during powder manufacture (measured by the extent of whey protein denaturation) is associated with a reduction in the solubility of dried skim milk during storage for six months at 30 °C.

The final and most important factor controlling shelf-life of dried milk is the condition in which it is stored. Although storage conditions are more critical for whole milk powder than for its fat-free analogue, the moisture content of all powders must be maintained in the critical range of 2–4% if deterioration is to be avoided. Skim-milk powder stored in barrier bags at normal ambient temperature has a shelf-life of at least one year and the deterioration observed during storage for a further year is slight. However, if moisture penetrates the powder rapid deterioration occurs even when enzyme activity is absent. The main cause of deterioration is associated with protein/lactose interaction. Such deterioration is exacerbated by storage of powder at high temperature.

In the case of dried whole milk, autoxidation of milk fat affects shelf-life. Where addition of antioxidants is permitted, a useful extension of shelf-life can be achieved but their use is associated with marked consumer resistance. To ameliorate the problem, dried whole milk is given a very severe heat treatment during manufacture. Such heating results in the liberation of free sulphydryl groups in the proteins and these reactive groups compete with lipids for oxidants. In addition, the oxygen level of the powder may be reduced by replacing the air with an inert gas but special rigid packaging must be used, adding significantly to the cost.

In summary, control of moisture content and protection from exposure to oxygen hold the key to extending the shelf-life of powders. Because all the reactions associated with powder deterioration are temperature sensitive, where possible powder should be stored in the cold (4–8 °C) and out of direct strong light.

9.8.3   In-can sterilised cream

In contrast to butter and dried milk, the shelf-life of sterilised cream is determined by chemical reactions involving minerals and protein. Bacteriological and enzymic deterioration are unusual in products sterilised in cans because of the severity of the heat treatment. Almost all the sterilised cream (23% butterfat) manufactured at present in the UK contains the sodium salts of orthophosphate and those of carbonate and citrate. These stabilisers inhibit calcium–protein interaction with considerable success. In addition, storage at refrigeration temperature has beneficial effects. Serum separation is almost completely inhibited and viscosity is increased. There is little penalty in terms of cream texture if storage is carried out at 6 °C but severe problems can occur if sterilised cream is frozen.

9.8.4   Sterile concentrated milk

Full cream evaporated milk is an important commodity in terms of the international trade in dairy products and is usually made to contain 9% fat and 31% total solids. Control of quality must take into account: (a) cream separation during storage, (b) age-gelation and (c) deposition of calcium salts. Cream separation is avoided by manipulation of the homogenisation conditions during manufacture. Homogenisation should be as severe as possible without prejudicing heat stability. Age gelation is inhibited by application of a severe heat treatment to the milk before concentration and by addition of mineral stabiliser. Finally, mineral deposition is moderated by limiting the use of mineral stabiliser. Where very extended shelf-lives are required, the addition of small amounts of lecithin to the concentrate can promote a useful increase in stability. While manufacture of in-can sterilised concentrated milk is well established and the control factors are known, successful manufacture of the equivalent UHT concentrate is more difficult. UHT sterilised concentrate is very susceptible to premature age-gelation and stringent conditions must be applied to the raw material to avoid contamination with bacterial proteinase.

9.8.5 Sterilised UHT processed milks and creams

UHT treatment is based on the principle that the thermal characteristics of bacterial destruction are substantially different from the rates of chemical reaction. By increasing the temperature of heat treatment and reducing exposure time (e.g. to 4 s at 142 °C), equivalent bacterial lethality can be maintained to that used in heat sterilising canned milk or cream but with a significant reduction in chemical interaction such as Maillard browning.

In UHT milk, the main cause of premature spoilage is a result of proteolytic action. Two sources of heat-stable enzyme have been implicated. Although plasmin has been implicated, its concentration in mid-lactation milk from normal, healthy cows is low and it is likely to be of secondary importance in spoilage. On the other hand, enzyme from psychrotrophic bacteria is important and the general rule is that product should not be manufactured from raw milk in which the bacterial load exceeds 10^6 cfu ml^{-1}.

The shelf-life of UHT cream is substantially shorter than that of milk even when proteolysis is absent. For UHT single cream (18% butterfat), the main customer complaint is associated with feathering when the cream is added to hot coffee. The problem has been identified as one of calcium-induced aggregation and can be ameliorated, but not overcome, by the careful use of mineral stabilisers that interact with calcium. In commercial practice, additions of sodium carbonate and tri-sodium citrate have been found to extend the period before the onset of feathering in hot coffee. Storage temperature also has a significant effect on shelf-life and, although not necessary for bacteriological stability, refrigeration promotes a marked improvement in shelf-life.

9.8.6 Cream liqueurs

Cream liqueur is a class of compound beverage containing a substantial proportion of dairy ingredients, e.g. 16% butterfat and 3% sodium caseinate. Shelf-life is determined by the onset of gelation, by creaming and fat plugging and, infrequently, by deposition of calcium citrate-rich deposits. The liqueurs are made by emulsifying cream in a solution of sodium caseinate to yield a dispersion of fat particles. Sugar, colour and flavour are then added and the mixture treated by severe homogenisation to obtain a very fine dispersion of the fat. Creaming during storage is related to the efficiency of homogenisation and it has been established that, by ensuring that all fat particles are less than 0.8 μm in diameter, creaming does not occur on extended storage.

The second problem which may limit the shelf-life of liqueurs is the onset of gelation. This defect is associated with calcium interactions with milk protein and can be avoided by the following:

- Addition of trisodium citrate.
- Reduction of the calcium content of cream.
- Use of anhydrous milk fat as a lipid source.
- Use of the citric acid ester of glycerol mono-stearate to replace some of the protein present for emulsification.

The third defect of cream liqueurs is associated with the use of trisodium citrate as an inhibitor of age-gelation. On prolonged storage, crystalline particles may form a deposit, largely of calcium citrate. This salt becomes progressively less soluble as temperature increases and its formation can be slowed by reducing processing temperatures after citrate addition or by reduction of the concentration of added salt.

9.8.7   Cheese
Cheese is a family of products ranging in shelf-life from several days to many years. It is thus difficult to generalise and, for this reason, only a single type – Cheddar – representing the most popular variety consumed in the UK will be considered here. The standard of identity limits the moisture to an upper limit of 39%, and the fat in dry matter to a minimum of 48%. Nevertheless, the 'Cheddar' label spans a wide range both in terms of flavour and texture. The major classification is on the basis of maturity. 'Mild' Cheddar may have been matured for only 3 months while 'extra-mature' cheese may be 18–24 months old. The complexity of cheese lies in the fact that it is a biologically and chemically active product. Manufacture is simple in theory but complex in practice. A lactic acid starter culture is added to heat-treated milk and, after a short ripening period during which the pH drops, the milk is coagulated by addition of rennet. The active ingredient of rennet is the enzyme chymosin that cleaves the κ-casein specifically. This action results in destabilisation of the micellar casein in the presence of calcium – in large excess in acidified milk – and a protein gel forms in which milk fat globules are entrapped. The coagulum or cheese curd is then cut into small pieces, and syneresis is encouraged by scalding, stirring and piling of the curd. After further curd processing and salting, the curd is pressed.

The pressed curd is then ripened by storage in permeable packaging at between 6 and 12 °C (sometimes complex temperature profiles are used). During ripening, simultaneous reactions occur which lead to breakdown of the curd texture and development of flavour. Proteolysis is the key reaction controlling maturation rate but its origin and control is complex. Lipase action plays a secondary, but probably underrated, role in flavour development. Clear guidelines for the relation between bacterial load in raw milk and off-flavour

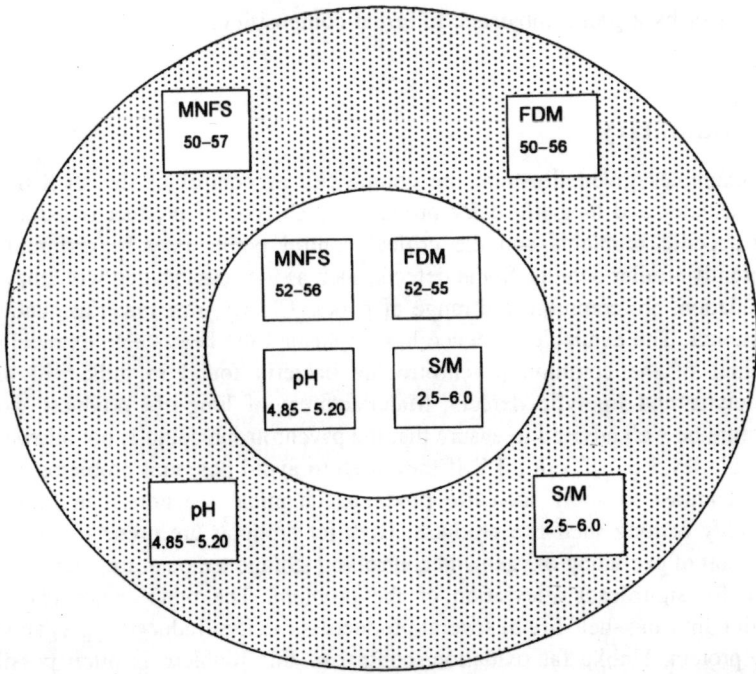

Fig. 9.2 Compositional range for optimising quality of Cheddar cheese. Adapted from Gilles and Lawrence. MNFS = moisture in non-fat solids; FDM = fat in dry matter; S/M = salt in moisture; pH = pH of cheese. Inner ring = premium grade; outer ring = first grade.

development associated with excessive lipolysis in cheddar cheese have been established. Rancid flavours developed in cheese after only 16 weeks' storage when the psychrotroph count of the raw milk used for manufacture reached a threshold of between 2×10^6 and 8×10^6 cfu ml^{-1}.

The maturation rate of cheese depends not only on the amount and type of enzyme present but also on the composition of the product, because composition determines the environment in which enzyme (and subsequent chemical) activity can be expressed. Guidelines proposed by the New Zealand Dairy Research Institute relate cheese composition to the ultimate quality of long-hold mature product and these have stood the test of time. The compositional ranges for first and premium grade cheese are shown schematically in Fig. 9.2. Four factors are important: salt in moisture (S/M), moisture in non-fat solids (MNFS), fat in dry matter (FDM) and pH. It has been found both in New Zealand and in the UK that by careful control of cheese composition, optimal quality and shelf-life can be attained.

Although space does not permit detailed consideration of other cheese varieties, similar principles apply, i.e. shelf-life is controlled by initial composition and by subsequent proteolysis. Flavour defects are usually associated with either residual enzyme activity derived from psychrotrophic bacteria or by a gross imbalance in initial composition.

9.9   Summary

The examples given illustrate the complexity of control of the shelf-life of intermediate- and long-life dairy products. Each type of product is associated with specific problems and the critical control points may be different for apparently similar defects. Some defects, such as those associated with enzymic degradation, are common to a range of goods. Clearly, raw material quality is paramount. The available evidence has implicated the heat-stable extracellular enzymes of the common psychrotrophic bacteria found in milk with both proteolytic and lipolytic defects. Manufacturers of long-life products would therefore be well advised to ensure that the psychrotroph count is not allowed to exceed a level of 10^6 cfu ml^{-1} if they wish to avoid potential problems.

In contrast to short shelf-life products, chemical reactions can limit the durability of long shelf-life products. High fat products are prone to oxidation and, short of excluding oxygen and controlling storage temperature, there is little scope for significant alleviation of the problem. The other major chemical reaction limiting shelf-life in several products is calcium-induced aggregation of milk protein. Unlike fat oxidation, control of this problem is often possible. Modifications to processing conditions, especially those involving heat treatment and homogenisation, are often successful and the addition of the appropriate mineral stabiliser can often be effective.

Cheese poses a particular problem for not only is composition important but the starter culture and coagulant used significantly affect the rate of ripening. It is perhaps inappropriate to define a shelf-life for cheese since many varieties are acceptable to the consumer for a large part of their maturation period – albeit with suboptimal flavour or texture.

In conclusion, no panacea can be provided for control of the shelf-life of dairy products. Each must be considered in turn and, as new products are developed, it is anticipated that further problems will emerge.

9.10   Acknowledgement

This work was funded by the Scottish Executive, Rural Affairs Department.

9.11   Bibliography

BORDE-LEKONA B, LEWIS M J and HARRIGAN W F Keeping quality of pasteurised and high pasteurised milk. In *Biochemistry of Milk Products*, eds. A T Andrews & J Varley. Cambridge, Royal Society of Chemistry, 1994, pp. 157–68.

BURTON H *Ultra-High-Temperature Processing of Milk and Milk Products*. Reading, Elsevier Applied Science, 1988.

CROSS H R and OVERBY A J (eds). *Meat Science, Milk Science and Technology*, Amsterdam, Elsevier Science Publishers BV, 1988.

EARLEY R (ed). *Technology of Dairy Products*, 2nd Edition, London, Blackie Academic & Professional, 1998.

FOX P F *Cheese: Chemistry, Physics and Microbiology, Volume 1 General Aspects*, Cork, Chapman & Hall, 1993.

GILLES J and LAWRENCE R C *New Zealand Journal of Dairy Science and Technology*, 1973, **8** 148.

GORMLEY T R (ed). *Chilled Foods. The State of the Art*. London, Elsevier Applied Science, 1990.

HORNE D S, LEAVER J and MUIR D D (eds). Caseins and Caseinates: Structures, Interactions, Networks. Hannah Symposium 1997. *International Dairy Journal incorporating Netherlands Milk & Dairy Journal Special Issue*, 1999, **9** (3/6) 161–417.

JEREMIAH L E (ed). *Freezing Effects on Food Quality*. New York, Marcel Dekker, 1995.

MASTERS K *Spray Drying Handbook*. London, George Goodwin, 1985.

McKELLAR ROBIN C *Enzymes of Psychrotrophs in Raw Food*. Boca Raton, CRC Press Inc, 1989.

MULDER K and WALSTRA P *The Milk Fat Globule: Emulsion Science as Applied to Milk Products and Comparable Foods*. Wageningen, Pudoc, CAB, 1974.

RENNER E (ed). *Micronutrients in Milk and Milk-based Food Products*. London, Elsevier Applied Science, 1989.

ROBINSON R K *Dairy Microbiology, Volume 1, The Microbiology of Milk*. Reading, Applied Science Publishers, 1981.

SPREER E *Milk & Dairy Product Technology*. New York, Marcel Dekker, 1998.

TAMIME A Y and ROBINSON R K *Yogurt Science and Technology* (2nd Edition). Cambridge, Woodhead Publishing, 1999.

WELCH R A S, BURNS D J W, DAVIS S R, POPAY A I and PROSSER C G (eds). *Milk Composition, Production and Biotechnology*. Wallingford, CAB International, 1997.

10

Testing the authenticity of milk and milk products

F. Ulberth, University of Agricultural Sciences, Austria

10.1 Introduction

The driving force behind any adulteration is to maximise revenues by either using a cheap ingredient to (partially) substitute a more expensive one, or to (partially) remove the valued component in the hope that the altered product passes undetected by the final user or consumer. Watering of milk or skimming off cream are good examples to illustrate the point, and these fraudulent operations have been practised for a long time. Dairy products account for a large share of the total value of agricultural production in the developed world. Major advances in agronomy, large-scale transport, processing, and the introduction of efficient distribution systems have resulted in increased technological complexity, a higher degree of globalisation and lower product prices. The economics of dairying are very complex and mostly governed by intricate guidelines and laws to balance production and demand, stabilise prices and protect local interests. A complicated market scheme for milk products is at the very heart of the European Union's Common Agricultural Policy (Rasmussen, 2003). Fraudulent malpractice creates unfair competition, leading to market distortions, which in turn may impact the local or even the international economy. Therefore, authentication of milk and milk products is of primary importance for both consumers and manufacturers, and at all levels along the process chain.

Extension of a product with a cheap ingredient, also known as 'economic adulteration', does usually not carry a health hazard for consumers. This statement is not generally valid regarding adulterated milk and milk products. Consumers allergic to cows' milk may suffer severely if they ingest, e.g., ovine or caprine milk fraudulently extended with bovine milk or whey. As a consequence most countries have set up a complicated legal framework to ensure proper consumer protection and to foster fair trade practices. Compositional product standards, codified by national as well as supranational authorities, e.g. FAO/WHO Codex Alimentarius, International Dairy Federation (IDF) and the European Commission (EC), represent an integral part of food legislation. Product labelling is a vital instrument to inform consumers about the identity of a product, thereby obliging producers to conform to predefined product standards. Infringement of labelling regulations could lead to criminal charges in the courts. Therefore, analytical data used in court or in other disputes have to stand up to scrutiny. A large number of methods have been developed and standardised with a view to that particular purpose. They can be found in method manuals issued, e.g., by the IDF, the Association of Analytical Chemists International (AOAC Internat.), or the EC.

Most of the product standards refer *inter alia* to hygienic quality parameters, e.g. total plate count, number of various indicator micro-organisms, somatic cell count, etc., which are at the borderline of product authenticity and product safety. These issues are beyond the scope of this chapter and readers are referred to the respective literature (e.g. Robinson, 2002).

10.1.1   Milk and milk product authenticity issues
In general, authenticity issues fall into at least one of the following categories:

- Non-compliance with legal requirements (product standards) such as:
    - Maximum/minimum content of water, solids-non-fat, and fat in certain dairy products (butter, cheese, yoghurt, etc.)
    - Geographical origin of the product.
- Wrongful addition of certain ingredients of dairy or non-dairy origin such as:
  - Watering of milk
  - Milk of different species
  - Addition of non-dairy protein
  - Altering the casein/whey protein ratio
  - Addition of buttermilk or whey powder to milk powder
  - Addition of vegetable or animal fats to milk fat
  - Addition of reconstituted milk to fluid milk
  - Non-authorised preservatives.
- Non-compliance regarding use of certain technological processes:
  - Heat treatment
  - Cheese ripening
  - Membrane technology.

Whatever type of fraud is perpetrated, authenticity testing relies either on a fundamental difference between the original and the adulterant, or on an intimate knowledge of their composition and possible ranges of compositional variation. The former case is much more tractable than the latter. Detection of foreign proteins added to milk of a certain species by exploiting differences in their electrophoretic mobilities is an example where a fundamental dissimilarity is used to check the purity of the product. If no tangible differences exist, compositional data of authentic samples have to be gathered, taking into account all possible natural variations, e.g. due to breed, stage of lactation, production systems, geographical origin, etc. The authenticity of a product is confirmed when its compositional data fit into the data space represented by authentic samples. This type of testing usually depends on some form of statistical decision-making procedure. As of lately, chemometrics, the discipline concerned with application of multivariate statistical methods, as well as those methods based on mathematical logic, to chemistry (Brown et al., 1992), are increasingly applied to compositional data in order to solve authenticity and classification problems.

10.2   Detecting and quantifying foreign fats

Milk represents a very complex physico-chemical system, where virtually all components present contribute information that is valuable for authenticity testing (Table 10.1). Clear-cut distinctions of different principles are of course not always possible, e.g. heat treatment results in an increased formation of Maillard products which are derived from the reaction of proteins with reducing sugars (lactose).

Milk fat (MF) is perhaps the most valued milk component and therefore has been the target for dubious manipulations for a long time. Traditional physico-

Table 10.1   Analytes of indicative value for the detection of adulteration of milk and milk products

Milk component	Source of adulteration	Analyte(s)
Fat	Non-dairy fat or oil Buttermilk added to milk	Fatty acids Triglycerides Phospholipids Sterols Fat-soluble vitamins
Protein	Non-dairy proteins Milk of a different species Whey added to milk Heat load	Caseins Whey proteins Glucomacropeptide Casein bound-P Protein-N Denatured proteins
Lactose	Water Heat load	Freezing point Furosin Lysinoalanin HMF Glycosylated proteins
Minerals	Water	Freezing point

chemical methods to verify the authenticity of MF, e.g. by determining the iodine value (a measure of the total unsaturation of a fat), Reichert-Meissel value (titrimetric determination of steam-volatile, water-soluble fatty acids (FA)), or Polenske value (titrimetric determination of steam-volatile but water-insoluble fatty acids) are only successful to recognise massive adulteration of MF, or even its substitution by another fat (Collomb and Spahni, 1991). With the advent of gas-liquid chromatography (GLC) techniques, the classical fat values were substituted by the analysis of the complete FA spectrum.

Strategies to detect adulterated MF are based either on the concentration ranges of individual FA or on the concentration ratios of two or more FA. A large number of different FA ratios have been proposed (Fox et al., 1988; Hughebaert and Hendrickx, 1971; Muuse et al., 1986; Toppino et al., 1982; Ulberth and Rogenhofer, 1989; Younes and Soliman, 1986). The effectiveness of 19 such indices was compared using the FA composition of a large number of authentic MF samples (Ulberth, 1994). The addition of vegetable fats or oils was easier to detect than commingling of animal fats. Additions of coconut fat or linoleic acid-rich vegetable oils (sunflower seed oil, corn oil, safflower oil, etc.) were traced down to a level of 2% by the ratios C12:0/C10:0 and C14:0/C12:0, and C18:2/C8:0, respectively. At a level of 10% commingling, palm oil and olive oil were detected by using C14:0/C18:2 and C18:2/C8:0 ratios. At 5% commingling, 50% of the adulterated samples passed the test undetected. Tallow was particularly difficult to detect, the ratio C16:0/C14:0 being the most suitable. However, it was possible to detect only 15% of the cases where 5% tallow had been added to MF. If the information content of a FA chromatogram was exploited in a more efficient way, i.e. subjected to linear discriminant analysis instead of forming FA ratios, more than 95% of cases where either tallow, lard, olive oil or palm oil were added to MF at the 3% level were correctly classified (Ulberth, 1994).

FA ratios have been used with success to discriminate between MF of different species (bovine, ovine and caprine milk). Iverson and Sheppard (1989) used the C12:0/C10:0 ratio to detect addition of bovine to ovine or caprine cheese milk. For instance, the ratio for bovine MF averages around 1.16, while it is 0.46 for caprine MF and 0.58 for ovine MF. This ratio was employed to indicate the level of cows' milk in cheeses labelled as goats' or ewes' milk cheese. Other FA indicators, mostly based on the ratio of a medium-chain and a volatile, short-chain FA (e.g. C14:0/C8:0), have been proposed and were summarised by Ramos and Juarez (1984). These authors also reported that the limit of detection for cows' MF in mixture with goats' or ewes' MF is 5–10%. Applying a more sophisticated methodology (pattern recognition techniques) to evaluate certain FA ratios (C14:0/C8:0, C14:1/C8:0 and C14:1/C16:1) an even more sensitive limit for the detection of cows' milk in ewes' milk cheese was established (Schwaiger and Vojir, 1995).

The difficulty of detecting fat of animal origin added to MF has led to the development of so-called triglyceride (TG) formulae for MF purity control. Originally, Timms (1980) described an approach using the information content inherent to the TG profile of MF and combined it with a multivariate evaluation of the results to allow the determination of non-MF, including animal depot fats, in MF down to a level of 5%. His basic idea was further refined by Precht and co-workers (Precht and Heine, 1986a, 1986b; Precht, 1992a, 1992b). Several collaborative studies organised by the EC demonstrated the general applicability of the approach (Precht, 1992c). It was adopted as a reference method for the detection of foreign fats in MF within the EC (Commission Regulation (EC) No 213/2001). Based on the TG profile of 755 different MF, so-called S-values were derived by regression analysis. The S-values for authentic MF fluctuate within a certain range. If these limits are transgressed, the presence of a foreign fat can be assumed with a given level of statistical confidence. All types of foreign fats can be detected using the formula:

$$S = -2.7575*C26 + 6.4077*C28 + 5.5437*C30 - 15.3247*C32 \\ + 6.2600*C34 + 8.0108*C40 - 5.0336*C42 + 0.6356*C44 \\ + 6.0171*C46$$

For authentic MF the S-value for the 'total formula' fluctuates within a range of 95.68 to 104.32 (99% confidence level). Typical values for the limit of detection are 4.5–5.0% for vegetable fats (soybean oil, olive oil, palm oil, etc.), 4.7% for lard and 5.4% for tallow. For a number of foreign fats (e.g. coconut fat, palm oil, lard, etc.) particular TG formulae have been developed which are more sensitive and allow detection at a level of 2–3% adulterant.

The validity and applicability of the TG formulae have been confirmed by others (Collomb *et al.*, 1998a; Luf, 1988; Povolo *et al.*, 1999; Ulberth *et al.*, 1998; Van Renterghem, 1997). Although packed column GLC has been used to establish the TG formulae, certain types of capillary columns are fully equivalent and can be used without impacting the approach (Collomb *et al.*, 1998b; Molkentin and Precht, 1994; Ulberth *et al.*, 1998). Besides multiple linear regression analysis, other ways of multivariate treatment of TG data to detect foreign fats have been suggested (principal components analysis, partial least-squares regression, artificial neural networks), but have not found widespread acceptance (Collomb *et al.*, 1998c; Lipp, 1996a, 1996b). Intensive lipolysis of MF, e.g. in (over)matured cheese, may lead to false-positive results when the TG formulae are applied, highlighting the need for the development of special formulae taking into account fat degradation (Battelli and Pellegrino, 1994). The TG formula approach to verify the authenticity of bovine MF was recently extended to caprine MF (Fontecha *et al.*, 1998).

Sterol analysis is a straightforward way to detect vegetable fats added to MF, since phytosterols do not occur in MF in measurable amounts. Detection of β-sitosterol, stigmasterol, campesterol, etc. is taken as an unequivocal proof that a vegetable fat is present. However, care has to be exercised in drawing correct conclusions as minor components (e.g. lanosterol) in chromatograms of the unsaponifiable part of MF may elute closely to β-sitosterol (Homberg, 1991). Currently, two methods standardised by IDF exist for the determination of sterols in MF; one is based on the difference in melting points of phytosteryl acetate and cholesteryl acetate (IDF Standard 32: 1965), the other on a GLC procedure (IDF Standard 54: 1970). A similar GLC procedure to detect β-sitosterol and stigmasterol was also described by the EC (Commission Regulation (EC) No 213/2001). As an alternative to the lengthy sample preparation described in those standards, a hyphenated LC-GC technique was introduced (Kamm et al., 2002). The limit of detection for the determination of β-sitosterol via LC-GC was found to be 2 mg/kg fat. This is considerably lower than detection limits of 40 mg/kg and 10 mg/kg, respectively, reported for the convential procedures (Homberg and Bielefeld, 1979). Considering the amount of β-sitosterol present in rapeseed oil (ca. 4000 mg/kg), this indicates that an addition of about 0.05% rapeseed oil to MF would be detectable. An adulteration at such a low level is of no practical concern. However, additions of only 1–2% vegetable oil will be detected with certainty. Even for palm oil, an example for a vegetable oil exhibiting only a relatively low content of β-sitosterol (200–400 mg/kg), the resulting limit of detection (0.5–1%) would be sufficient.

Misbranding of spreadable fats, which contain MF and suitable non-MF, is another problem area. Products introduced on the spreadable fats market within the EU must comply with Council Regulation (EC) No 2991/94. Up to now, no official method for the determination of the MF proportion in the fat blend has been specified. Usually, butyric acid (C4:0), which occurs exclusively in MF of ruminant animals, is used as a marker to estimate the amount of MF in the blend. A number of reliable methods have been suggested for the determination of C4:0 in spreadable fats by GLC (Molkentin and Precht, 1998a, 1998b; Pocklington and Hautfenne, 1986; Ulberth, 1998a, 1998b) or by HPLC (Christie et al., 1987). A major drawback of the approach is the natural variation of the C4:0 content in MF (Molkentin and Precht, 1997). For a representative number of samples taken all over Europe the figures varied between 3.07 g and 3.75 g per 100 g MF, with a mean value of 3.42 g per 100 g. The variations were due to differences in feeding regimen, lactation stage and breed. By using the average content of C4:0 in MF the proportion of MF in an unknown fat blend may thus deviate to up to $\pm 10\%$ from the true value, without taking into account any additional analytical errors (Molkentin and Precht, 1998b). When a sample of the MF used for blend formulation is available for analytical testing, the performance of the method in terms of accuracy and precision can be improved. The EU Expert Group 'Milk and Milk Products' (Agriculture DG) has collaboratively tested the latter methodology in order to gain precision data. Reproducibility of the method was 1.7% MF for a mixture containing 25% MF, and 3.2% MF for a mixture containing 60% MF (Molkentin and Precht, 2000).

Alternatives to chromatographic techniques for MF authentication, such as differential scanning calorimetry (Bringer et al., 1991; Coni et al., 1994) and infra-red spectroscopic techniques (Sato et al., 1990; Laporte and Paquin, 1998), were proposed, but have not found wide application. In particular, spectroscopic techniques would be highly welcome, since they do not need lengthy sample preparation and therefore have a high throughput, and are non-destructive testing methods.

10.3   Detecting milk of different species

In most countries producers of dairy products are required to label the milk type (bovine, ovine, caprine) used for manufacture. Since the production volume of ovine and caprine milk is much smaller and their supply varies to a considerable extent, an incentive for economic adulteration exists. Moreover, certain traditional products that are highly valued by consumers on a worldwide scale, such as Mozzarella, Roquefort, Manchego, Pecorino or Feta cheese, are exclusively made from non-bovine milk. Hence, analytical methods are needed to check for the presence of cows' milk in products declared to be made solely from ewes', goats' or water-buffaloes' milk. In some production areas the addition of goats' milk to ewes' milk used for the production of traditional cheese varieties could also be an issue.

Differences in the molecular make-up of milk proteins are the primary route to discriminate milk of different species. Various forms of electrophoresis, chromatography and immunochemistry are used as analytical tools to track down those differences. The protein-based methods may be supplemented by the analysis of the fat phase (FA ratios, TG profile) as described in the preceding chapter.

Separation of milk proteins by various forms of electrophoresis is one of the most widely applied techniques in dairy products authentication. Early attempts focused on the higher electrophoretic mobility in polyacrylamide gels (PAGE) of the α_{s1}-casein of bovine milk as compared to ovine and caprine milk (Aschaffenburg and Dance, 1968; Foissy, 1976; Freimuth and Krause, 1968). A limit of detection of 1% of cows' milk in goats' milk was reported by those authors. As the caseins are partially degraded during cheese ripening, newly formed peptides obscure to a certain extent the region of the bovine α_{s1}-casein. As a result the sensitivity of the method drops, and data interpretation becomes much more difficult. Discontinuous electrophoresis of β-caseins was used as an alternative by Mayer and Hörtner (1992) for the determination of bovine caseins in milk and dairy products.

Due to its high separation efficiency, isoelectric focusing in thin polyacrylamide gels (PAGIF) has become a preferred technique for the separation of complex protein mixtures. Applying this technique, Krause et al. (1982) made use of the γ-caseins, proteolytic breakdown products of β-casein, as an indicator for the detection of an admixture of bovine to ovine and caprine milk and cheese. Ovine and caprine milk cannot be distinguished by this technique. The addition of plasmin to cheese caseins in order deliberately to create γ-caseins and their subsequent separation by PAGIF greatly enhances the sensitivity of the method (Addeo et al., 1990a). It has been officially adopted for the control of cheese within the EU (Commission Regulation (EC) No 213/2001). Evaluation is performed by comparing the protein patterns of the unknown sample with reference standards on the same gel. Detection of cows' milk in cheeses from ewes', goats' or water-buffaloes' milk and mixtures of ewes', goats' and buffaloes' milk is done via the γ_3- and γ_2-caseins, whose isoelectric points range between pH 6.5 and pH 7.5. The limit of detection is less than 0.5% of cows' milk. The method is suitable for a sensitive and specific detection of native and heat-treated cows' milk and caseinate in fresh and ripened cheeses made from non-bovine milk, but it is not suitable for the detection of milk and cheese adulteration by heat-treated bovine whey protein concentrates.

PAGIF of para-κ-caseins allows not only the detection of an addition of bovine milk to cheese from other species but also the differentiation between cheese of ovine or caprine origin. However, in the case of ripened Roquefort cheese, a peptide migrating with cows' milk para-κ-casein was identified, leading to a false-positive response (Addeo et al., 1990b). Such difficulties were not noticed in another study with Camembert made from milk of different species (Mayer et al., 1997). The method can be extended to other dairy products. The addition of rennet to ewes' yoghurt to produce para-κ-caseins artificially and subsequent separation of the caseins by cationic PAGE allowed the detection of cows' milk down to 1% (Kaminarides and Koukiassa, 2002).

Whey proteins are not markedly altered by proteolysis during cheese ripening. In order to adequately exploit this feature, separation systems have been set up based on differences in electrophoretic mobilities of whey proteins, in particular of β-lactoglobulin (Addeo et al., 1989; Amigo et al., 1991; Rispoli et al., 1991). When silver nitrate was used for staining, cows' milk at a level of 1% was detectable in various types of cheese (Amigo et al., 1991). The drawback of the method is that heat treatment denatures whey proteins to a variable extent, thus affecting the test results. For example, heating to 90°C for 30 min denatured the whey proteins and gave negative results when cows' milk was added to milk for cheese making (Amigo et al., 1991).

The increased availability of commercial capillary electrophoresis instrumentation has led to an increased transfer of traditional electrophoretic assay formats to this novel technique. The high resolution power and the speed of analysis are its most attractive features. Both the casein fraction and the whey proteins can be analysed and used for authentication purposes. As is the case with traditional PAGE, α_{s1}-casein of bovine milk had the highest mobility among the different caseins by applying capillary zone electrophoresis (CZE) in an uncoated tube, which proved to be useful for the detection of cows' milk in goats' milk (Lee et al., 2001). However, caprine para-κ-caseins and bovine β-casein were also found to be good markers for the presence of the milk of these species in Iberico-type cheese (Molina et al., 2000). The differences between the CZE patterns of the casein fraction of bovine, ovine and caprine milk allowed identification and even quantification of the milk of each species in binary and ternary mixtures by multivariate regression analysis (Molina et al., 1999). The mean errors in prediction were lower than 3% in all cases. A similar chemometric approach was reported by Vallejo Cordoba (1998).

Whey proteins of different species were successfully separated by CZE and can also serve as authenticity indicators (Cartoni et al., 1999; Cattaneo et al., 1996; Recio et al., 1995). The ratio of the corrected peak areas of bovine β-

lactoglobulin B to ovine α-lactalbumin was linearly related to the amount of cows' milk present within a range of 0–20% (Cartoni *et al.*, 1999).

High performance liquid chromatography (HPLC) is another route to protein separation and was effectively used to determine individual milk proteins. Different chromatographic profiles are obtained for the proteins from different species. Ion-exchange as well as reversed-phase (RP) columns were applied to fractionate either the caseins or the whey proteins or total milk proteins. Bovine, ovine and caprine para-κ-caseins were baseline separated by cation-exchange HPLC and used for quantifying the mixture, i.e. the proportions of the milk types used for cheese making (Mayer *et al.*, 1997). Others used RP columns to separate primarily α-, β- and κ-casein fractions of different species (Bordin *et al.*, 2001; Urbanke *et al.*, 1992; Veloso *et al.*, 2002). By analogy to the official EC method, Volitaki and Kaminarides (2001) added plasmin to the isolated caseins to intensify the γ-casein fraction and separated the mixture by RP-HPLC. The caseinomacropeptides of different species are separable by HPLC and can serve as markers (Lopez Fandino *et al.*, 1993). HPLC analysis of whey proteins is also of interest for species discrimination (Bobe *et al.*, 1998a; de Frutos *et al.*, 1991; de Noni *et al.*, 1996; Romero *et al.*, 1996).

When quantitative aspects regarding mixture proportions are considered, the different casein contents of bovine, caprine and in particular ovine milk used for cheese making have to be taken into account. Since ewes' milk has a much higher casein content than cows' milk, the resulting relationships are non-linear (Addeo *et al.*, 1990a, 1990b; Mayer *et al.*, 1997).

Recently, new strategies for the structural analysis of milk proteins based on mass spectrometric technologies, in particular matrix-assisted laser desorption–time of flight mass spectrometry (MALDI–TOF), have been developed. Owing to its speed and the minimum of sample preparation required, the MALDI–TOF technique is very attractive. Using particularly α-lactalbumin and β-lactoglobulin as markers, addition of cows' milk to the milk of other species and to water-buffalo Mozzarella were easily detected by MALDI–TOF (Angeletti *et al.*, 1998; Cozzolino *et al.*, 2001, 2002; Fanton *et al.*, 1998).

Due to their excellent sensitivity and minimal sample preparation requirements, immunochemical methods have found wide acceptance for the discrimination of milk of different species. Various assay formats and antibodies directed against different antigens have been described (Table 10.2). Many of the assays target bovine β-casein, as this fraction has the highest allergenic potential of all caseins (Anguita *et al.*, 1996a). The limit of detection for most of the assays is 0.1–1.0% depending on the assay format. If polyclonal antibodies were used, they were usually purified by affinity chromatography to eliminate cross-reactivity. Commercial test kits are now on the market and have found wide application.

Immunological methods can fail when the targeted antigen is substantially degraded by either heating or proteolysis. DNA from somatic milk cells (mostly leucocytes) is suggested to persist in ripened cheese and may be amplified by polymerase chain reaction (PCR) and analysed for species discrimination. Plath *et al.* (1997) used primers encoding a partial sequence of the β-casein gene to

Table 10.2 Immunochemical assay formats used for the discrimination of milk of different species

Assay	Antibody	Antigen	Reference
Competitive indirect ELISA	Polyclonal	Bovine γ-caseins	Richter et al. (1997)
Competitive indirect ELISA	Polyclonal	Native and heat denatured bovine β-lactoglobulin	Beer et al. (1996)
Indirect ELISA	Monoclonal	Bovine β-casein	Anguita et al. (1995)
Indirect ELISA	Monoclonal	Bovine α_{s1}-casein	Rolland et al. (1993)
Indirect ELISA	Monoclonal	Caprine α_{s2}-casein	Haza et al. (1996)
Indirect ELISA	Polyclonal	Bovine caseinomacropeptide	Bitri et al. (1993)
Indirect ELISA	Polyclonal	Caprine whey proteins	García et al. (1994)
Sandwich ELISA	Monoclonal	Bovine β-lactoglobulin	Levieux and Venien (1994)
Sandwich ELISA	Polyclonal	Bovine caseins	Rodriguez et al. (1993)
Immunostick ELISA	Monoclonal	Bovine β-casein	Anguita et al. (1996b)
Western blotting	Monoclonal	Bovine β-lactoglobulin	Molina et al. (1996)

detect the corresponding genomic DNA in milk and cheese. The PCR product from ovine or caprine β-casein DNA contained a specific restriction enzyme site that was not present in bovine β-casein DNA. After restriction enzyme analysis and subsequent separation of the fragments by PAGE, the undigested bovine β-casein fragment was detected as an additional band if cows' milk was present. A similar approach was described for the identification of water-buffalo, bovine, ovine and caprine milk in cheese, based on amplification of a 359 bp fragment of the cytochrome-b gene and restriction fragment chain length polymorphism analysis (Branciari et al., 2000). A single-step PCR method with bovine-specific primers for a fragment of the cytochrome-b gene to detect cows' in goats' milk was described by Bania et al. (2001).

Genomic DNA was extracted from cheese and PCR double-stranded amplifications were conducted using various suitable sets of primers for species-specific DNA amplification to detect the milk source (bovine, ovine and caprine) in cheese (Calvo et al., 2002). A duplex PCR was developed to identify cows' milk and buffaloes' milk in cheese products, particularly in buffalo Mozzarella cheese (Bottero et al., 2002).

Mitochondrial (mt) DNA shows also species-diagnostic sequence variations and, on top of that, the number of copies of mtDNA is much higher than that of genomic DNA. Cow-specific primers were designed to target the control region of mtDNA and the resulting PCR product of 413 bp separated by agarose gel electrophoresis. The limit of detection of cows' milk in goats' cheese was less than 0.1% (Maudet and Taberlet, 2001).

A DNA-based technique which combines PCR, ligase chain reaction (LCR) and an enzyme immunoassay (EIA) to detect the presence of cows' milk in ewes', goats' and buffaloes' milk and corresponding cheeses was developed by Klotz and Einspanier (2001). It is based on subtle differences in the β-casein gene of cow, sheep, goat and buffalo species. DNA, extracted from milk or cheese samples, served as a template to amplify a universal β-casein PCR product. Subsequently, LCR with species-specific primers was performed using the PCR product as a template. LCR primers were labelled with biotin or digoxygenin for further sensitive detection by EIA. This screening technique allowed clear discrimination of cow species from sheep, goat and buffalo species in milk and cheese.

The sensitivity of the DNA-based methods is very high; limits of detection are reported to be better than 0.1% of the targeted species. However, quantification of mixture proportions seems to be difficult as the source of the DNA is somatic milk cells. It is well known that the somatic cell count is affected by a number of factors (number and stage of lactation, udder health) which are out of control.

10.4   Detection of non-milk proteins, watering of milk and alteration of the casein/whey protein ratio

Non-dairy proteins of vegetable or animal origin are generally cheaper than milk proteins and are sometimes added to extend the product (economic adulteration) or because of their functional properties. In particular, soy protein has good water holding and binding capacity and therefore can improve the texture of a product (e.g. soft cheese). A number of electrophoretic (Cattaneo et al., 1994; Kanning et al., 1993; Manso et al., 2002), chromatographic (Cattaneo et al., 1994; Espeja et al., 2001) and immunochemical (Turin and Bonomi, 1994; Sanchez et al., 2002) methods have been devised to detect the addition of non-milk proteins.

10.4.1   Watering of milk

Addition of water to a beverage is the epitome of food adulteration. Dilution with water alters the density of milk, the refractive index of the lactoserum and, most importantly, its freezing point. The thermistor cryoscopic determination of the freezing point of raw milk is probably the most widely and frequently applied technique for food authenticity testing. The freezing point of authentic raw milk varies only within narrow limits. Breed, stage and parity of lactation, feeding regimens, udder health, production region, season and milking time are seen as the most important factors influencing the freezing point (Buchberger, 1994, 2000; Rohm et al., 1991; Wiedemann et al., 1993). Mean values were reported for different countries in a range between −0.5310°C and −0.5209°C (Buchberger, 1990; Coveney, 1993; Rohm et al., 1992; Slaghuis, 2001). The procedure for the determination of the freezing point has been standardised (IDF Standard 108B:1991; Commission Decision 91/180/EEC). Although the method is considered to be robust, a number of operating parameters may influence the test result and have to be controlled carefully (Rohm, 1993).

10.4.2   Alteration of the casein/whey protein ratio

The by-product of cheese making, rennet whey, is of low value but the volumes produced abound. Therefore, it is tempting to add whey fraudulently to other dairy products. Advances in membrane filtration technology opened up interesting possibilities to split skim milk into different protein fractions to give products with an added value on one hand and less valuable fractions on the other (Creamer et al., 2002). Furthermore, protein standardisation of milk and milk products is now permitted, provided that milk components only are added or removed and the ratio of casein to whey protein is not altered. Therefore, reliable methods are needed to check the protein composition of dairy products. The methods proposed are either indirect, for example by determining certain protein fractions not as such but in terms of an inherent characteristic feature, or direct, for example using electrophoretic or chromatographic methods to separate the protein mixture into individual components.

Whey proteins contain significantly more sulphur-containing amino acids (cysteine and cystine) and more aromatic amino acids (tryptophan, tyrosine and phenylalanine). Additions of whey proteins therefore increase those values as compared to the genuine product. The former can be·determined by a modified ninhydrin reaction (De Koning and Van Rooijen, 1971) or by polarography (Mrowetz and Klostermeyer, 1976; Lechner and Klostermeyer, 1981). The limitation of the polarographic method, although very effective and reliable, is that it uses hazardous chemicals (methylmercury chloride). A very elegant way to determine the casein/whey protein ratio is the application of derivative spectroscopy. Second-order (Luf and Brandl, 1987) and even fourth-order derivatives (Lüthi-Peng and Puhan, 1999; Meisel, 1995; Miralles et al., 2000) have been proposed. The method quantifies aromatic amino acid residues of milk proteins and is unaffected by other absorbing non-protein material in the sample solution. The different content of protein-bound phosphorus of casein and whey protein is the basis of an effective though laborious testing principle that detects whey additions (Wolfschoon-Pombo and Furtado, 1989).

Direct measurement of all relevant protein fractions by electrophoretic (Basch et al., 1985; Meisel and Carstens, 1989; Miralles et al., 2000) or chromatographic (Bobe et al., 1998b; Bordin et al., 2001) methods is more laborious but gives a more detailed insight. The casein to whey protein ratio can be determined directly from the chromatographic trace obtained, after careful calibration using reference compounds.

The caseinomacropeptide (CMP), which results from the cleavage of κ-casein during renneting of milk, is a good indicator for the presence of rennet whey. Two methods based on gel-filtration HPLC have been adopted by the EC (Commission Regulation (EC) No 213/2001) to check skim milk powder for the presence of rennet whey powder. Instead of UV detection, pulsed electrochemical detection of CMP, which was very sensitive and selective, was proposed (Van Riel and Olieman, 1995a). As an alternative to the HPLC procedures, CMP was determined by capillary electrophoresis (Recio *et al.*, 2000; Van Riel and Olieman, 1995b). Proteolytic activity, particularly from psychrotrophic bacteria, during cold storage of milk produces peptides similar to CMP, which may interfere with CMP detection. This could give rise to false-positive results (Martinez Penagos *et al.*, 1993; Recio *et al.*, 1996). Other, less often applied techniques to estimate the casein/whey protein ratio are photoacoustic spectroscopy (Doka *et al.*, 1999) and pyrolysis mass spectrometry (Schmidt *et al.*, 1999).

10.5   Measuring heat load

The primary aim of heating milk is to ensure its microbiological safety and stability. However, heating of milk profoundly alters the physico-chemical state of its components, leading primarily to the denaturation of certain vulnerable protein fractions (immunoglobulins, enzymes, whey proteins) and the formation of so-called browning products (Maillard reaction).

According to Council Directive 92/46/EEC pasteurised milk is obtained by heat treatment, at least 71.7°C for 15 seconds, or any other temperature–time combination producing an equivalent effect. Pasteurised milk has to show a negative reaction to the phosphatase test and a positive reaction to the peroxidase test. However, the production of pasteurised milk which shows a negative reaction to the peroxidase test is authorised, provided that the milk is labelled as 'high-temperature pasteurised'. The required tests (phosphatase and peroxidase) have been standardised (Commission Decision 91/180/EEC); alternative, more rapid testing methods (e.g. Fluorophos®, Reflectoquant®) have also been proposed (Berger *et al.*, 2001; Lechner, 1996).

Higher heat loads result from a number of other processes applied during manufacture of dairy products, primarily UHT treatment, sterilisation, concentration by water evaporation and drying. Therefore, methods are needed that can (i) discriminate between the severity of heat treatment applied, and (ii) detect products with a high heat load that have been added to other milk products (e.g. addition of dried milk to fluid milk).

The American Dry Milk Institute (ADMI) has standardised a turbidimetric method developed by Harland and Ashworth to distinguish between different heat loads (low, medium, high) in skim milk powder (ADMI, 1971). In this test, casein and heat-denatured whey proteins are precipitated with NaCl at neutral pH; the supernatant is then acidified to coagulate the native whey proteins and the resulting turbidity is taken as a measure for the content of non-denatured whey proteins. More recently, the amount of non-denatured, soluble whey proteins has been quantified directly by HPLC procedures (IDF Standard 178: 1996; Kneifel and Ulberth, 1985; Resmini *et al.*, 1989; Villamiel *et al.*, 2000).

Immunochemical methods were also successfully employed to determine heat-denatured whey proteins (Jeanson *et al.*, 1999; Rosenthal *et al.*, 1999).

Methods based on the determination of native whey proteins are particularly suited to discriminate products with rather low heat load (pasteurisation conditions). The presence of several Maillard reaction products such as lactose isomerisation and protein-glycation are indicative of severe heat treatment. The two main markers are furosine and lactulose. Furfurals are another group of heat treatment indicators, which have found wide application not only in the dairy industry (Albalá-Hurtado *et al.*, 1997; Ferrer *et al.*, 2000), but throughout the food industry.

Furosine is an amino acid obtained by acid hydrolysis of glycosylated proteins, in particular of the lysine–lactose adduct formed in the Maillard reaction. It can be determined by HPLC (Hartkopf and Erbersdobler, 1993; Henle *et al.*, 1995; Nicoletti *et al.*, 2000; Resmini *et al.*, 1990) or by capillary electrophoresis (Corradini *et al.*, 1996). Furosine has been used not only to distinguish between different types of heat treatment (Clawin-Raedecker *et al.*, 2000; Pellegrino *et al.*, 1995; Villamiel *et al.*, 2000), but also to determine whether milk powder has been added to fluid milk or as an indicator for reconstituted milk (Ohta *et al.*, 2002; Van Renterghem and De Block, 1996).

Lactulose is formed by isomerisation of lactose during the heating of milk, and has been proposed as an analytical index to distinguish UHT from sterilised milk (Clawin-Radecker *et al.*, 1992); it is not found in pasteurised milk. A variety of methods were used for its determination: GLC (Martinez-Castro *et al.*, 1987), HPLC (Cataldi *et al.*, 1999; IDF Standard 147: 1991), capillary electrophoresis (Soga and Serwe, 2000), enzymology (Amine *et al.*, 2000a; Kuhlmann *et al.*, 1991), colorimetry (Amine *et al.*, 2000b) and continuous-flow amperometry (Mayer *et al.*, 1996; Moscone *et al.*, 1999).

Another Maillard reaction product, lysinoalanine (LAL), was shown to be a sensitive indicator for heat treatment of milk and for addition of dairy-based substitutes rich in LAL (caseinates, etc.) to other milk products, in particular cheese (Faist *et al.*, 2000; Moret *et al.*, 1997; Pellegrino *et al.*, 1996). Maillard products have fluorescent properties and this feature was used for a very sensitive and rapid determination of the heat load, which was in good agreement with more established procedures (Birlouez-Aaragon *et al.*, 2002). Novel strategies for the estimation of heat load are the direct determination of glycosylated proteins, either by immunology (Pallini *et al.*, 2001), by HPLC (Pellegrino and Cattaneo, 2001) or by mass spectrometry (Cozzolino *et al.*, 2001).

10.6 Identifying geographical origin

Products manufactured in a particular way in a specific geographical region have always found a following, although they usually command a higher price. Marketing of agricultural products has recently focused on promotion of premium goods in affluent countries. Traditional cheese varieties such as

Camembert, Parmesan or Stilton are in high demand, and to protect their market legal instruments have been introduced in the EU (Council Regulation (EEC) 2081/92). To be eligible to use a protected designation of origin (PDO) or a protected geographical indication (PGI), an agricultural product or foodstuff must comply with strict specifications. On-site inspections by a control authority are currently the only accepted way to safeguard the PDO/PGI label, as reliable and validated analytical testing methods do not exist yet.

The most promising approach seems to be to characterise the products by determining stable isotope ratios ($^{13}C/^{12}C$, $^{15}N/^{14}N$, $^{16}O/^{18}O$) and subsequent application of mathematical pattern recognition techniques. This has been applied to the characterisation of the geographical origin of milk (Kornexl et al., 1997), butter (Rossman et al., 2000) and Pecorino Sardo cheese (Manca et al., 2001). It was found that the feeding regimen, in particular maize silage, can influence the $^{13}C/^{12}C$ ratio, use of industrial fertilisers the $^{15}N/^{14}N$ ratio, and the water supply the $^{16}O/^{18}O$ ratio of milk and milk products.

A number of chemical (fat content and pH value), biochemical (L- and D-lactate, and pyruvate), microbiological (lactobacilli and enterococci), colour and sensory parameters were investigated to discriminate between Emmental cheeses of different origin (Pillonel et al., 2002). Although some promising results have been obtained, the analytical approach is in its infancy and much needs to be done to give a reliable indication that verifies the origin of a product.

10.7   Conclusions

Detection of fraud is complicated by the fact that the quantities of certain indicators vary due to biological, climatic, agronomic and temporal factors. Moreover, processing can dramatically change the composition of minor constituents. Therefore, too stringent specifications cannot be set by food inspection, as this will eventually increase the number of false-positive results. Since unscrupulous manufacturers or vendors have developed an excellent understanding of the underlying principles to detect fraud, they have managed in many cases to tailor blends in such a way that they comply with product specifications.

In many cases no fundamental differences, ideally the lack or presence of a product-specific component, between the genuine and the adulterated product exist. Consequently, purity criteria have to be empirically determined by analysing a wide array of genuine products and creating and regularly updating a database holding information about the concentration ranges of certain indicative components of the commodity concerned. In order to solve difficult cases more than one analyte has to be considered for detecting fraud. Likewise, a combination of different analytical techniques to determine dissimilar characteristics of a commodity (e.g. a combination of spectroscopic and chromatographic methods) could be more useful than relying on one single methodology. Given the complexity of some problems, univariate statistics (measures of location and dispersion) have to be substituted by intricate statistical algorithms to aid in pattern recognition and classification of genuine and adulterated products. The merits of such procedures, though scientifically sound, are difficult to comprehend for those not familiar with advanced statistical data interpretation techniques, and might, therefore, find little acceptance in a court of law.

The challenge for food law enforcement agencies is to be a step ahead and to develop constantly new methods to get a better insight into the complex chemical mixture representing food, in order to identify a set of possible marker components for authentication purposes.

10.8 References

ADDEO, F., MOIO, L., CHIANESE, L. and DI LUCCIA, A. (1989). *Ital. J. Food Sci.* **1**: 45–52.

ADDEO, F., MOIO, L., CHIANESE, L., STINGO, C., RESMINI, P., BERNER, I., KRAUSE, I., DI LUCCIA, A. and BOCCA, A. (1990a). *Milchwissenschaft* **45**: 708–711.

ADDEO, F., MOIO, L., CHIANESE, L., STINGO, C. and DI LUCCIA, A. (1990b). *Milchwissenschaft* **45**: 221–224.

ALBALÁ-HURTADO, S., VECIANA-NOGUÉS, M.T., IZQUIERDO-PULIDO, M. and VIDAL-CAROU, M.C. (1997). *J. Agric. Food Chem.* **45**: 2128–2133.

AMERICAN DRY MILK INSTITUTE (1971). *Bulletin* **916**.

AMIGO, L., RAMOS, M., MARTIN ÁLVAREZ, P.J. and BARBOSA, M. (1991). *J. Dairy Sci.* **74**: 1482–1490.

AMINE, A., MOSCONE, D., BERNARDO, R.A., MARCONI, E. and PALLESCHI, G. (2000a). *Anal. Chim. Acta* **406**: 217–224.

AMINE, A., MOSCONE, D. and PALLESCHI, G. (2000b). *Anal. Letters* **33**: 125–135.

ANGELETTI, R., GIOACCHINI, A.M., SERAGLIA, R. and PIRO, R. (1998). *J. Mass Spectrom.* **33**: 525–531.

ANGUITA, G., MARTÍN, R., GARCÍA, T., MORALES, P., HAZA, A.I., GONZÁLEZ, I., SANZ, B. and HERNÁNDEZ, P.E. (1995). *J. Dairy Res.* **62**: 655–659.

ANGUITA, G., MARTÍN, R., GARCÍA, T., MORALES, P., HAZA, A.I., GONZÁLEZ, I., SANZ, B. and HERNÁNDEZ, P.E. (1996a). *Milchwissenschaft* **51**: 21–25.

ANGUITA, G., MARTÍN, R., GARCÍA, T., MORALES, P., HAZA, A.I., GONZÁLEZ, I., SANZ, B. and HERNÁNDEZ, P.E. (1996b). *J. Food Protect.* **59**: 436–437.

ASCHAFFENBURG, R. and DANCE, J.E. (1968). *J. Dairy Res.* **35**: 383–384.

BANIA, J., UGORSKI, M., POLANOWSKI, A. and ADAMCZYK, E. (2001). *J. Dairy Res.* **68**: 333–336.

BASCH, J.J., DOURGLAS JR, F.W., PROCINO, L.G., HOLSINGER, V.H. and FARELL JR, H.M. (1985). *J. Dairy Sci.* **68**: 23–31.

BATTELLI, G. and PELLEGRINO, L. (1994). *Italian J. Food Sci.* **6**: 407–419.

BEER, M., KRAUSE, I., STAPF, M., SCHWARZER, C. and KLOSTERMEYER, H. (1996). *Z. Lebensm. Unters. Forsch.* **203**: 21–26.

BERGER, T., BOSSET, J.O., BUETIKOFER, U., EBERHARD, P., MEYER, J. and TANZER, D. (2001). *Trav. Chim. Aliment. Hyg.* **92**: 663–677.

BIRLOUEZ-AARAGON, I., SABAT, P. and COUTI, N. (2002). *Int. Dairy J.* **12**: 59–67.

BITRI, L., ROLLAND, M.P. and BESANCON, P. (1993). *Milchwissenschaft* **48**: 367–371.

BOBE, G., BEITZ, D.C., FREEMAN, A.E. and LINDBERG, G.L. (1998a). *J. Agric. Food Chem.* **46**: 1321–1325.

BOBE, G., BEITZ, D.C., FREEMAN, A.E. and LINDBERG, G.L. (1998b). *J. Agric. Food Chem.* **46**: 458–463.

BORDIN, G., CORDEIRO RAPOSO, F., DE LA CALLE, B. and RODRIGUEZ, A.R. (2001). *J. Chromatogr. A* **928**: 63–76.

BOTTERO, M.T., CIVERA, T., ANASTASIO, A., TURI, R.M. and ROSATI, S. (2002). *J. Food Protect.* **65**: 362–366.

BRANCIARI, R., NIJMAN, I.J., PLAS, M.E., DI ANTONIO, E. and LENSTRA, J.A. (2000). *J. Food Protect.* **63**: 408–411.

BRINGER, R., RUDZIK, L., WEBER, T. and WUST, E. (1991). *Milchwissenschaft* **46**: 304–307

BROWN, S.D., BEAR JR., R.S. and BLANK, T.B., (1992). *Anal. Chem.* **64**: 22R–49R.

BUCHBERGER, J. (1990). *Arch. Lebensm. Hyg.* **41**: 71–74.

BUCHBERGER, J. (1994). *DMZ Lebensm. Ind. Milchwirt.* **115**: 376–383.

BUCHBERGER, J. (2000). *DMZ Lebensm. Ind. Milchwirt.* **121**: 1054–1056, 1058–1059.

CALVO, J.H., OSTA, R. and ZARAGOZA, P. (2002). *Milchwissenschaft* **57**: 444–446.

CARTONI, G., COCCIOLI, F., JASIONOWSKA, R. and MASCI, M. (1999). *J. Chromatogr. A* **846**: 135–142.

CATALDI, T.R.I., ANGELOTTI, M. and BUFO, S.A. (1999). *Anal. Chem.* **71**: 4919–4925.

CATTANEO, T.M.P., FEROLDI, A., TOPPINO, P.M. and OLIEMAN, C. (1994). *Neth. Milk Dairy J.* **48**: 225–234.

CATTANEO, T.M.P., NIGRO, F. and GREPPI, G.F. (1996). *Milchwissenschaft* **51**: 616–619.

CHRISTIE, W.W., CONNOR, K., NOBLE, R.C., SHAND, J.H. and WAGSTAFFE, P.J. (1987). *J. Chromatogr.* **390**: 444–447.

CLAWIN-RADECKER, I., KUHLMANN, B., WEISS, G., KLOSTERMEYER, H. and SCHLIMME, E. (1992). *Kieler Milchw. Forsch. Ber.* **44**: 129–141.

CLAWIN-RAEDECKER, I., KIESNER, C. and MARTIN, D. (2000). *Milchwissenschaft* **55**: 679–682.

COLLOMB, M. and SPAHNI, M. (1991). *Trav. Chim. Aliment. Hyg.* **82**: 615–662.

COLLOMB, M., SPAHNI, M. and BÜHLER, T. (1998a). *Trav. Chim. Aliment. Hyg.* **89**: 59–74.

COLLOMB, M., SPAHNI, M. and BÜHLER, T. (1998b). *Trav. Chim. Aliment. Hyg.* **89**: 75–83.

COLLOMB, M., BÜTIKOFER, U., SPAHNI, M. and BÜHLER T. (1998c). *Trav. Chim. Alimant. Hyg.* **89**: 617–624.

Commission Decision 91/180/EEC of 14 February 1991 laying down certain methods of analysis and testing of raw milk and heat-treated milk.

Commission Regulation (EC) No. 213/2001 of 9 January 2001 laying down detailed rules for the application of Council Regulation (EC) No. 1255/1999 as regards methods for the analysis and quality evaluation of milk and milk products and amending Regulations (EC) No. 2771/1999 and (EC) No. 2799/1999. *Official Journal of the European Communities* **L37**: 1–99.

CONI, E., DI PASQUALE, M., COPPOLELLI, P. and BOCCA, A. (1994). *J. Am. Oil Chem. Soc.* **71**: 807–810.

CORRADINI, D., CANNARSA, G., CORRADINI, C., NICOLETTI, I., PIZZOFERRATO, L. and VIVANTI, V. (1996). *Electrophoresis* **17**: 120–124.

Council Directive 92/46/EEC of 16 June 1992 laying down the health rules for the production and placing on the market of raw milk, heat-treated milk and milk-based products. *Official Journal of the European Communities* **L268**: 1–32.

Council Regulation (EC) No. 2991/94 of 5 December 1994 laying down standards for spreadable fats. *Official Journal of the European Communities* **L316**: 2–7.

Council Regulation (EEC) No. 2081/92 of 14 July 1992 on the protection of geographical indications and designations of origin for agricultural products and foodstuffs. *Official Journal of the European Communities* **L208**: 1–8.

COVENEY, L. (1993). *J. Soc. Dairy Technol.* **46**: 43–46.

COZZOLINO, R., PASSALACQUA, S., SALEMI, S., MALVAGNA, P., SPINA, E. and GAROZZO, D. (2001). *J. Mass Spectrom.* **36**: 1031–1037.

COZZOLINO, R., PASSALACQUA, S., SALEMI, S. and GAROZZO, D. (2002). *J. Mass Spectrom.* **37**: 985–991.

CREAMER, L.K., PEARCE, L.E., HILL, J.P. and BOLAND, M.J. (2002). *J. Agric. Food Chem.* **50**: 7187–7193.

DE FRUTOS, M., CIFUENTES, A., DIEZ MASA, J.C., AMIGO, L. AND RAMOS, M. (1991). *J. High Res. Chromatogr.* **14**: 289–291.

DE KONING, P.J. and VAN ROOIJEN, P.J. (1971). *Milchwissenschaft* **26**: 1–6.

DE NONI, I., TIRELLI, A. and MASOTTI, F. (1996). *Sci. Tecnica Latt. Casearia* **47**: 7–17.

DOKA, O., BICANIC, D. and FRANKHUIZEN, R. (1999). *Z. Lebensm. Unters. Forsch.* **208**: 1–5.

ESPEJA, E., GARCIA, M.C. and MARINA, M.L. (2001). *J. Separation Sci.* **24**: 856–864.

FAIST, V., DRUSCH, S., KIESNER, C., ELMADFA, I. and ERBERSDOBLER, H.F. (2000). *Int. Dairy J.* **10**: 339–346.

FANTON, C., DELOGU, G., MACCIONI, E., PODDA, G., SERAGLIA, R. and TRALDI, P. (1998). *Rapid Commun. Mass Spectrom.* **12**: 1569–1573.

FERRER, E., ALEGRÍA, A., COURTOIS, G. and FARRÉ, R. (2000). *J. Chromatogr. A* **881**: 599–606.

FOISSY, H. (1976). *Österr. Milchwirt.* **31**: 5–8.

FONTECHA, J., DIAZ, V., FRAGA, M.J. and JUAREZ, M. (1998). *J. Am. Oil Chem. Soc.* **75**: 1893–1896.

FOX, J.R., DUTHIE, A.H. and WULFF, S. (1988). *J. Dairy Sci.* **71**: 574–581.

FREIMUTH, U. and KRAUSE, I. (1968). *Nahrung* **12**: 881–883.

GARCÍA, T., MARTÍN, R., RODRIGUEZ, E., MORALES, P., GONZÁLEZ, I., SANZ, B. and HERNÁNDEZ, P.E. (1994). *Food Agric. Immunol.* **6**: 113–118.

HARTKOPF, J. and ERBERSDOBLER, H.F. (1993). *J. Chromatogr.* **635**: 151–154.

HAZA, A.I., MORALES, P., MARTÍN, R., GARCÍA, T., ANGUITA, G., GONZÁLEZ, I., SANZ, B. and HERNÁNDEZ, P.E. (1996). *J. Agric. Food Chem.* **44**: 1756–1761.

HENLE, T., ZEHETNER, G. and KLOSTERMEYER, H. (1995). *Z. Lebensm. Unters. Forsch.* **200**: 235–237.

HOMBERG, E. (1991). *Fat Sci. Technol.* **93**: 516–517.

HOMBERG, E. and BIELEFELD, H. (1979). *Z. Lebensm. Unters. Forsch.* **169**: 464–467.

HUGHEBAERT, A. AND HENDRICKX, H. (1971). *Milchwissenschaft* **26**: 613–617.

International Dairy Federation Standard 32:1965.

International Dairy Federation Standard 54:1970.

International Dairy Federation Standard 108B:1991.

International Dairy Federation Standard 147:1991.

International Dairy Federation Standard 178:1996.

IVERSON, J.L. and SHEPPARD, A.J. (1989). *J. Dairy Sci.* **72**: 1707–1712.

JEANSON, S., DUPONT, D., GRATTARD, N. and ROLET-RÉPÉCAUD, O. (1999). *J. Agric. Food Chem.* **47**: 2249–2254.

KAMINARIDES, S.E. and KOUKIASSA, P. (2002). *Food Chem.* **78**: 53–55.

KAMM, W., DIONISI, F., HISCHENHUBER, C., SCHMARR, H.G. and ENGEL, K.H. (2002). *Eur. J. Lipid Sci. Technol.* **104**: 756–761.

KANNING, M., CASELLA, M. and OLIEMAN, C. (1993). *LC-GC Int.* **34**: 1–4.

226 Dairy processing

KLOTZ, A. and EINSPANIER, R. (2001). *Milchwissenschaft* **56**: 67–70.

KNEIFEL, W. and ULBERTH, F. (1985). *Milchwissenschaft* **40**: 265–269.

KORNEXL, B.E., WERNER, T., ROßMANN, A. and SCHMIDT, H.-L. (1997). *Z. Lebensm. Unters. Forsch.* **205**: 19–24.

KRAUSE, I., BELITZ, H.D. and KAISER, K.P. (1982). *Z. Lebensm. Unters. Forsch.* **174**: 195–199.

KUHLMANN, B., KLOSTERMEYER, H. and FRIES, A. (1991). *Milchwissenschaft* **46**: 555–558.

LAPORTE, M.F. and PAQUIN, P. (1998). *Seminars Food Anal.* **3**: 173–190.

LECHNER, E. (1996). *Dtsch. Milchw.* **47**: 6–10.

LECHNER, E. and KLOSTERMEYER, H. (1981). *Milchwissenschaft* **36**: 267–270.

LEE, S.C., CHEN, M.C. and LIN, C.W. (2001). *Aust. J. Dairy Technol.* **56**: 24–27.

LEVIEUX, D. and VENIEN, A. (1994). *J. Dairy Res.* **61**: 91–99.

LIPP, M. (1996a). *Z. Lebensm. Unters. Forsch.* **202**: 193–198.

LIPP, M. (1996b). *Food Chem.* **55**: 389–395.

LOPEZ FANDINO, R., ACEDO, M.I. and RAMOS, M. (1993). *J. Dairy Res.* **60**: 117–121.

LUF, W. (1988). *Dtsch. Milchw.* **21**: 699–701.

LUF, W. and BRANDL, E. (1987). *Milchwissenschaft* **42**: 275–278.

LÜTHI-PENG, Q.Q. and PUHAN, Z. (1999) *Milchwissenschaft* **54**: 74–77.

MANCA, G., CAMIN, F., COLORU, G.C., DEL CARO, A., DEPENTORI, D., FRANCO, M.A. and VERSINI, G. (2001). *J. Agric. Food Chem.* **49**: 1404–1409.

MANSO, M.A., CATTANEO, T.M., BARZAGHI, S., OLIEMAN, C. and LOPEZ FANDINO, R. (2002). *J. AOAC Int.* **85**: 1090–1095.

MARTINEZ-CASTRO, I., CALVO, M.M. and OLANO, A. (1987). *Chromatographia* **23**: 132–136.

MARTINEZ PENAGOS, A., EZQUERRA PLASENCIA, R., GARCIA ALVAREZ, J.A. and RODRIGUEZ LOPERENA, M.A. (1993). *Alimentaria* **243**: 47–50.

MAUDET, C. and TABERLET, P. (2001). *J. Dairy Res.* **68**: 229–235.

MAYER, H.K., HEIDLER, D. and ROCKENBAUER, C. (1997). *Int. Dairy J.* **7**: 619–628.

MAYER, M., GENRICH, M., KUENNECKE, W. and BILITEWSKI, U. (1996). *Anal. Chim. Acta* **324**: 37–45.

MAYER, W. and HÖRTNER, H. (1992). *Electrophoresis* **13**: 803–804.

MEISEL, H. (1995). *Milchwissenschaft* **50**: 247–251.

MEISEL, H. and CARSTENS, J. (1989). *Milchwissenschaft* **44**: 271–277.

MIRALLES, B., BARTOLOME, B., AMIGO, L. and RAMOS, M. (2000). *J. Dairy Sci.* **83**: 2759–2765.

MOLINA, E., FERNANDEZ FOURNIER, A., DE FRUTOS, M. and RAMOS, M. (1996). *J. Dairy Sci.* **79**: 191–197.

MOLINA, E., MARTIN ÁLVAREZ, P.J. and RAMOS, M. (1999). *Int. Dairy J.* **9**: 99–105.

MOLINA, E., DE FRUTOS, M. and RAMOS, M. (2000). *J. Dairy Res.* **67**: 209–216.

MOLKENTIN, J. and PRECHT, D. (1994). *Chromatographia* **39**: 265–270.

MOLKENTIN, J. and PRECHT, D. (1997). *Milchwissenschaft* **52**: 82–85.

MOLKENTIN, J. and PRECHT, D. (1998a). *Z. Lebensm. Unters. Forsch.* **206**: 213–216.

MOLKENTIN, J. and PRECHT, D. (1998b). *Chromatographia* **48**: 758–762.

MOLKENTIN, J. and PRECHT, D. (2000). *Eur. J. Lipid Sci. Technol.* **102**: 194–201.

MORET, S., CHERUBIN, S. and LERCKER, G. (1997). *Latte* **22**: 80–81.

MOSCONE, D., BERNARDO, R.A., MARCONI, E., AMINE, A. and PALLESCHI, G. (1999). *Analyst* **124**: 325–329.

MROWETZ, G. and KLOSTERMEYER, H. (1976). *Milchwissenschaft* **31**: 346–349.

MUUSE, B.G., WERDMULLER, G.A., GEERTS, J.P. and DE KNEGT, R. (1986). *Neth. Milk Dairy J.* **40**: 189–201.

NICOLETTI, I., COGLIANDRO, E., CORRADINI, C., CORRADINI, D. and PIZZOFERRATO, L. (2000). *J. Liquid Chromatogr.* **23**: 717–726.

Official Journal of the European Communities **L93**: 1–48.

OHTA, T., YOSHIDA, T., KANZAKI, B., HOSONO, A. and SUYAMA, K. (2002) *Milchwissenschaft* **57**: 70–73.

PALLESCHI, G. (2001). *Analyst* **126**: 66–70.

PALLINI, M., COMPAGNONE, D., DI STEFANO, S., MARINI, S., COLETTA, M. and PALLESCHI, G. (2001). *Analyst* **126**: 66–70.

PELLEGRINO, L. and CATTANEO, S. (2001). *Nahrung* **45**: 195–200.

PELLEGRINO, L., DE NONI, I. and RESMINI, P. (1995). *Int. Dairy J.* **5**: 647–659.

PELLEGRINO, L., RESMINI, P., DE NONI, I. and MASOTTI, F. (1996). *J. Dairy Sci.* **79**: 725–734.

PILLONEL, L., BADERTSCHER, R., BÜTIKOFER, U., CASEY, M., DALLA TORRE, M., LAVANCHY, P., MEYER, J., TABACCHI, R. and BOSSET, J.O. (2002). *Eur. Food Res. Technol.* **215**: 260–267.

PLATH, A., KRAUSE, I. and EINSPANIER, R. (1997). *Z. Lebensm. Unters. Forsch.* **205**: 437–441.

POCKLINGTON, W.D. and HAUTFENNE, A. (1986). *Pure Appl. Chem.* **58**: 1419–1428.

POVOLO, M., BONFITTO, E., CONTARINI, G. and TOPPINO, P.M. (1999). *High Res. Chromatogr.* **22**: 97–102.

PRECHT, D. (1992a). *Z. Lebensm. Unters. Forsch.* **194**: 1–8.

PRECHT, D. (1992b). *Z. Lebensm. Unters. Forsch.* **194**: 107–114.

PRECHT, D. (1992c). *Dtsch. Molkerei Ztg.* **113**: 796–803.

PRECHT, D. and HEINE, K. (1986a). *Milchwissenschaft* **41**: 329–334.

PRECHT, D. and HEINE, K. (1986b). *Milchwissenschaft* **41**: 406–410.

RAMOS, M. and JUAREZ, M. (1984). *FIL-IDF Bulletin* **181**: 3–9.

RASMUSSEN, K.W. (2003). In *Encyclopedia of Dairy Sciences*, ed. H. Roginski, J.W. Fuquay and P.F. Fox, Academic Press, Amsterdam, pp. 15–20.

RECIO, I., MOLINA, E., RAMOS, M. and DE FRUTOS M. (1995). *Electrophoresis* **16**: 654–658.

RECIO, I., LOPEZ FANDINO, R., OLANO, A., OLIEMAN, C. AND RAMOS, M. (1996). *J. Agric. Food Chem.* **44**: 3845–3848.

RECIO, I., GARCIA RISCO, M.R., LOPEZ FANDINO, R., OLANO, A. and RAMOS, M. (2000). *Int. Dairy J.* **10**: 333–338.

RESMINI, P., PELLEGRINO, L., HOGENBOOM, J.A. and ANDREINI, R. (1989). *Ital. J. Food Sci.* **3**: 51–62.

RESMINI, P., PELLEGRINO, L. and BATTELLI, G. (1990). *Ital. J. Food Sci.* **2**: 173–183.

RICHTER, W., KRAUSE, I., GRAF, C., SPERRER, I., SCHWARZER, C. and KLOSTERMEYER, H. (1997). *Z. Lebensm. Unters. Forsch.* **204**: 21–26.

RISPOLI, S., RIVEMALE, M. and SAUGES, R. (1991). *Lait* **71**: 501–510.

ROBINSON, R.K. (2002). *Dairy Microbiology Handbook*, 3rd edn, Wiley Interscience, New York.

RODRIGUEZ, E., MARTÍN, R., GARCÍA, T., GONZÁLEZ, I., MORALES, P., SANZ, B. and HERNÁNDEZ, P.E. (1993). *J. Sci. Food Agric.* **61**: 175–180.

ROHM, H. (1993). *Z. Lebensm. Unters. Forsch.* **197**: 558–561.

ROHM, H., PLESCHBERGER, C. and FOISSY, H. (1991). *Ernährung/Nutrition* **15**: 333–337.

ROHM, H., SÖLKNER, J. and PLESCHBERGER, C. (1992). *Ernährung/Nutrition* **16**: 135–140.

ROLLAND, M.P., BITRI, L. and BESANCON, P. (1993). *J. Dairy Res.* **60**: 413–420.

ROMERO, C., PEREZ ANDUJAR, O., OLMEDO, A. and JIMENEZ, S. (1996). *Chromatographia* **42**: 181–184.

ROSENTHAL, I., BERNSTEIN, S. and MERIN, U. (1999). *Milchwissenschaft* **54**: 367–368.

ROSSMAN, A., HABERHAUER, G., HÖLZL, S., HORN, P., PICHLMAYER, F. and VOERKELIUS, S. (2000). *Eur. Food Res. Technol.* **211**: 32–40.

SANCHEZ, L., PEREZ, M.D., PUYOL, P., CALVO, M. and BRETT, G. (2002). *J. AOAC Int.* **85**: 1390–1397.

SATO, T., KAWANO, S. and IWAMOTO, M. (1990). *J. Dairy Sci.* **73**: 3408–3413.

SCHMIDT, M.A.E., RADOVIC, B.S., LIPP, M., HARZER, G. and ANKLAM, E. (1999). *Food Chem.* **65**: 123–128.

SCHWAIGER, I. and VOJIR, F. (1995). *Ernährung/Nutrition* **19**: 67–69.

SLAGHUIS, B.A. (2001). *Int. Dairy J.* **11**: 121–126.

SOGA, T. and SERWE, M. (2000). *Food Chem.* **69**: 339–344.

TIMMS, R.E. (1980). *J. Dairy Res.* **47**: 295–303.

TOPPINO, P.M., CONTARINI, G., TRAVERSI, A.L., AMELOTTI, G. and GARGANO, A. (1982). *Riv. Ital. Sost. Grasse* **54**: 592–610.

TURIN, L. and BONOMI, F. (1994). *J. Sci. Food Agric.* **64**: 39–45.

ULBERTH, F. (1994). *J AOAC Int.* **77**: 1326–1333.

ULBERTH, F. (1998a). *Z. Lebensm. Unters. Forsch.* **206**: 305–307.

ULBERTH, F. (1998b). *Int. Dairy J.* **7**: 799–803.

ULBERTH, F. and ROGENHOFER, M. (1989). *Ernährung/Nutrition* **13**: 3–9.

ULBERTH, F., GABERNIG, R. and ROUBICEK, D. (1998). *Z. Lebensm. Unters. Forsch A* **206**: 21–24.

URBANKE, W., LUF, W. and BRANDL, E. (1992). *Z. Lebensm. Unters. Forsch.* **195**: 137–142.

VALLEJO CORDOBA, B. (1998). *J. Capillary Electrophoresis* **5**: 133-137.

VAN RENTERGHEM, R. (1997). *Milchwissenschaft* **52**: 79–82.

VAN RENTERGHEM, R. and DE BLOCK, J. (1996). *Int. Dairy J.* **6**: 371–382.

VAN RIEL, J.A.M. and OLIEMAN, C. (1995a). *Anal. Chem.* **67**: 3911–3915.

VAN RIEL, J.A.M. and OLIEMAN, C. (1995b). *Electrophoresis* **16**: 529–533.

VELOSO, A.C.A., TEIXEIRA, N. and FERREIRA, I.M.P.L.V.O. (2002). *J. Chromatogr. A* **967**: 209–218.

VILLAMIEL, M., VAZQUEZ, A., MORAIS, F. and CORZO, N. (2000). *Milchwissenschaft* **55**: 320–322.

VOLITAKI, A.J. and KAMINARIDES, S.E. (2001). *Milchwissenschaft* **56**: 207–210.

WIEDEMANN, M., BUCHBERGER, J. and KLOSTERMEYER, H. (1993). *DMZ Lebensm. Ind. Milchwirt.* **114**: 634–644.

WOLFSCHOON-POMBO, A.F. and FURTADO, M.A.M. (1989). *Z. Lebensm. Unters. Forsch.* **188**: 16–21.

YOUNES, N.A. and SOLIMAN, M.M.A. (1986). *Grasas y Aceites* **37**: 200–203.

11

Functional dairy products

M. Saxelin, R. Korpela and A. Mäyrä-Mäkinen, Valio Ltd, Finland

11.1 Introduction

Dairy products form the major part of functional foods. To understand their success it is important to know that milk is a natural and highly nutritive part of a balanced daily diet. Designing and developing functionality in dairy-based products simply means modifying and/or enriching the healthy nature of the original base. This chapter is a brief introduction to the composition of milk and the nature of fermented milk products. It also gives a few definitions and introduces some of the functional dairy products on the market. The purpose of this chapter is not to evaluate the quality and depth of the science behind each product: some of these products are tested in their final state, while the functionality of others is based on accepted knowledge of a particular compound. At the same time, this chapter offers some 'good guesses' as to the potential development of functional dairy foods in the future.

11.2 Composition of milk

The milks of various mammalian species differ in the amount and type of their components. This review focuses on cows' milk and those products of which cows' milk forms a prominent ingredient. Cows' milk is mainly composed of water, with approximately 4.8% lactose, 3.2% protein, 3.7% fat, 0.19% non-protein nitrogen and 0.7% ash. The principal families of proteins in milk are caseins, whey proteins and immunoglobulins. About 80% of proteins are caseins (Banks and Dalgleish, 1990).

Caseins (α_{s1}-, α_{s2}-, β- and κ-) and whey proteins differ in their physiological and biological properties. Caseins form complexes called micelles with calcium. Globular α-lactalbumin and β-lactoglobulin are the main whey proteins. They constitute 70–80% of the total whey proteins, the remainder being immuno-globulins, glycomacropeptide, serum albumin, lactoferrin and numerous enzymes. Some of the biological properties of milk proteins are shown in Table 11.1. Milk proteins are a rich source of precursors of biologically active peptides. Bioactive peptides are formed by the enzymatic hydrolysis of proteins or by the proteolytic activity of lactic acid bacteria in microbial fermentations. Many of the peptides survive through the intestinal tract. Bioactive peptides are also formed *in vivo* by the enzymatic hydrolysis of the digestive enzymes. Table 11.2 shows some bioactive peptides derived from milk proteins, and also their functions.

Milk fat is a complex of lipids, and exists in microscopic globules in an oil-in-water emulsion in milk. The majority of milk lipids are triglycerides or the esters of fatty acids combined with glycerol (97–98%), and the minority are phospholipids (0.2–1%), free sterols (0.2–0.4%) and traces of free fatty acids. About 62% of milk fat is saturated, 30% monounsaturated (oleic acid), 4% polyunsaturated and 4% of minor types of fatty acids (Miller *et al.*, 2000).

Lactose is the principal carbohydrate in milk. It is a disaccharide formed from galactose and glucose. Lactose forms about 54% of the total non-fat milk solids. It also provides 30% of the energy of milk. In addition to high-value protein, milk also provides vital minerals and vitamins. It is an important source of minerals, in particular of calcium, phosphorus, magnesium, potassium and trace elements such

Table 11.1 Biological activities of major cows' milk proteins (Korhonen *et al.*, 1998)

Protein	Suggested functions	Concentration (g/l)
Caseins (α, β and κ)	Iron carrier (Ca, Fe, Zn, Cu) Precursors of bioactive peptides	28
α-Lactalbumin	Lactose synthesis in mammary gland, Ca carrier, immunomodulation, anticarcinogenic	1.2
β-Lactoglobulin	Retinol carrier, fatty acids binding, possible antioxidant	1.3
Immunoglobulins A, M and G	Immune protection	0.7
Glycomacropeptide	Antiviral, antibacterial, bifidogenic Releases protein to cause satiety?	1.2
Lactoferrin	Toxin binding Antimicrobial, antiviral Immunomodulation Anticarcinogenic Antioxidative Iron absorption	0.1
Lactoperoxidase	Antimicrobial	0.03
Lysozyme	Antimicrobial, synergistic with immunoglobulins and lactoferrin	0.0004

Table 11.2 Bioactive peptides derived from cows' milk proteins (Korhonen *et al.*, 1998; Clare and Swaisgood, 2000)

Bioactive peptides	Protein precursor	Bioactivity
Casomorphins	α- and β-Casein	Opioid agonists
α-Lactorphin	α-Lactalbumin	Opioid agonists
β-Lactorphin	β-Lactoglobulin	Opioid agonists
Lactoferroxins	Lactoferrin	Opioid antagonists
Casoxins	κ-Casein	Opioid antagonists
Casokinins	α- and β-Casein	Antihypertensive
Casoplatelins	κ-Casein, transferrin	Antithrombotic
Casecidin	α- and β-Casein	Antimicrobial
Isracidin	α-Casein	Antimicrobial
Immunopeptides	α- and β-Casein	Immunostimulants
Phosphopeptides	α- and β-Casein	Mineral carriers
Lactoferricin	Lactoferrin	Antimicrobial
Glycomacropeptide	Caseins	Anti-stress

as zinc. In many countries, especially in Europe, milk is the principal source of calcium, providing about 60–80% of the total calcium intake. Calcium forms soluble complexes with milk protein, casein, and phosphorus, and is easily absorbed. Milk contains all the vitamins known to be essential to humans. Vitamins A, D, E and K are associated with the fat component of milk. In northern countries where there is a shortage of sunshine in winter, milk and milk fat has traditionally been the major source of vitamin D. Milk also provides water-soluble vitamins (ascorbic acid, thiamin, riboflavin, niacin, pantothenic acid, vitamin B6, folate and vitamin B12) in variable quantities (Miller *et al.*, 2000).

11.3   Fermented milk products

The Scandinavian countries have a long tradition of using fermented dairy products. In the old days, the seasonal variation in milk production led the farms to preserve milk for the cold winter in the forms of butter and its by-product, buttermilk, as well as other traditional fermented milk products (Leporanta, 2001). Later, the industrial production of these products began, and selected product-specific starter cultures became commercially available. The consumption of milk and fermented milks in selected countries in Europe and some other countries is shown in Fig. 11.1. Cultured buttermilks, or fermented milk products as they are also called, are primarily consumed plain, but flavoured varieties are available, too. Mesophilic *Lactococcus lactis* subsp. *lactis/cremoris/diacetylactis* and *Leuconoctoc cremoris* strains are used for fermentation at 20–30°C for 16–20 h. Starter cultures other than mesophilic lactococci/leuconostoc can also be used for the fermentation of milk drinks. There are products on the market which are fermented with a special strain of lactobacilli (e.g. *L. casei*) or a mixture of several lactobacilli, lactococci and

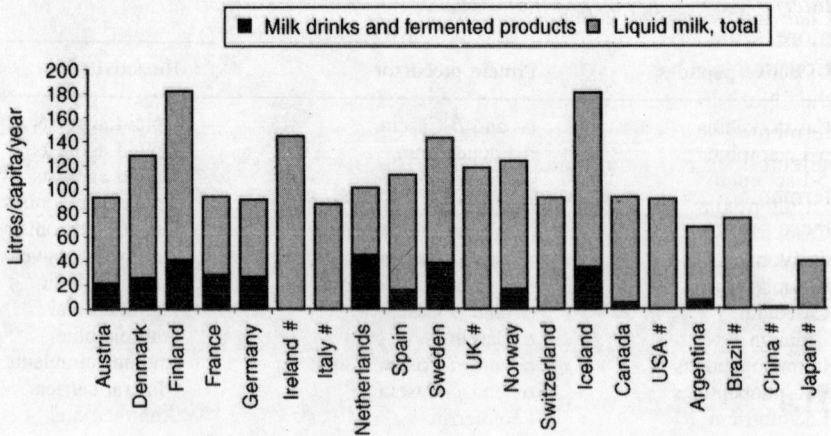

Fig. 11.1 The consumption of milk drinks and fermented products and total consumption of liquid milk in selected countries. #Data not available for fermented products.

other genera/species. For example kefir, a traditional fermented milk drink originating from the Balkans, is produced by a starter culture containing various species of *Lactococcus*, *Leuconostoc*, *Lactobacillus*, *Acetobacter* and yeasts, giving the product its special flavour and aroma.

The health effects of fermented milk products became known through the works of Professor Elie Metchnikoff (Pasteur Institute, Paris), who about a hundred years ago discovered that the secret of the long life of Bulgarian peasants lay in their high consumption of a fermented milk product, yoghurt. Since the 1950s, the flavouring of yoghurt with fruits has increased consumption radically. Today yoghurt is of ever-increasing popularity and there are various types of yoghurt on the market. All yoghurts have this in common: that the milk is fermented with *Streptococcus thermophilus* and *Lactobacillus delbrueckii* subsp. *bulgaricus*, which grow in synergy in milk. The fermentation is carried out at 30–43°C for 2.5–20 h. The selection of the starter culture strains defines the fermentation time and thus the structure and flavour of the final product. Fruit preparations may then be added to the fermented milk base before packaging.

Quark-based products (fresh cheeses, etc.) are also made with microbial fermentations of milk, but the whey is separated after milk coagulation. The production processes vary, but many products contain live lactic acid bacteria. Matured cheeses are formed if coagulated milk protein and milk fat are further processed by pressing, salting and maturing in a cool temperature for various periods of time.

All fermented milk products contain live lactic acid bacteria, unless they are pasteurised after fermentation. In 2000 the total consumption of fermented milks and yoghurts in the EU was about 6.35 million tonnes (*Bulletin of the*

International Dairy Federation **368**, 2001). That means a total consumption of more than 10^{20} colony-forming units (cfu) of lactic acid bacteria. Consumption varies considerably according to country, the highest being in the Nordic countries and the Netherlands. Since Metchnikoff's time, fermented milks have been thought to offer health benefits. The addition of selected, well-documented health-effective strains (probiotics) to the fermentations is an easy and natural way of enhancing the functionality of these products. When one considers the healthy nature of milk, consumed on a daily basis, it is hardly surprising that the major part of functional foods is dairy based.

11.4   What do we mean by functional dairy products?

Functional foods are not defined in the EU directives. Some countries (e.g. the UK, Sweden, Finland) have national rules (guidelines on health claims) for the interpretation of the current legislation (Directives 65/65/EEC and 2000/13/EC) in relation to health claims, but as more products are advertised and marketed across borders, harmonisation at the EU level is needed (Smith, 2001). A draft proposal (working document Sanco/1832/2002) is under discussion. In Finland new guidelines were launched in June 2002. The European Functional Food Science Programme, funded by the European Union and led by the International Life Sciences Institute (ILSI), defines functional foods as follows (Diplock, 1999):

> A food can be regarded as 'functional' if it is satisfactorily demonstrated to affect beneficially one or more target functions in the body, beyond adequate nutritional effects in a way that is relevant to either an improved state of health and well-being and/or reduction of risk of disease.

What is actually meant by 'satisfactorily demonstrated'? One of the interpretations is that a food product can be called functional only if its health benefit has been shown in the consumption of a normal daily dose of the final product, or an effective dose of the ingredient is used and the impact of the food matrix is known. There is a general consensus that, in order to be 'satisfactorily demonstrated', at least two high-quality human intervention studies must have been completed.

Dairy foods can be divided into three groups:

- Basic products (milk, fermented milks, cheeses, ice cream, etc.).
- Added-value products, in which the milk composition has been changed, e.g. low-lactose or lactose-free products, hypoallergenic formulae with hydrolysed protein for milk-hypersensitive infants, milk products enriched with Ca, vitamins, etc. Primarily, these products are targeted at specific consumer groups, and, depending on individual opinions, are included or not in the functional food category.

• Functional dairy products with a proven health benefit. Products are based on milk that is enriched with a functional component, or the product is based on ingredients originating from milk. The most common functional dairy products are those with probiotic bacteria, quite frequently enriched with prebiotic carbohydrates.

11.5 Examples of functional dairy products: gastrointestinal health and general well-being

11.5.1 Probiotic products

Probiotic bacteria are live microbial strains that, when applied in adequate doses, beneficially affect the host animal by improving its intestinal microbial balance. **Probiotic foods** are food products that contain a living probiotic ingredient in an adequate matrix and in sufficient concentration, so that after their ingestion, the postulated effect is obtained, and is beyond that of usual nutrient suppliers (De Vrese and Schrezenmeir, 2001).

It is clear, then, that the tradition of fermented dairy products is long, and to make these products 'functional' is a natural and fairly simple concept (Lourens-Hattingh and Viljoen, 2001). The probiotic strains used in dairy products most commonly belong to *Lactobacillus* and *Bifidobacterium* genera (see Table 11.3). The characteristics of probiotic strains vary, and each strain has to be studied individually. The primary requirement of a probiotic strain is that it should be adequately identified with methods based on genetics, and that the strain should be defined in the text of the product package. This makes it possible to analyse the scientific data behind any claims made.

Some probiotic strains are sufficiently proteolytic to grow excellently in milk, but others need growth stimulants. Those that do not ferment lactose need monosaccharides (Saxelin *et al.*, 1999; De Vrese and Schrezenmeir, 2001). Sometimes the texture or the taste of a milk product fermented with a probiotic does not meet with consumer approval or is technologically impractical. For this reason it is common to use probiotic strains together with standard starter cultures (yoghurt, mesophilic, etc). Probiotics can be added before the fermentation of the milk, or part of the milk can be fermented separately with the probiotic strain and the two parts mixed after the fermentations.

Table 11.3 The most common species of bacteria used in probiotic dairy foods

• *Lactobacillus acidophilus* group:
   L. acidophilus, L. johnsonii,
   L. gasseri, L. crispatus
 • *L. casei/paracasei*
 • *L. rhamnosus*
 • *L. reuteri*
 • *L. plantarum*
	• *Bifidobacterium lactis*
	 • *B. bifidum*
	 • *B. infantis*
	 • *B. breve*
	 • *B. animalis*
	 • *B. adolescentis*

Alternatively, a probiotic strain can be added to the fermented product after fermentation. Sometimes the milk is not fermented at all.

The level of a probiotic strain has to be stable and viable during the shelf-life of the product. There are reports showing that this is not always the case (Shah, 2000). However, research on the subject has changed the situation and will further improve the quality of probiotic products. Today most of the defined probiotic strains used in dairy products have good storage stability. As to the testing of functionality, the easiest method is to develop one type of product and to test its health benefits. Multinational companies often operate in several countries with the same product image marketed under the same trade mark. The small bottle – the 'daily dose' concept – is a good example of this. Identical bottles of Yakult (with the *Lactobacillus casei* Shirota strain) or those of Danone Actimel (with the *L. casei* Imunitass strain DN 114 001) are marketed with the same product concept and the same marketing message all over the world.

However, to meet consumers' demands for probiotic foods in different countries, different types of products are also needed. One way to meet this challenge is to try to define an effective daily dose to be used in various types of products. For example, *Lactobacillus rhamnosus* GG is used in Finland in cultured buttermilks, 'sweet' milk, yoghurts, fermented whey-based drinks, set-type fermented milks ('*viili*'), cheeses, juices, and mixtures of milk and juice. It is not reasonable or scientifically interesting to repeat clinical studies with all the different types, especially when the overall claims to be used in marketing are the same general level. Milk is a protective food matrix for probiotics and improves the survival of the strain in the intestine. As can be seen in Fig. 11.2, if one wishes to re-isolate the strain in stool samples during daily consumption, much lower doses of *Lactobacillus* GG can be used in milk or cheese than in capsules or in powders.

The most common probiotic dairy products worldwide are various types of yoghurt, other fermented dairy products (e.g. cultured buttermilks in Finland), various lactic acid bacteria drinks ('Yakult-type') and mixtures of probiotic (fermented) milks and fruit juice. Probiotic cheeses, both fresh and ripened, have also been launched recently. From January 2000 to May 2002, 25 functional cheeses were launched in Europe, 19 of which, it was claimed, contained an active culture or a probiotic strain (Mintel's Global New Products Database; www.gnpd.com). In addition to everyday products, probiotics are also used in indulgence products, e.g. ice creams.

Probiotic dairy foods (with certain specific strains) are known to relieve intestinal discomfort, prevent diarrhoea and improve recovery. However, no country will accept this claim, as it is too medical for use in the marketing of food. The most common health claim used for probiotic dairy foods may be 'improves natural defence systems', but as far as we know, the science behind that statement is not officially evaluated in any country for any product. In Japan, where functional food legislation is organised best, the package claims for the accepted Food for Specified Health Use (FOSHU) regulation lactobacilli products are that they balance gastrointestinal functions. Recently a claim that a

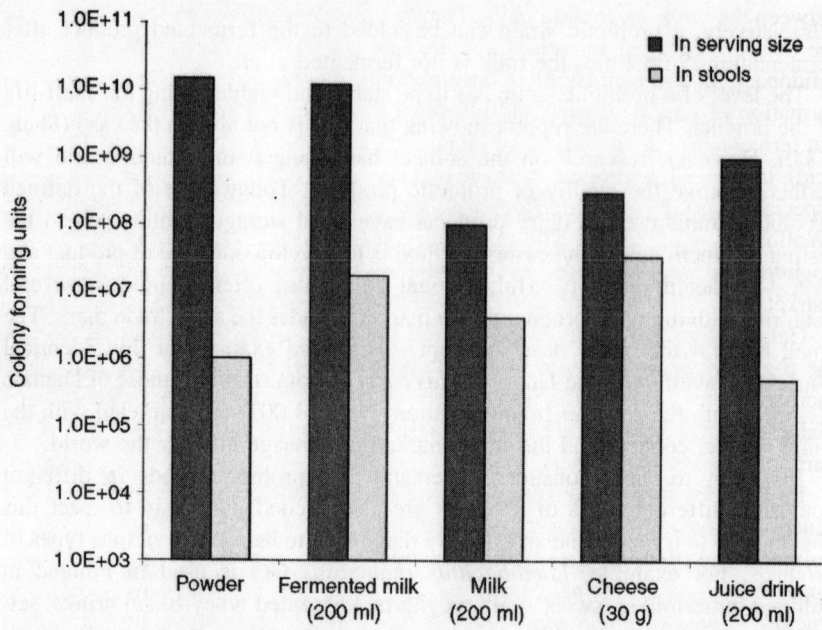

Fig. 11.2 The recovery of *Lactobacillus* GG in faecal samples during daily consumption of different product forms. The daily dose of the probiotic strain (log cfu) per serving and the level in stool samples (log cfu/g wet mass) are indicated in the vertical axis.

yoghurt product enriched with a strain of *L. gasseri* suppressed *Helicobacter pylori* (one cause of peptic ulcers) was also accepted. There are other products that supposedly suppress the growth and activity of *H. pylori*, both in Europe and in the Korean Republic.

11.5.2   Prebiotic and synbiotic dairy products
Prebiotics are non-digestible food ingredients that beneficially affect the host by selectively stimulating the growth and/or activity of one or a limited number of bacteria in the colon. **Prebiotic foods** are food products that contain a prebiotic ingredient in an adequate matrix and in sufficient concentration, so that after their ingestion, the postulated effect is obtained, and is beyond that of usual nutrient suppliers. **Synbiotics** are mixtures of pro- and prebiotics that beneficially affect the host by improving the survival and implantation of selected live microbial strains in the gastrointestinal tract (De Vrese and Schrezenmeir, 2001).

In contrast to probiotics, which introduce exogenous bacteria into the human intestine, prebiotics stimulate the preferential growth of a limited number of bacteria already existing in a healthy, indigenous microbiota. The clue to prebiotic compounds is that they are not digested in the upper gastrointestinal tract, because of the inability of the digestive enzymes to hydrolyse the bond between the monosaccharide units. They act as soluble fibres and are digested in the colon, enhancing microbial activity and stimulating the growth mainly of bifidobacteria and lactobacilli. Consumption of higher doses may encourage the formation of gas, flatulence and intestinal discomfort. The end-products in the gut fermentation are mainly short chain fatty acids (acetic, propionic and butyric acid), lactic acid, hydrogen, methane and carbon dioxide. Short chain fatty acids, especially butyric acid, are known to act as an energy source for enterocytes (Wollowski *et al.*, 2001). The main dairy products enriched with prebiotics are yoghurts and yoghurt drinks, but spreads, fresh cheeses and milks are also on the market.

Galactooligosaccharide, a milk-based prebiotic, is derived from lactose by the β-galactosidase enzyme. It is a natural prebiotic of human breast milk, and facilitates the growth of bifidobacteria and lactobacilli in breast-fed infants. Galactooligosaccharides are commercially used principally in Japan and other parts of Asia.

In Europe inulin and fructooligosaccharides are widely used in various functional foods, including dairy-based products. Inulin is a group of fructose polymers linked by $\beta(2-1)$ bonds that limit their digestion by enzymes in the upper intestine. Their chain lengths range from 2 to 60. Oligofructose is any fructose oligosaccharide containing two to ten monosaccharide units linked with glycosidic linkage. Both inulin and fructooligosaccharides (oligofructoses) are extracted from plant material (e.g. chicory) or synthesised from sucrose. The role of inulin and the oligofructoses in a food matrix is bi-functional. They do not increase the viscosity of a milk product but give a richer texture to liquid products and spreads.

11.5.3 Low-lactose and lactose-free milk products

In the human intestine lactose is hydrolysed by a lactase enzyme developed in the brush border of the small intestine. When a person has a lactase deficiency and lactose causes intestinal discomfort and other symptoms, this is called lactose intolerance, and is quite common in most parts of the world. The incidence of lactose intolerance is low only in the Nordic countries, the British Isles, Australia and New Zealand. Most people can drink one glass of milk (~10 g lactose) in a single dose taken with a meal, without suffering symptoms, but not a 50 g dose ingested on an empty stomach, the dose used in lactose tolerance tests.

There is a general consensus of opinion that probiotic dairy products alleviate lactose intolerance. This is true of all fermented dairy products, especially yoghurt, owing to the β-galactosidase activity of the yoghurt culture and the higher consistency of fermented milks compared with ordinary milk. However, a much more sophisticated and efficient way of reducing symptoms caused by lactose is to hydrolyse it in the milk enzymatically. In long-life milks the enzyme is generally added to the milk after sterilisation, and the product is released for sale after a certain period, when the level of lactose has decreased.

In fermented milks the enzyme is added before fermentation or at the same time as the culture. If added with the culture, the enzyme must be active in acidic conditions. In Finland, Valio Ltd has a large range of lactose-hydrolysed (HYLA®) milk products, altogether around 80 varieties.

The hydrolysis of lactose changes the taste of the milk, making it sweeter, because glucose and galactose are sweeter than lactose. This is an accepted fact in fermented milk products, especially if they are additionally sweetened. However, this sweetness is not popular in milk for drinking, and thus milk consumption drops. Recently, this problem, too, has been solved. In 2001 Valio Ltd launched a lactose-free milk in which the lactose has been completely removed physically. The sweetness has been restored to its normal level and the taste is that of normal fresh milk.

11.5.4   Others

Sphingolipids contain compounds such as ceramides, sphingomyelin, cerebrosides, sulphatides and gangliocides. Sphingolipids are found in millk, butter and cheese – approximately 2 mg/100 g milk. Because they exist in cell membranes rather than in fat droplets, they are found in fat-free, low-fat as well as in full-fat dairy products. *In vitro* and experimental studies indicate that sphingolipids influence cell regulation, and thus carcinogenesis and tumour formation (Miller *et al.*, 2000). In 2000, a yoghurt brand called 'Inpulse' was launched in Belgium (Büllenger Butterei). The low-fat product was said to be rich in natural milk lecithin (45 mg/100 g) and sphingolipids (phospholipids 144 mg/100 g). A variety launched since then contains 0.6 g fat, 115 mg phospholipids, 36 mg phosphatidylcholine and 18.4 mg sphingolipids. The information on the product declares that 'lecitin and sphingolipids are biomembranes, which re-establish the biological equilibrium of the cells, protect against bacterial infections and help digestion'.

11.6   Examples of functional dairy products: cardiovascular health

Coronary heart disease (CHD) is a serious form of cardiovascular disease and the most common – the leading cause of death in developed industrialised countries. Many risk factors, both genetic and environmental, contribute to the development of coronary heart disease. The three most important modifiable risk factors for this are cigarette smoking, high blood pressure and high blood cholesterol levels, particularly of low-density lipoprotein (LDL) cholesterol. Other risk factors likely to contribute to the risk of CHD are diabetes, physical inactivity, low high-density lipoprotein (HDL) cholesterol, high blood triglyceride levels, and obesity. Oxidative stress, homocysteine, lipoprotein and psychosocial factors may also increase the risk. To choose a healthy, low-fat diet with high levels of fruits and vegetables, an active lifestyle and no smoking seems to reduce the risk of heart diseases. The inclusion of semi-skimmed or non-fat milk products in an otherwise healthy diet adds many essential vitamins, not to mention milk calcium, which has a vital role in controlling blood pressure (Miller *et al.*, 2000). Milk products specifically developed to reduce dietary risk factors are already on the market.

11.6.1   Products for controlling hypertension

There are a few products on the market for lowering blood pressure. Several milk peptides are known to have an inhibitory effect on the angiotensin converting enzyme (ACE inhibition). ACE is needed for converting angiotensin I to angiotensin II, increasing blood pressure and aldersterone, and inactivating the depressor action of bradykinin. ACE inhibitors derived from caseins are called casokinins, and they are derived from the tryptic digestion of bovine β- and κ-caseins. In two commercial products, these peptides are isoleucine–proline–proline and valine–proline–proline, which are formed from β-casein by the fermentation of milk with *Lactobacillus helveticus*. The *L. helveticus* bacterium is generally used in cheese-making and the fermentation is a normal dairy process. The Calpis Amiel drink (Japan) is a sterile product, without living bacterial cells. The fermented milk drink Evolus, more recently developed by Valio Ltd (Finland), contains, in addition to the active tripeptides, living bacterial cells and an improved composition of minerals (Ca, K, Mg). Both products have been tested in animal studies with spontaneously hypertensive rats (Sipola, 2002) and in clinical human trials (Hata *et al.*, 1996; Seppo *et al.*, 2003). The Japanese product has official FOSHU status.

In Finland there is a cheese on the market that has been shown to have ACE inhibitory activity (Festivo cheese, Agricultural Research Centre, Jokioinen, Finland). The bioactive peptides are shown to be α_{s1}-casein N-terminal peptides but the researchers thought that they might be too long to be absorbed intact in the intestine. The quantity also varied during the maturation and age of the cheese, and the effect of the cheese on human blood pressure remains to be tested (Ryhänen *et al.*, 2001). Another idea, not yet commercially launched in dairy products, is based on whey proteins that are hydrolysed so that the whey protein isolate has an ACE inhibitory activity (Davisco Foods International Inc., USA). The effect of this product seems to be much faster than those based on the tripeptides, but the mechanism is not yet known (Pins and Keenan, 2002).

11.6.2   Products for controlling cholesterol

Natural cows' milk fat contains high levels of saturated fatty acids. Replacing the consumption of full-cream milk with semi-skimmed or non-fat milk will reduce the intake of saturated fatty acids. Sometimes it is not enough just to reduce the intake of saturated fats and cholesterol, since most cholesterol is synthesised within our own bodies. On the other hand, plant sterols and stanols have long been known to reduce the assimilation of dietary cholesterol. Since the mid-1990s there have been products enriched with plant stanols specially targeted at those people with (moderately) high cholesterol levels. A few years later plant sterols were also accepted as food ingredients by the EU Novel Foods legislation, and now the Food and Drug Administration in the USA has also accepted plant sterols and stanols. Sterols are building blocks of the cell membranes in both plant and animal cells. Isolated plant stanols, hydrated forms of sterols, are crystallised particles. They effectively bind cholesterol and are not absorbed by the human body. Esterified plant stanols are fat-soluble and easy to use as a food ingredient. Intestinal enzymes hydrolyse the ester bond and the insoluble stanol is free to bind cholesterol and to be secreted. Basically, the effect of plant sterols is based on the same mechanism.

Several milk-based functional foods including plant sterols or stanols are commercially available. They all are semi-skimmed or non-fat products. Products containing Benecol (Raisio Benecol Ltd, Finland), the only **plant stanol** ester ingredient, are on the market in several countries. In some products the 'effective daily dose' has to be collected from several servings (e.g. Benecol milk, yoghurt, various spreads in the UK), in some other countries the dose is contained in one serving (e.g. Valio Benecol yoghurt in Finland). **Plant sterols** are also added to functional milk products, especially to milk (e.g. Mastellone Hnos SA, Argentina). In March 2001, Marks & Spencer launched a range of 20 products, including yoghurt, enriched with **soy proteins** (& More brand, UK). The daily consumption of 25 g soy proteins has been shown to lower cholesterol by 10%.

The safety risk of overdosing with plant sterols and stanols has been the subject of discussion by the scientific committee on food of the European Commission. The consumption of this kind of product requires a fairly good knowledge on the part of the consumer, as she or he has to be familiar with the products with the compound and also to know the quantity of the active ingredient in various products. For that reason the labelling must be informative enough.

Matured cheeses contain quite high levels of milk fats. Replacing milk fat with vegetable oil can reduce the intake of saturated fatty acids. In Finland there are cheeses on the market in which milk fat has been replaced by rapeseed oil (Julia and Julius with 17% and 25% rapeseed oil, respectively; Kyrönmaan Osuusmeijeri, Finland). The products, when included daily in a low-fat diet, reduced blood cholesterol statistically significantly (Karvonen et al., 2002).

11.6.3   Omega-3 fatty acids

There are two major classes of polyunsaturated fatty acids: omega-3 fatty acids found in fish oils and as a minor constituent of some vegetable oils, and omega-6 fatty acids, which include the essential fatty acid linoleic acid, found in vegetable oils such as corn, sunflower and soybean. Omega-3 fatty acids are said to contribute to the good functioning of the cardiovascular system, on the basis of various physiological effects. Before omega-3 fatty acids could be added to milk products, the fishy taste and odour had to be disguised and the easy oxidation of the oil overcome. It took several years before these problems were solved, but nowadays there are a few suppliers selling good-quality fish-oils to be added to milk. The pioneer in launching an omega-3-enriched milk was the Italian dairy company Parmalat. Its 'Plus Omega 3' milk was launched in 1998 and is a semi-skimmed milk enriched with 80 mg omega-3. It is recommended for use by all health-conscious consumers in a dose of half a litre per day (Mellentin and Heasman, 1999). Since then other producers all over the world have followed with their own omega-3-enriched milks. Milk is often also enriched with the antioxidative vitamins A, C and E.

11.7   Examples of functional dairy products: osteoporosis and other conditions

The cause of osteoporosis, as with other chronic diseases, is multifactorial, involving both genetic and environmental factors. An accumulation of scientific evidence indicates that a sufficient intake of calcium throughout one's life offers protection against osteoporosis. The bone mass reaches its peak when a person is 30 years of age and then the density decreases with age, especially after the menopause. The fortification of semi-skimmed and non-fat milk with vitamin D is important, as this vitamin is essential to improve calcium absorption and is also removed when fat is removed. Milk is the richest source of calcium. There are several milks and milk products enriched with calcium, and both inorganic and milk-based calcium (e.g. TruCal, Glanbia Ingredients Inc.) are used. The absorption of calcium may be enhanced with bioactive milk proteins. Caseino-phosphopeptides (CPPs) are known to increase the solubility of calcium, but controversy exists as to whether CPPs enhance calcium absorption in the body. The authors do not know of any commercial applications of CPPs in dairy products.

11.7.1   Products for enhancing immune functions

Some of the probiotic dairy products have been shown to enhance immune functions and thus to reduce the risk of infection. Milk contains natural immunoglobulins, which can be isolated and concentrated, either from normal milk or from colostrum, which contains a high proportion of them. There are milk-based products on the market in which the product is further enriched with immunoglobulins. In the USA and Australia, Lifeway Foods is marketing kefir under the brand name Basic Plus. The product is said to be probiotic, although the probiotic strains are not specified. The active ingredient, an extract of colostrum, has been developed by GalaGen Inc. and is targeted at maintaining intestinal health and the natural microbiota. Basic Plus was launched in 1998 and is the first dairy-based food supplement sold in the USA in the refrigerated sections of health food and grocery stores.

Milk immunoglobulins are used in new drinks in the USA under the brand name of 'NuVim'. The production of immunoglobulins is boosted in a selected herd in New Zealand by an immune stimulant, and isolated under carefully controlled conditions in order to preserve the micronutrients. The product is said to be lactose-free and fat-free, to have beneficial effects on the immune system and to improve the health of muscles and joints (Heasman and Mellentin, 2002).

11.7.2 Milks to help with sleeping problems

Melatonin is a hormone that controls the body's day and night rhythm. The secretion of melatonin is high in early childhood and decreases rapidly with ageing. Stress conditions and age cause a lowering of the level of melatonin. It is secreted at nights in both humans and bovines. The concentration at night in cows' milk is about four times higher than in milk collected during the day. The first product based on a standardised milking system at night was launched in Finland in 2000 (Yömaito, Ingman Foods Ltd). Since no human trials have been published so far, the company does not make any health claims. In spring 2002 an organic milk, 'Slumbering Bedtime Milk' (Red Kite Farm, UK), was launched in the UK. It is said to contain higher levels of melatonin than ordinary milk. The company says that the level of melatonin in the milk complements that of the human body and the drink will not induce drowsiness if drunk during the day, or the following morning if drunk at night/late in the evening.

11.8   Future trends

Research and discussion on pro- and prebiotics have encouraged basic research in the field of the intestinal microbial flora and its metabolism. This has also led to improved research funding from public resources, both nationally and from the European Union. Not enough is known of the composition and metabolism of the bacteria in the intestines in health and disease. Also the knowledge on the role of the microbiota in the development and function of immune response needs more investigation. Development and improvements in research methods, and *in vitro*, *ex vivo* and *in vivo* models, have provided important information on the mechanisms behind the effects, and new biomarkers to be followed in human studies. The more we know about the composition and function of the intestinal microbiota, the greater the potential to develop functional foods for targeted consumer groups. Considering the healthy population there may be potential to develop targeted products for different age groups. In the reduction of risk and treatment of various diseases, pro- and prebiotics have resulted in promising benefits. However, it is important to understand the mechanisms behind the effects. When the mechanisms are known, it will be also possible to control the activity or the dose of the effective compounds. We also need official definitions of functional foods, and relevant regulation of physiological claims and health claims. The production of functional foods that have to follow the rules of production of medicines is hardly in the interest of normal dairy companies. It may be unrealistic to apply the same rules to medicines as to everyday foods with a short shelf-life.

Milk is a rich source of nutritive compounds which can be enriched and/or further modified. Milk fat does not consist merely of saturated fatty acids, but also of monounsaturated and polyunsaturated fatty acids. The role of conjugated linoleic acid (CLA) in preventing the risk of certain diseases, and in particular, the problem of how to increase its quantity in milk has evoked wide interest among several research groups. Milk proteins and bioactive peptides may supply new products to help protect against several common health risk factors. There are bioactive peptides potentially to be used to give satiety or to better tolerate stress. Lactose derivatives can be used as soluble fibre to relieve constipation and to modulate the intestinal flora. Milk minerals can be used to replace sodium in salt, supporting a healthy diet for avoiding hypertension. Milk components are natural, and applications for novel foods are seldom needed. There is also a huge selection of lactic acid bacteria used for milk fermentations, which have a long tradition of safe use. Genetically modified strains may be needed for special purposes, though perhaps not in products for the general public.

In developing functional dairy products, various groups of experts are needed. The basis must be in the scientific research of effects, requiring medical experts, nutritionists and microbiologists. Food technologists are needed for product development, process technologists and biotechnologists for processing the compounds, chemists to analyse the compounds and, finally, experts for marketing the products. Marketing is a big challenge, as it has to tell the public about the health benefits in such a simple way that every layperson understands. Medical and nutritional messages need to be simplified. It is important to remember that functional dairy products are mainly for supplying nutritive foods for everyday consumption. Nutrimarketing is also needed to explain research results to health-care professionals and to convince them of the benefits of functional foods.

11.9   Sources of further information and advice

www.gnpd.com
www.new-nutrition.com
www.scirus.com
www.just-food.com
www.ifis.org
http://www.foodlineweb.co.uk
www.fst.ohio-state.edu/People/HARPER/Functional-foods/Functional-Foods.htm
www.valio.com
www.benecol.com
www.daviscofoods.com
www.kefir.com

www.ific.org
www.effca.com
www.usprobiotics.org
www.elintarvikevirasto.fi/english

11.10   References

BANKS W and DALGLEISH D G (1990), 'Milk and milk processing' in Robinson R K, *Dairy Mircobiology*, Volume 1, *The Microbiology of Milk*, second edition, London, Elsevier Science Publishers Ltd, 1–35.

CLARE D A and SWAISGOOD H E (2000), 'Bioactive milk peptides: a prospectus', *J Dairy Sci*, **83**, 1187–1195.

DE VRESE M and SCHREZENMEIR J (2001), 'Pro and prebiotics', *Innov Food Technol*, **May/June**, 49–55.

DIPLOCK A T (1999), 'Scientific concepts of functional foods in Europe: Consensus document', *Br J Nutr*, **81**(Suppl 1), S1–S27.

HATA Y, YAMAMOTO M, OHNI M, NAKAJIMA K, NAKAMURA Y and TAKÀNO T (1996), 'A placebo-controlled study of the effect of sour milk on blood pressure in hypertensive subjects', *Am J Clin Nutr*, **64**, 767–771.

HEASMAN M and MELLENTIN J (2002), 'New NuVim prepares to be swallowed up', NNB, 7(8), 29–30.

KARVONEN H M, TAPOLA N S, UUSITUPA M I AND SARKKINEN E S (2002), 'The effect of vegetable oil-based cheese on serum total and lipoprotein lipids', *Eur J Clin Nutr*, **56**, 1094–1101.

KORHONEN H, PIHLANTO-LEPPÄLÄ A, RANTAMÄKI P and TUPASELA T (1998), 'Impact of processing on bioactive proteins and peptides', *Trends Food Sci Technol*, **8**, 307–319.

LEPORANTA K (2001), 'Developing fermented milks into functional foods', *Innov Food Technol*, **10**, 46–47.

LOURENS-HATTINGH A and VILJOEN B C (2001), 'Yoghurt as probiotic carrier food', *Int Dairy J*, **11**, 1–17.

MELLENTIN J and HEASMAN M (1999), 'Functional foods are dead. Long live functional foods', *NNB*, **4**(7), 16–19.

MILLER G D, JARVIS J K and MCBEAN L D (2000), *Handbook of Dairy Foods and Nutrition*, second edition, Boca Raton, London, New York, Washington DC, CRC Press.

PINS J and KEENAN J M (2002), 'The antihypertensive effects of a hydrolysed whey protein isolate supplement (BioZate 1®)', *Cardiovasc Drugs Ther*, **16** (Suppl 1), 68.

RYHÄNEN E-L, PIHLANTO-LEPPÄLÄ A and PAHKALA E (2001), 'A new type of ripened, low-fat cheese with bioactive properties', *Int Dairy J*, **11**, 441–447.

SAXELIN M, GRENOW B, SVENSSON U, FONDEN R, RENIERO R and MATTILA-SANDHOLM T (1999), 'The technology of probiotics', *Trends Food Sci Technol*, **10**, 387–392.

SEPPO L, JAUHIAINEN T, POUSSA T and KORPELA R (2003), 'A fermented milk, high in bioactive peptides, has a blood pressure lowering effect in hypertensive subjects', *Am J Clin Nutr*, **77**, 326–330.

SHAH N P (2000), 'Probiotic bacteria: selectivè enumeration and survival in dairy foods', *J Dairy Sci*, **83**(4), 894–907.

SIPOLA M (2002), 'Effects of milk products and milk protein-derived peptides on blood pressure and arterial function in rats', PhD Thesis, Institute of Biomedicine/ Pharmacology, University of Helsinki; electronic PDF version: http:// ethesis.helsinki.fi/julkaisut/laa/biola/vk/sipola/.

SMITH J (2001), 'Defining health claims for Europe', *Funct Foods Nutraceut*, **November/ December**, 12.

WOLLOWSKI I, RECHKEMMER G and POOL-ZOBEL B L (2001), 'Protective role of probiotics and prebiotics in colon cancer', *Am J Clin Nutr*, **73**(2 Suppl), 451S–455S.

12

Developing and approving health claims for functional dairy products

J. Snel and R. van der Meer, NIZO Food Research, The Netherlands

12.1 Introduction

There is an increasing commercial interest in *Lactobacillus* cultures that aim to improve human health. These cultures and their products are generally called probiotics, although the exact definition of probiotics has changed over the course of time. Initially, Fuller (1989) stated that probiotics are live microbial feed supplements that beneficially affect the host animal by improving its intestinal microbial balance. Later, Guarner and Schaafsma (1998) defined probiotics as living microorganisms which upon ingestion exert health effects beyond basic nutrition (in humans and animals). It is increasingly recognised that inactivated probiotic microorganisms may also have beneficial effects on human health. Therefore, Salminen and co-workers (1999) proposed that probiotics are microbial cell preparations, or components of microbial cells, that have a beneficial effect on health and well-being of the host. This variety in definitions is mainly due to the discussions about applications other than in food or feed, the necessity to use living bacteria, and whether the health-promoting mechanism is related to the functionality of the microflora as a total.

The majority of the current probiotics belong to the genera *Lactobacillus* and *Bifidobacterium*. The health benefits of these strains have been investigated using *in vitro* approaches, as well as animal and human studies. On the basis of human studies, it is demonstrated that fermented products containing these probiotic strains can benefit human health in many ways. This could be shortening the duration of rotavirus-induced diarrhoea (Shornikova *et al.*, 1997; Guandalini *et al.*, 2000), improving control of atopic eczema (Isolauri *et al.*, 2000), reduction of colonisation by *Helicobacter pylori* (Felley *et al.*, 2001), relieving the symptoms of irritable bowel syndrome (Niedzielin *et al.*, 2001), and delaying the recurrence of superficial bladder cancer (Aso *et al.*, 1995). For consumer products, the most prevalent claim deals with increasing the natural resistance of the body.

There is a general agreement that health claims on probiotics for the human market should be validated in human studies. Since the health benefits are strain specific, results obtained with one strain cannot directly be extrapolated to other strains. A good probiotic strain should also possess technologically interesting properties, such as the possibility to cultivate the organism on an industrial scale. Strains should be able to grow on a fermentable substrate (e.g. milk) and the final product should have an attractive colour, taste, aroma and texture. Furthermore, a sufficient number of probiotic bacteria should be present in the final product to induce the health benefit.

This chapter will focus on how lactic acid bacteria, either dead or alive, can contribute to health by increasing resistance towards pathogenic microorganisms. Since infection experiments cannot easily be performed in humans, other ways to substantiate health claims are necessary. *In vitro* and animal studies can provide the mechanism(s) by which a probiotic strain is active. Human volunteer studies and clinical trials should provide evidence that the same mechanisms play a role in humans too. Here, we will describe how these studies can be translated into health claims.

12.2   The body's defence mechanisms

In order to enable efficient absorption of nutrients from the food flow, the intestinal mucosal surface is greatly increased through the formation of villi and microvilli. However, the enormous surface area gets easily colonised by a variety of microbes, either commensal or pathogenic. This makes the gut a major site of entrance for several bacterial pathogens such as *Escherichia coli*, *Salmonella*, or *Campylobacter* species (Wells *et al.*, 1988). Fortunately, commensal bacteria usually outnumber pathogens and form a stable ecosystem that hampers colonisation by pathogens.

Pathogenic microorganisms are excluded from the body by various barriers. After ingestion, the microorganisms are exposed to digestive juices in the stomach and small intestine that form a first line of defence that interferes with survival of the pathogen. The low pH and the presence of pepsin in the stomach, and the bile salts and proteolytic enzymes of the small intestine, efficiently kill many newly ingested bacteria.

Also the microflora contribute to a large extent to the host defence system by preventing colonisation of pathogens. Commensal bacteria can compete for nutrients that are necessary for growth of the pathogens. Furthermore, pathogens depend on adhesion sites on the mucosa to maintain themselves in the intestinal tract. Commensal bacteria can prevent adhesion of pathogens by specific blocking of the receptor or by steric hindrance. Next to that, the microflora contain bacteria that produce antimicrobial substances such as bacteriocins or volatile fatty acids that can kill other bacteria or reduce their growth.

Evidence for the role of the microflora in resistance to infections is obtained from comparison of germ-free (lacking any microbes) and conventional animals (Freter and Abrams, 1972; Berg and Savage, 1975). These studies have raised the belief that the addition of selected probiotic strains may change the composition of the microflora from potentially harmful to beneficial for the host. Probiotic bacteria that survive gastrointestinal transit and are active in the gut may compete for nutrients and adhesion sites, and produce antimicrobial factors. Ideally, this leads to a reduction in potentially pathogenic bacteria. A more thorough understanding of probiotic mechanisms has revealed that a change in microflora composition by itself is not a guarantee of better resistance against pathogens. For immunomodulating properties of probiotic strains, the effects are probably caused by direct interactions between probiotic bacteria and the host rather than by a change in microflora composition.

The intestinal epithelium forms a second line of defence, aiming to prevent pathogens from translocation through the gut wall to peripheral organs such as the spleen and liver. This single-cell layer contains enterocytes, and goblet cells producing mucins that cover the surface of the epithelium. The stability of this mucus layer is improved by trefoil peptides. Tight junctions form strong bonds between epithelial cells and prevent migration of bacteria through the paracellular pathway. At the bottom of the small intestinal crypts, Paneth cells are found that produce antimicrobial peptides called defensins (Selsted et al., 1992).

Invasive pathogens that enter the body are recognised by the mucosal immune system that serves as a third line of defence. Initially, translocating pathogens evoke an innate immune reaction by macrophages and neutrophilic granulocytes that destroy pathogens after phagocytosis, and natural killer cells that destroy infected host cells. Although these are fast actions that can kill pathogens within minutes, these immune cells produce reactive molecules such as NO and oxygen radicals that are harmful to the host as well. Therefore, an adaptive immune response is triggered if the pathogens escape the innate immune response or if they infect the host for a second time. This adaptive immune response takes several days to build up, and is based on the specific recognition of the pathogen by antibody proteins and T-lymphocytes (Kuby, 1997).

The mucosal immune system needs to discriminate between nutrients, non-pathogenic commensal bacteria and potentially harmful pathogens. Although the microflora stimulates the alertness of the mucosal immune system (Berg and Savage, 1975), it usually does not induce immune responses against commensal bacteria or nutrients. These components induce so-called immunological tolerance. The first step in this process is continuous sampling of bacteria and macromolecules from the intestinal contents by dendritic cells that are just below the epithelial barrier, and by M-cells. M-cells form a specialised type of epithelial cells that covers the lymphoid follicles in the small intestine called

Peyer's patches. How the balance between tolerance against nutrients and commensal bacteria and immune reactivity against pathogens is maintained is still unclear, especially since pathogenic and commensal microorganisms share multiple antigens (MacDonald, 1995).

There are numerous mechanisms by which probiotics potentially can stimulate host resistance against pathogens in humans. Basically, all three barriers mentioned above could be improved, since probiotics are active in the intestinal contents and have direct interactions with the epithelium and mucosal immune system. However, hard evidence is limited, obviously due to a lack of controlled infection models in humans. Mechanistic studies using animals or *in vitro* models have demonstrated the potential of probiotics to improve host defence.

12.3 *In vitro* studies

In vitro studies are very suitable to select for new candidate strains that can be evaluated in further animal or human trials. Using human or animal faeces as a source of lactic acid bacteria, several thousand strains have been isolated and screened for *in vitro* characteristics (Dunne *et al.*, 2001). Advanced *in vitro* models have been described that are provided with a complete microflora (Alander *et al.*, 1999), or contain dynamic devices to mimic gastrointestinal conditions as closely as possible (Marteau *et al.*, 1997). However, it is important to note that results from such studies never reflect the *in vivo* situation. For example, many *in vitro* systems lack the absorption of probiotic metabolites. Also the development of an immune response cannot be mimicked *in vitro*, and interactions with mucin-producing goblet cells and other epithelial cells are usually studied in cancer cell lines with culture medium rather than digestive juices. Nevertheless, *in vitro* screening is the only solution to select probiotic candidates for further *in vivo* evaluation on a large scale.

Many screening strategies primarily focus on intestinal survival and temporary colonisation, since it is strongly believed that probiotics should survive gastrointestinal conditions in order to be active in the gut. Important factors are the ability to deal with the low pH of the stomach, the presence of bile salts and adherence to epithelial surfaces or mucus. These prior conditions, however, do not predict a health benefit of a candidate probiotic and should be extended by investigation of the health promoting activity *in vivo*.

Screening of probiotics for adhesion to epithelial cell lines such as Caco-2 or HT29 cells has become an important selection criterion, although a good correlation between *in vitro* adherence characteristics and *in vivo* colonisation has not been made. A comparison of 12 probiotic strains revealed that there is a considerable difference between strains that are currently on the market (Tuomola and Salminen, 1998). Since the mucus layer forms the first contact of probiotic bacteria with the intestinal mucosa, the adhesion to mucus has also gained interest (Kirjavainen *et al.*, 1998).

The basic hypothesis has been for a long time that a good interaction between epithelial cells and probiotic bacteria is important for a functional health effect. Although that might be true, the cell line studies show no saturation in the adhesion: adding more bacteria to the cell culture does not change the fraction of bacteria that adhere (Tuomola and Salminen, 1998). This suggests that the adhesion is rather non-specific without any receptor–ligand interactions. Therefore, strong but non-specific adhesion to cell lines is unlikely to predict any health benefit.

Epithelial cells in culture can be used to demonstrate an effect of probiotic bacteria on the adhesion of pathogens. It has been shown that probiotics and enteropathogens share binding sites for adhesion to epithelium (Neeser et al., 2000). In a similar concept, it was shown that probiotics can also interfere with the adhesion of probiotics to mucus (Tuomola et al., 1999). A mathematical approach to analyse the interaction between probiotics and pathogen for adhesion to cells and mucus has been described (Lee et al., 2000). The inhibition of adhesion might also be related to production of antimicrobial substances by probiotics. It has been shown that lactobacilli can produce antimicrobial factors with an inhibiting activity against Gram-positve as well as Gram-negative bacteria (Talarico and Dobrogosz, 1989).

Several studies have investigated the interactions between probiotics and cells of the immune system to explore an immunomodulating effect. These could be either transformed macrophage or T-cell lines (Marin et al., 1997), or cells obtained from blood or lymphoid organs (Kitazawa et al., 1994). From these studies, it becomes clear that strains of lactic acid bacteria have a differential effect on cytokine production by immune cells. However, since probiotics are generally not invasive, it seems unlikely that immune cells from blood or spleen get in direct contact with probiotic cells. This makes the direct extrapolation of the results to humans questionable. To circumvent this problem, immunological studies with lymphoid cells from murine Peyer's patches have been described (Yasui and Ohwaki, 1991). Since the relative amounts of different cell types in Peyer's patches is highly variable, it might be difficult to reproduce the outcome of experiments. Therefore, this method has not gained much attention yet.

Two recent developments have created breakthroughs for in vitro screening on immunomodulating properties. A first important discovery is that co-cultivation of human Caco-2 cells and mouse lymphocytes results in the formation of an M-cell-like cell type (Kerneis et al., 1997). M-cells are part of Peyer's patches, and are important for antigen sampling. It is thought that these cells can bring probiotics in contact with the immune system. At this time, the first probiotic studies using this system need to be published. A second promising approach is the use of dendritic cells, since these cells are also used for antigen sampling from the gut (Rescigno et al., 2001). Intestinal dendritic cells cannot be used for in vitro stimulation with probiotics since they have already been stimulated by various antigens from the microflora. Using naive bone marrow-derived dendritic cells that were stimulated with various probiotic lactobacilli, Christensen *et al.* (2002) showed a differential cytokine expression favouring either immunological tolerance, or cellular or antibody immune responses depending on the strain of *Lactobacillus*.

12.4   Animal studies

Animal studies in which enteric pathogens are orally administered offer realistic controlled models for food-borne infections. They have the advantage that the infection process can be followed in time with a focus on the mechanism behind the health benefit. The intact intestinal physiology and presence of a microflora make extrapolation to humans much better than the *in vitro* studies.

Probiotics can in principle contribute to three different stages of the *in vivo* host defence. They can improve colonisation resistance, strengthen the mucosal barrier or improve the response of the body by stimulating the immune system. We have developed a *Salmonella enteritidis* infection model that allows a simultaneous study of all three barriers of host defence (Bovee-Oudenhoven *et al.*, 1999). Colonisation resistance is measured by monitoring faecal excretion of *Salmonella* in time. Nitric oxide-derived nitrite and nitrate in urine serves as a marker for translocation. Furthermore, antibody titres provide information on the humoral immune response. The first probiotics that have been studied with this model demonstrate the ability of some strains to improve colonisation resistance (unpublished data).

In the absence of an endogenous microflora, lactic acid bacteria can grow out to high colonisation levels and efficiently compete with enteric pathogenic bacteria. For example, colonisation of germ-free animals with a *Lactobacillus casei* strain delayed mortality and reduced colonisation of pathogens in mice infected with a lethal *Salmonella* dose (Hudault *et al.*, 1997). Similar effects were shown for *L. salivarius* and resistance to *Helicobacter pylori* in mice (Kabir *et al.*, 1997), and for *L. plantarum* and resistance against *E. coli* infection in rats (Herias *et al.*, 1999). Although such studies are very useful for elucidating mechanisms by which probiotics may act under gastrointestinal conditions, the use of germ-free animals is rather artificial since the functionality of probiotics is always complementary to the normal microflora.

Several studies have provided evidence that lactic acid bacteria can suppress colonisation of pathogens in animal feeding trials. A study in which yoghurt containing *L. bulgaricus* and *Streptococcus thermophilus* was fed to mice infected with *Salmonella typhimurium* demonstrated a reduction of the pathogen (De Simone *et al.*, 1988). Since both strains of lactic acid bacteria cannot survive gastrointestinal conditions, the effect is probably explained by the presence of large amounts of lactate in the yoghurt. Lactate that is produced by all lactic acid bacteria has a strong antimicrobial activity against Gram-negative bacteria such as *Salmonella*. Less clear is another study that used a *L. acidophilus* strain (Coconnier *et al.*, 1997). Spent supernatant of this strain showed antimicrobial activity against a broad range of Gram-positive and Gram-negative bacteria. A *Salmonella typhimurium* infection experiment in mice demonstrated that feeding probiotic bacteria together with the spent culture supernatant inhibited colonisation of the pathogen. It is uncertain, however, whether lactate might have played a role in this study too, which demonstrates the necessity of choosing proper controls.

Studies with a specific focus on intestinal permeability are rare. It has been demonstrated that *L. casei* can decrease intestinal permeability in suckling rats (Isolauri *et al.*, 1993). Nevertheless, this study intended to unravel the mechanism by which this strain can contribute to prevent antigenic uptake and the subsequent development of cow's milk allergy. The relevance for infections still needs to be demonstrated.

In order to study an immunomodulatory effect of probiotics, several models have been described in which animals are infected by oral or parenteral routes with a broad variety of pathogens. We have previously chosen to use an oral infection model with the helminth *Trichinella spiralis*. Encapsulated muscle larvae of this parasite get released in the stomach after consumption of contaminated meat, pass towards the jejunum, and mature within 3–4 days. Viviparous females penetrate the small intestinal epithelium and produce larvae. New-born larvae migrate through the intestinal mucosa via lymphatic and blood vessels towards host striated muscle tissue, where they are encapsulated within a host-derived structure. A rat model making use of this parasite has the advantage that the immunity to *T. spiralis* depends on multiple cell types at the mucosal and systemic, specific and non-specific, and humoral and cellular levels. A *Lactobacillus casei* strain, but not two *Bifidobacterium* strains, was shown to enhance cellular immunity, although no difference in helminth load was observed (De Waard *et al.*, 2001). Since an infection with *Listeria monocytogenes* is highly dependent on cellular immunity, a follow-up study was performed with this pathogen. This revealed that the probiotic *Lactobacillus casei* strain improved cellular immunity and reduced the numbers of *Listeria* in the intestinal tract as well as in liver and spleen (De Waard *et al.*, 2002).

12.5   Human studies

Since most probiotics are marketed for healthy consumers, it is important to demonstrate the benefits in healthy subjects. On the other hand, as long as probiotics are marketed as food products, it is not recommended that probiotics largely change the normal physiology of the body since this might turn probiotics into pharmaceutical preparations. One of the first human studies aiming to show an effect in healthy adult volunteers demonstrated that a *Lactobacillus casei* strain was able to modulate the composition and metabolic activity of the microflora (Spanhaak *et al.*, 1998). Demonstration of the presence of live probiotic bacteria in the microflora might demonstrate that a probiotic bacterium is active, but it cannot be considered as a functional health effect. This

L. casei strain did not alter any of the immune parameters that were measured, although the same strain has shown a strong immunomodulating activity in rat experiments (De Waard *et al.*, 2002).

Some probiotics have an immunomodulating effect that can be detected in healthy volunteers. As an example, it has been reported that elderly volunteers consuming *L. rhamnosus* had a stimulation of natural killer cell activity as determined *ex vivo* (Gill *et al.*, 2001). Whether this can be translated into a functional health effect requires further study. Although it is possible to determine a direct immunomodulation in healthy subjects by monitoring immune parameters such as natural antibodies or leukocyte differentiation, several volunteer studies focus on the body's reaction against some kind of challenge, e.g. vaccination, that induce a change in normal immune parameters.

A vaccination approach was used to demonstrate the effect of a probiotic product containing *L. acidophilus* and bifidobacteria (Link-Amster *et al.*, 1994). Volunteers consumed this product for three weeks after which an attenuated *Salmonella typhi* was administered for oral vaccination. An increased count of faecal *Lactobacillus* and *Bifidobacterium* was found during the fermented milk intake. Furthermore, a four-fold increase of specific serum-IgA antibodies was observed. Extrapolation of these results predicts a better protection after infection with a virulent *Salmonella* strain for persons who have consumed the probiotic product.

A realistic approach focusing on a direct health effect on pathogenic microorganisms is to demonstrate benefits in patients recovering from spontaneous infections. The first evidence for health benefits from probiotics during infection comes from a Finnish study on recovery of young children from acute diarrhoea caused by rotavirus (Isolauri *et al.*, 1991). These authors showed that a probiotic strain is effective in shortening the hospitalisation time from 2.4 to 1.4 days. Subsequently, a multicentre trial confirmed a shorter duration of diarrhoea, less chance of a protracted course, and earlier discharge from the hospital (Guandalini *et al.*, 2000).

Another target group that might be useful for probiotic health studies are people at risk, such as persons getting antibiotic treatment or patients suffering from inflammatory bowel diseases. A meta-analysis showed that certain probiotic lactobacilli can be used for prevention or treatment of antibiotic-associated diarrhoea (D'Souza *et al.*, 2002). A first pilot study gives indications for an effect of *L. rhamnosus* in prevention of Crohn's disease, although a permanent clinical trial should give final evidence (Gupta *et al.*, 2000). A study using patients suffering from irritable bowel syndrome reported an improvement of the symptoms in 95% of the patients treated with *L. plantarum* versus 15% in the placebo-treated group (Niedzielin *et al.*, 2001).

A drawback of many human studies is their focus on a therapeutic effect whereas the main benefit for the consumer is a preventive effect. Although controlled human infection studies with pathogenic microorganisms would be the gold standard to show whether probiotic strains are indeed beneficial, the possibilities of doing this are for obvious ethical reasons highly limited, if not impossible. Recently, we have overcome this problem by developing a new model in which healthy human volunteers were infected with a modified *E. coli* derived from a strain causing traveller's diarrhoea. This mutant strain is non-invasive and lacks the ability to produce toxins, but survives intestinal conditions and causes mild, short-lived symptoms. Using this approach, we have found that subjects consuming calcium-rich dairy products developed significantly less diarrhoea (Bovee-Oudenhoven *et al.*, 2002). Probiotic studies have not been performed with this model yet.

12.6   Making health claims

There is no doubt that health claims on probiotics should be supported by scientific evidence. The studies described in the previous sections of this chapter, however, illustrate that there is presently a wide variety of approaches. The only way to keep the confidence of consumers in probiotic products is for the scientific community to accept health claims. A thorough understanding of the working mechanism facilitates the acceptance, but at least two independent positive human studies seem to be required. The difficulty of demonstrating health effects in healthy humans as described earlier is a major handicap for general acceptance. Several countries including The Netherlands, Belgium, Sweden and the United Kingdom have introduced organisations that should judge the scientific information on functional foods (Feord, 2002). Leading scientists participate in committees that evaluate the evidence on probiotic strains in relation to the claims that are made.

Probiotic health claims have long been hampered by the notion that the activity of lactic acid bacteria is strain-dependent. This means that health benefits obtained with one strain cannot be directly extrapolated to another strain. As a consequence, all strains should have their own dossier to support health claims, although the strength of the scientific support varies from strain to strain.

At the moment, strains are mostly promoted for a general benefit to digestive health. In the perception of the consumer, this is a generic characteristic for all probiotic products, not for specific strains. As there are many strains of probiotics available, data need to be generated on the specific health benefits related to a specific strain, or final product. It will become increasingly important to associate a specific strain with a specific claim, and possibly with a specific target group of consumers. Only in this way can probiotic strains be marketed for their unique health benefits.

The legislative relation between claims and health benefits is far from clear (for a review, see Feord, 2002). An important problem is that medicinal legislation worldwide prohibits associating medicinal claims with food products. In several countries even health claims are prohibited. The basic rule is that food laws dictate that food labelling must not mislead the consumer. It is, however, difficult to objectively judge misleading of the consumer in the field of probiotics and improved resistance since it is impossible to perform controlled infection experiments in humans.

12.7   Future trends

Currently, the search for new probiotic strains is handicapped by our limited knowledge of the mechanism behind the health benefit. Studying health benefits for probiotics on a trial and error basis for each single strain remains a costly operation that can only be funded by large companies and governments. Our increasing knowledge of probiotic mechanisms and the rapid progress in genomic techniques enables the identification of biochemical structures or bacterial genes that are essential for health benefit. This allows rational selection and subsequent validation of promising new strains.

An example of a potential target for *in vitro* selection of probiotics is the ability to adhere to carbohydrate binding sites at the epithelium that are also used for adhesion by enteropathogenic bacteria (Neeser *et al.*, 2000). These probiotics can reduce effects of food-borne infections. A more thorough understanding of bacterial cell characteristics could result in strain selection for immunomodulatory purposes (Christensen *et al.*, 2002). This might be useful for the development of probiotics preventing relapses of inflammatory bowel diseases, or for reduction of allergy symptoms. The major advantage of a first focus on a functional activity is that the potential as well as the limitations of the health benefits are known. The second focus should therefore be the optimisation of the health benefit of a strain. The addition of prebiotics to a probiotic product might give the strain a selective advantage in the gut, and encapsulation could help to pass the stomach.

A new promising area of research on probiotics is the field of genomics. The availability of complete genome sequences of several lactic acid bacteria (Klaenhammer *et al.*, 2002) will facilitate the identification of bacterial genes that are responsible for the probiotic effect. DNA microarray analysis and real-time PCR enable the study of genes at the transcription level under controlled conditions. Molecular techniques are available to study gene expression of bacteria under *in vivo* circumstances such as in the gastrointestinal tract (Slauch and Camilli, 2000). We strongly believe that in-depth studies in this direction will improve our understanding of probiotic effects and generate new leads for the identification and selection of probiotic strains. For those reasons, our research efforts are increasingly focused on genomic approaches.

The wide variety of mechanisms by which probiotics can potentially improve health make it likely that some strains can be used for certain applications, whereas other strains have different health benefits. This has raised the belief that a differentiation of strains for specific purposes will develop. As an example, *Lactobacillus* GG has been demonstrated to be active against rotavirus diarrhoea in young children (Isolauri *et al.*, 1991; Guandalini *et al.*, 2000). Nevertheless, this same strain failed to reduce the incidence of urinary tract infections, bacterial sepsis and necrotising enterocolitis in preterm infants (Dani *et al.*, 2002). Apparently, the mechanism by which this strain contributes to resistance against rotavirus cannot be generalised to other infections. Therefore, we expect that in future strains are marketed specifically for allergy reduction, food-poisoning, prevention of traveller's diarrhoea, resistance to flu and common colds, and so on. Furthermore, there will be a focus on specific consumer groups, such as patients suffering from inflammatory bowel diseases, infants and the elderly.

Although most probiotics are used for intestinal applications, there is an increasing interest in alternative applications such as the treatment or prevention of urinary tract infections (Reid and Bruce, 2001). For this application, the ability to produce hydrogen peroxide is considered to be an important feature for a probiotic strain (Ocana *et al.*, 1999). Another application for probiotics might be the reduction of *Streptococcus mutans* in the oral cavity, which is responsible for dental caries, or the improvement of skin health. These applications have received little attention until now (Ouwehand *et al.*, 2002).

An unexplored new field for probiotics is the use of recombinant lactic acid bacteria as vehicles for the delivery of active molecules. It has been shown that immunisation of mice with recombinant *Lactococcus lactis* expressing tetanus toxin fragment C elicits a protective immune response against a challenge with the complete toxin (Robinson *et al.*, 1997). Using a similar approach, others showed that the delivery of an interleukin-10 producing *L. lactis* to mice could reduce the symptoms of TNBS-induced colitis and spontaneous colitis in IL-10-/- mice (Steidler *et al.*, 2000). Despite the straightforward approach and promising results, it is questionable to what extent the use of recombinant microorganisms is accepted by the consumer.

The scientific community, as well as consumers, increasingly accepts the health benefits of selected probiotic strains. The use of lactic acid bacteria to enhance the resistance to infections has become a major application of probiotics. Several double-blind placebo-controlled studies have been performed to demonstrate the effects in humans. In particular, shortening of rotavirus-induced diarrhoea is well established. Nevertheless, although many mechanisms behind the health effects have been proposed, the selection of new strains takes place mainly on a trial and error basis.

12.8 Sources of further information and advice

A recent overview of probiotic strains that are currently on the market and their documented health benefits in human clinical trials is given by Ouwehand and colleagues (Ouwehand *et al.*, 2002). Further information with respect to legal affairs, describing differences between the European, American and Japanese market, is given in a recent overview by Feord (2002).

12.9   References

ALANDER, M., DE SMET, I., NOLLET, L., VERSTRAETE, W., VON WRIGHT, A. and MATTILA-SANDHOLM, T. (1999) The effect of probiotic strains on the microbiota of the Simulator of the Human Intestinal Microbial Ecosystem (SHIME). *Int J Food Microbiol* 46: 71–79.

ASO, Y., AKAZA, H., KOTAKE, T., TSUKAMOTO, T., IMAI, K. and NAITO, S. (1995) Preventive effect of a *Lactobacillus casei* preparation on the recurrence of superficial bladder cancer in a double-blind trial. The BLP Study Group. *Eur Urol* 27: 104–109.

BERG, R.D. and SAVAGE, D.C. (1975) Immune responses of specific pathogen-free and gnotobiotic mice to antigens of indigenous and nonindigenous microorganisms. *Infect Immun* 11: 320–329.

BOVEE-OUDENHOVEN, I.M., WISSINK, M.L., WOUTERS, J.T. and VAN DER MEER, R. (1999) Dietary calcium phosphate stimulates intestinal lactobacilli and decreases the severity of a salmonella infection in rats. *J Nutr* 129: 607–612.

BOVEE-OUDENHOVEN, I., LETTINK-WISSINK, M., VAN DOESBURG, W. and VANDER MEER, R. (2002) Abstract 347: Dietary calcium inhibits traveler's diarrhea in humans.

CHRISTENSEN, H.R., FROKIAER, H. and PESTKA, J.J. (2002) Lactobacilli differentially modulate expression of cytokines and maturation surface markers in murine dendritic cells. *J Immunol* 168: 171–178.

COCONNIER, M.H., LIEVIN, V., BERNET-CAMARD, M.F., HUDAULT, S. and SERVIN, A.L. (1997) Antibacterial effect of the adhering human *Lactobacillus acidophilus* strain LB. *Antimicrob Agents Chemother* 41: 1046–1052.

DANI, C., BIADAIOLI, R., BERTINI, G., MARTELLI, E. and RUBALTELLI, F.F. (2002) Probiotics feeding in prevention of urinary tract infection, bacterial sepsis and necrotizing enterocolitis in preterm infants. A prospective double-blind study. *Biol Neonate* 82: 103–108.

DE SIMONE, C., TZANTZOGLOU, S., BALDINELLI, L., DI FABIO, S., BIANCHI-SALVADORI, B., JIRILLO, E. and VESELY, R. (1988) Enhancement of host resistance against *Salmonella typhimurium* infection by a diet supplemented with yogurt. *Immunopharmacol Immunotoxicol* 10: 399–415.

DE WAARD, R., GARSSEN, J., SNEL, J., BOKKEN, G.C., SAKO, T., VELD, J.H. and VOS, J.G. (2001) Enhanced antigen-specific delayed-type hypersensitivity and immunoglobulin G2b responses after oral administration of viable *Lactobacillus casei* YIT9029 in Wistar and Brown Norway rats. *Clin Diagn Lab Immunol* 8: 762–767.

DE WAARD, R., GARSSEN, J., BOKKEN, G.C. and VOS, J.G. (2002) Antagonistic activity of *Lactobacillus casei* strain *shirota* against gastrointestinal *Listeria monocytogenes* infection in rats. *Int J Food Microbiol* 73: 93–100.

D'SOUZA, A.L., RAJKUMAR, C., COOKE, J. and BULPITT, C.J. (2002) Probiotics in prevention of antibiotic associated diarrhoea: meta-analysis. *BMJ* 324: 1361.

DUNNE, C., O'MAHONY, L., MURPHY, L., THORNTON, G., MORRISSEY, D., O'HALLORAN, S., FEENEY, M., FLYNN, S., FITZGERALD, G., DALY, C., KIELY, B., O'SULLIVAN, G.C., SHANAHAN, F. and COLLINS, J.K. (2001) *In vitro* selection criteria for probiotic bacteria of human origin: correlation with *in vivo* findings. *Am J Clin Nutr* 73: 386S–392S.

FELLEY, C.P., CORTHESY-THEULAZ, I., RIVERO, J.L., SIPPONEN, P., KAUFMANN, M., BAUERFEIND, P., WIESEL, P.H., BRASSART, D., PFEIFER, A., BLUM, A.L. and MICHETTI, P. (2001) Favourable effect of an acidified milk (LC-1) on *Helicobacter pylori* gastritis in man. *Eur J Gastroenterol Hepatol* 13: 25–29.

FEORD, J. (2002) Lactic acid bacteria in a changing legislative environment. *Antonie van Leeuwenhoek* 82: 353–360.

FRETER, R. and ABRAMS, G.D. (1972) Function of various intestinal bacteria in converting germfree mice to the normal state. *Infect Immun* 6: 119–126.

FULLER, R. (1989) Probiotics in man and animals. *J Appl Bacteriol* 66: 365–378.

GILL, H.S., RUTHERFURD, K.J. and CROSS, M.L. (2001) Dietary probiotic supplementation enhances natural killer cell activity in the elderly: an investigation of age-related immunological changes. *J Clin Immunol* 21: 264–271.

GUANDALINI, S., PENSABENE, L., ZIKRI, M.A., DIAS, J.A., CASALI, L.G., HOEKSTRA, H., KOLACEK, S., MASSAR, K., MICETIC-TURK, D., PAPADOPOULOU, A., DE SOUSA, J.S., SANDHU, B., SZAJEWSKA, H. and WEIZMAN, Z. (2000) Lactobacillus GG administered in oral rehydration solution to children with acute diarrhea: a multicenter European trial. *J Pediatr Gastroenterol Nutr* 30: 54–60.

GUARNER, F. and SCHAAFSMA, G.J. (1998) Probiotics. *Int J Food Microbiol* 39: 237–238.

GUPTA, P., ANDREW, H., KIRSCHNER, B.S. and GUANDALINI, S. (2000) Is lactobacillus GG helpful in children with Crohn's disease? Results of a preliminary, open-label study. *J Pediatr Gastroenterol Nutr* 31: 453–457.

HERIAS, M.V., HESSLE, C., TELEMO, E., MIDTVEDT, T., HANSON, L.A. and WOLD, A.E. (1999) Immunomodulatory effects of *Lactobacillus plantarum* colonizing the intestine of gnotobiotic rats. *Clin Exp Immunol* 116: 283–290.

HUDAULT, S., LIEVIN, V., BERNET-CAMARD, M.F. and SERVIN, A.L. (1997) Antagonistic activity exerted *in vitro* and *in vivo* by *Lactobacillus casei* (strain GG) against *Salmonella typhimurium* C5 infection. *Appl Environ Microbiol* 63: 513–518.

ISOLAURI, E., JUNTUNEN, M., RAUTANEN, T., SILLANAUKEE, P. and KOIVULA, T. (1991) A human *Lactobacillus* strain (*Lactobacillus casei* sp strain GG) promotes recovery from acute diarrhea in children. *Pediatrics* 88: 90–97.

ISOLAURI, E., MAJAMAA, H., ARVOLA, T., RANTALA, I., VIRTANEN, E. and ARVILOMMI, H. (1993) *Lactobacillus casei* strain GG reverses increased intestinal permeability induced by cow milk in suckling rats. *Gastroenterology* 105: 1643–1650.

ISOLAURI, E., ARVOLA, T., SUTAS, Y., MOILANEN, E. and SALMINEN, S. (2000) Probiotics in the management of atopic eczema. *Clin Exp Allergy* 30: 1604–1610.

KABIR, A.M., AIBA, Y., TAKAGI, A., KAMIYA, S., MIWA, T. and KOGA, Y. (1997) Prevention of *Helicobacter pylori* infection by lactobacilli in a gnotobiotic murine model. *Gut* 41: 49–55.

KERNEIS, S., BOGDANOVA, A., KRAEHENBUHL, J.P. and PRINGAULT, E. (1997) Conversion by Peyer's patch lymphocytes of human enterocytes into M cells that transport bacteria. *Science* 277: 949–952.

KIRJAVAINEN, P.V., OUWEHAND, A.C., ISOLAURI, E. and SALMINEN, S.J. (1998) The ability of probiotic bacteria to bind to human intestinal mucus. *FEMS Microbiol Lett* 167: 185–189.

KITAZAWA, H., TOMIOKA, Y., MATSUMURA, K., ASO, H., MIZUGAKI, M., ITOH, T. and YAMAGUCHI, T. (1994) Expression of mRNA encoding IFN alpha in macrophages stimulated with *Lactobacillus gasseri*. *FEMS Microbiol Lett* 120: 315–321.

KLAENHAMMER, T., ALTERMANN, E., ARIGONI, F., BOLOTIN, A., BREIDT, F., BROADBENT, J., CANO, R., CHAILLOU, S., DEUTSCHER, J., GASSON, M., VAN DEN GUCHTE, M., GUZZO, J., HARTKE, A., HAWKINS, T., HOLS, P., HUTKINS, R., KLEEREBEZEM, M., KOK, J., KUIPERS, O., LUBBERS, M., MAGUIN, E., MCKAY, L., MILLS, D., NAUTA, A., OVERBEEK, R., PEL, H., PRIDMORE, D., SAIER, M., VAN SINDERSEN, D., SOROKIN, A., STEELE, J., O'SULLIVAN, D., DE VOS, W., WEIMER, B., ZAGOREC, M. and SIEZEN, R. (2002) Discovering lactic acid bacteria by genomics. *Antonie van Leeuwenhoek* 82(1–4): 29–58.

KUBY, J. (1997) *Immunology*, Third edition. W.H. Freeman, New York.

LEE, Y.K., LIM, C.Y., TENG, W.L., OUWEHAND, A.C., TUOMOLA, E.M. and SALMINEN, S. (2000) Quantitative approach in the study of adhesion of lactic acid bacteria to intestinal cells and their competition with enterobacteria. *Appl Environ Microbiol* 66: 3692–3697.

LINK-AMSTER, H., ROCHAT, F., SAUDAN, K.Y., MIGNOT, O. and AESCHLIMANN, J.M. (1994) Modulation of a specific humoral immune response and changes in intestinal flora mediated through fermented milk intake. *FEMS Immunol Med Microbiol* 10: 55–63.

MACDONALD, T.T. (1995) Breakdown of tolerance to the intestinal bacterial flora in inflammatory bowel disease (IBD) [editorial; comment]. *Clin Exp Immunol* 102: 445–447.

MARIN, M.L., LEE, J.H., MURTHA, J., USTUNOL, Z. and PESTKA, J.J. (1997) Differential cytokine production in clonal macrophage and T-cell lines cultured with bifidobacteria. *J Dairy Sci* 80: 2713–2720.

MARTEAU, P., MINEKUS, M., HAVENAAR, R. and HUIS IN'T VELD, J.H. (1997) Survival of lactic acid bacteria in a dynamic model of the stomach and small intestine: validation and the effects of bile. *J Dairy Sci* 80: 1031–1037.

NEESER, J.R., GRANATO, D., ROUVET, M., SERVIN, A., TENEBERG, S. and KARLSSON, K.A. (2000) *Lactobacillus johnsonii* La1 shares carbohydrate-binding specificities with several enteropathogenic bacteria. *Glycobiology* 10: 1193–1199.

NIEDZIELIN, K., KORDECKI, H. and BIRKENFELD, B. (2001) A controlled, double-blind, randomized study on the efficacy of *Lactobacillus plantarum* 299V in patients with irritable bowel syndrome. *Eur J Gastroenterol Hepatol* 13: 1143–1147.

OCANA, V.S., PESCE DE RUIZ HOLGADO, A.A. and NADER-MACIAS, M.E. (1999) Selection of vaginal H_2O_2-generating *Lactobacillus* species for probiotic use. *Curr Microbiol* 38: 279–284.

OUWEHAND, A.C., SALMINEN, S. and ISOLAURI, E. (2002) Probiotics: an overview of beneficial effects. *Antonie van Leeuwenhoek* 82: 279–289.

REID, G. and BRUCE, A.W. (2001) Selection of lactobacillus strains for urogenital probiotic applications. *J Infect Dis* 183 Suppl 1: S77–S80.

RESCIGNO, M., URBANO, M., VALZASINA, B., FRANCOLINI, M., ROTTA, G., BONASIO, R., GRANUCCI, F., KRAEHENBUHL, J.P. and RICCIARDI-CASTAGNOLI, P. (2001) Dendritic cells express tight junction proteins and penetrate gut epithelial monolayers to sample bacteria. *Nat Immunol* 2: 361–367.

ROBINSON, K., CHAMBERLAIN, L.M., SCHOFIELD, K.M., WELLS, J.M. and LE PAGE, R.W. (1997) Oral vaccination of mice against tetanus with recombinant *Lactococcus lactis*. *Nat Biotechnol* 15: 653–657.

SALMINEN, S., OUWEHAND, A., BENNO, Y. and LEE, K.Y. (1999) Probiotics: how should they be defined? *Trends in Food Science and Technology* 10: 107–110.

SELSTED, M.E., MILLER, S.I., HENSCHEN, A.H. and OUELLETTE, A.J. (1992) Enteric defensins: antibiotic peptide components of intestinal host defense. *J Cell Biol* 118: 929–936.

SHORNIKOVA, A.V., CASAS, I.A., MYKKANEN, H., SALO, E. and VESIKARI, T. (1997) Bacteriotherapy with *Lactobacillus reuteri* in rotavirus gastroenteritis. *Pediatr Infect Dis J* 16: 1103–1107.

SLAUCH, J.M. and CAMILLI, A. (2000) IVET and RIVET: use of gene fusions to identify bacterial virulence factors specifically induced in host tissues. *Methods Enzymol* 326: 73–96.

SPANHAAK, S., HAVENAAR, R. and SCHAAFSMA, G. (1998) The effect of consumption of milk fermented by *Lactobacillus casei* strain *Shirota* on the intestinal microflora and immune parameters in humans. *Eur J Clin Nutr* 52: 899–907.

STEIDLER, L., HANS, W., SCHOTTE, L., NEIRYNCK, S., OBERMEIER, F., FALK, W., FIERS, W. and REMAUT, E. (2000) Treatment of murine colitis by *Lactococcus lactis* secreting interleukin-10. *Science* 289: 1352–1355.

TALARICO, T.L. and DOBROGOSZ, W.J. (1989) Chemical characterization of an antimicrobial substance produced by *Lactobacillus reuteri*. *Antimicrob Agents Chemother* 33: 674–679.

TUOMOLA, E.M. and SALMINEN, S.J. (1998) Adhesion of some probiotic and dairy *Lactobacillus* strains to Caco-2 cell cultures. *Int J Food Microbiol* 41: 45–51.

TUOMOLA, E.M., OUWEHAND, A.C. and SALMINEN, S.J. (1999) The effect of probiotic bacteria on the adhesion of pathogens to human intestinal mucus. *FEMS Immunol Med Microbiol* 26: 137–142.

WELLS, C.L., MADDAUS, M.A. and SIMMONS, R.L. (1988) Proposed mechanisms for the translocation of intestinal bacteria. *Rev Infect Dis* 10: 958–979.

YASUI, H. and OHWAKI, M. (1991) Enhancement of immune response in Peyer's patch cells cultured with *Bifidobacterium breve*. *J Dairy Sci* 74: 1187–1195.

Part II

New technologies to improve quality

13

On-line measurement of product quality in dairy processing

G. Ellen and A. J. Tudos, NIZO Food Research, The Netherlands

13.1 Introduction

The dairy industry has to guarantee that the quality and safety of products meets well-defined specifications. This can be implemented by thoroughly checking the quality of each batch of the final product. The problem with this approach is that deviations are signalled at a stage when corrections are usually not possible. Probably, a more attractive approach is a thorough analysis of not only the input and output streams, but also control of all relevant processing parameters in between. This approach yields better product quality because slight deviations of relevant process parameters can be rapidly detected and corrected for. Safety margins can be minimised, yielding increased productivity and profitability. Finally, a faster product release to the market is possible.

For end-product testing, a properly working analytical laboratory is sufficient. The decision of product release will be based on reliable analytical results. From the viewpoint of business efficiency, immediate release of finished products is vital. This can be achieved by chain management of the whole process, i.e. total quality assurance. The tools to achieve this goal include fast measurements, discussed in this chapter, and rapid feedback systems for process control, dealt with elsewhere in this book.

Sampling and analysis can be carried out *on-line*, *in-line*, *at-line* or *off-line*. The distinction between on-line and in-line is not always clear. In this chapter we define these categories as follows. *On-line* analysis means that the data on a process stream segment are available in real time or with only a short delay after the segment has passed the measuring point. The measurement is called *in-line* if the measuring point is in the main process line enabling feedback for process control. Samples taken from the line can be analysed *at-line* with instruments located in the production area. If none of the aforementioned is applicable, samples have to be sent for *off-line* measurement to a laboratory.

The controllability of a process can be evaluated based on objective parameters such as process controllability (van der Grinten 1968, Leemans 1971). Process controllability (*r*) ranges from 0 (totally uncontrollable process) to 1 (total control on process). This parameter can be calculated based on results from a process audit and will determine the opportunities to improve product quality through process control. Process controllability can be expressed on the basis of disturbances as follows:

$$r^2 = \frac{\sigma_p^2 - \sigma_\varepsilon^2}{\sigma_p^2}$$

where σ_p is the standard deviation of the process fluctuations before control, a measure for the initial disturbance, and σ_ε is the standard deviation of the process fluctuations after control, a measure for the remaining disturbance after process adjustment.

Table 13.1 demonstrates the effect of the analysis speed and measurement precision on process control. In the table vital parameters are comprised for off-line, at-line and in-line analysis systems. In Table 13.1 the measurement time (the time period between sampling and availability of the analytical result) of the off-line analysis was assumed to be 1 h. In practice this time lag often amounts to several days due to delays at transportation to a central facility, scheduling of analyses and delays with reporting of results. At-line analysis provides a faster turnover, as transportation and scheduling delays are eliminated (0.2 h in Table 13.1). In-line analysis provides results practically instantaneously. For off-line analysis the sampling interval was chosen to be 1 h, for at-line analysis this parameter was set at 0.5 h, whereas in-line analysis was assumed to provide results continuously.

A vital parameter, measurement uncertainty, represents the precision of measurements. In analytical laboratories skilled staff, sophisticated instrumentation, validated and standardised procedures, in combination with frequent calibration and stringent quality control, ensure high precision and accuracy of the measurements. At-line instruments usually compromise accuracy due to time

Table 13.1 Effect of analysis speed and measurement uncertainty on controllability of a process with a response time on corrections of 0.1 h (adapted from Tummers and Wienke 2002)

Parameter	Off-line analysis	At-line analysis	In-line analysis
Measurement time	1 h	0.2 h	0 h
Sampling interval	1 h	0.5 h	0 h
Measurement uncertainty	1%	30%	50%
Process controllability (*r*)	0.46	0.73	0.87
Remaining disturbance (σ_ε)	90%	70%	50%

and cost limitations. In- and on-line apparatus mostly provides even less accuracy. In the example of Table 13.1 this parameter was chosen to be 1% for off-line analysis, 30% for at-line and 50% for in-line measurement.

The process controllability in case of in-line and at-line analysis appears quite high, whereas off-line analysis provides poor controllability. In practice, controllability values below 0.5 indicate uncontrollable processes, because only 10% of the disturbance is compensated. Based on the parameter of remaining disturbance, in-line analysis is clearly advantageous over at-line analysis. A striking conclusion of the above example is how vital the time lag between sampling and analytical results can be for process control. A central laboratory can guarantee process control only for relatively slow processes.

Dairy processes are usually complete within a time frame of hours, sometimes minutes or even seconds. Process control requires fast measurement, with less stringent demand on accuracy. Often, in- and on-line analysis is the method of preference with restrictions posed by the optically dense, inhomogeneous and fouling matrix. In-line analysis eliminates the need for batch sampling and can minimise sampling error by averaging of virtually instantaneous, continuous measurements. A prerequisite is that the instrument is placed at the correct analysis spot and timely changes can be made to the process. A restriction is that any component of the probes in contact with the product needs to comply with HACCP requirements. The advantages of effective process control are better compliance with product specification, hence narrower margins; faster release of products to the market, therefore less storage needed at the production site; less wasted product or products sold under the regular market price; and a decrease in the number of customer recalls.

In this chapter the existing technology for fast measurement is discussed for the determination of physical parameters, chemical concentration and micro-organisms. Examples are given for in-line measurements for process control in fermentation of yoghurt, renneting of milk, preparation of milk powder and pasteurisation. Applications for monitoring (bio)fouling and cleaning are also included. The chapter ends with a short review of exciting technologies suited to solve outstanding issues and an outlook on future trends.

13.2   On-line measurement of physical parameters

Measurement systems used in a food production environment must comply with stringent regulations. First, the choice of material in contact with the product is limited to food-grade materials. Secondly, in the design dead-zones must be avoided, and the surfaces must be smooth. Finally, the system must fulfil the requirements for cleaning and sterilisation in place, enduring the often harsh environment used for the various cleaning and disinfecting steps (pH < 1 and pH > 11). These requirements are common for all instruments applied in-line. In this section an overview is given of the available principles and measurement systems for the determination of physical parameters, concentration of

Table 13.2 Sensors for physical parameters, their principle of operation and relevant examples in dairy processing

Sensor	Principle of operation	Relevant processes
Temperature	Pt resistance wire	thermisation, pasteurisation, sterilisation, cooling, renneting
Pressure	(piezo)resistance, capacitance	filtration, pasteurisation, homogenisation
Flow	electromagnetism, displacement, turbine, ultrasonic, differential pressure, thermal mass	standardisation of fat content, mixing, heating, filtration
Level	conductivity, hydrostatic, vibration, ultrasonic, optical	storage tanks, mixing, packaging, CIP
Density	vibrating tubes, microwave	standardisation of fat content, powder production, mixing
Conductance	electrodes, microwave	cleaning in place (CIP)
Heat flux	thermopile (array of thermocouples)	fouling
Particle size, shape and distribution	focused beam reflectance, light scattering, microwave, video	cheese, yoghurt and powder production
Turbidity	IR and visible light scattering	CIP, filtration
Viscosity	diffusing wave spectroscopy, oscillation, vibration, NIR, hot wire, laser doppler anemometry, magnetic resonance imaging (MRI), NMR	cheese and yoghurt production, fermentation
Colour, optical density	optical reflection and absorbance	fermentation, powder production

compounds, and micro-organisms. Each section ends with relevant examples of application of the technology for process control in the dairy industry.

Various measurement systems have been successfully developed for the in-line determination of physical parameters. Table 13.2 is a compilation of the most commonly applied sensors in the dairy industry. The table contains the basic principles of operation together with relevant examples for use in dairy processing. For a comprehensive review on the measurement principles for pressure, temperature, flow and level, the reader is referred to Chapters 10 and 11 in *Instrumentation and Sensors for the Food Industry* (Berrie 2001a, 2001b). Up-to-date information on commercially available systems can be found at the websites of manufacturers.

Two examples of widespread application of sensors for physical parameters in the dairy industry are control of heat load and fat standardisation. Heat load is a quality parameter determined by the combination of temperature and residence time (i.e. flow). The organoleptic and storage quality of dairy products are largely determined by the heat load. The classification of pasteurised, sterilised and UHT milk, and of milk powders, is based on the heat load. In order to meet stringent specifications the temperature needs to be controlled within ±0.1°C and at a time scale of <1 second, imposing high demands on the response time and sensitivity of the sensors.

The second example of in-line process control in the dairy industry is fat standardisation. Narrowly defined by legal regulations and product specifications, the fat content of liquid dairy products is adjusted in-line using fat standardisation units. This process is based on the fact that differences in the density of milk are determined by variations in fat content. Therefore, systems available on the market for fully automatic in-line fat standardisation rely on measuring the density of the skimmed milk and whole milk or cream phases in combination with controlling the flow of each component to standardise the milk to the required fat content. Using current technology, fat content can be regulated within ±0.02% (m/m) of the target level in the final product.

A powerful new tool for in-line monitoring of texture changes is based on diffusing wave spectroscopy (DWS). DWS is an optical measuring technique based on multiple scattering of laser light by colloids and polymers in turbid systems (Pine et al. 1990). It is a non-destructive method applicable in a broad temperature range suited to determine the mobility of the colloidal particles (oil droplets, protein particles) even in concentrated systems such as emulsions and protein gels (Ten Grotenhuis et al. 1999). Physical contact of the probe with the product can be avoided by measuring through a window.

Incident laser light is multiply scattered due to the turbidity of the system. Scattered light can be detected at the opposite side of the incidence (transmission) or at the same side using a light fibre probe (back-scattering). The detected light intensity is a stochastic signal due to the mobility of the particles. Via determination of the intensity correlation curve, a numeric value for the mobility of the scattering particle can be obtained. The mobility of particles is determined by their surroundings and therefore reflects the visco-elastic properties of the system.

DWS-based systems have been used for monitoring acid-induced gelation of milk (Arikainen 2000, Vasbinder et al. 2001). A DWS-based measuring instrument called NIZO RheoLight (NIZO Food Research, Ede, The Netherlands) was developed to monitor curd formation in-line during cheese manufacturing (Ten Grotenhuis 1999). During standard and test production of more than 80 batches of cheese, the renneting process was followed for a period of 3 months with NIZO RheoLight. The fat content and amount of curd fines in the whey were determined (Fig. 13.1).

For the test batches the cutting programme started at gel strengths below or above the usual value. The critical gel strength was determined to be approximately 30 DWS units. When the curd was too soft at cutting, dramatic losses of fat and curd fines were seen: a renneting time approximately 2 minutes shorter (20 DWS units instead of 30) increased the losses in curd fines sixfold and increased fat loss by 50%. At this stage, the gel is not yet strong enough to be cut without damage. Longer cutting times result in slightly higher cheese

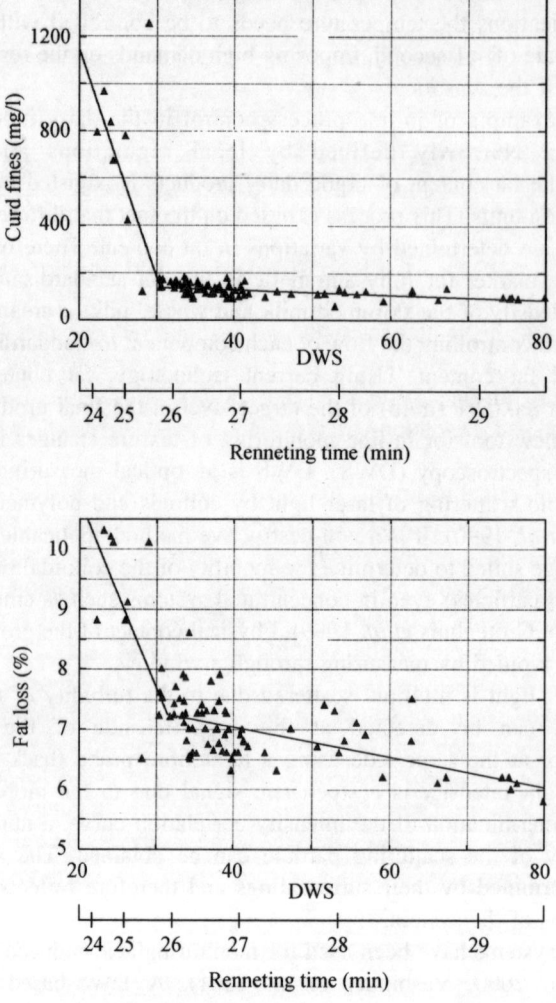

Fig. 13.1 Curd fines and fat content in whey depending on the gel strength and renneting time in cheese manufacturing.

yield, but can be disadvantageous for the production throughput (Table 13.3). The in-line sensor has been successfully installed in cheese factories where it contributes to cheese yield and process control (Straatsma *et al.* 2001, 2002).

The NIZO RheoLight system provides distinct advantages for the cheese-making process. For example, the complete process of cheese-making can be automated, and the renneting process can be continuously monitored with improved control over the water content of the product. Additionally, the final product shows less variation in shape. Finally, the product composition is less prone to seasonal effects. The applications have been extended to follow

Table 13.3 Effect of cutting time and gel strength on fat and protein yield in cheese processing, at an annual production of 25 000 000 kg cheese

Gel strength (DWS)	Renneting time (min)	Yield increase (kg/year)	
		Fat	Protein
20	23.5	−27 300	−142 590
30 (ref)	25.7	−	−
50	27.8	4195	3205
70	28.9	8345	6406

changes in the rheology characteristics of turbid systems such as desserts, drinks, sauces and the production of yoghurt (Ten Grotenhuis *et al.* 2000). An advantage of this in-line system is that dosing errors of ingredients are immediately detected. Deviations from normal process trend can be traced at an early stage.

An alternative optical technique for cutting time control in cheese-making is represented by the CoAguLite (REFLECTronics Inc., Lexington, KY, USA). The CoAguLite sensor measures changes in light back-scattering during coagulation of milk. From the reflectance profile, a prediction is made for the optimal cutting time. The two systems, CoAguLite and NIZO RheoLight, show a major difference in determining the optimal cutting time. The RheoLight measures real-time gel strength throughout the process, whereas the CoAguLite extrapolates the optimal cutting time from measurement data obtained during the first stages of flocculation. Extrapolation can be hampered by unexpected effects during the process, resulting in incorrect prediction of the optimal cutting time.

Further systems for viscosity determination are based on induced mechanical effects (shear, torsion, ultrasound) which by themselves can disrupt the structure to be measured (Bourne 2002). Additionally, a heated thermistor was used for monitoring curd formation, based on decrease of thermal conductivity on flocculation of milk. The error of prediction was 1.9 min in 16 experiments (Passos *et al.* 1999). As seen in Table 13.3, this precision is not sufficient.

13.3   Measuring product composition

The use of process analytical equipment grew by more than 5% annually during the 1990s (McMahon and Robertson 1995, McIvor 1997). As a consequence, the number of laboratory-based analyses has been shrinking and the work has been shifting away from chemists and chemical technicians to plant operators trained to make analytical determinations. Various measurement systems have been successfully developed; Table 13.4 is a compilation of the most commonly applied systems for concentration measurement in dairy processes. The table contains the basic principles of operation together with relevant examples for use in dairy processing. For information on the operating principles behind the

Table 13.4 Chemical parameters, the principle of their determination and relevant examples for application in dairy processing

Parameter	Principle	Relevant applications
pH	ion selective electrode (ISE), field effect transistor (FET)	fermentation, cleaning-in-place
Water content	(near) infrared spectrometry, sensors	powder and cheese production
Fat content	(near) infrared spectrometry	standardisation, quality control of dairy products
Protein content	(near) infrared spectrometry	standardisation, quality control of dairy products
Lactose/ carbohydrates	flow injection analysis, (near) infrared spectrometry, sensors	fermentation process control, quality control
Lactic acid	flow injection analysis, sensors	fermentation process control
Flavour components	fast mass spectrometry, electronic nose, electronic tongue, sensors, spectroscopic techniques, dedicated mass spectrometry	process control, quality control, cleaning
Residues/ contaminants	fast mass spectrometry, electronic nose, electronic tongue, sensors	process control, quality control, cleaning
(Bio)fouling	heat transfer resistance, pressure drop	production processes
Byproducts	sensors, optical measurements	smouldering of milk powder
Cleaning/ disinfecting	conductivity, electronic nose, electronic tongue, sensors, spectroscopic techniques, dedicated mass spectrometry, ISE	cleaning-in-place

analytical techniques, the reader is referred to basic literature on sensors (Taylor and Schultz 1996, Kress-Rogers 1997, Kress-Rogers and Brimelow 2001) and spectrometry (Skoog and Holler 1996).

One of the most established techniques, infrared (IR) spectrometry, provides a rapid and direct method for process analysis. Based on the wavelength of irradiation, infrared techniques can be divided into mid- and near-infrared, often called MIR ($\lambda = 2\text{--}14\,\mu\text{m}$) and NIR ($\lambda = 0.75\text{--}2.6\,\mu\text{m}$) (Scotter 1997). IR is a non-destructive and non-invasive technique suited for at-, on- or in-line application in food processing plants. Determination of more than one component is possible within one spectral acquisition time, i.e. within minutes, seconds or less. MIR is mostly applied for analysis in gas and liquid phase, whereas NIR is applicable for the analysis of solid or liquid products.

Few analytical methods are capable of direct measurements in complex food matrices. Infrared techniques are suited for such matrices but lack the potential of 'seeing through' thick layers of inhomogeneous samples such as an intact cheese. Nevertheless, the technologies represent probably the most successful analytical tools in food analysis, because they are fast, versatile and non-invasive. IR measurements can be carried out in solid, liquid and gas samples and are not hampered by viscosity or turbidity of the sample. Analysis can be implemented in the transmission, reflection or attenuated total reflection (ATR) mode. Even immersion probes are commercially available. Various manufacturers provide dedicated systems suited for process analysis in the food industry. An overview of the companies, the measuring principle and applications is provided in Table 13.5.

Originally used for the identification of organic compounds, mid-infrared spectrometry has gained widespread application for quantitative measurements and recently for process control of high moisture content dairy products. A typical example is an FT-MIR-based on-line analyser and dedicated process controller developed by FOSS for standardisation of milk used in the manufacture of dairy products. The standardisation is carried out on multiple components, such as fat, protein, lactose and total solids, to within <0.01% of the target value. The idea of on-line standardisation is to decrease the spread in distribution of, for example, the fat content in the processed dairy product. With manual standardisation, the distribution is very broad as indicated by curve 1 in Fig. 13.2. By using the standardisation control system of FOSS, the fat distribution curve was considerably narrowed around the old target value (curve 2), but as long as the target is not changed, the average of the production will be the same. The improved fat distribution figures make it possible to move the average of the production down from 3.07 to 3.02 and at the same time get

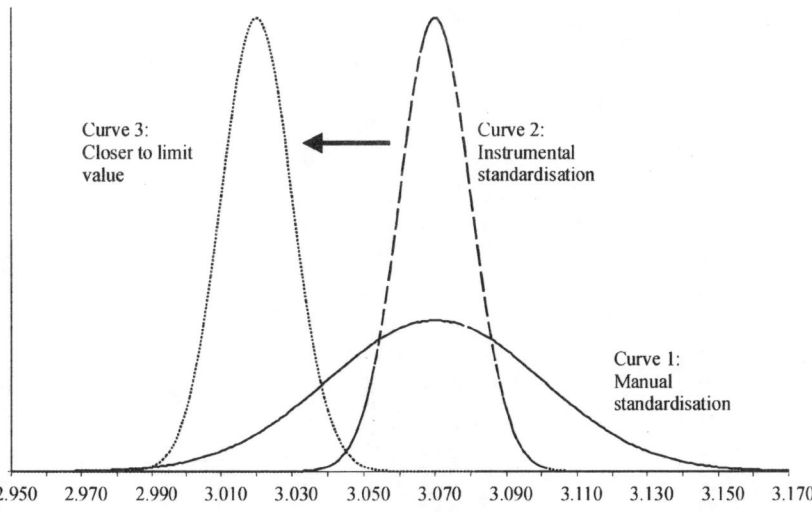

Fig. 13.2   Effect of improving standardisation accuracy on the economy of production (courtesy of FOSS).

Table 13.5 Producers of dedicated IR instruments

Company	URL	Measurement principle	Applications	Remarks
ABB Bomem Inc., Quebec, Canada	www.bomem.com	FT-NIR	fat, salt, protein moisture in butter; standardisation of fat, protein and moisture in liquid dairy products	at-line, 2 min/sample in-line and on-line 1-5 samples/min
AIS-Tech	www.adnex.de	NIR	moisture in solid food products	on-line probe
Analyticon Instruments Corp., Springfield, NJ	www.analyticon.com	NIR	moisture in solid food products	on-line probe
Analyticai Spectral Devices Inc., Boulder, CO	www.asdi.com	NIR	fat and moisture in cheese	at-line fibre optic probe
Axiom Analytical Inc., Irvine, CA	www.goaxiom.com	NIR FT-MIR	food and other applications	in-line ATR probe, immersion probe, non-contact analyser and on-line sampling system
ChemQuip Ltd, Stockport, UK	www.chemquip.co.uk	NIR	gas, liquid and solid samples including food	in-line ATR probe, single and double path cell
FOSS, Hillerød, Denmark	www.foss.dk	NIT	fat, moisture, protein, TS[a] in cheese, butter, quark, yoghurt	at-line, approx. 1 min per sample
		NIR	solids, liquids, powders	at-line, approx. 1 min per sample
		FT-MIR	in-line fat, protein, lactose, SNF[b] in milk	in-line milk standardisation
Kett Electric Laboratory, Tokyo, Japan	www.kett.co.jp	NIR	moisture, protein, fat, lactose content in milk powder	at-line

Company	Website	Technique	Application	Mode
Leco Corp., St Joseph, MI	www.leco.com	NIR	moisture and fat in cheese; moisture, salt, fat, ash and protein in whey powder	at-line at-line
Thermo Electron Corporation, Chelmsford, MA	www.thermo.com	NIR	fat, protein, moisture in foods including dairy products	at-line
NDC Infrared Engineering, Maldon, Essex, UK	www.ndcinfrared.com	NIR	moisture, fat, protein in dairy powders	on-line
Perten Instruments, Huddinge, Sweden	www.perten.com	NIR	fat, protein, salt and moisture in foods including dairy products	at-line, <1 min per sample
Polytec GmbH, Waldbronn, Germany	www.analytic-web.com	NIR	fat, protein, moisture in foods including dairy products moisture in powder	at-line on-line
Process Sensors Corp., Milford, MA	www.processsensors.com	NIR	moisture in dairy powders	at-line
Wilks Enterprise Inc., South Norwalk, CT	www.wilksir.com	MIR	fluids	in-line ATR plug sensor
Zeltex Inc., Hagerstown, MD	www.zeltex.com	NIR	fat, protein, moisture in cheese and other foods	at-line, <1 min per sample

[a] TS = total solids.
[b] SNF = solids-non-fat.

batches within the legal limit (curve 3). In this way expensive milk components are saved, and both production economy and product quality are improved.

An example of *in situ* fermentation monitoring of glucose, fructose, lactose, galactose, lactic acid and ethanol was demonstrated using an attenuated total reflection (ATR) sensor connected to a remote dispersive mid-IR spectrometer with an optical fibre (Fayolle *et al.* 2000). A well-established application proven in daily practice is the early warning system for fire in drying installations, based on IR detection of carbon monoxide in the drying air (Steenbergen *et al.* 1991; see also Chapter 20 in this book). The system, called NICOSYS, is currently marketed by Hobré Instruments (Purmerend, the Netherlands). Another system, called STUVEXCOPS by StuvEx Sicherheitssysteme GmbH (Hamm, Germany), is also on the market.

Near infrared (NIR) plays a key role in the analysis and process control of dairy products. The technique offers flexibility in the determination of protein moisture, fat and lactose contents in a wide range of dairy products, e.g. liquid milk, dairy powders, cream, cheese and processed cheese. Many of these products are emulsions, whose sampling for classical chemical analysis is cumbersome. Fundamental literature on NIR is available (Burns and Ciurczak 1992, Osborne *et al.* 1993) as well as a review on food analysis (Osborne 2000). NIR instruments are generally very fast and easy to operate, providing results similar in accuracy to the reference methods to which they are calibrated. NIR requires little or no sample preparation and no chemicals, and is ideal for complex matrices, e.g. food. For some in-line applications, fibre optic probes are used. The applications span the range from purely quantitative measurements such as protein, moisture and fat content to qualitative measurements and product identification.

It is profitable to make products which narrowly match the required specifications. Milk powders are analysed on-line, enabling the moisture content to be narrowly controlled as demonstrated by Holroyd (2002). A FOSS 5500 scanning NIR apparatus was placed after the fluid bed drier. Via a sample grab arm operated with compressed air, 100 g of sample is presented to the instrument. The sample is either returned to the flow or retained for later reference. In Fig. 13.3 the results of the on-line NIR and an off-line reference method (IDF 26A:1993) are compared. An overall match of the two methods is easily seen, though at the indicated time region serious deviation from the target value occurred, unseen by the reference method due to low sampling frequency. An additional disadvantage of the reference measurement is that the analysis data do not become available until after more than 3 hours, whereas the NIR measurement provides data instantaneously. The economic benefits for process control are obvious.

Sometimes at-line measurements provide sufficient benefits and are cheaper than in-line options (Holroyd 2002). The example shown in Fig. 13.4, the determination of moisture, salt and fat in butter, takes less than 1 min. Other examples for application of NIR for dairy process control include the continuous in-line determination of moisture, protein and fat in cottage cheese and

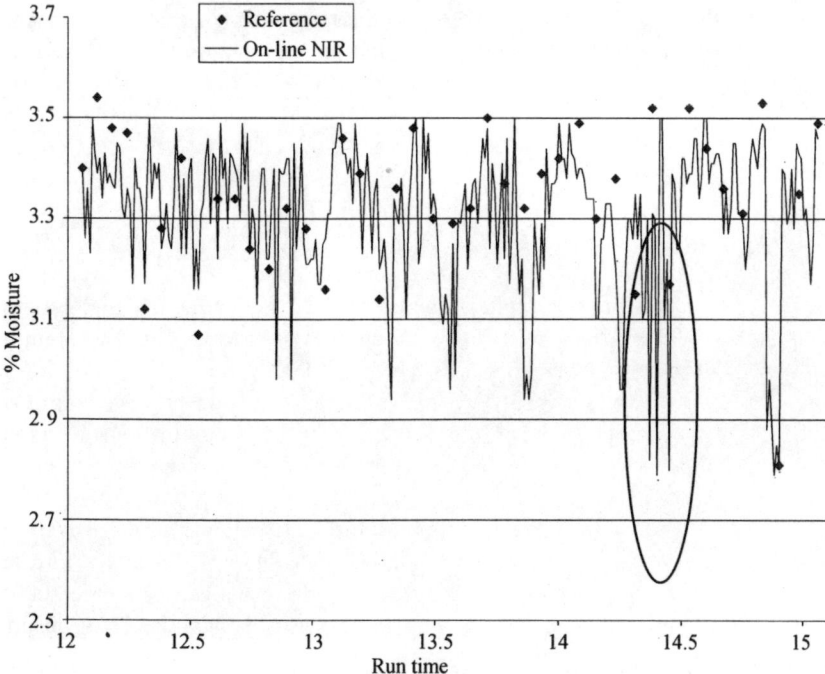

Fig. 13.3   Comparison of on-line and reference (IDF 26A:1993) measurements of moisture in milk powder (Holroyd 2002).

processed cheese (Hoyer 1997). Correlation coefficients between 0.988 and 0.999 were found between the NIR and reference methods in 35 samples of processed cheese and 49 of cottage cheese. The standard errors of prediction varied from 0.06% to 0.38%. No information on the reference methods is provided in the publication.

A specific example for in-line measurements is represented by testing of return PET milk bottles for abuse. Before refilling, glass bottles undergo steam cleaning, whereas plastic bottles do not endure this treatment. Therefore, the air inside each bottle is tested for the presence of organic compounds, mainly hydrocarbons and remnants of household chemicals, using a dedicated mass spectrometry system. These systems are commercially available, but the sampling device usually needs to be tailor-made.

Flow injection analysis (FIA), first described by Růžička and Hansen (1975), is a well-established analytical technique, known for its high sample throughput combined with good precision, reproducibility and accuracy. The basis for the technology is a continuous flow of liquid into which reagents are injected as small liquid segments that are transported, mixed, diluted and reacted under well-controlled conditions. The technique allows chemists to easily automate and optimise well-developed wet chemical methods for routine laboratory use, and even for at-line or on-line process analysis. Reagents can also be

Fig. 13.4   At-line NIR determination of moisture, salt and fat in butter (Holroyd 2002).

immobilised in small reactors, limiting the cost per sample. This technology is especially useful when biochemical reactions are required in FIA systems, e.g. by using enzymes (Mattiasson 1994). Present commercially available FIA systems and producers are listed in Table 13.6. The table also contains system characteristics such as sample volume and throughput, detection systems and areas of application. The table is based on a recent publication (Smith and Hinson-Smith 2002). As the field is developing rapidly, the reader is advised to check product reviews of periodicals for updated information.

An example of the at-line application of FIA in dairy processes is the determination of D- and L-lactate in butter, yoghurt and buttermilk production (Becker *et al.* 1995). The FIA system contained a microreactor with immobilised D- and L-lactate dehydrogenase enzymes for the production of pyruvate in the presence of nicotinamide adenine dinucleotide (NAD$^+$). The produced NADH was detected photometrically. The analysis could be performed within 5 minutes. The only sample preparation required was dilution. The analysis cost 10% of the reference method. The FIA analysis results of 15 different dairy products were within 3% of those obtained with the reference method (DIN 10335).

A similar on-line application in an accelerated, fed-batch yoghurt fermentation process was developed at NIZO Food Research by de Jong (1994) using in-line dialysis and fluorometric detection (Fig. 13.5). The sample throughput was 20 per hour and the results were in agreement with HPLC. The

Table 13.6 Overview of commercially available FIA systems (adapted from Smith and Hinson-Smith 2002)

Company	AMKO Systems, Richmond Hill, Ontario, Canada	FIAlab instruments, Bellevue, WA	FOSS, Hillerød, Denmark	Global FIA, Fox Island, WA	Lachat Instruments, Milwaukee, WI	OI Analytical, College Station, TX	Skalar Inc., Breda, The Netherlands
URL	www.amkosystems.com	www.flowinjection.com	www.foss.dk	www.globalfia.com	www.lachatinstruments.com	www.oico.com	www.skalar.com
Detection principles	colorimeters, ISE[a] conductivity	light absorbance, fluorescence, bioluminescence	dual-wavelength photometer	UV-vis absorbance, chemiluminescence amperometric	photometric, ISE, conductivity, flame, photometric, amperometric, pH, fluorimetric	photometrics, ISE, amperometric	photometric, UV, IR, fluorimetric, flame, conductivity, pH, ISE
Applications	chemical, environmental, biotechnology, pharmaceutical, food and beverage	water quality, environmental, proteomics, food sample handling for FTIR, ICP-MS, chemical sensors, immunoassays	food, environmental and industrial	organic and inorganic analytes on-line, lab and field analysis	high throughput, environmental, industrial QC, bioreactor monitoring, food and beverage, in-line digestions	water and waste, industrial QC, agricultural, food and beverage	water and waste, industrial QC, agricultural, food and beverage, detergent and pharmaceuticals
Sample volume and throughput	2–100 μl 20 samples/h		20–400 μl 60–120 samples/h	variable, 1–3 min/sample	1 μl to 2 μl 60–120 samples/h	20–75 samples/h	20–140 samples/h/manifold 16 manifolds simultaneously

[a] ISE = ion selective electrode.

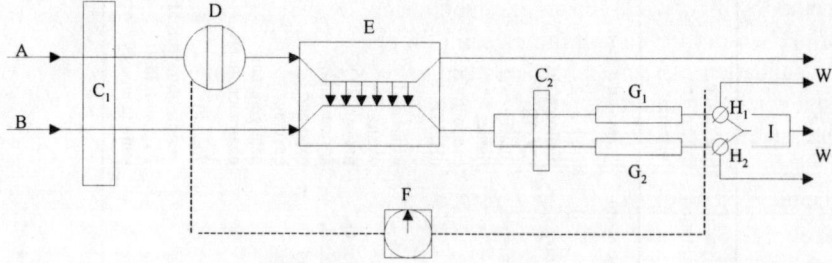

Fig. 13.5   Scheme of the FIA setup for simultaneous determination of *D*- and *L*-lactate.
(A) 5% Na-citrate carrier solution; (B) 2.5 mM NAD in hydrazine–glycine–EDTA buffer
at pH 9.0; (C) pumps, flow $C_1 = 1.2$ ml/min, $C_2 = 0.6$ ml/min; (D) injection valve 200 μl;
(E) dialyser unit; (F) timer/controller; (G_1) reactor column width with immobilised *D*-
lactate dehydrogenase; (G_2) reactor column with immobilised *L*-lactate dehydrogenase;
(H) valves; (I) fluorescence detector (340/460 nm); (W) waste.

system provides a useful tool for on-line control of product claims in the
production of novel and functional foods.

Well-known devices for in-line concentration measurement are sensors. The
most common example is the glass electrode for pH sensing. A chemical sensor
or a biosensor can be defined as an analytical device comprised of a chemical or
biological recognition element directly interfaced to a signal transducer, which
together relate the concentration of an analyte or group of analytes to a
measurable response. Hence, a sensor can provide continuous information about
its environment, and in principle is ideal for in-line measurements. In
recognition of this promise, several journals are specialising in sensors, large
professional societies have sensor divisions and frequent international
conferences are organised. At the turn of the millennium, more than 2000
sensor-related articles were published per year (Janata 2001). Yet, all these
efforts have so far yielded few examples in process analysis, most sensors
having been developed for the determination of sugars (mainly glucose) and
ethanol in fermentation processes.

The main hurdles for the application of chemical and biosensors in a process
environment are the price vs. lifetime ratio, mismatch between analytical
characteristics (reproducibility, robustness, drift, sensitivity, etc.) and
requirements, and deterioration of analytical characteristics on cleaning-in-
place. Further limitations, practical problems and future demands are outlined in
reviews by Mehrvar *et al.* (2000) and O'Connell and Guilbault (2001).

A process example of the application of (bio)sensors in fermented milk and
yoghurt was provided by Mannino *et al.* (1999). Two parallel amperometric
biosensors were applied to the simultaneous detection of glucose and galactose.
The two rhodium-on-carbon paste sensors were constructed using glucose
oxidase and galactose oxidase enzymes, respectively. The sample throughput
was 70 per hour. All results were within 10% agreement with the HPLC results.
The advantage of fast data acquisition is manifested in better controllability of
the process (see Table 13.1). If extended with a microdialysis system, the

method will be suited for on-line monitoring. Further examples include the use of pH sensors for monitoring cleaning-in-place.

Validation of chemical sensors and concentration measurement systems can be a costly adventure. A useful workaround is to measure physical parameters (pressure, temperature, conductivity) which are correlated to the compound to be measured. If the correlation is sufficiently robust, the determination of the chemical parameter(s) can be replaced by monitoring the physical parameters.

13.4   On-line microbiological testing

Microbiological testing in the dairy plant is critical to ensure the quality of raw milk and finished products. The presently available methods include standard plate count (SPC), direct microscopic count (DMC), preliminary incubation (PI)-SPC, direct microscopic somatic cell count (DMSCC), and fast detection methods such as Bactoscan (FOSS, Denmark), Bactoscope (Delta Instruments, the Netherlands) and ATP-based measurements. Finally, indirect methods, such as the determination of conductivity, titratable acidity and gas formation, are also available.

The traditional methods usually require several hours or days of culturing, but provide relatively low limits of detection (in the range of 1 cfu/ml or lower). Fast methods can provide results within approximately 10 minutes; however, the limits of detection are in the range 10^4–10^5 cfu/ml. With the majority of indirect methods the effects of the growth of micro-organisms are only traceable at a stage when the product is already spoiled.

Micro-organisms presenting problems in dairy production are divided into two categories, pathogens and spoilage microbes. Production steps such as pasteurisation, (ultra) high temperature (UHT) treatment and sterilisation inactivate all pathogens. UHT and sterilisation also inactivate spoilage micro-organisms. The major problem for UHT and sterilised products is post-sterilisation contamination: spoilage micro-organisms can reach high levels during the long shelf-life of the products. Early detection of contamination is essential and requires determination at very low levels.

Despite extensive efforts to develop reliable and rapid analysis technology, no commercial methods are available as yet. Promising developments include a plastic food wrap suited for indicating bacterial contamination (Kleiner 2000). The food wrap, presently at the verge of market introduction by Toxin Alert (Mississauga, Ontario, Canada), will signal bacterial contamination without the need to open the package. Magnetic resonance imaging (MRI) has also been used to detect spoilage in closed packages (Schenz et al. 1999). Conductance and impedance techniques offer yet another non-destructive approach to detect bacterial growth in closed packages (Raaska and Mattila-Sandholm 2000). Extensive description of the technology and the practice can be found in Gibson (2001). Also ultrasonic imaging can be used for testing closed packages as well as calorimetric and volumetric methods (Raaska and Mattila-Sandholm 2000).

The detection limits of these techniques do not allow in-line measurements during production. The closed packages need to be incubated, sometimes for as long as several days. Additionally, the reliability of these techniques is not yet fully established.

The running times of continuous-flow process equipment such as pasteurisers are limited mainly by thermoresistant Streptococci (TRS). Raw milk may contain 10^2–10^4 TRS/ml. These micro-organisms attach to surfaces up to 10^7 TRS/cm^2. TRS are not completely inactivated by pasteurisation and proliferate at temperatures between 30° and 50°C, i.e. in the regenerative section of heat exchangers. In the course of a running period the TRS are released into the product flow. Depending on the initial level in the raw milk, running times of approximately 4 to over 11 hours can be realised before the critical level of 10^5 TRS/ml is reached and the pasteuriser must be cleaned. Bactoscan and ATP measurements were tested for indication of reaching the critical level (Te Giffel *et al.* 2001). The results revealed that, owing to the detection limits (10^4–10^5 cfu/ml), both systems are suited only as an 'emergency break', but not as a timely indicator that cleaning is necessary. If equipped with a suited filtration–concentration unit (e.g. Aquamarijn Microfiltration B.V., Zutphen, the Netherlands), the technology can reach the target detection limits.

13.5   Monitoring fouling and cleaning-in-place

The formation of fouling deposits within processing equipment has a significant economic impact in the dairy industry. Monitoring of fouling can provide useful information on when cleaning is necessary, and ensure effective operation of pasteurisers, sterilisers and drying equipment. When the tolerance level is reached, production has to be stopped and the equipment is cleaned in place (CIP). Monitoring of (bio)fouling and of CIP provides examples of the concerted application of physical sensors and devices for microbial growth detection and for concentration measurement.

An established technique for the monitoring of fouling in dairy processing lines is based on heat transfer measurements (Otten and Van Boxtel 1989, Truong and Anema 2002). An early example of monitoring the build-up of a fouling layer was provided by Otten and Van Boxtel (1989) by on-line measurement of the level of deposit based on the disturbance of hydrodynamic characteristics and on disturbance of heat transfer. The build-up of deposits on the inner wall of a pipe creates an additional thermal resistance and reduces the heat transport through the wall. Heat flux sensors consist of an array of thermocouples in which the elements are separated by a thin layer of thermal resistance material. Under a temperature gradient the thermocouple junctions are at different temperatures and therefore generate a voltage difference, proportional to the heat flux. These sensors provide more accurate information than simple temperature measurements, improving the accuracy of temperature-based control systems.

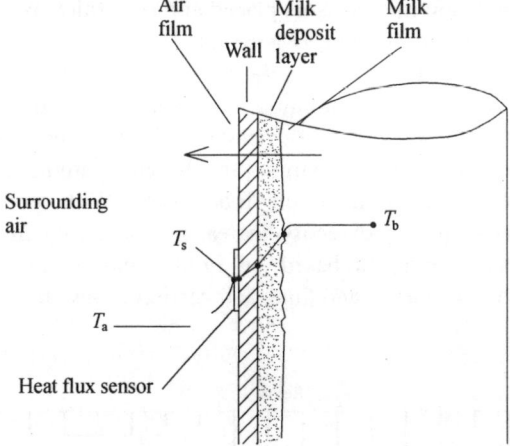

Fig. 13.6 Sectional view of a fouled pipe showing heat flux and temperature profile across the pipe wall. Temperature profile: bulk milk (T_b), sensor (T_s) and ambient air (T_a).

Truong and Anema (2002) measured fouling using a heat-flux sensor attached to the outer surface of a pipe of a direct steam injection milk heater (Fig. 13.6). The figure shows the temperature profile from the bulk milk (T_b) through the deposit layer and the pipe wall to the ambient air (T_a). The thicker the deposit layer on the wall, the smaller the temperature difference between the sensor (T_s) and the ambient temperature (T_a), resulting in a decreased heat flux.

The heat flux in relation to the average deposit thickness was measured in a pilot plant and in a commercial plant with the heat-flux-based system shown in Fig. 13.7. The method is suited for mapping critical points most sensitive to

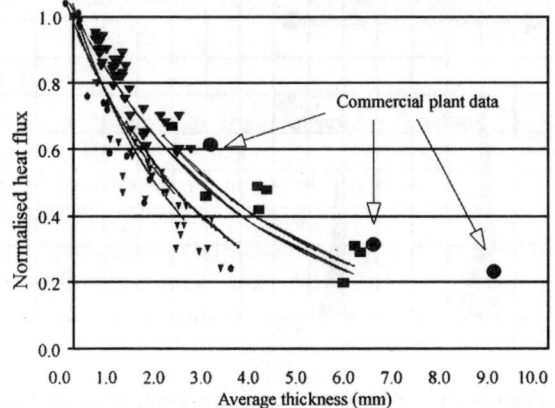

Fig. 13.7 Relation between the normalised heat flux and the average desposit layer thickness, both measured at the end of runs of heating whole milk to 85°C (■ top line), 95°C (▼ middle line) and 100°C (• bottom line).

fouling in the production line. Sensors placed at these critical points provide on-line information on when cleaning is necessary.

Cleaning and disinfection are essential for ensuring and maintaining quality and safety in the food industry. In liquid food processing frequent cleaning is a prerequisite. Dairy processes require even daily cleaning. These procedures are often based on experience. Large margins are chosen regarding the intensity and length of the cleaning steps to ensure food safety. With production batches getting smaller and product diversity increasing, flexibility in CIP processes gains in relevance. Strategies based on in-line and on-line monitoring of cleaning steps can save energy and time, and decrease consumption of water and

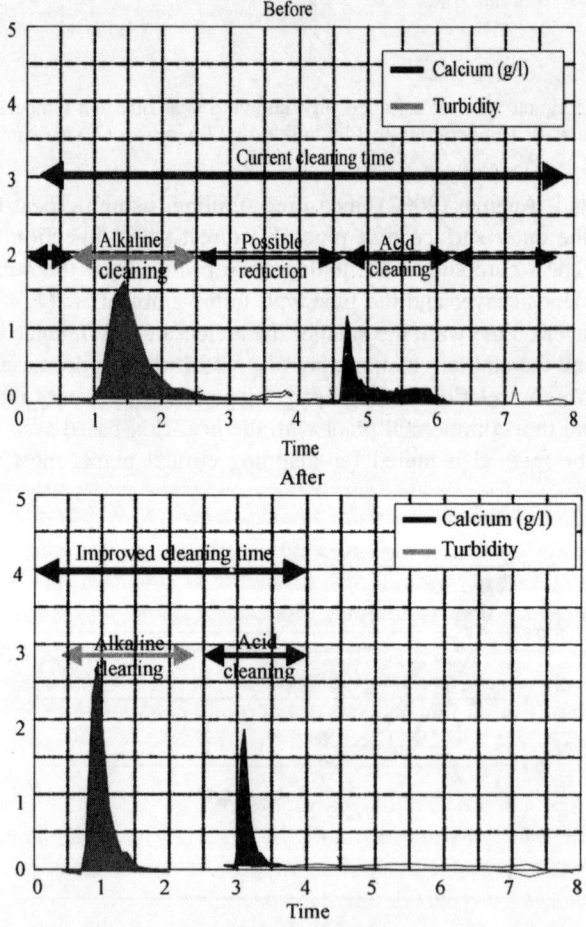

Fig. 13.8 Optimisation of CIP based on in- and at-line measurements. Turbidity corresponds with the amount of undissolved organic and inorganic material removed by alkaline cleaning. Calcium ion measurements: removal of inorganic deposition during acidic cleaning.

raw materials. Cleaning and disinfecting protocols include pumping an alkaline solution through the system to remove organic material (mainly proteins) and an acidic cleaning step to remove inorganic deposits, mainly calcium phosphate. Each step is preceded by aqueous rinsing, and the procedure ends with a thorough rinsing with water to ensure complete removal of the cleaning agents.

NIZO Food Research has developed a monitoring system, called OPTI-CIP, based on in- and at-line measurements of removal of deposits and cleaning agents (van Asselt *et al.* 2002). With OPTI-CIP, processes can be continuously analysed and optimised. Figure 13.8 demonstrates how optimisation of CIP can be accomplished by monitoring organic and inorganic material in the effluent. In a plant a two-step cleaning process was followed using a turbidity sensor (Type AF 56-N, OPTEK, Essen, Germany) and monitoring calcium. The efficiency of cleaning was improved by reducing the cleaning time by 50%.

13.6   Future trends

As shown in the previous sections, the challenge of in-line determination of most *physical parameters* relevant in dairy processing has been successfully tackled. In the near future, existing in-line methods can be used to acquire data on processes for predictive modelling and feed-forward process control (see Chapter 20 in this book). This approach will result in products narrowly matching the required specifications and depending less on fluctuations in the composition of raw materials.

Further outstanding issues are still to be solved in the area of on-line determination of *chemical compounds*. A challenging area is early detection of veterinary drug residues and contaminants in raw milk. The solution for this issue is urgently awaited owing to problems in fermentation processes, as well as to guarantee the safety and quality of final products. With proper 'farm to fork' chain management, abnormalities in composition will be detected very early in the chain, preferably during milking. Other outstanding issues include detecting abnormal milk in automatic milking systems, monitoring of the development of flavour compounds during fermentation, and the determination of the water content of intact cheeses before brining.

The technology of on-line analysis of *microbial contamination* at the required level is presently not available at all. In-line methods are urgently needed to trace microbes and spores.

There is light at the end of the tunnel in the guise of novel analytical techniques. In the following paragraphs a few innovative techniques that promise a breakthrough are discussed. Most of the illustrations of applications for these techniques are outside the dairy area.

Innovative *sensing systems* are currently under development to detect 'abnormal milk'. Abnormal milk, i.e. milk with clots, blood or a watery consistency, is not suited for human consumption and according to European Council Directive 92/46/EEC shall not reach the farm milk tank. Automatic detection of abnormal milk has gained importance due to the introduction of automatic milking systems where visual inspection is not possible (Rasmussen 2001). Present systems are based on conductivity sensors, yielding significant numbers of false positive as well as false negative results (de Mol 2000). Novel systems under development for the detection of abnormal milk are based on colour analysis (Espada and Vijverberg 2002), enzyme detection (Pemberton *et al.* 2001) and the electronic tongue (Rudniskaya 2002, Vlasov *et al.* 2002). If further developed, these sensor systems could also be used in the production line: the colour determination of products (custards, chocolate drinks, fermented dairy drinks), deviations in the composition of fermented products, authenticity and product control (e.g. sweeteners and flavours).

Another commercially available sensor suited for in-line process applications is based on surface plasmon resonance. The Spreeta^{TM} sensor (Texas Instruments, Austin, TX, USA) can be used to control the mixing ratio of fluid ingredients. If suited selective coatings are developed, Spreeta technology can in future also provide contamination monitoring.

The *electronic nose* (e-nose) is another example of an innovative sensor. An e-nose uses an array of chemical sensors to detect volatile analytes, and pattern recognition software to check the resulting chemical fingerprint. Most commercially available e-noses are built of metal oxides, conductive polymers or polymer composites as sensing surfaces. An overview of commercially available instruments can be found in a recent product review (Zubritsky 2000). All e-noses are subject to drift of two categories: sensor drift, which is due to the ageing or degradation of the individual sensors, and system drift, which encompasses all sensors. Volatile sulphur-containing compounds in food matrices cause additional problems as they can poison the sensing materials. The above effects cause the most common problem with e-noses, their poor reproducibility (Van Ysacker and Ellen 1998). An illustration of the application of e-noses in the dairy area was presented by classifying cheddar cheeses (Kress-Rogers 1997). In 80% of the tested samples the e-nose could distinguish among mild, medium and mature cheeses.

Several of the commercially available e-noses are based on gas-phase *quartz crystal microbalance* (QCM) sensors. QCM is a technology to measure the mass of a material deposited on an oscillating quartz crystal surface. The mass difference is a linear function of the observed change in the crystal's resonant frequency. QCMs can measure masses ranging from micrograms to fractions of a nanogram, the mass of a layer or even a partial layer of atoms. However, a practical disadvantage lies in the high sensitivity: not all that is measured is an interpretable signal. The selectivity of the sensor can sometimes be regulated by varying the surface layer. QCM is suited for applications where the sample matrix is very well defined (Henry 1996). The versatility of QCM is demonstrated by its ability to be used in liquid environments as well as gas or vacuum. Its fast response and versatility make it a promising candidate for process analysis. Early examples of applications in the liquid and gas phase of QCM-based devices are listed in D'Amico *et al.* (1997).

Contrary to the vast number of applications, the use of *biosensors* is often hampered by practical problems. Some of the most common are poor reproducibility, short lifetime, lengthy cycle times due to sluggish reaction, and the need for regeneration. In general, spectroscopic techniques are more established, and although not always matching biosensors in terms of selectivity and sensitivity, they are considerably more robust. Spectroscopic techniques can often be applied non-contacting, through a suited window.

In addition to MIR and NIR, *Raman spectrometry* is a third molecular spectroscopic technique for qualitative and quantitative analysis (Doyle 2001). Raman spectrometry is based on inelastic light scattering to measure the vibrational frequencies in components of the sample. Raman spectrometry can provide a very attractive alternative to both MIR and NIR, as it combines the functional group-specificity of MIR with the optical convenience of NIR, with considerable potential for on-line analysis. In addition, Raman spectrometry provides the advantage of no interference by water nor by extensive scattering by emulsion particles. Flexible waveguides and probes for FT-Raman spectrometers allow in-line monitoring directly in the reaction vessel or process line. Backscattering detection permits the evaluation of coatings and thin films. The widespread application of the technique has been hampered by slow instrumental development. Recently, NIR/FT-Raman has been successfully applied to the monitoring of an emulsion polymerisation reaction: qualitative and quantitative results were obtained in lab and pilot-scale systems (Charmot *et al.* 1999). Raman spectroscopy provided valuable insight at the molecular level for process development. As the instrumental and sampling equipment for on-line analysis has only recently become available, examples in food processing are expected to follow.

Nuclear magnetic resonance (NMR) spectroscopy provides quantitative information on the chemical composition of a sample. NMR is an extremely versatile, non-invasive, non-destructive technique. It can be used to gain static and dynamic information from intact, highly complex, heterogeneous materials such as foods (Belton *et al.* 1999). Contrary to many other techniques, the NMR signal is directly proportional to the amount of analyte in the sample, without the need for determining response factors. With high-resolution NMR, within a few seconds the contents of water, fat, protein, lactose and additives can be determined in a dairy product. The technique has been extended to determine the structure of food matrices. One of the widest applications of bench-top NMR spectrometers is the determination of the solid/liquid ratio of fats. Currently, NMR is considered to be a relatively slow analytical technique, and therefore high-throughput applications are scarce. A practical limitation of the throughput in NMR is the filling of the special, expensive sample tubes, which is a time-consuming operation. With a newly introduced concept, BEST-NMR (Bruker Efficient Sample Transfer, Bruker Analytik, Karlsruhe, Germany), this step can be automated using a FIA system, enabling a sample throughput up to 720 per day (Spraul *et al.* 1999). So far, the system has applications mainly in the pharmaceutical industry.

Table 13.7 Novel techniques suited for on-line analysis in the dairy process industry

Technique	Applications	Predicted year of application on-line
NMR and MRI	composition, texture, spoilage	before 2005
Raman spectrometry	composition, standardisation	before 2005
ISFETS, CHEMFETS	composition, CIP	before 2005
Colour sensor	quality control of composite products	2005 to 2010
Dedicated mass spectrometer	fermentation, flavour compounds, authenticity, off-flavours, contaminants	2005 to 2010
Ion mobility spectrometry	composition, authenticity, off-flavours, contaminants	2005 to 2010
Ion selective electrodes	composition, CIP	2005 to 2010
Electronic nose	fermentation, flavour compounds, authenticity, off-flavours, contaminants	2005 to 2010
Quartz crystal microbalance	fermentation, flavour compounds, authenticity, off-flavours, contaminants	2005 to 2010
Fast gas chromatography	fermentation, flavour compounds, authenticity, off-flavours, contaminants	2005 to 2010
(Photo)acoustic techniques	micro-organisms, flavour compounds, authenticity, off-flavours, contaminants	2005 to 2010
Biosensors	various	after 2010
Electronic tongue	fingerprint of compounds, authenticity, off-flavours, enzyme detection	after 2010
Capillary electrophoresis	composition, CIP, micro-organisms, contaminants	after 2010
Fibre optic biosensors	micro-organisms	after 2010
FT-MIR and FT-NIR	micro-organisms	after 2010
Micro total analysis concepts (μTAS)	composition, various	after 2010

Ion mobility spectrometry (IMS) offers attractive features for in-line analysis. IMS is a technique based on the analyte molecules being ionised by ion–molecule interactions in a radioactive ion source. The ions are subsequently separated according to differences in their mobility in a weak electric field at atmospheric pressure (Eiceman and Karpas 1994). The main advantage of the technique is that no vacuum is needed for its operation. This instrumental simplicity and facile operation has allowed it to be widely implemented in airports to detect narcotics and explosives. Although application examples in process analysis are limited, the system is ideal for this purpose owing to its high sensitivity, small size and low energy consumption together with high throughput (<30 seconds per sample) and reliable operation. Applications of IMS include measurements in fermentation processes (Kotiaho *et al.* 1995), and verification of cleaning between production batches of pharmaceuticals (Walia *et al.* 2002).

Undoubtedly, many more promising examples can be found. However, it is beyond the scope of this chapter to provide an exhaustive list of possible techniques. The authors are convinced that methods using mass spectrometry, fast gas chromatography, capillary electrophoresis (maybe on-a-chip), micro total analysis concepts (TAS), ion selective electrodes, ISFETs and CHEMFETs, fibre optic biosensors, (photo)acoustic techniques and more will be used for on-line process monitoring sometime in the future.

In- and on-line techniques are essential for improving quality in production processes. The tools are available, and as shown in this chapter several of them have found application in the dairy industry. There is a distinct need for more. Table 13.7 gives an overview of promising techniques, their possible applications in the dairy field and the expected time required for fully-fledged introduction in the dairy process industry.

13.7   Sources of further information and advice

BALTES H., GÖPEL W., HESSE J. (2001) *Sensors, Sensors Update, 9*, John Wiley & Sons, Chichester, West Sussex, UK.

BELTON P.S., HILLS B.P., WEBB G.A. (1999) *Advances in Magnetic Resonance in Food Science*, RSC, Cambridge, UK.

BOURNE M.C. (2002) *Food Texture and Viscosity: Concept and Measurement*, second edition, Academic Press, San Diego, CA.

BURNS D.A., CIURCZAK E.W. (1992) *Handbook of Near Infrared Analysis*, Marcel Dekker, New York.

EICEMAN G.A., KARPAS Z. (1994) *Ion Mobility Spectrometry*, CRC Press, Boca Raton, FL.

KRESS-ROGERS E. (ED.) (1997) *Handbook of Biosensors and Electronic Noses Medicine, Food and the Environment*, CRC Press, Boca Raton, FL.

KRESS-ROGERS E., BRIMELOW J.B. (eds) (2001) *Instrumentation and Sensors for the Food Industry*, CRC Press, Boston, MA and Woodhead Publishing, Cambridge, UK.

OSBORNE B.G. (2000) 'Near-infrared spectroscopy in food analysis', in Meyers R.A. (ed.) *Encyclopedia of Analytical Chemistry*, John Wiley & Sons, Chichester, West Sussex, UK.

OSBORNE B.G., FEARN T., HINDLE P.H. (1993) *Practical NIR Spectroscopy*, second edition, Longman, Harlow, Essex, UK.

ROBINSON R.K., BATT C.A., PATEL P.D. (eds) (2000) *Encyclopedia of Food Microbiology*, Vol. 3, Academic Press, San Diego, CA.

SKOOG D.A., HOLLER F.J. (1996) *Fundamentals of Analytical Chemistry*, Saunders College Publishing, Fort Worth, TX.

STEFFE J.F. (1996) *Rheological Methods in Food Process Engineering*, second edition, Freeman Press, East Lansing, MI.

TAMIME A.Y., LAW B.A. (2001) *Mechanisation and Automation in Dairy Technology*, Sheffield Academic Press, Sheffield, UK.

TAYLOR R.F., SCHULTZ J.S. (1996) *Handbook of Chemical and Biological Sensors*, IOP Publishing, Bristol, UK.

13.8   References

ARIKAINEN E.O. (2000) 'A diffusing wave spectroscopy study of acidified milk gel under shear', *Progr. Colloid Polym. Sci.*, **115**, 166–170.

BECKER T., SCHMIDT H.-L., LECHNER E. (1995) 'D- and L-lactate determination in dairy products: presentation of a fast automated analysis system', *Z. Lebensm. Unters. Forsch.*, **201**, 537–540.

BELTON P.S., HILLS B.P., WEBB G.A. (1999) *Advances in Magnetic Resonance in Food Science*, RSC, Cambridge, UK.

BERRIE P.G. (2001a) 'Pressure and temperature measurement in food process control', in Kress-Rogers E., Brimelow J.B. (eds), *Instrumentation and Sensors for the Food Industry*, CRC Press, Boston, MA and Woodhead Publishing, Cambridge, UK, 280–302.

BERRIE P.G. (2001b) 'Level and flow measurement in food process control', in Kress-Rogers E., Brimelow J.B. (eds), *Instrumentation and Sensors for the Food Industry*, CRC Press, Boston, MA and Woodhead Publishing, Cambridge, UK, 303–325.

BOURNE M.C. (2002) *Food Texture and Viscosity: Concept and Measurement*, second edition, Academic Press, San Diego, CA.

BURNS D.A., CIURCZAK E.W. (1992) *Handbook of Near Infrared Analysis*, Marcel Dekker, New York.

CHARMOT D., AMRAM B., AGNELY M., PERÉ E., BAUER C., HUVENNE J.P., ASUA J., LEIZA J., ARMITAGE P., SIMON A., LEHENER C., SAWATZKI J. (1999) 'NIR FT-Raman spectroscopy: in-line control of emulsion polymerisation – from the laboratory to the production plant', *Bruker Report*, **147**, 32–33.

D'AMICO A., DI NATALE C., VERONA E. (1997) 'Acoustic devices', in Kress-Rogers E. (ed.), *Handbook of Biosensors and Electronic Noses Medicine, Food and the Environment*, CRC Press, Boca Raton, FL.

DE JONG E.A.M. (1994) Unpublished results, NIZO Food Research, Ede, The Netherlands.

DE MOL R.M. (2000) 'Automated detection of oestrus and mastitis in dairy cows', Thesis, Wageningen University, the Netherlands.

DOYLE W.M. (2001) 'Comparison of near-IR and Raman analysis for potential process applications', Axiom Analytical, Inc., Irvine, CA, Technical Note AN-922.

EICEMAN G.A., KARPAS Z. (1994) *Ion Mobility Spectrometry*, CRC Press, Boca Raton, FL.

ESPADA E., VIJVERBERG E. (2002) 'Milk colour analysis as a tool for the detection of abnormal milk', presented at the First North American Conference on Robotic Milking, 20–22 March, Toronto, Canada.

FAYOLLE P., PICQUE D., CORRIEU G. (2000) 'On-line monitoring of fermentation processes by a new remote dispersive middle-infrared spectrometer', *Food Control*, **11**, 291–296.

GIBSON D.M. (2001) 'Conductance/impedance techniques for microbial assay', in Kress-Rogers E., Brimelow J.B. (eds), *Instrumentation and Sensors for the Food*

Industry, CRC Press, Boston, MA and Woodhead Publishing, Cambridge, UK, 485–517.

HENRY C. (1996) 'Measuring the masses: quartz crystal microbalances', *Anal. Chem.*, **68**, 625A–628A.

HOLROYD S. (2002) 'In-line analysis', presented at the Symposium Laboratories in Transition, IDF/ISO/AOAC Analytical Week, Toledo, Spain.

HOYER H. (1997) 'NIR on-line analysis in the food industry', *Process Control and Quality*, **9**, 143–152.

JANATA J. (2001) 'Centennial retrospective on chemical sensors', *Anal. Chem.*, **73**, 151A–153A.

KLEINER K. (2000) 'It won't kill you. Now you can see your fish isn't foul without opening the pack', *New Scientist*, 8 April.

KOTIAHO T., LAURITSEN F.R., DEGN H., PAAKKANEN H. (1995) 'Membrane inlet ion mobility spectrometry for on-line measurement of ethanol in beer and in yeast fermentation', *Anal. Chim. Acta*, **309**, 317–325.

KRESS-ROGERS E. (ed.) (1997) *Handbook of Biosensors and Electronic Noses Medicine, Food and the Environment*, CRC Press, Boca Raton, FL.

KRESS-ROGERS E., BRIMELOW J.B. (eds) (2001) *Instrumentation and Sensors for the Food Industry*, CRC Press, Boston, MA and Woodhead Publishing, Cambridge, UK.

LEEMANS F.A. (1971) 'Selection of an optimum analytical technique for process control', *Anal. Chem.*, **43**, 36A–49A.

MANNINO S., COSIO M.S., BUCATTI S. (1999) 'Simultaneous determination of glucose and galactose in dairy products by two parallel amperometric biosensors', *Ital. J. Food Sci.*, **11**, 57–65.

MATTIASSON B. (1994) 'Flow injection bioanalysis – a convenient tool in process monitoring and control', in Alberghina L., Frontali L., Sensi P. (eds), *ECB6, Proc. 6th Eur. Congr. on Biotechnology (Firenze 1993)*, Elsevier, Amsterdam.

MCIVOR M.C. (1997) 'Process analyser benchmarking', *AT-Process*, **3**(1–2), i.

MCMAHON T.K., ROBERTSON A.J. (1995) *The Process Analyser Market (1994–99)*, PAI Partners, Leonia, NJ.

MEHRVAR M., BIS C., SCHARER J.M., MOO-YOUNG M., LUONG J.H. (2000) 'Fiber-optic biosensors – trends and advances', *Anal. Sci.*, **16**, 677–692.

O'CONNELL P.J., GUILBAULT G.G. (2001) 'Sensors and food quality', in Baltes H., Göpel W., Hesse J., *Sensors, Sensors Update 9*, John Wiley & Sons, Chichester, West Sussex, UK.

OSBORNE B.G. (2000) 'Near-infrared spectroscopy in food analysis', in Meyers R.A. (ed.) *Encyclopedia of Analytical Chemistry*, John Wiley & Sons, Chichester, West Sussex, UK.

OSBORNE B.G., FEARN. T., HINDLE P.H. (1993) *Practical NIR Spectroscopy*, second edition, Longman, Harlow, Essex, UK.

OTTEN Z.E.H., VAN BOXTEL A.J.B. (1989) 'On-line measurement of foul deposition in heat exchangers', *Voedingsmiddelentechnologie*, **22**(21), 18–13.

PASSOS E.F., MONTEIRO P.S., OLIVEIRA R.C., MARTINS J.G.O., ALVES H.G., BRANDÃO S.C.C. (1999) 'Predicting the cutting time of coagulating milk for cheese production using a heated thermistor', *J. Food Sci.*, **64**, 879–882.

PEMBERTON R.M., HART J.P., MOTTRAM T.T. (2001) 'An assay for the enzyme N-acetyl-β-D-glucosaminidase (NAGase) based on electrochemical detection using screen-printed carbon electrodes (SPCEs)', *Analyst*, **126**, 1–11.

PINE D.J., WEITZ D.A., ZHU J.X., HERBHOLZHEIMER E. (1990) 'Diffusing wave spectroscopy:

dynamic light scattering in the multiple scattering limit', *J. Phys. France*, **51**, 2101–2127.

RAASKA L., MATTILA-SANDHOLM T. (2000) 'Ultrasonic imaging/non-destructive methods to detect sterility of aseptic packages', in Robinson R.K., Batt C.A., Patel P.D. (eds), *Encyclopedia of Food Microbiology*, Vol. 3, Academic Press, San Diego, CA, 2195–2201.

RASMUSSEN M.D. (2001) 'Automatic milking, how to define a threshold for dumping mastitic milk?', *Proc. 2nd Int. Symp. on Mastitis and Milk Quality*, AABP and NMC, 401–404.

RUDNISKAYA A. (2002) Private communication.

RŮŽIČKA J., HANSEN E.H. (1975) 'Flow injection analyses Part I. A new concept of fast continuous flow analysis', *Anal. Chim. Acta*, **78**, 145–157.

SCHENZ T.W., DAUBER B., NICHELLS C., GARDNER C., SCOTT W.A., ROBERTS S.P., HENNESY M.J. (1999) 'Online magnetic resonance imaging for detection of spoilage in finished packages', in Belton P.S., Hills B.P., Webb G.A., *Advances in Magnetic Resonance in Food Science*, RSC, Cambridge, UK, 265–271.

SCOTTER C.N.G. (1997) 'Non-destructive spectroscopic techniques for the measurement of food quality', *Trends Food Sci. Techn.*, **8**, 285–292.

SKOOG D.A., HOLLER F.J. (1996) *Fundamentals of Analytical Chemistry*, Saunders College Publishing, Fort Worth, TX.

SMITH J.P., HINSON-SMITH V. (2002) 'Flow injection analysis: quietly pushing ahead', *Anal. Chem.*, **74**, 385A–388A.

SPRAUL M., HOFMANN M., NEIDIG P. (1999) 'High-throughput flow-injection NMR and its applications', *Bruker Report*, **147**, 14–17.

STEENBERGEN A.E., VAN HOUWELINGEN G., STRAATSMA J. (1991) 'System for early detection of fire in a spray drier', *J. Soc. Dairy Technol.*, **44**, 76–79.

STRAATSMA H., VAN DEN HOVEN G., TEN GROTENHUIS E. (2001) 'Optische tool voor in-line procesbewaking van geleringsprocessen', *Voedingsmiddelentechnologie*, **34**(4), 16–18.

STRAATSMA H., VAN DEN HOVEN G., KANNING M., TEN GROTENHUIS E. (2002) *EDM*, 6 February, 31–32.

TAYLOR R.F., SCHULTZ J.S. (1996) *Handbook of Chemical and Biological Sensors*, IOP Publishing, Bristol, UK.

TE GIFFEL M.C., MEEUWISSE J., DE JONG P. (2001) 'Control of milk processing based on rapid detection of micro-organisms', *Food Control*, **12**, 305–309.

TEN GROTENHUIS E. (1999) 'Prediction of cutting time during cheese production', *Eur. Dairy Mag.*, **11**, 40–41.

TEN GROTENHUIS E., VAN DEN BERG G., DE KRUIF C.G. (1999) 'Science evolving into a versatile industrial tool: the diffusing wave spectroscopy story', *Eur. Dairy Mag.*, **2**, 44–46.

TEN GROTENHUIS E., PAQUES M., VAN AKEN G. (2000) 'The application of diffusing wave spectroscopy to monitor the phase behaviour of emulsion–polysaccharide systems', *J. Coll. Interf. Sci.*, **227**, 495–504.

TRUONG T., ANEMA S. (2002) 'The use of a heat-flux sensor for in-line monitoring of fouling of non-heated surfaces', *Trans. Inst. Chem. Eng.*, accepted for publication.

TUMMERS P., WIENKE D. (2002) Adapted from the presentation 'Process analytical audit' presented at the Process Analysis Day of the Royal Dutch Chemical Society, 19 April, Arnhem, The Netherlands.

VAN ASSELT A.J., VAN HOUWELINGEN G., TE GIFFEL M.C. (2002) 'Monitoring system for improving cleaning efficiency of CIP processes in dairy environments', *Trans. Inst. Chem. Eng.*, **80** (Part C), accepted for publication.

VAN DER GRINTEN P.M.E.M. (1968) 'Uncertainty in measurement and control', *Statistica Neerlandica*, **22**, 43–63.

VAN YSACKER P., ELLEN G. (1998) 'Restricted possibilities for electronic nose applications in dairy industry', *Voedingsmiddelentechnologie*, **31**, 11–13.

VASBINDER A.J., VAN MIL P.J.J.M., BOT A., DE KRUIF C.G. (2001) 'Acid-induced gelation of heat-treated milk studied by diffusion wave spectroscopy', *Coll. and Surf. B: Biointerfaces*, **21**, 245–250.

VLASOV Y., LEGIN A., RUDNITSKAYA A. (2002) 'Electronic tongues and their analytical application', *Anal. Bioanal. Chem.*, **373**, 136–146.

WALIA G., DAVIS M., STEFANOU S., DEBONO R. (2002) 'Using ion mobility spectrometry for cleaning verification in pharmaceutical manufacturing', *Pharmaceutical Technology*, 72–78.

ZUBRITSKY E. (2000) 'E-noses keep an eye on the future', *Anal. Chem.*, **72**, 421A–426A.

14

Rapid on-line analysis to ensure the safety of milk

**A. Amine, Université Hassan II-Mahammedia, Morocco and
L. Micheli, D. Moscone and G. Palleschi, Università di Roma
'Tor Vergata', Italy**

14.1   Introduction

With the increasing requirement for pre-prepared and processed food, as consumers become less willing to spend significant periods of time preparing fresh food, problems with the quality and safety of prepared or processed foods will increase. A major issue is food safety, highlighted by recent outbreaks such as those concerning BSE, foot and mouth, and *E coli* 0157. There is a general and urgent need for rapid procedures, applicable to process control, to monitor food safety and quality. This chapter addresses this issue in relation to milk quality. It first discusses the safety of the product at the initial point of product collection: the farm. It then looks at ensuring safety and quality during processing by monitoring a number of key parameters, and investigates the possibilities of new markers of product quality.

14.1.1   Contamination monitoring in the milking parlour

Concerns over milk contamination are growing as the labour available for milking cows diminishes and milking systems are increasingly automated. Companies and research institutions within the EU lead the world in the development and introduction of robotic milking. Although high standards have been set for animal welfare and milk hygiene by legislation, the technical means of achieving these standards are still lacking. Close control, in real time, of milk contamination markers will improve the milking system by allowing operators to make quick decisions about milk quality, ensuring that freshly-collected milk is hygienically acceptable for human use.

The two most important contamination factors in fresh collected milk are faecal contamination and mycotoxin contamination. As a result of the cow's anatomy and the farm environment, faecal contamination during the production of milk is an enduring problem. There is a need to avoid introducing undesirable colour and flavouring taints into the milk, combined with the ever-present risks associated with the introduction of faecal pathogens. Milk is also susceptible to contamination from external sources. One of the most important hazards is aflatoxin M_1, a hepatocarcinogenic mycotoxin that could occur in the milk of cows fed with aflatoxin B_1-contaminated feedstuffs (Miraglia, 1998).

14.1.2   Monitoring processed milk

There is a need to define and develop fast and reliable procedures to identify markers of milk quality in order to distinguish effectively-processed milks (heated/lactose hydrolysed) from those for which treatments have been omitted or carried out unsuccessfully. Developments in dairy technology have introduced new heating processes and new time/temperature combinations for the thermal treatment of milk (for example thermized, pasteurised, UHT in bottle sterilised). This trend is leading to the availability of milks with different characteristics, which may be marketed under the same designation (EU Commission Doc VI/5726/92, 1992; EU Directive 92/46, 1992; Pellegrino et al., 1995).

Some thermal markers, such as alkaline phosphatase (ALP) and lactoperoxidase (LPO), are already in use as indices of adequate milk heat treatment (EU Commission Doc VI/844/93, 1993; Griffiths, 1986; IDF Doc 442, 1990; IDF, 1991). Other indices, such as lactulose and lactosilated proteins, have been proposed as indices of heat damage (Andrews, 1984; Burton, 1984; Erbersdoler and Dehn-Müller, 1989; Geier and Klostermeyer, 1983; Henle et al., 1991; O'Brien, 1995; Staal, 1986) and are still being studied by working groups of both the International Dairy Federation (IDF) and the European Union (EU) (EU Commission Doc VI/5726/92, 1992; EU Commission Doc VI/844/93, 1993; EU Directive 92/46, 1992; EU Commission Doc VI/CG/1018/94, 1994; IDF Doc 557, 1993a). There is therefore a continuing need for the development of fast and reliable thermal markers to monitor process effectiveness and product safety.

In this chapter we will report on a number of new procedures based on monitoring key markers for processed milk. These include rapid procedures for lactulose based on an electrochemical sensor and spectrophotometric analysis and an immunosensor procedure for the detection of lactosilated milk proteins. The detection of these marker compounds in fresh and processed milk has been carried out using biosensor and immunosensor technologies. Currently, not many bio- and immunosensor devices are used in the food industry. However, the increasing concern for more efficient detection of chemical contaminants and pathogens and their metabolites in milk has stimulated interest in the use of rapid methods of analysis based of biosensors and immunosensors (Turner, 2000).

14.2 Monitoring contamination during milking: faecal contamination and mycotoxins

The main point of contamination of milk by faecal material during milking is the teats of cows. Teats could be washed automatically within the teat cup and electronic cameras could be used to examine the cleanliness of the teats of cows standing in a stall (Bull *et al.*, 1996; Mottram, 1997). Close inspection would require sensors mounted above a teat cup and an automated monitoring system. However if the quality/cleanliness of the wash water can be verified, the absence of milk contamination downstream can be assured without direct sensing. Chlorophyll derived from bovine faeces is a recognised marker of faecal contamination of milk. The development of a sensor for chlorophyll determination in washing water before milking is a part of an EU funded project: ROSEPROMILK (EU Project, 2002).

Spectroscopic techniques have been used successfully to detect contamination in marine and freshwater (Arar, 1997). However, they are not practical when dealing with the pre-milking washing water, which may contain absorbing components. More recently, the ROSEPROMILK team have developed an electrochemical sensor based on screen-printing technology for the rapid electrochemical determination of chlorophyll. Cyclic voltammetric studies using screen-printed carbon electrodes showed that chlorophyll could not be determined directly in a quiescent buffer solution. However, using a medium exchange protocol which involved substrate accumulation through stirring in phosphate buffer solution containing acetone, followed by brief rinsing in water and final cyclic or linear sweep voltammetry in a phosphate buffer, a clear peak response was obtained for chlorophyll at an applied potential of +400 mV versus Ag/AgCl. To obtain an optimum detection of chlorophyll required an accumulation for 60 s at open circuit in 0.1 M phosphate buffer pH 7.0 containing 1% acetone, followed by rinsing in water and cyclic voltammetry at 50 mV/s in 0.1 M phosphate buffer at pH 7.0. Calibration plots of chlorophyll concentration were linear over the range 0.25–2.25 μM ($r^2 = 0.998$). The oxidation peak measured at around +500mV is directly proportional to a concentration of chlorophyll in the submicromolar range. The pH has no effect on response of chlorophyll oxidation in the range of pH 5.0–8.0. The development of an operational on-line sensor needs further research

14.2.1 Mycotoxin contamination

Mycotoxins are a group of chemically diverse secondary fungal metabolites that induce a variety of toxic responses in humans and animals when foods or feeds containing these compounds are ingested. Aflatoxins are a class of mycotoxins produced by the fungal strains *Aspergillus flavus* and *Aspergillus parasiticus* during growth, harvest or storage. In particular aflatoxin B_1 has been implicated in lethal episodic outbreaks of mold poisoning in exposed human and animal populations (Miraglia, 1998). Aflatoxin M_1 a hepatocarcinogenic mycotoxin, could occur in the milk of cows fed with aflatoxin B_1-contaminated feedstuffs.

The maximum content of aflatoxin M_1 allowed in milk under EU directives is 0.05 ppb (Rosner, 1998). The level of aflatoxin M_1 can be kept so low only if the analytical controls are accurate and sensitive. At present, aflatoxin analysis is carried out using ELISA kits for screening M_1 and B_1 (Biancardi, 1997), with confirmation by HPLC (which is the official method) using post-columns derivatisation after sample clean-up (Markaki and Melisseri, 1997). Dragacci *et al.* (2001) have reported on 'proficiency testing for the evaluation of the ability of EU-national reference laboratories to determine aflatoxin M_1 in milk at levels corresponding to the new EU legislation'. They tested samples of milk powder and liquid milk at various levels of aflatoxin M_1 contamination. Two trials were conducted in 1996 and 1998 according to ISO guide 43, in particular for the homogeneity testing of sample batches and for the calculation of laboratory z-scores. The samples used were naturally-contaminated milk obtained by feeding cows with aflatoxin B_1-contaminated feed. The levels of aflatoxin M_1 in the samples ranged from 0.2 to 0.7 μg/kg in milk powder and from 0.05 to 0.07 μg/kg in liquid milk. These levels were chosen as being close to the EU-regulated limit of 0.05 μg/kg of aflatoxin M_1 per litre. Results produced by the participating laboratories were compiled and statistically analysed to detect variations and to calculate the individual z-scores. Except for one laboratory in each exercise, all laboratories exhibited acceptable z-scores. The interlaboratory relative standard deviation for reproducibility (RSD_R) obtained were in the range 15.7–30.3%. Compared with other published studies, this indicated a very good precision for the performance of this laboratory network in the analysis of traces of aflatoxin M_1 in milk. Tables 14.1 and 14.2 report the raw data and their statistical summary in the 1998 exercise.

These aflatoxin M_1 tests were carried out using a HPLC procedure including an immunoaffinity clean-up step. However this procedure, standardised by the International Dairy Federation (IDF) in 1995 (IDF, 1995) and then by the ISO and CEN (ISO, 1998) is slow and requires highly-qualified personnel, expensive instrumentation and reagents. Recent research has concentrated on developing more rapid methods with a comparable level of sensitivity. Andreou and Nikolelis (1998) have reported the application of lipid-based biosensors for monitoring aflatoxin M_1 in milk and milk preparation. This is based on electrochemical flow injection monitoring of aflatoxin M_1 using stabilized systems of filter-supported bilayer lipid membranes. Injections of aflatoxin M_1 were made into flowing streams of a carrier electrolyte solution, and a transient current signal appeared less than 10 s after exposure of the lipid membranes to the toxin. The magnitude of this signal was linearly related to the concentration of aflatoxin M_1, with detection limits at the subnanomolar level. The mechanism of signal generation was investigated by differential scanning calorimetric experiments. Using this technique aflatoxin M_1 could be determined in continuous flowing systems with a rate of at least 4 samples min. Figure 14.1 reports some experimental results involving injection of aflatoxin M_1 into milk

Table 14.1 Raw data (blind duplicated 1 and 2) and laboratory means in the 1998 exercise. The results are expressed in μg of aflatoxin M_1L

Laboratory codes	Batch A			Batch B		
	Blind duplicate 1	Blind duplicate 2	Mean	Blind duplicate 1	Blind duplicate 2	Mean
1	0.038	0.031	0.035	0.067	0.073	0.070
2	0.037	0.036	0.037	0.056	0.058	0.057
3	0.163	0.180	0.172	0.210	0.284	0.247
4	0.053	0.053	0.053	0.081	0.079	0.080
5	0.046	0.044	0.045	0.075	0.071	0.073
6	0.042	0.059	0.051	0.104	0.081	0.093
7	0.030	0.025	0.028	0.072	0.055	0.064
8	0.033	0.042	0.038	0.076	0.056	0.066
9	0.042	0.043	0.043	0.063	0.063	0.063
10	0.058	0.054	0.056	0.082	0.085	0.084
11	0.053	0.049	0.051	0.074	0.075	0.075
12	0.046	0.045	0.046	0.069	0.071	0.070
13	0.048	0.061	0.055	0.082	0.078	0.080
14	0.041	0.050	0.046	0.080	0.050	0.065
15	0.044	0.040	0.042	0.066	0.064	0.065
16	0.052	0.054	0.053	0.080	0.083	0.082

and Table 14.3 reports some results of aflatoxin M_1 added in commercial milk preparations.

Sibanda et al. (1999) reported a membrane-based flow-through enzyme immunoassay for the detection of aflatoxin M_1 in milk. The assay comprised nylon Immunodyne ABC membrane spotted with anti-mouse antibodies, a plastic snap-fit device, absorbent cotton wool, mouse anti-aflatoxin M_1, monoclonal antibodies and aflatoxin B_1-horseradish peroxidase conjugate. This assay was coupled to an immunoaffinity column. The visual detection limit was 0.05 ng/g AFM_1 in milk. Assay time for the immunoaffinity column clean-up was 12 min, and 18 min for the flow-through assay, making the total assay time 30 min. This method allowed for a rapid screening of milk consignments not conforming to the maximum permissible limit of 50 ppt, hence enabling their

Table 14.2 Statistical summary for precision parameters in the 1998 exercise. Assigned values for batches A and B were respectively 0.050 and 0.071 μg of aflatoxin M_1/L

Batch	N	m μg/l	SD_r (μg/l)	r (μg/l)	RSD_r (%)	SD_R (μg/l)	R (μg/l)	RSD_R (%)
A	16	0.045	0.0050	0.0142	11.1	0.0090	20.1	0.0256
B	16	0.072	0.0086	0.0244	11.9	0.0114	15.7	0.0322

m: overall mean; SD_r: standard deviation for repeatability; r: repeatability value; RSD_r: relative standard deviation for repeatability; SD_R: standard deviation for reproducibility; R: reproducibility value; RSD_R: relative standard deviation for reproducibility.

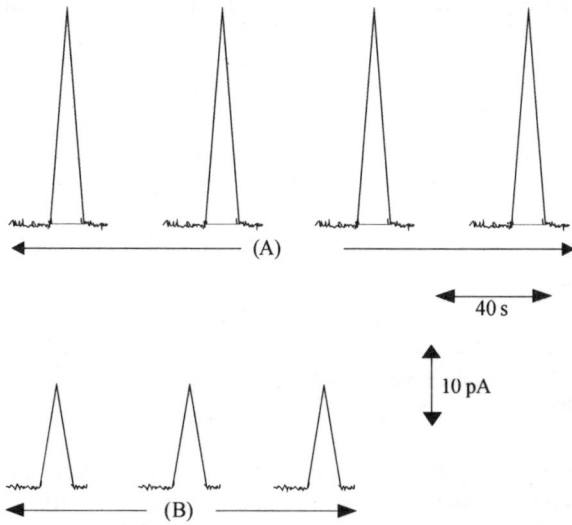

Fig. 14.1 Recordings showing the variability of response of the BLMs to repetitive AFM,-spiked milk samples injections at a flow rate value of 4.0 ml min^{-1}. AFM$_1$ concentrations were (A) 6.09 and (B) 3.05 nM. The injection of each sample was made at the beginning of each recording.

immediate rejection at the farm. Laboratory validation was done using certified reference materials (CRM) with aflatoxin M$_1$ concentrations of <0.05, 0.09 and 0.76 ppb. The high precision of the assay was shown by the high repeatability of the assay results. There were no significant differences in recovery between standard in buffer and CRM ($P > 0.05$), and assay responses for these two were highly correlated (99.63%). Tables 14.3 and 14.4 report respectively the quantification of aflatoxin M$_1$ from commercial spiked milk, and the comparison of the recovery of aflatoxin M$_1$ from spiked milk compared to toxin in buffer at concentrations of 0.00, 0.05, 0.1 and 1 ppb. Table 14.5 shows the summary statistics.

Table 14.3 Results of quantification of AFM$_1$ added in commercial milk preparations (numbers in parentheses are the spike amounts of AFM$_1$)[a]

Sample ID	AFM$_1$ content (nM)
FAGE Dairy Products S.A., skimmed milk	(7.15) 6.61 ± 0.30
Delta Dairy Products S.A., half cream milk	(3.81) 4.14 ± 0.21
Delta Dairy Products S.A., full cream milk	(14.6) 14.7 ± 0.97
Carnation instant non-fat dry milk, Société des Produits Nestlé S.A. (reconstituted)	(11.1) 10.2 ± 0.58
Noulat, Fiesland Dairy Foods	(11.1) 11.6 ± 0.70

[a] Results presented are the average of five determinations ±1SD.

Table 14.4 Recovery of aflatoxin M_1 from spiked milk compared to toxin in buffer at concentrations of 0.00, 0.05, 0.1 and 1.0 ng/ml[a]

	AFM_1 in buffer	AFM_1 spiked milk	AFM_1 in buffer	AFM_1 spiked milk	AFM_1 in buffer	AFM_1 spiked milk	AFM_1 in buffer	AFM_1 spiked milk
AFM_1 concentration (ng/ml)	0.0	0.0	0.05	0.05	0.1	0.1	1.0	1.0
$(\bar{x})\Delta E_{ab}^{*b}$	9.13	9.48	4.73	4.87	4.58	4.84	4.56	5.04
SD ($\pm$)	0.82	0.33	0.16	0.59	0.20	0.14	0.20	0.86
Sample variance	0.67	0.10	0.03	0.35	0.04	0.02	0.04	0.75

[a] $n = 10$ (number of samples/assays ran for each concentration).
[b] Colour development.

A new immunoaffinity fluorimetric biosensor has been developed by Carlson *et al.* (2000) to detect and to quantify all aflatoxins including aflatoxin M_1. The handheld, self-contained biosensor is fully automatic, highly sensitive, rapid and requires no special storage. Approximately 100 measurements can be made before refurbishment is required, and concentrations from 0.1 ppb to 50 ppb can be determined in less than 2 minutes with a 1 ml sample volume. The device operates on the principles of immunoaffinity for specificity and fluorescence for a quantitative assay. The analytical procedure is flexible so that other chemical and biological analytes could be detected with minor modifications to the current device. Figure 14.2 illustrates the immunochemical-based capture, purification and detection process.

Recently, Micheli *et al.* (2002) reported on the development of a disposable immunosensor for aflatoxin M_1 detection in spiked milk, which can combine the high selectivity of immunoanalysis with the convenience of electrochemical probes. Immunoassay parameters, such as amounts of antibody and labelled antigen, buffer and pH, length of time and temperature of each precoating,

Table 14.5 Summary statistics of the flow-through assay for the detection of AFM_1 in buffer and (CRM)[a]

	Standard in buffer	Zero level CRM No. 282	Standard in buffer	Zero level CRM No. 283	Standard in buffer	Zero level CRM No. 285
AFM_1 concentration (ng g^{-1})	0.00	<0.05	0.09	0.09 ($\pm$0.04, 0.02)	0.76	0.76 ($\pm$0.05)
	10.44	10.40	5.66	6.01	5.69	5.58
SD ($\pm$)	1.08	2.07	0.78	0.70	0.50	0.46
Sample variance	1.16	4.29	0.60	0.48	0.25	0.20

[a] $n = 10$ (number of samples/assays ran for each concentration).
[b] Colour development.

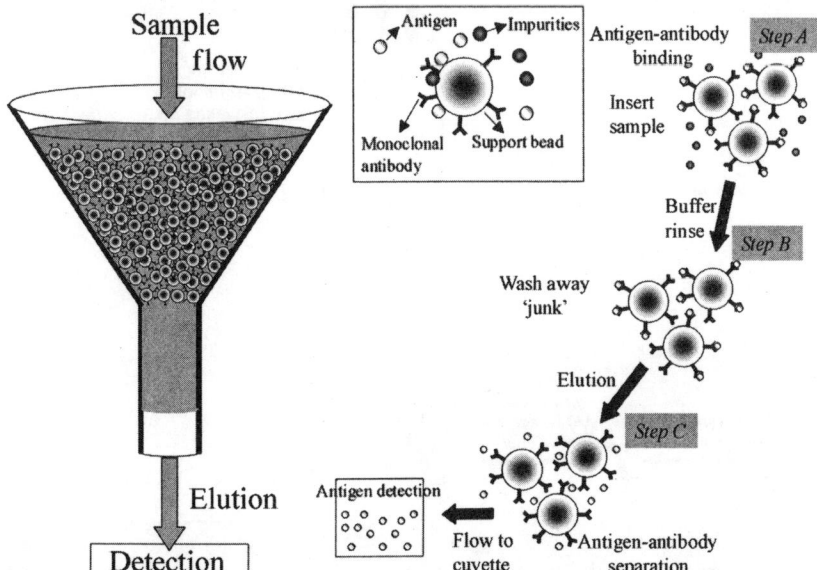

Fig. 14.2   Pictorial representation of the immunochemical-based capture, purification and detection process. The antibody coated beads capture the antigen (step A) as the liquid is passed over the beads. In step B, the beads/antibodies/antigen are rinsed clean of any impurities. Once clean, the antigens are then released back into solution (step C), where their concentration is measured.

coating, binding and competition steps were evaluated and optimised in setting up a spectrophotometric Enzyme-Linked ImmunoSorbent Assay (ELISA) procedure, a powerful tool in biochemical trace analysis. A working range between 0.03 and 0.12 ppb was obtained in a direct competitive format. Electrochemical immunosensors have been fabricated immobilising the antibodies directly on the surface of screen-printed electrodes (SPEs), and allowing competition between aflatoxin M_1 free and that conjugated with HRP. Electrochemical techniques, such as Chronoamperometry and Differential Pulse Voltammetry (DPV) have been evaluated and the most sensitive selected for the final detection step. The sensor has been evaluated for the analysis of aflatoxin M_1 directly in milk. Figure 14.3 illustrates a screen-printing electrode detection system (SPE, used as support and transducer, and direct competitive ELISA format) and Fig. 14.4 a calibration curve for aflatoxin detection in spiked milk.

14.3   Measuring the effectiveness of heat treatment

Milk is heat treated to ensure a longer shelf-life and to guarantee its micro-biological safety. However, heat treatment can damage the milk's nutritional properties. It should therefore meet the minimum time/temperature combinations required to make the milk safe without significant heat damage.

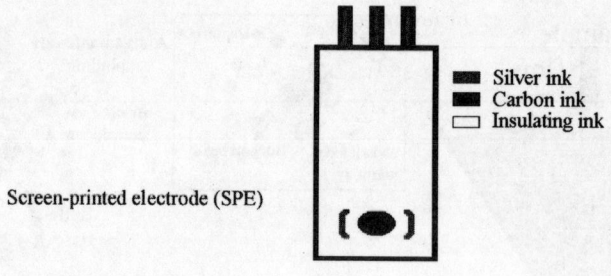

Screen-printed electrode (SPE)

■ Silver ink
■ Carbon ink
☐ Insulating ink

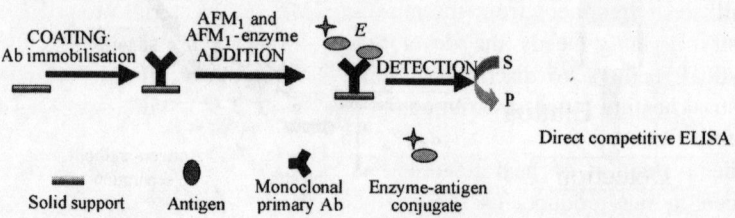

Fig. 14.3 Scheme of a screen-printing electrode detection system: SPE, used as support and transducer, and direct competitive ELISA format.

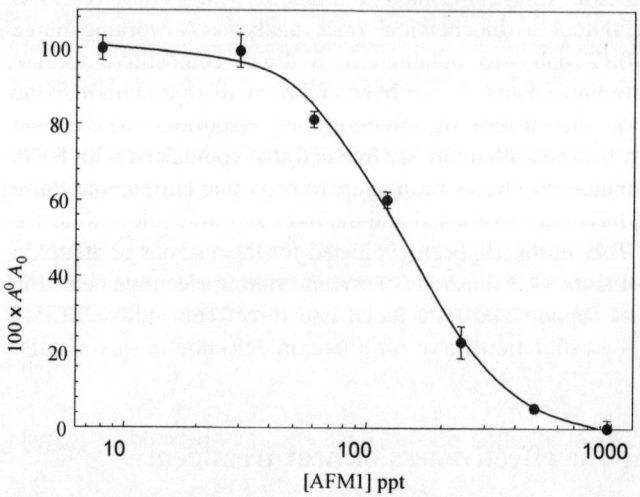

Fig. 14.4 Typical calibration curve for direct competitive ELISA for aflatoxin M_1 detection, calculate with the '4 -parameter logistic equation'
$$[f(x) = \{[a - d]/[1 + (X/c)^b]\} + d].$$

Table 14.6   Example of heat treatments commonly used by the dairy industry

Heat treatment	Conditions
Thermisation	65°C/30 s
Pasteurisation	72°C/15 s
High temperature	90°C/5 min
Ultrapasteurisation	120°C/2–4 s
UHT	140°C/3–8 s
Sterilisation	110°C/5–10 min

So far there is no one universal marker, which can distinguish differing degrees of milk heat treatment from thermisation to in-bottle sterilisation. The dairy industry urgently needs the development of rapid, sensitive and low-cost analytical methods to discriminate milk heat treatment effects. Examples of industrial heating processes commonly used by the dairy industry are presented in Table 14.6.

The evaluation of heat treatment is possible if irreversible changes are induced in the product. These can then be identified by suitable chemical markers. Chemical markers should in principle be easy to determine by rapid instrumental techniques preferably at an early stage than when food deterioration becomes detectable by sensory methods. Two types of chemical markers may be used to assess heat treatments (Mortier et al., 2000):

- the degradation, denaturation and inactivation of heat labile components, e.g. whey proteins or enzymes
- the formation of 'new' substances, such as lactulose or products of the Maillard reaction (MR), which are not present, or present only at trace levels, in the raw milk.

It is useful to consider three stages in the MR (Van Boekel, 1998): the initial, advanced and final stages. The initial stage of the MR, in which Amadori compounds are formed, does not give rise to colour. Upon prolonged heating, the Amadori rearrangement products undergo dehydration and fission and yield colourless reductones as well as fluorescent substances, some of which may be pigmented. The final stage of MR is where most of the colour is produced. This stage is characterised by the formation of unsaturated brown polymers (IDF, 1971).

14.3.1   Measurement of alkaline phosphatase and lactoperoxidase activity in milk

Alkaline phosphatase (EN, 1984a) is a thermolabile enzyme which is indigenous to all dairy products, including raw milk. It has an inactivation temperature slightly above that which is required to destroy the most resistant disease organisms likely to be found in milk. This method can be used to determine whether or not the pasteurisation process was adequate or to detect post-process contamination of pasteurised products with raw milk. However false-positive results might occur in three different situations:

- Microorganisms present in milk after pasteurisation may produce phosphatases.
- Reactivation of phosphatase enzyme may be observed in milk processed by high-temperature/short-time (HTST) pasteurisation or may be caused by exposure of the product to the room temperature in the presence of Mg^{++}.
- Interfering substances reacting directly with reagent assays and producing a background coloration.

Confirmation tests are required when positive phosphatase results are observed. The standard method uses sodium phenylphosphate as substrate and quantitative determination of phenol by the 'indophenol reaction'. The qualitative statement 'phosphatase negative' means an alkaline phosphatase activity (ALP) lower than 4 mg phenol/mL of milk (IDF, 1971). The new IDF standard (IDF Method 155A, 1999) specifies the use of the fluorimetric method for determination of ALP in milk and milk-based drinks. The cost of this method is higher than colorimetric tests. However, the fluorimetric method is more sensitive and can be used to measure ALP not only in milk but also in many milk and dairy products. It can be used to measure ALP in coloured/flavoured pasteurised products whereas colorimetric tests cannot.

Lactoperoxidase (LPO) is grouped under the general class of peroxidases (EN, 1984b) which catalyse the oxidation of suitable electron donors by hydrogen peroxide. Since lactoperoxidase is a heat stable enzyme and is very sensitive to temperature changes around 80°C, its activity has been used for the determination of the upper limit of pasteurisation. Pasteurised milk must show a positive LPO reaction and must be labelled as 'high-temperature pasteurised' when a negative result is obtained. Before measuring LPO activity spectrophotometrically at 412 nm with ABTS (2,2'-azinobis (3-ethyl-benzothiazoline-6-sulphonic acid)) and H_2O_2 as substrate, milk proteins require precipitation and filtration steps for turbidity elimination (Hernandez *et al.*, 1990). Blel *et al.* (2001) have described a very easy and rapid colorimetric method which avoids preliminary casein precipitation and filtration steps using a clarifying Reagent[R].

14.3.2   Determination of lactulose in processed milk

Lactulose, which is formed during milk heat treatment, is the most widely studied index for differentiating heated milks (Pellegrino *et al.*, 1995; Corzo *et al.*, 1996). It has been proposed by the IDF (IDF, 1993b) and by the European Commission (EC) (EU Commision Doc VI/844/93, 1993) as an analytical index to distinguish UHT milk from in-bottle sterilised milk. There are several analytical methods for detection of lactulose:

- gas chromatography (Martinez-Augustin *et al.*, 1995)
- the IDF official method based on liquid chromatography (IDF, 1991),
- enzymatic methods based on spectrophotometric detection (De Block *et al.*, 1996) or amperometric detection (Mayer *et al.*, 1996; Sekine and Hall, 1998)

As with other established methods, these techniques are time-consuming. An example is provided by a kit commercially available from Roche Diagnostic (formerly Boehringer Mannheim, Germany) based on an enzymatic procedure (Boehringer Mannheim, 1995). One drawback of this method is the potential interference from glucose, which is quite high in milk where the molar ratio lactose/lactulose could be equal to 1000/1. While it is possible to minimise the effects of glucose interferences by sample pre-treatment with glucose oxidase and catalase, this approach makes the assay more difficult to automate, because it requires six different enzymes, expensive reagents and about 15 hours to perform the analysis.

Moscone *et al.* (1999) have developed a simple and rapid flow method based on the use of an electrochemical biosensor and microdialysis. It is based on the hydrolysis of lactulose to galactose and fructose by the enzyme β-galactosidase immobilised in a reactor. The amount of fructose produced was measured with an electrochemical biosensor based on the fructose dehydrogenase enzyme, $K_3[Fe(CN)_6]$ as mediator and a platinum-based electrochemical transducer (Fig. 14.5). The use of a microdialysis probe as the sampling system permitted the direct measurement of lactulose in milk samples without pre-treatment in the range 4–1700 mgL. The sensitivity of the procedure allows pasteurised, UHT and in-container sterilised milks to be distinguished.

Amine *et al.* (2000a) have developed a new enzymatic spectrophotometric method for the determination of lactulose according to the following reactions:

$$\text{Lactose} \xrightarrow{\beta\text{-galactosidase}} \text{D-fructose} + \text{galactose}$$

$$\text{D-fructose} + \text{MTT} \xrightarrow[\text{PMS}]{\text{FDH}} \text{5-Keto-D-fructose} + \text{MTT Formazan}$$

This method entailed the use of β-galactosidase, which hydrolyses lactulose to fructose and galactose, and fructose dehydrogenase (FDH), which reacts with fructose in the presence of a tetrazolium salt (MTT), giving a coloured compound which can be detected spectrophotometrically at 570 nm. The assay showed a lactulose detection limit in milk of about $10\,\text{mgL}^{-1}$, a linear range of 20–$800\,\text{mgL}^{-1}$ and a relative deviation of 5%. The correlation with the determination of lactulose in milk using reference procedures was good (Tables 14.7 and 14.8). Moreover this procedure was found suitable for the quantification of lactulose in milk after the heat treatment process, and more convenient for the rapid and sensitive estimation of lactulose if compared with previous published enzymatic methods.

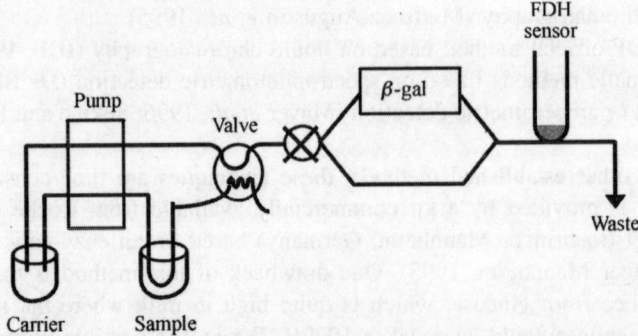

Fig. 14.5 Flow manifold for determination of lactulose in milk samples. β-galactosidase immobilised in a reactor and fructose dehydrogenase immobilised on platinum electrode. Carrier is citrate buffer and mediator, ferricyanide. The sampling system is microdialyse probe. B = buffer + mediator; P = peristaltic pump; S = sample ; M = microdialysis probe; T = three-way stopcock; β-gal = β-galactosidase reactor; FDH = fructose dehydrogenase biosensor; C = cell; D = detector; R = recorder; W = waste.

Table 14.7 Total lactulose content of different UHT milk samples determined by the Roche spectrophotometric kit and the proposed method

Milk samples	Spectrophotometric kit A (mgL^{-1})	Proposed method B (mgL^{-1})	(A − B)/A %
UHT A	131	120	8
UHT B	140	131	6
UHT C	116	128	−10
UHT D	75	82	−9
UHT E	124	134	−8
UHT F	166	173	−4

Table 14.8 Recovery of lactulose added to commercial low pasteurised milk determined by the official HPLC method and by the proposed method[a]

Added lactulose (mgL^{-1})	HPLC official method A Recovery (mgL^{-1})	(%)	Proposed method B Recovery (mgL^{-1})	(%)
225	206	92	217	96
280	246	88	267	95
300	287	96	325	108
450	472	105	417	93
600	581	97	577	96

[a] Correlation coefficients A − B, $r = 0.980$.

Table 14.9 Absorbance measurement using Seliwanoff's reaction of raw milk and of different types of milk commercially available. Number of samples (n) and minimum, maximum, mean, median and relative standard deviation (RSD) of the absorbance values are indicated

	Raw ($n = 7$)	Pasteurised ($n = 15$)	UHT ($n = 12$)	Sterilised ($n = 4$)
Mean	0.152	0.174	0.240	0.367
RSD %	7	16	18	10
Min	0.136	0.143	0.185	0.340
Max	0.165	0.223	0.326	0.422
Median	0.154	0.158	0.239	0.350

A more rapid and simple method to distinguish between UHT and sterilised milk has also been developed (Amine *et al.*, 2000b). This method uses a Seliwanoff's reagent and is based on the assumption that lactulose is the only source of ketose (fructose) in milk. This method determines lactulose directly in milk with no treatment. This method showed a linear range between 17 and 170 mg dL^{-1} and a detection limit lower than that of the official HPLC method. This novel procedure was compared with a commercially available enzymatic method and the results correlated well (Table 14.9).

14.3.3   Glycated proteins in milk

Lactose reacts non-enzymatically with lysine residues of milk proteins to form a Schiff base, which is stabilized through an Amadori rearrangement in the first stage of the MR. So far, the most widely used method to evaluate the Amadori compound (lactuloselysine), the major form of modified lysine during the initial stage of glycosylation in thermally treated milk, is the furosine method (Resmini *et al.*, 1990). The main drawbacks of this procedure are the time of analysis and the fact that only part of lactuloselysine is converted into furosine. The formation of hydroxymethylfurfural (HMF) from the Amadori compound has also been studied (Furth, 1988; Morales *et al.*, 1997). However the yield of HMF is only about 10% of the content of the Amadori component. A direct method for measuring lactuloselysine after complete enzymatic hydrolysis by an amino acid analyser has also been proposed (Henle *et al.*, 1991).

Pizzano *et al.* (1998) have developed an immunological approach to direct detect protein bound Amadori compounds. The polyclonal antibodies raised against a lactosylated synthetic peptide were used to specifically detect the Amadori compounds in milk. More recently, monoclonal antibodies for lactosylated proteins were produced, characterised and used in a competitive assay format (Pallini *et al.*, 2001). The data obtained indicate that the ELISA is applicable to diluted milk samples and is able to distinguish between milk samples that have undergone different heat treatments (UHT and pasteurised milk). The main drawback of the quantification of lactuloselysine is the lack of a pure standard for comparison.

A new fluorimetric FAST (Fluorescence of Advanced Maillard products and Soluble Tryptophan) method to estimate the intensity of heat treatment applied to milk from thermization to "in-bottle" sterilisation has also been developed (Leclere and Birlouez-Aragon, 2001; Birlouez-Aragon et al., 2002). The FAST method is a global approach for quantifying the MR by measuring the formation of fluorescent advanced products (AMP) in the pH 4.6 milk supernatant. The FAST method gives an estimate of nutritional damage and it is a rapid alternative for measuring the furosine concentration of heat treated milk.

14.4   Future trends

Public concern for milk safety and quality, and increased general demands for information about food, are likely to provide more impetus for innovative approaches to food analysis in the future. In this context, rapid methods of analysis are increasingly important, particularly where they involve portable instrumentation, have a high sensitivity, need no reagents, and are cost effective, reproducible and accurate. One technology, which matches most of the features reported, is that of bio- and immunosensors not only for fresh milk contamination control but also to improve milk process control. This is particularly important in improving UHT milk so that it matches the nutritional and sensory quality of fresh milk while remaining safe for the consumer.

14.5   References

AMINE A, MOSCONE D, BERNANDO R, MARCONI E and PALLESCHI G (2000a), 'A new enzymatic spectrophotometric assay for the determination of lactulose in milk', Anal Chim Acta, 406 217–224.

AMINE A, MOSCONE D and PALLESCHI G (2000b), 'Rapid determination of lactulose in milk using Seliwanoff's reaction', Anal Lett, 33(1) 125–135.

ANDREOU VG and NIKOLELIS DP (1998), 'Flow injection monitoring of aflatoxin M1 in milk and milk preparations using filter-supported BLMs', Anal Chem, 68 1735.

ANDREWS GR (1984), 'Distinguishing pasteurized, UHT and sterilized milks by their lactulose content', J Soc Dairy Technol, 37 92–96.

ARAR EJ (1997), 'In vitro determination of chlorophylls a,b,c_1 + c_2 and pheopigments in marine and freshwater algae by visible spectrophotometry', US Environmental Protection Agency, Method 446.0.

BIANCARDI A (1997), 'Determinazione di aflatossina M1 nel latte', Industrie Alimentari XXXVI, 870–876.

BIRLOUEZ-ARAGON I, SABAT P and GOUTI N, (2002), 'A new method for discriminating milk heat treatment', Int Dairy J, 12(1) 59–67

BLEL M, GUINGAMP -F, GAILLARD JL and HUMBERT G (2001), 'Improvement of a method for the measuring of lactoperoxidase activity in milk', Int Dairy J, 11 795–799.

BOEHRINGER MANNHEIM (1995), 'Lactulose in milk', in: Keesey J (ed.), *Methods of Enzymatic Bioanalysis and Food Analysis*, Indianapolis (USA), Boehringer Mannheim Biochemicals, Cat. N 139106

BULL CR, MCFARLANE NJB, ZWIGGELAAR R, ALLEN CJ and MOTTRAM TT (1996), 'Inspection of teats by colour image analysis for automatic milking systems', *Computers and Electronics in Agriculture*, **15** 15–26.

BURTON H (1984), 'Reviews of the progress of dairy science: the bacteriological, chemical, biochemical and physical changes that occur in milk at temperatures of 100-150°C', *J Dairy Res*, **51** 341–363.

CARLSON MA, BARGERON CB, BENSON RC, FRASER AB, PHILIPS TE, VELKY JT, GROOOPMAN JD, STRICKLAND PT and KO HW (2000), 'An automated, handheld biosensor for aflatoxin', *Bios Bioel*, **14** 841–848.

CORZO N, VILLAMIEL M and MARTINEZ-CASTRO I (1996), 'Lactulose, monosaccharides and undenatured serum protein contents in commercial UHT creams and their usefulness for thermal treatment assessment', *Food Chem*, **56**(4) 429–432.

DE BLOCK J, MERCHIERS M, VAN RENTERGHEM R and MOERMANS R (1996), 'Evaluation of two methods for the determination of lactulose in milk', *Int Dairy J*, **6**(2) 217–222.

DRAGACCI S, GROSSO F, PFAUWATHEL-MARCHOND M, FREMY JM, VENANT A and LOMBARD B (2001), 'Proficiency testing for the evaluation of the ability of European Union-National Reference laboratories to determine aflatoxin M1 in milk at levels corresponding to the new European Union legislation', *Food Add Contam*, **18**(5) 405–415.

EU COMMISSION (1992), Dairy Chemistry Group. Doc VI/5726/92: Projet de decision de la commission fixant les limites et les méthodes permettant de distinguer le differents types de lait de consom traites thermiquement.

EU COMMISSION (1993), Dairy Chemistry Group. Doc. VI/844/93: Peroxidase inactivation and β-lactoglobulin in commercial samples of pasteurised milk.

EU COMMISSION (1994), Dairy Expert Group. Doc VI/CG/1018/94. Determination of furosine (ϵ-furoylmethyl-lysine) content.

EC DIRECTIVE 92/46, 16-6-1992. EC O.J. NO L268, 14-9-1992 (1992), Council Directive laying down the health rules for production and placing on the market of raw milk, heat-treated milk and milk-based products.

EN (ENZYME NOMENCLATURE) (1984a), Alkaline Phosphatase – EC 3.1.3.1, Webb EC (ed.), Academic Press, London.

EN (ENZYME NOMENCLATURE) (1984b), Lactoperoxidase – EC 1.11.1.7, Webb EC (ed.), Academic Press, London.

ERBERSDOBLER HF and DEHN-MÜLLER B (1989), 'Formation of early Maillard products during UHT treatment of milk', in: *Heat-induced Changes in Milk*, Fox PF (ed.), *Int Dairy Fed Bul*, **238** 62–70.

EU PROJECT (2002), 'Quality of life and management of living resources – ROSEPROMILK Contract n. QLK1-CT-2001-01617 ROBUST CHEMICAL SENSORS AND BIOSENSORS FOR RAPID ON-LINE IDENTIFICATION OF FRESHLY COLLECTED MILK', First Annual Report: 1 December 2001–30 November 2002.

FURTH AJ (1988), 'Methods for assaying non enzymatic glycosylation', *Anal Biochem*, **175**, 347–360.

GEIER H and KLOSTERMEYER H (1983), 'Formation of lactulose during heat treatment of milk', *Milchwissenschaft*, **38** 475–477.

GRIFFITHS MW (1986), 'Use of milk enzymes as indices of heat treatment', *J Food Prot* **49**

696–705.

HENLE R, WALTER H and KLOSTERMEYER H (1991), 'Evaluation of the extent of the early Maillard reaction in milk products by direct measurement of the Amadori product lactuloselysine', *Z. Lebensm Unters. Forsch*, **193** 119–122.

HERNANDEZ M, VAN MARKWIJK B and VREEMAN H (1990), 'Isolation and properties of lactoperoxidase from bovine milk', *Met Milk Dairy J*, **44** 213–231

INTERNATIONAL DAIRY FEDERATION (IDF) (1971), Standard 63. 'Milk and milk powder, buttermilk and buttermilk powder, whey and whey powder: determination of phosphatase activity (reference method)'.

INTERNATIONAL DAIRY FEDERATION (IDF) (1990), E-Doc 442: Phosphatase activity.

INTERNATIONAL DAIRY FEDERATION (IDF) (1991), 'Alkaline phosphatase test as a measure of correct pasteurisation', *Int Dairy Fed Bul*, **262** 32–35.

INTERNATIONAL DAIRY FEDERATION (IDF) (1993a), E-Doc 557: 'Lactulose determination and other methods for distinguishing heat treatment of milk'.

INTERNATIONAL DAIRY FEDERATION (IDF) (1993b), B-Doc 235. 'Influence of technology on the quality of heated milk and fluid milk products'.

INTERNATIONAL DAIRY FEDERATION (IDF) (1995), E-Doc 171. 'Immunoaffinity column/HPLC determination of AFM1'.

INTERNATIONAL DAIRY FEDERATION (IDF) (1999), Milk and milk-based drinks. 'Determination of alkaline phosphatase activity using a fluorimetric method. Method 155A'.

ISO (INTERNATIONAL STANDARD ORGANIZATION) (1998), EN ISO 14501, 'Milk and milk powder – determination of aflatoxin M1 content: Clean up by immunoaffinity chromatography and determination by high-performance liquid chromatography'.

LECLÈRE J and BIRLOUEZ-ARAGON I (2001), 'The fluorescence of advanced Maillard products is good indicator of lysine damage during the Maillard reaction', *J Agric Food Chem*, **49** 4682–4687.

MARKAKI P and MELISSARI E (1997), 'Occurrence of aflatoxin M1 in commercial pasteurized milk determined with ELISA and HPLC', *Food Add Contam*, **14**(5) 451–456.

MARTINEZ-AUGUSTIN O, BOZA JJ, ROMER JM and GIL A (1995), 'A rapid gas-liquid chromatography method for the determination of lactulose and mannitol in urine: clinical application in studies of intestinal permeability', *Clin Biochem*, **28**(4) 401–405.

MAYER M, GENRICH M, KÜNNECKE W and BILITEWSKI U (1996), 'Automated determination of lactulose in milk using an enzyme reactor and flow analysis with integrated dialysis', *Anal Chim Acta*, **324**(1) 37–45

MICHELI L, GRECCO R, PALLESCHI G, and MOSCONE D (2002), 'Development of a disposable immunosensor for aflatoxin M1 detection in milk', in: *Euroanalysis 12*, Dortmund, Germany 8–13 September 2002, 326.

MIRAGLIA M (1998), 'Mycotoxins and phycotoxins – developments in chemistry, toxicology and food safety', in: Miraglia M, van Egmond HP, Bresa C and Gilbert J (eds), *Proceeding of the International IUPAC Symposium on Mycotoxin and Phycotoxin*, Colorado (USA), Alaken, Inc. Fort Collins, 67, 151, 181.

MORALES FJ, ROMEO C and JIMENEZ-PEREZ S (1997), 'Chromatographic determination of bound hydroxymethylfurfural as an index of milk protein glycosylation', *J Agric Food Chem*, **45** 1570–1573.

MORTIER L, BRAEKMAN A, CARTUYVELS D, RENTERGHEM RV and BLOCK JD (2000), 'Intrinsic indicators for monitoring heat damage of consumption milk', *Biotechnol Agron*

Soc Environ, **4**(4) 221–225.

MOSCONE D, BERNARDO RA, MARCONI E, AMINE A and PALLESCHI G (1999), 'Rapid determination of lactulose in milk by microdialysis and biosensors', *Analyst,* **124** 325–329.

MOTTRAM TT (1997), 'Requirements for teat inspection and cleaning in automatic milking systems', *Computers and Electronics in Agriculture,* **17** 63–77.

O'BRIEN J (1995), 'Heat-induced changes in lactose: isomerization, degradation, Maillard browning', in *Heat-induced Changes in Milk* (2nd edition), Int Dairy Fed., Brussels (Belgium), 134–170.

PALLINI M, COMPAGNONE D, DI STEFANO S, MARINI S, COLETTA M and PALLESCHI G (2001), 'Immunodetection of lactosylated proteins as a useful tool to determine heat treatment in milk samples', *Analyst,* **126** 66–70.

PELLEGRINO L, RESMINI P and LUF W (1995), 'Assessment (indices) of heat treatment of milk', in: *Heat-induced Changes in Milk* (2nd edition), Fox PF (ed.), Int Dairy Fed. Special Issue n 9501, 409–453.

PELLEGRINO L, DE NONI I and RESMINI P (1995), 'Coupling of lactulose and furosine indices for quality evaluation of sterilized milk', *Int Dairy J,* **5**(7) 647–659.

PIZZANO R, NICOLAI MA, SICILIANO R and ADDEO F (1998), 'Specific detection of the Amadori compounds in milk by using polyclonal antibodies raised against a lactosylated peptide', *J Agric Food Chem,* **46** 5373–5379.

RESMINI, P, PELLEGRINO L and BATELLI G (1990), 'Accurate quantification of furosine in milk and dairy products by a direct HPLC method', *Ital J Food Science,* **3**, 173–183.

ROSNER H (1998), 'Mycotoxin: limits in European union and effects on trade', in: *Mycotoxin and Phycotoxins – Developments in Chemistry, Toxicology and Food Safety,* Miraglia M, van Egmond HP, Brera C and Gilbert J (eds), Alaken, Inc. Fort Collins, Colorado USA, 203–212.

SEKINE Y and HALL EAH (1998), 'A lactulose sensor based on coupled enzyme reactions with a ring electrode fabricated from tetrathiafulvalen-tetracyanoquinodimetane', *Bios Bioel,* **13**(9) 995–1005.

SIBANDA L, DE SAEGER S and VAN PETEGHEM C (1999), 'Development of a portable field immunoassay for the detection of aflatoxin M1 in milk', *Int J Food Microbiol,* **48**(3) 203–209.

STAAL PFJ (1986), 'Legislation/statutory regulations applicable to pasteurized fluid milk in a selected number of countries', *Int Dairy Fed Bull,* **200** 71–89

TURNER APF (2000), 'Biosensors – sense and sensitivity', *Science,* **290**, 1315–1317.

VAN BOEKEL MAJS (1998), 'Effect of heating on Maillard reactions in milk', *Food Chem,* **62**(4) 403–414.

15

High-pressure processing to improve dairy product quality

W. Messens, Agricultural Research Centre, Ghent, Belgium and
J. Van Camp and K. Dewettinck, Ghent University, Belgium

15.1 Introduction: high-pressure principles and technologies

Although preliminary research into the application of HP to foods was carried out over a century ago, various HP-processed foods have only recently been launched, such as fruit preparations, fruit juices, rice cakes, and raw squid in Japan, fruit juices in France and guacamole in the USA (Smelt, 1998). This is principally due to the recent availability of suitable equipment and to the increasing consumer demand for minimally processed additive-free, shelf-stable products. So far, no HP-processed dairy products are known to be available on the market, although various studies have dealt with high-pressure (HP) processing of dairy products, including milk, yoghurt and cheese, as is described in this chapter.

First, an overview is given of the HP principle and equipment. The treatment of milk by HP is described in Section 15.2, including the effect on its nutritional properties. Effects on the endogenous microflora and the pathogenic bacteria are described in Section 15.3 and on the indigenous milk enzymes and pro-enzymes in Section 15.3.1. The effect of HP on the milk proteins is described in Section 15.4. Effects on other milk properties, including its appearance, viscosity and pH, are described in Section 15.5 and on its rennet coagulation properties in Section 15.5.1. Effects of HP on milk's cheese-making properties are described in Section 15.6 and on its yoghurt-making properties in Section 15.6.1. The treatment of cheeses by HP is described in Section 15.7, with the purpose of reducing the brining time (Section 15.7.1), preserving cheeses and/or destroying pathogenic microorganisms in cheese (Section 15.7.2) and accelerating the ripening (Section 15.7.3). Rheological property changes may also occur in cheese when HP is applied, as described in Section 15.7.4. Future trends and research needed in this area are described in Section 15.8. Sources of further information on this topic are given in Section 15.9. Unless specified otherwise, 'milk' refers to 'bovine milk' in this chapter. Also, treatment temperature is near room temperature unless stated otherwise.

Two principles underlie the effect of HP. Firstly, the principle of Le Chatelier according to which any phenomenon (phase transition, chemical reactivity, change in molecular configuration, chemical reaction) accompanied by a decrease in volume (negative ΔV) will be enhanced by an increase in pressure and vice versa. Secondly, pressure is instantaneously and uniformly transmitted independently of the size and the geometry of the food. This is known as isostatic pressure (Heremans, 1982; Tauscher, 1995).

HP equipment generally consists of four main parts: a HP vessel and its closure, a pressure-generating system, a temperature-control device and a material-handling system. The most important part is the pressure vessel of which the wall thickness is determined by the maximum working pressure, the vessel diameter and the number of cycles the vessel is designed to perform. The pressure-generating system causes a slight rise in the temperature of the food, and makes the temperature-control device necessary for some applications (Mertens and Deplace, 1993). Non-liquid products are usually sealed in flexible packages before being placed in the HP vessel filled with water (sometimes mixed with a small amount of oil) that is used as a pressure-transmitting medium. Liquid products are placed directly in the HP vessel (Earnshaw, 1996). The former is referred to as indirect compression, the latter as direct compression. Next to batch operation, semi-continuous and continuous operations are used in food processing. In semi-continuous processing, several vessels are connected in series; while some are under constant pressure, others are being pressurised, loaded or unloaded. This minimises the operation time and allows energy recuperation. Continuous operation is suitable for liquid products, such as milk and fruit juices (Vardag et al., 1995).

In the food industry, vessels with a volume of several thousand litres are in use. The typical operating pressures are in the range 100–500 MPa and holding times of 5–10 min (Myllymäki, 1996). Recent advances in equipment design now allow foods to be processed up to 900 MPa (Linton and Patterson, 2000).

15.2 The effects of high pressure on nutritional and other qualities in milk

The nutritional value of milk and dairy products is determined by the presence of both macronutrients (carbohydrates, proteins, lipids) and micronutrients (minerals, trace elements, vitamins). Since HP processing has only a limited influence on covalent bonds, it is expected that this technology will only marginally influence the nutritional characteristics of these food products in comparison to traditional thermal processing. Only in a limited number of studies have the nutritional characteristics of pressure-treated milk and dairy products been evaluated. In some cases, the HP treatment was combined with moderate heating. Attention will be given here to the influence of pressure on Maillard browning reactions, selective hydrolysis and digestibility of milk proteins, and the stability of vitamins in milk during and after pressure treatment.

The effect of pressure on Maillard browning has been investigated in model systems. Hill *et al.* (1996) used an aqueous solution of glucose and lysine at different initial pH values (5.1–10.1) and temperatures (40–60°C). The Maillard reaction was followed by measuring the absorbance of the solutions post-pressurisation (600 MPa) at 420 nm. Compared to ambient pressure, the rate of Maillard browning at 50°C was retarded by pressure at pH 5.1 and 6.5 but enhanced at pH 8.0 and 10.1. The effect of pressure was negligible at pH 7.0–7.5. By gas chromatography and mass spectrometry, it was demonstrated that yields for volatile reaction products obtained from the reaction of glucose with lysine at pH 10.1 and 60°C were suppressed after pressurisation. It was suggested that under these conditions, pressure increased the rate of aldol condensation reactions (Hill *et al.*, 1999).

More recently, Schwarzenbolz *et al.* (2000) demonstrated that Maillard-type reactions with ribose were increased under pressure. A solution of N^{α}-acetylarginine, N^{α}-acetyllysine and ribose in equimolar ratios at pH 7.4 was pressurised at 600 MPa for 2 h and at 60°C. Pressurisation resulted in a pressure-dependent increase of the pentosidine content, which is a fluorescent marker for the advanced Maillard reaction. This marker was also found in an enhanced yield in protein-bound form after pressure treatment of β-casein with ribose (ratio 1:10). Heating the β-casein/ribose solution for 2 h at 60°C did not result in a detectable amount of pentosidine, while the application of 600 MPa compared to 200 MPa was followed by a doubling of the amount of protein-bound pentosidine. However, by studying the effect of pressure (400 MPa, 30 min, 25°C) on raw milk, López-Fandiño *et al.* (1996) could not detect furosine in the milk, indicating that no significant loss of available lysine occurred. As a consequence, although the work with model systems suggests an effect of HP on the Maillard reaction, work with dairy products does not directly confirm these trends, and more research will be required to investigate the influence of HP on the protein–carbohydrate interaction in milk and milk products.

One of the first papers demonstrating that HP can influence the preferential hydrolysis of milk proteins was by Hayashi *et al.* (1987). Casein was digested by thermolysin at both ambient and high pressure (200 MPa). On the contrary, β-lactoglobulin (β-Lg) was only selectively digested by the enzyme under pressure, while α-lactalbumin (α-La) was resistant to hydrolysis at both ambient and high pressure. The stability of α-La was attributed to its rigid structure, which is stabilised by four intramolecular disulphide bonds. β-Lg is more pressure-sensitive than α-La, and begins to denature around 200 MPa, thereby facilitating thermolysin digestion. Similarly, Okamoto *et al.* (1991) used pressures of 100–300 MPa to selectively eliminate β-Lg in milk whey by a 3-h digestion with thermolysin at 30°C. Using pure β-Lg, maximum digestion (almost 60%) was obtained at 150 MPa. Using milk whey concentrate, the extent of β-Lg digestion was increased with increasing pressure, with less than 20% of β-Lg remaining post-pressurisation at 200 MPa. The difference in optimal pressure to digest β-Lg in the pure form and in the whey protein mixture (150 versus 200 MPa) might be related to the protective effects of the concentrated proteins in the whey concentrate on thermolysin and/or on its activity. The thermolysin digests had no binding affinity to five different types of anti-β-Lg monoclonal antibodies with distinct epitope specificity after treatment at 200 MPa, as evaluated by competitive ELISA.

Nakamura et al. (1993) investigated the use of HP as a pre-treatment of enzymatic hydrolysis to prepare hypoallergenic hydrolysates from whey protein concentrate (WPC) to apply in infant formulas. Hydrolysis of WPC with two proteases (papain W-40 from *Carica papaya* and proleather® from *Bacillus subtilis*) at 45°C for 6 h was investigated by HPLC. Compared to hydrolysis at ambient pressure, the pressure pre-treatment of WPC produced peptides with a narrower range of molecular weights. No difference between the different pressurisation conditions (200 MPa for 10 min, 400 MPa for 5 min, 600 MPa with no holding time) could be found, although the antigenicity of the protein hydrolysates as evaluated by ELISA decreased with the level of pressure applied. The preparation hydrolysed after compressing at 600 MPa resembled a hydrolysate treated at 60°C for 30 min. The authors concluded that HP before hydrolysis might be a promising procedure for the preparation of low antigenic WPC hydrolysates.

Van Willige and Fitzgerald (1995) used human digestive enzymes (trypsin and chymotrypsin) to evaluate the effect of pressure on the selective enzymatic hydrolysis at 37°C of different variants of β-Lg (A, B and AB). At ambient pressure, native β-Lg A was hydrolysed approximately three times faster than β-Lg B. At high pressures (100 and 300 MPa, for 0–180 min), the genetic variant associated differences in β-Lg hydrolysis disappeared. HP (<300 MPa, 30 min, 30°C) can also facilitate the hydrolysis of β-Lg B by pepsin and by trypsin, which was associated with the denaturation of the protein under pressure, as assessed with high-pressure fluorescence spectroscopy. The changes in conformation of the protein reversed slowly after decompression, whereby the enhanced digestibility of the protein was maintained at ambient pressure for several hours (Stapelfeldt et al., 1996). All these studies clearly indicate that HP can selectively influence the digestion of milk proteins, which may find its application in altering digestibility and/or antigenicity of milk proteins.

Studies on the effect of pressure on vitamin retention in milk and milk products are limited. Sierra et al. (2000) found no loss in retention of vitamin B1 and B6 after pressure processing (400 MPa, 30 min) of raw milk. For vitamin B6, also the contents of pyridoxamine (36 μg/l) and pyridoxal (291 μg/l) did not change significantly.

15.3   The effects of high pressure on bacteria and enzymes

Heat treatments are still the most commonly used means of inactivating food spoilage and pathogenic bacteria in raw milk. Although efficient, thermal treatment may fail to destroy bacterial spores and may affect the appearance, taste and nutritional value of milk as well as its processing characteristics. Sensitivity to pressure varies greatly from one bacterial species to another, Gram-positive cells being generally more resistant than Gram-negative cells and spores more resistant than vegetative cells (Smelt, 1998).

Hite (1899) reported six decimal reductions in the microbial load of milk when subjected to 689 MPa for 10 min. Later, various studies have examined pressure inactivation of the indigenous microflora in milk. Combination of a treatment at 122 MPa and 13°C for 83 min was reported to result in a complete destruction of microbial vegetative cells in milk (Johnston, 1995). Mussa and Ramaswamy (1997) found first-order rate kinetics for inactivating microorganisms present in raw whole milk. Although higher pressures are more effective, treatment at a higher pressure for a shorter time or at a lower pressure for a longer time may bring about a given reduction in microbial count. At pressures above 350 MPa, complete destruction was observed after 10 min exposure. The shelf-life of milk treated at 350 MPa for 32 min was 18 days if stored at 5°C. Only a slight decrease in total aerobic count, but a pronounced reduction in psychrotrophic count, were found by treating raw whole milk at 200 MPa (López-Fandino et al., 1996) which may resemble thermisation, a mild heat treatment of milk. Treatment of goat's milk for 15 min at 500 MPa was as efficient as pasteurisation in reducing the bacterial population of milk (Trujillo et al., 1999b, Buffa et al., 2001b). Garcia-Risco et al. (1998) did not observe a baroprotective effect of fat on microbial inactivation by HP. It was suggested that this effect could become noticeable only at fat levels higher than that of whole milk.

Lactococci inoculated into reconstituted skim milk were more sensitive than lactobacilli to pressures of 100–350 MPa. The treated cells exhibited lower acidification rates, even without affecting cell viability. HP increased the hydrolytic activity of lactococci and lactobacilli on the carboxyl-terminal fragment from β-casein, which contributes to bitterness in cheese, while the aminopeptidase or dipeptidase activity was not or only partly inhibited. It was suggested to apply HP to cheese milk to create an additional supply of enzymes with debittering properties (Casal and Gomez, 1999).

Various studies have been undertaken to assess the destruction of pathogenic bacteria in milk. A 3–4 log reduction of Listeria innocua by pressurisation at 200 MPa for five 1-min cycles (Kheadr et al., 2002) and a 7–8 log reduction of L. innocua in ewe's milk by pressurisation at 450–500 MPa (10–15 min) were found (Gervilla et al., 1997). The decimal reduction time (D-value) at 340 MPa of L. monocytogenes in ultra-high-temperature (UHT) treated milk was 13.2 min. In raw milk, the D-value was lower (9.3 min), which could be due to the presence of heat-labile antimicrobial compounds acting synergistically with pressure to enhance inactivation (Styles *et al.*, 1991). The destruction by HP (100–500 MPa, 15 min) of various microorganisms inoculated in ovine milk was in the order *Pseudomonas fluorescens* > *Escherichia coli* ≥ *Listeria innocua* > *Lactobacillus helveticus* > *Staphylococcus aureus*. Pressurisations at temperatures below room temperature produced greater inactivation on *P. fluorescens*, *Listeria innocua* and *Lactobacillus helveticus*, whereas for *E. coli* and *S. aureus* the opposite was true. The fat content (0–50%) did not show a baroprotective effect (Gervilla *et al.*, 2000). For *S. aureus* in whole milk, the extent of inactivation increased with pressure (50–350 MPa) and treatment time (4–12 min) (Erkmen and Karatas, 1997).

A study by McClements *et al.* (2001) indicates the importance of the history of a bacterial culture prior to HP treatment and that bacterial spores require more severe treatments, probably in combination with other preservation techniques, to ensure inactivation. A more effective inactivation of bacterial contaminants can be achieved by combination of HP with heat or bacteriocins. This could improve the quality of minimally processed foods at lower pressure levels. This has been demonstrated for the destruction of *E. coli* and *S. aureus* using mild heating (up to 60°C) (Patterson and Kilpatrick, 1998), for the destruction of *S. aureus* and *L. innocua* using lacticin 3147 (Morgan *et al.*, 2000), and for the destruction of *E. coli* using mild heating (50°C) and lysozyme and nisin (Garcia-Graells *et al.*, 1999). Dynamic high pressure (DHP), i.e. the use of consecutive, short pressure treatments interrupted by brief decompressions, has also been shown to be very effective for the destruction of *E. coli* (Garcia-Graells *et al.*, 1999; Vachon *et al.*, 2002) and *Salmonella enteritidis* (Vachon *et al.*, 2002), offering a promising alternative for the cold pasteurisation of milk (Vachon *et al.*, 2002).

15.3.1   Effect on indigenous milk enzymes and pro-enzymes in milk

Because of the relative economic significance of the various enzymes in milk, their stability to HP has been investigated. In a buffer system, almost no reduction in catalase activity was found at 600 MPa (Trujillo *et al.*, 1997). Lactoperoxidase in raw milk is resistant to pressure of 400 MPa (López-Fandino *et al.*, 1996) up to 700 MPa combined with temperatures between 20°C and 65°C. Application of pressure even exerted a protective effect (Ludikhuyze *et al.*, 2001). Trujillo *et al.* (1999b) found that pasteurised and HP-treated goat's milk (500 MPa, 15 min) had different lipase activity. Alkaline phosphatase, used for evaluating the effectiveness of pasteurisation, was still active in raw milk samples treated at 400 MPa for 20–60 min (Johnston, 1995; López-Fandino *et al.*, 1996). Almost complete inactivation was obtained above 700 MPa (Johnston, 1995). Mussa and Ramaswamy (1997) have shown that alkaline phosphatase cannot be used as an indicator of the effectiveness of milk pressurisation. The barostability of lysozyme in milk has not yet been studied. However, since its three-dimensional structure is similar to that of α-La, lysozyme could be pressure resistant (Trujillo *et al.*, 1997). The proteolysis by plasmin in milk kept post-pressurisation at 37°C for 48 h has been studied. López-Fandino et al. (1996) found no effect of pressures between 100 and 400 MPa, while Scollard et al. (2000) found little effect for milk treated at 50 MPa, but at 300–500 MPa proteolysis was increased, and above 500 MPa, proteolysis was less than that of raw milk. It was suggested that the increase of proteolysis in milk (at 300–500 MPa) could be due to changes in micelle structure facilitating increased availability of substrate bonds to plasmin (Scollard et al., 2000). HP treatments at higher temperatures increased plasmin inactivation, which reached 86.5% at 60°C. Pressurisation at 40–60°C compared to 25°C reduced the proteolytic activity and improved the organoleptic properties of milk, and could be used to produce milk of good sensory properties with an increased shelf-life (Garcia-Risco et al., 2000).

15.4   The effects of high pressure on milk proteins

15.4.1   Casein micelles in milk

HP treatment causes changes to casein micelle size of skim milk (Needs et al., 2000b) and reconstituted skim milk (Desobry-Banon et al., 1994; Gaucheron et al., 1997). At 200 MPa, partial disintegration of casein micelles occurred and at ≥400 MPa the disintegration was complete (Desobry-Banon et al., 1994; Gaucheron et al., 1997; Needs et al., 2000b). The turbidity decreased as a result of treatments up to 300 MPa; applying higher pressures up to 600 MPa caused little further decrease in turbidity (Needs et al., 2000b). The size of micelles in milk also depends on the temperature during treatment (Gaucheron et al., 1997) and the heat treatment of the milk before HP treatment (Schrader et al., 1997). The casein micelles in raw or pasteurised skim milk are more sensitive to pressure than the heat-induced casein–whey protein complexes in UHT-treated milk (Schrader et al., 1997). Also, subsequent heating of skim milk at 30°C post-pressurisation restored the original size distribution (Shibauchi et al., 1992). The ionic calcium concentration was unaltered (Johnston et al., 1992; De La Fuente et al., 1999) or slightly increased (López-Fandino et al., 1998) by HP treatment while levels of total serum calcium and phosphorus were both increased to a similar extent by HP treatment of skim milk (Shibauchi et al., 1992), reconstituted skim milk (Desobry-Banon et al., 1994) and raw whole milk (López-Fandino et al., 1998). It is believed that this additional non-ionic calcium and phosphorus are released by the fragmentation of the micelle structure by pressure (Johnston, 1995). Schrader and Buchheim (1998) suggested that these changes in casein micelles in milk by HP are due to three discrete processes:

- Irreversible HP-induced dissolution of heat-precipitated colloidal calcium phosphate (CCP) formed by severe heat treatment of milk
- HP-induced partial dissolution of indigenous CCP, resulting in largely reversible disintegration of casein micelles or casein–whey protein aggregates
- HP-induced denaturation of whey proteins.

Pressurisation increased the levels of non-sedimentable casein in raw milk (Desobry-Banon *et al.*, 1994; López-Fandino *et al.*, 1998). The dissociation of individual caseins was in the order $\beta > \kappa > \alpha_{s1} > \alpha_{s2}$, corresponding to the ester-phosphate content. This indicates that the caseins more tightly bound to the CCP dissociated to a lesser extent (López-Fandino *et al.*, 1998). Also, HP possibly resulted in the formation of large fragments (possibly containing denatured β-Lg) and/or some reaggregation (Johnston *et al.*, 1992). Indeed, β-Lg in skim milk was found to be denatured above 200 MPa and reaggregated to casein micelles or submicelles (Schrader *et al.*, 1997; López-Fandino *et al.*, 1998; Schrader and Buchheim, 1998). The surface hydrophobicity increased post-pressurisation, particularly at higher pressures and greater treatment times. This effect persisted for 8 days at 5°C, and could have resulted from micellar casein fragmentation and/ or from unfolding of individual casein chains (Johnston *et al.*, 1992).

15.4.2 Other milk proteins

HP treatment of raw milk led to an increased denaturation of β-Lg by increasing pressures above 100 MPa (López-Fandino *et al.*, 1996; López-Fandino and Olano, 1998b; Arias *et al.*, 2000; Garcia-Risco *et al.*, 2000; Scollard *et al.*, 2000). Above 400 MPa, relatively little further denaturation occurred (Scollard *et al.*, 2000). The level of denaturation of β-Lg is influenced by heating the milk before pressurisation (Gaucheron *et al.*, 1997; Needs *et al.*, 2000a), by the temperature during HP treatment (López-Fandino and Olano, 1998b; Garcia-Risco *et al.*, 2000), by the pH of the milk during treatment (Arias *et al.*, 2000) and by the species the milk is derived from (Felipe *et al.*, 1997; López-Fandino and Olano, 1998a). Compared to β-Lg, α-La is much more resistant to denaturation by HP. It appeared to be completely resistant to pressures up to 500 MPa (López-Fandino *et al.*, 1996; Felipe *et al.*, 1997; Gaucheron *et al.*, 1997; López-Fandino and Olano, 1998a, 1998b; Garcia-Risco *et al.*, 2000; Needs *et al.*, 2000a). The higher number of disulphide bonds in α-La (four compared to two in β-Lg) (Gaucheron *et al.*, 1997) and the lack of a free sulphydryl group in α-La (López-Fandino *et al.*, 1996) giving it a more rigid molecular structure than β-Lg, may explain these differences in pressure sensitivity. The conformation of bovine serum albumin (BSA) remains fairly stable at 400 MPa; which may be explained by the high number of disulphide bonds (17) stabilising the three-dimensional structure of BSA (López-Fandino *et al.*, 1996). Immunoglobulins are resistant to pressures up to 300 MPa (Felipe *et al.*, 1997).

15.5 The effects on other properties of milk

Some studies did not observe changes in the pH values of skim milk post-pressurisation (Johnston. *et al.*, 1992; López-Fandino *et al.*, 1996). In later studies, an increase in the pH value by HP treatment of raw and UHT-treated skim milk (Schrader *et al.*, 1997; Schrader and Buchheim, 1998) and caprine milk (De La Fuente *et al.*, 1999) was found. The pH increase was higher when the milk was treated at higher pressures or lower temperatures and when UHT-treated milk was pressure-treated compared to raw and pasteurised milk (Schrader and Buchheim, 1998). According to Schrader and Buchheim (1998), this pH shift is caused by the pressure-induced partial dissociation of the micellar CCP. In UHT-treated milk, also a pressure-induced dissociation of the heat-induced insoluble calcium phosphate takes place. The first pH shift is reversible while the latter is irreversible.

The disintegration of casein micelles into small fragments leads to a reduction of the milk's lightness (*L*)-values (Johnston *et al.*, 1992; Shibauchi *et al.*, 1992; Desobry-Banon *et al.*, 1994). This leads to a change in appearance: from 400 MPa onwards, the skim milk became almost transparent (Johnston *et al.*, 1992; Shibauchi *et al.*, 1992; Desobry-Banon *et al.*, 1994; Gaucheron *et al.*, 1997). The *L*-value of whole raw milk was only slightly decreased by HP treatment (Mussa and Ramaswamy, 1997).

HP treatment increased the dynamic viscosity of skim milk (Shibauchi *et al.*, 1992) and reconstituted skim milk (Desobry-Banon *et al.*, 1994), depending on the pressure intensity and to lesser extent on the treatment time (Shibauchi *et al.*, 1992). The changes started at 200 MPa and levelled off at 400 MPa. An increase in viscosity of 19% and 38% was observed for reconstituted skim milk at 430 MPa and skim milk at 500 MPa, respectively. For pressure-treated (400 MPa for 20 min) whole raw milk, a 21% increase in viscosity was found (Mussa and Ramaswamy, 1997). According to Desobry-Banon *et al.* (1994), the viscosity increase can be explained by the disintegration of the casein particles into smaller ones leading to an increased fraction of casein micelles in the total volume.

15.5.1   Effect on the rennet coagulation properties of milk

The time necessary for rennet coagulation (RCT) of milk is affected by the pressure intensity, the duration of the treatment at certain pressures, the temperature of the treatment, the pH of the milk and the milk species. At pressures up to 200 MPa, most studies agree that the RCT of bovine, ovine and caprine milk decreases (Desobry-Banon *et al.*, 1994; López-Fandino *et al.*, 1996; López-Fandino and Olano, 1998a; Arias *et al.*, 2000; Needs *et al.*, 2000b). Desobry-Banon *et al.* (1994) suggested that this is caused by the disruption of casein micelles by HP, giving them an increased specific surface area that increases the probability of interparticle collision. Processing of milk at higher pressures increased the RCT again to reach values that were close to those of untreated milk (López-Fandino *et al.*, 1996; López-Fandino and Olano, 1998a; Arias *et al.*, 2000; Needs *et al.*, 2000b; Buffa *et al.*, 2001d) or that were higher (Needs *et al.*, 2000b). The disruption of casein micelles appeared to be complete at treatments at and above 400 MPa. Whey proteins, particularly β-Lg, were denatured at increasing pressure, and the denatured β-Lg was incorporated into the gels. Its presence interfered with the secondary aggregation phase and reduced the overall rate of coagulation (Needs *et al.*, 2000b). One study reported that the RCT of milk treated at pressures above 200 MPa remained similar to that treated at 200 MPa (Desobry-Banon *et al.*, 1994). Treatments of ovine and caprine milk at 400 MPa did not considerably lengthen the RCT (López-Fandino and Olano, 1998a), while treatment of goat's milk at 500 MPa increased the RCT (Buffa *et al.*, 2001d). The duration of the treatment at 400 MPa, but not at 200 MPa, also affected the RCT: a 10 min treatment reduced the RCT, while longer times increased the RCT (López-Fandino *et al.*, 1996). The combined use of HP with temperatures of at least 40°C delayed RCT (López-Fandino and Olano, 1998b). Acidification of milk before pressurisation decreased the RCT, while alkalisation increased the RCT (Arias *et al.*, 2000).

The rennet coagulation process was investigated under pressure at 30°C. Initial proteolysis by chymosin (primary phase) was hardly affected up to 130 MPa, while the coagulation time (secondary phase) was approximately nine times higher than at ambient pressure (Ohmiya *et al.*, 1987). López-Fandino and Olano (1998b) reported that HP treatment reduced the rate of release of caseinomacropeptide (CMP) from κ-casein at 200–300 MPa by rendering κ-casein less susceptible to the action of chymosin, possibly because of interactions between denatured β-Lg and κ-casein.

Curd firmness was increased by treatment of milk for 30 min at 300 MPa, but not at 100, 200 or 400 MPa. The firmness was also dependent on the duration of the treatment (López-Fandino *et al.*, 1996). However, Needs *et al.* (2000b) found that skim milk treated at 200–600 MPa yielded higher curd firmness values than untreated milk. The microstructure of these curds differed. Curds produced from pressure-treated (600 MPa) milk contained dense networks of fine strands, which were continuous over much bigger distances than in curds produced from untreated milk, where the strands were coarser with large interstitial spaces. Pandey *et al.* (2000) found an increase in the gel strength of the rennet curds with a decrease in pressure level (200–400 MPa), temperature (3–21°C) and holding time (10–110 min). Molina *et al.* (2000) observed that the curd firmness of milk with reduced fat content treated at 400 MPa for 15 min was higher than that of equivalent untreated milk. For goat's milk, a treatment at 400–500 MPa improved the curd's consistency (López-Fandino and Olano, 1998a, Buffa *et al.*, 2001d).

15.6   The effects on cheese and yoghurt-making properties of milk

The wet curd yield was increased by up to 20% by pressurisation of milk at 300–400 MPa for 30 min compared to untreated milk. In addition, the loss of proteins in the whey was reduced. Lower levels of β-Lg (not of α-La) were found in the rennet whey of pressurised milks, indicating that at least part of the denatured β-Lg was retained in the curd (López-Fandino *et al.*, 1996; López-Fandino and Olano, 1998b; Arias *et al.*, 2000; Molina *et al.*, 2000; Needs *et al.*, 2000b).

Syneresis from the curds was similar to control samples when the milk was treated at up to 400 MPa, but was reduced by 600 MPa (Needs et al., 2000b). Pandey et al. (2000), however, found a decrease in water-holding capacity of the rennet curds with a decrease in pressure (200–400 MPa), temperature (3–21°C) and holding time (10–110 min). The combined application of 400 MPa and 40°C was found to increase the curd yield compared to 20°C (López-Fandino and Olano, 1998b). With increasing pH of milk, the wet curd yield and the moisture retention in the curd increased for samples treated at 400 MPa (Arias et al., 2000). Wet curd yield of caprine milk was also increased above 300 MPa, while it was increased above 200 MPa for ovine milk (López-Fandino and Olano, 1998a).

Cheddar cheeses made from pressurised milk retained more moisture and protein than cheeses made from pasteurised milk. They produced 7% higher yields using 586 MPa for three 1-min cycles (Drake et al., 1997) and 4% higher yields using 200 MPa for five 1-min cycles (Kheadr et al., 2002). Pressurisation of semi-skim milk (400 MPa, 15 min) increased the yield of reduced-fat cheese by 9% (Molina et al., 2000). In cheese-making experiments with pressurised goat's milk (500 MPa, 15 min) increased yields were also found (Trujillo et al., 1999b). The higher yields are due to retention of β-Lg and, especially, moisture. The latter is explained by the less close reaggregation of the cascin micelles and fat globules post-pressurisation, allowing more moisture to be entrapped in the cheese. The presence of whey proteins can also facilitate increased moisture binding in the cheese (Drake et al., 1997) which may have adverse effects as well. The goat's milk and reduced-fat cheeses made from HP-treated milk had higher levels of salt (Trujillo et al., 1999a; Molina et al., 2000), which may be due to the effect of the moisture content on the rate of salt absorbed by cheese.

Sensory and microbiological analysis of Cheddar cheeses indicated no differences between pasteurised and pressurised milk cheeses, but the latter had a pasty and weak texture (Drake et al., 1997) or were more firm, elastic and cohesive and less brittle than the first (Kheadr et al., 2002). Pressurisation of reduced-fat milk, however, improved cheese texture (Molina et al., 2000). Goat's milk cheeses made from HP-treated milk had higher pH and salt, matured more quickly (higher extent of proteolysis) and developed stronger flavours than cheeses made from pasteurised milk (Trujillo et al., 1999a). Cheeses made from HP-treated goat's milk were firmer and less fracturable than those made from pasteurised milk, but differences became less notable towards the end of ripening (Buffa et al., 2001c). Cheeses made from HP-treated goat's milk showed a similar level of lipolysis to cheeses made from raw milk, whereas the level of lipolysis in cheese made from pasteurised milk was lower. This behaviour could be explained by heat-sensitive but pressure-resistant characteristics of the milk lipase. No differences in the sensorial attributes between cheeses were found (Buffa et al., 2001a). Goat's cheese made from pressurised milk had similar microbiological characteristics to pasteurised milk cheeses (Buffa et al., 2001b).

15.6.1   Effect on the yoghurt-making properties of milk

Acid-set gels obtained using glucono-δ-lactone (GDL) from HP-treated skim milk showed an improved rigidity and gel breaking strength, a greater resistance to syneresis and an increased index of protein hydration with increasing pressure and treatment time (Johnston et al., 1993). Coagulation started at a higher pH and yielded a stronger gel than untreated milk (Desobry-Banon et al., 1994). Also, solvation of the pellets was higher. These changes were in accordance with micelle disruption into small clusters or aggregates (Famelart et al., 1997).

The microstructure and rheological properties of set yoghurts made from skim milk subjected to heat and pressure (600 MPa, 15 min), fortified by addition of whey proteins, were very different. Pressure-treated milk yoghurt had a much higher storage modulus but yielded more readily to large deformation than the heated milk yoghurt (Needs et al., 2000a). In stirred yoghurt, hydrodynamic properties and viscosity were improved when the milk was treated for 1 h in the 100–600 MPa range (Johnston et al., 1994). The firmness of yoghurt made from HP-treated ewe's milk (200–500 MPa, 10–55°C, 15 min) increased with increasing pressure, and an additional increase in firmness was observed at 55°C. The level of syneresis increased during storage for yoghurts made from pasteurised or heat-treated milk, but not from HP-treated milk (Ferragut et al., 2000).

The acidification of milk with GDL under pressure (50–200 MPa) was examined by Schwertfeger and Buchheim (1999). Coagulation of samples treated at higher pressures and/or for longer times occurred. The structures of these aggregates differed distinctly from the homogeneous gel formed by acidification of milk at ambient pressure; a fine-stranded, coherent coagulum was formed at 200 MPa for 20 min.

HP may also induce the gelation of milk concentrates at low temperature and neutral pH in the absence of any coagulating enzyme or gelling agent (Kumeno et al., 1993; Vélez-Ruiz et al., 1998).

15.7   High-pressure treatment of cheese

HP treatments have been applied to cheese to assess whether the brining time could be shortened, which could reduce processing time and improve cheese quality (Morris et al., 1985). The preservation and destruction of pathogenic microorganisms in fresh cheese by HP has been the object of some studies. To compensate for the considerable cost associated with cheese storage, the use of the HP technology to accelerate cheese ripening was evaluated. Other changes, such as rheological property changes, also occur in cheese when HP is applied. Some of these changes may be advantageous; others may be drawbacks of the method.

15.7.1   High-pressure brining of cheese

Neither salt uptake nor salt diffusion was accelerated by brining of Gouda cheese (Messens *et al.*, 1999a) and Manchego-type cheese (Pavia *et al.*, 2000) under HP, but the water loss of Gouda cheese was reduced by brining at pressures above 200–300 MPa (Messens *et al.*, 1999a). This pressure-brining of Gouda cheese at 300 MPa for 30 min, however, disrupted the paracasein micelle structure, yielding more proteins, particularly β-casein and peptides in the cheese serum. The hydrolysis of β-casein by plasmin is accelerated by HP brining as indicated by UREA-PAGE (Messens *et al.*, 1998).

15.7.2   Elimination of microorganisms in cheese by high pressure

The refrigerated shelf-life of pasteurised goat's milk cheese can be extended by HP treatment (400–500 MPa for 5–15 min) since any bacterial growth during refrigerated storage was observed (Capellas *et al.*, 1996). HP can also be used to inactivate *Listeria monocytogenes* in goat's milk cheeses manufactured from strongly contaminated raw milk without any modifications on its organoleptic characteristics (Gallot-Lavallee, 1998). The combination of 400–500 MPa with mild heat (50°C) gave a reduction of *Staphylococcus carnosus* inoculated in fresh goat's milk cheese. The combination of 500 MPa and nisin was the most effective treatment. Inactivation of *Bacillus subtilis* spores inoculated in fresh cheese can be achieved by germination followed by vegetative cells inactivation (Capellas *et al.*, 2000).

The effectiveness of HP treatment to inactivate microbial contaminants in Cheddar cheese (slurry) has been assessed by O'Reilly *et al.* (2000a). The relative sensitivities of the isolates to HP were *Penicillium roqueforti* > *Escherichia coli* > *S. aureus*. The organisms were more sensitive to pressure in cheese than in slurry. In addition to cell death, the presence of sub-lethally injured cells in slurries post-pressurisation was demonstrated (O'Reilly *et al.*, 2000a). Pressurisation at 500 MPa for 15 min reduced the numbers of *L. monocytogenes* in Gouda, Edamski and Poslaski cheese by approximately 6 log units. The indigenous microflora was less pressure sensitive than *L. monocytogenes* (Szczawinski *et al.*, 1997). Pressurisation at 200 MPa caused approximately a 2 log reduction of the numbers of *L. monocytogenes* and *E. coli* O157:H7 in smear-ripened cheese manufactured using raw milk. From 300 MPa onwards, pressurisation resulted in complete inactivation of both pathogens (O'Reilly *et al.*, 2001). HP treatment (340 and 544 MPa for 10–30 min) of Swiss cheese slurries reduced the microbial population during prolonged storage at 30°C for up to 5 days (Jin *et al.*, 1996).

15.7.3   Accelerated ripening of cheese by high pressure

Accelerated cheese ripening by HP (3 days at 50 MPa) has been demonstrated for the first time in a patent by Yokoyama *et al.* (1992). This yielded a Cheddar cheese with a taste comparable to that of a matured commercial cheese. Using the same pressure conditions, O'Reilly *et al.* (2000b) also observed an increase in the levels of proteolysis of immature Cheddar cheese but the differences became smaller during ripening. The degradation of α_{s1}-casein was enhanced by HP resulting in an accumulation of α_{s1}-I-casein. The enhancement of Cheddar cheese ripening was far less pronounced than in the patent, which could be attributed to the higher level of starter bacteria added to the cheese milk in the latter than conventionally. In both studies, the enhancement of proteolysis by HP could be partly due to a temperature effect, since cheeses were treated at a higher temperature than conventionally used for Cheddar cheese storage. For goat's milk cheese, Sendra *et al.* (1999) found that the enhanced proteolysis by exposure to 50 MPa for 3 days at 25°C compared to 3 days at 14°C and ambient pressure was due more to the elevated storage temperature than to the pressure level applied.

Yokoyama *et al.* (1992) also described the addition of lipase and protease to Parmesan-type cheese curd at salting, followed by treatment at 50 MPa for 3 days. This resulted in a Parmesan-type cheese equivalent to a commercial cheese. Pressure-treated Gouda cheese (14°C) obtained a higher pH than the untreated equivalent, particularly shortly post-pressurisation (Messens *et al.*, 1999b). Various indexes of cheese proteolysis (Reps *et al.*, 1998; Messens *et al.*, 1999b) and the SDS-PAGE profiles (Messens *et al.*, 1999b) were similar in treated and untreated cheeses. Hence, the proteolysis by chymosin and plasmin, and the proteinase/peptidase system of the starter, were not influenced by HP, although pressures above 225 MPa decreased starter bacterial growth (Messens *et al.*, 1999b). Butyric acid and acetoin were found in lower concentrations after ripening of the pressurized Gouda cheeses (Butz *et al.*, 2000). Pressurisation for 3 days at 50 MPa did not lead to an enhancement of proteolysis (Messens *et al.*, 1999b). Other semi-hard cheeses with a composition different from that of Gouda cheese, e.g. Saint-Paulin (higher water content), and Loo Light (lower fat content) also showed no increased proteolysis after treatment at 50 MPa for 8 h (Messens, 2000).

HP treatment of white mould-ripened cheeses, such as Camembert, led to an increase in its proteolysis (Reps *et al.*, 1998; Messens *et al.*, 2001), depending on the pressure and the maturity of the cheese. For 10-day-old Camembert, the highest degree of proteolysis was observed when 50 MPa for 2 h was applied (Reps *et al.*, 1998). Treatment at 50 MPa for 8 h enhanced the levels of pH 4.6-SN (soluble nitrogen) and trichloroacetic acid soluble nitrogen (TCA-SN) near the rind. Messens *et al.* (2001) suggested that this could have resulted from the increased pH caused by HP treatment leading to a higher action of the metalloproteinase of *Penicillium camemberti* (Messens *et al.*, 2001).

Coryneform bacteria, especially *Brevibacterium linens*, dominate the surface microflora of smear-ripened cheeses, such as Père Joseph. Treatment at 50 MPa for 8 h markedly affected pH and proteolysis of Père Joseph. Treated samples had a higher concentration of a typical breakdown product resulting from the caseinolytic action of an extracellular proteinase of *B. linens*. This is possibly a result of the pH increase leading to a higher amount and/or activity of the proteolytic enzymes of *B. linens* that are capable of breaking intact caseins (Messens *et al.*, 2000a).

Goat's milk cheese proteolysis was enhanced by exposure to 400 MPa for 5 min at 14°C. Cheeses were ripened in 14 days compared to the conventional 28 days, possibly due to the higher pH or the enhanced enzyme activity from inoculated starter culture. Sensory analysis, however, indicated bitter notes in the accelerated ripened cheese (Saldo *et al.*, 2000). Levels of proteolysis in hard caprine milk cheese treated at 50 MPa for 72 h were only slightly different from those in untreated cheese. Treatment at 400 MPa for 5 min increased secondary proteolysis, or conversion of peptides into FAA, whereas coagulant activity was decreased (Saldo *et al.*, 2002a).

15.7.4   Rheology and microstructure of pressure-treated cheese

HP treatment has been shown to overcome the texture problem of half-fat Cheddar cheese. Treatment at 200 MPa gave the most similar performance to full-fat Cheddar. However, the browning time of half-fat Cheddar was less than for full-fat Cheddar (Johnston *et al.*, 2002). HP treatment (200 MPa for 60 min) of immature Mozzarella cheese increased its meltability and resulted in cheeses not different from matured samples. Moisture redistribution was found to play a major part in the changes (Johnston and Darcy, 2000).

While the proteolysis of Gouda cheese was not affected by HP treatment (Messens *et al.*, 1999b), its rheological properties were altered. The samples treated at 400 MPa got less rigid, less solid-like, and more viscoelastic; from 50 MPa onwards, the samples had less resistance to flow. It was shown that HP weakened hydrophobic interactions in Gouda cheese. This could have led to structural changes of the paracasein network causing the rheological property changes. The effects on proteins in Gouda cheese are reversible as both hydrophobic interactions and rheological properties were restored during ripening (Messens *et al.*, 2000b). Saldo *et al.* (2001) concluded that the incidence of hydrophobic and hydrogen bonds in treated hard cheeses was reduced after HP treatment (50 MPa for 72 h). Water was bound more strongly and cheese became more fluid-like compared to the untreated cheese.

Goat's milk cheeses treated at 400 MPa for 5 min were less crumbly and more elastic than untreated cheeses (Saldo *et al.*, 2000). The texture and colour of Mato cheese, a fresh cheese made from goats' milk, changed slightly by treatment at 500 MPa. HP-treated cheese lost more whey with a higher total nitrogen content than untreated cheese (Capellas *et al.*, 2001). During ripening post-pressurisation, HP-treated (400 MPa) hard caprine cheese had lower lightness and higher chroma values than untreated cheese (Saldo *et al.*, 2002b).

Pressure-shift freezing and thawing of Cheddar was shown to prevent the paste-like body and appearance typically for conventionally frozen and thawed Cheddar. The product was, however, different from fresh cheese, e.g. in being more readily deformed. Pressure-shift freezing and thawing gave no advantages in the case of immature Mozzarella cheese (Johnston, 2000).

15.8   Future trends

The shelf-life of thermally pasteurised milk may be obtained by HP treatment of milk at 400–500 MPa. However, this treatment may not be sufficient to inactivate pathogens. To overcome this problem, more effective inactivation of bacterial contaminants can be achieved by combination of HP with heat or by applying bacteriocins or by the use of DHP. Inactivation then occurs at lower pressure levels, improving the milk quality. More efforts could be done to investigate the combined use of HP with bacteriocins, because this research is still premature. Since HP technology is more costly than traditional heat technologies, other substantial changes should be introduced to apply this technology in the dairy industry. The use of HP-treated milk for cheesemaking has several advantages. Depending on the treatment intensity, this could reduce the RCT and increase the cheese yield and/or produce cheeses that are microbiologically safer than raw milk cheeses. To overcome the texture problem of low-fat cheeses, pressurised skim milk can be used for cheesemaking. This outcome still needs to be confirmed and should be compared with other means to overcome the texture defects of low-fat cheeses. Possible applications can also be found in yoghurt production, due to the improvement of the texture of yoghurt made from HP-treated milk which leads to an increased firmness and a decreased syneresis.

Safer cheese can be manufactured using pressurised milk, but also by HP treatment of the cheese itself. From a technological point of view, smaller volumes will need to be used in the latter case, but the process will be more complicated than for liquid processing. HP treatment of some cheese varieties increases proteolysis. Increased proteolysis was found for cheeses with a secondary flora, such as mould-ripened and smear-ripened cheeses and for goat's milk cheeses. The texture of several cheeses is affected in a positive way for some cheese varieties. The texture defect of low-fat cheeses can be overcome and Mozzarella cheese can be produced with improved meltability.

Nutritional consequences of HP processing of milk and dairy products, and food products in general, have been given little attention. More research should be done in this area because HP processing may give less nutritional damage than traditional processes. For future applications, this should be taken into account.

15.9   Sources of further information and advice

A review on the nutritional effects of HP and other new processing technologies is given in Gould (2001). The modification of the functionality of proteins has been reviewed by Messens et al. (1997), while Hendrickx et al. (1998) have reviewed the effects of HP on enzymes related to foods. The mechanism and efficacy of HP for the destruction of microorganisms has been reviewed by Smelt (1998), Knorr (1999), Linton and Patterson (2000) and Lado and Yousef

(2002). Recently, several review articles have been published concerning the HP processing of milk and dairy products. The paper by Datta and Deeth (1999) gives a general overview of HP processing of foods, followed by a description of the effects of HP on dairy products and processes. A review of the principles of HP and the equipment is also given. O'Reilly *et al.* (2001) focus on the applications of HP treatments on cheese manufacture and ripening. Both the treatment of milk prior to cheesemaking and the treatment of cheese are discussed in detail. The current state of knowledge of the effects of HP on constituents and properties of milk and possible applications of HP treatment of milk prior to the production of yoghurt and cheese are reviewed by Huppertz *et al.* (2002). The ongoing work towards the development of HP applications for the cheese industry is summarised in a paper by Trujillo *et al.* (2000).

15.10   References

ARIAS, M, LÓPEZ-FANDINO, R and OLANO, A (2000), 'Influence of pH on the effects of high pressure on milk', *Milchwiss,* 55(4), 191–194.

BUFFA, M, GUAMIS, B, PAVIA, M and TRUJILLO, A J (2001a), 'Lipolysis in cheese made from raw, pasteurized or high-pressure-treated goats' milk', *Int Dairy J,* 11(3), 175–179.

BUFFA, M, GUAMIS, B, ROYO, C and TRUJILLO, A J (2001b), 'Microbiological changes throughout ripening of goat cheese made from raw, pasteurized and high-pressure-treated milk', *Food Microbiol,* 18(1), 45–51.

BUFFA, M, TRUJILLO, A, PAVIA, M and GUAMIS, B (2001c), 'Changes in textural, micro structural, and colour characteristics during ripening of cheeses made from raw, pasteurized or high-pressure-treated goats' milk', *Int Dairy J,* 11(11–12), 927–934.

BUFFA, M, TRUJILLO, A J and GUAMIS, B (2001d), 'Rennet coagulation properties of raw, pasteurised and high pressure-treated goat milk', *Milchwiss,* 56(5), 243–246.

BUTZ, P, FERNANDEZ, A, KOLLER, W D, MESSENS, W and TAUSCHER, B (2000), 'Effects of high pressure treatment on fermentation processes during ripening of Gouda cheese', *High Pressure Res,* 19(1–6), 427–431.

CAPELLAS, M, MOR-MUR, M, SENDRA, E and GUAMIS, B (2001), 'Effect of high-pressure processing on physico-chemical characteristics of fresh goats' milk cheese (Mato)', *Int Dairy J,* 11(3), 165–173.

CAPELLAS, M, MOR-MUR, M, GERVILLA, R, YUSTE, J and GUAMIS, B (2000), 'Effect of high pressure combined with mild heat or nisin on inoculated bacteria and mesophiles of goat's milk fresh cheese', *Food Microbiol,* 17(6), 633–641.

CAPELLAS, M, MOR-MUR, M, SENDRA, E, PLA, R and GUAMIS, B (1996), 'Populations of aerobic mesophils and inoculated *E. coli* during storage of fresh goat's milk cheese treated with high pressure', *J Food Prot,* 59(6), 582–587.

CASAL, V and GOMEZ, R (1999), 'Effect of high pressure on the viability and enzymatic activity of mesophilic lactic acid bacteria isolated from caprine cheese', *J Dairy Sci,* 82(6), 1092–1098.

DATTA, N and DEETH, H C (1999), 'High pressure processing of milk and dairy products', *Aust J Dairy Technol,* 54(1), 41–48.

DE LA FUENTE, M A, OLANO, A, CASAL, V and JUAREZ, M (1999), 'Effects of high pressure and heat treatment on the mineral balance of goat's milk', *J Dairy Res,* 66, 65–72.

DESOBRY-BANON, S, RICHARD, F and HARDY, J (1994), 'Study of acid and rennet coagulation of high pressurized milk', *J Dairy Sci*, 77, 3267–3274.

DRAKE, M A, HARRISON, S L, ASPLUND, M, BARBOSA-CANOVAS, G and SWANSON, B G (1997), 'High pressure treatment of milk and effects on microbiological and sensory quality of cheddar cheese', *J Food Sci*, 62(4), 843.

EARNSHAW, R (1996), 'High pressure food processing', *Nutr Food Sci*, (2), 8–11.

ERKMEN, O AND KARATAS, S (1997), 'Effect of high hydrostatic pressure on *Staphylococcus aureus* in milk', *J Food Eng*, 33, 257–262.

FAMELART, M H, GAUCHERON, F, MARIETTE, F, LE GRAËT, Y, RAULOT, K and BOYAVAL, E (1997), 'Acidification of pressure-treated milk', *Int Dairy J*, 7, 325–330.

FELIPE, X, CAPELLAS, M and LAW, A J R (1997), 'Comparison of the effects of high-pressure-treatments and heat pasteurization on the whey proteins in goat's milk', *J Agric Food Chem*, 45, 627–631.

FERRAGUT, V, MARTINEZ, V M, TRUJILLO, A J and GUAMIS, B (2000), 'Properties of yoghurts made from whole ewe's milk treated by high hydrostatic pressure', *Milchwiss*, 55, 267–269.

GALLOT-LAVALLEE, T (1998), 'Efficiency of high pressure treatment for destruction of *Listeria monocytogenes* in goat cheese from raw milk', *Sci Aliments*, 18(6), 647–655.

GARCIA-GRAELLS, C, MASSCHALCK, B and MICHIELS, C W (1999), 'Inactivation of *Escherichia coli* in milk by high-hydrostatic-pressure treatment in combination with antimicrobial peptides', *J Food Prot*, 62(11), 1248–1254.

GARCIA-RISCO, M R, CORTES, E, CARRASCOSA, A V and LÓPEZ-FANDINO, R (1998), 'Microbiological and chemical changes in high-pressure-treated milk during refrigerated storage', *J Food Prot*, 61(6), 735–737.

GARCIA-RISCO, M R, OLANO, A, RAMOS, M and LÓPEZ-FANDINO, R (2000), 'Micellar changes induced by high pressure. Influence in the proteolytic activity and organoleptic properties of milk', *J Dairy Sci*, 83(10), 2184–2189.

GAUCHERON, F, FAMELART, M H, MARIETTE, F, RAULOT, K, MICHEL, F and LE GRAËT, Y (1997), 'Combined effects of temperature and high-pressure treatments on physicochemical characteristics of skim milk', *Food Chem*, 59, 439–447.

GERVILLA, R, CAPELLAS, M, FERRAGUT, V and GUAMIS, B (1997), 'Effect of high hydrostatic pressure on *Listeria innocua* 910 CECT inoculated into ewe's milk', *J Food Prot*, 60(1), 33–37.

GERVILLA, R, FERRAGUT, V and GUAMIS, B (2000), 'High pressure inactivation of microorganisms inoculated into ovine milk of different fat contents', *J Dairy Sci*, 83(4), 674–682.

GOULD, G W (2001), 'Symposium on "nutritional effects of new processing technologies". New processing technologies: an overview', *Proc Nutr Soc*, 60(4), 463–474.

HAYASHI, R, KAWAMURA, Y and KUNUGI, S (1987), 'Introduction of high pressure to food processing: preferential proteolysis of b-lactoglobulin in milk whey', *J Food Sci*, 52(4), 1107–1108.

HENDRICKX, M E, LUDIKHUYZE, L, VAN DEN BROECK, I and WEEMAES, C (1998), 'Effects of high pressure on enzymes related to food quality', *Trends Food Sci Technol*, 9, 197–203.

HEREMANS, K (1982), 'High pressure effects on proteins and other biomolecules', *Ann Rev Biophys Bioeng*, 11, 1–21.

HILL, V M, LEDWARD, D A and AMES, J M (1996), 'Influence of high hydrostatic pressure and pH on the rate of Maillard browning in a glucose–lysine system', *J Agric Food*

Chem, 44, 594–598.

HILL, V M, ISAACS, N S, LEDWARD, D A and AMES, J M (1999), 'Effect of high hydrostatic pressure on the volatile components of a glucose–lysine model system', *J Agric Food Chem,* 47, 3675–3681.

HITE, B H (1899), 'The effect of pressure in the preservation of milk', *Bull. W. Virginia Univ. Agr. Exp. Stat,* 58, 15–35.

HUPPERTZ, T, KELLY, A L and FOX, P F (2002), 'Effects of high pressure on constituents and properties of milk', *Int Dairy J,* 12(7), 561–572.

JIN, Z T, HARPER, W J and FARKAS, D (1996), 'Effects of high pressure treatment on changes of microflora and aroma profile in accelerated ripening of cheese slurry', *J Dairy Sci,* 79, suppl. 1, 114.

JOHNSTON, D E (1995) 'High pressure effects on milk and meat', in Ledward, D A, Johnston, D E, Earnshaw, R G and Hasting, A P M, *High Pressure Processing of Foods,* Nottingham, University Press, 99–121.

JOHNSTON, D E (2000), 'The effects of freezing at high pressure on the rheology of Cheddar and Mozzarella cheeses', *Milchwiss,* 55(10), 559–562.

JOHNSTON, D E and DARCY, P C (2000), 'The effects of high pressure treatment on immature Mozzarella cheese', *Milchwiss,* 55(11), 617–620.

JOHNSTON, D E, AUSTIN, B A and MURPHY, P M (1992), 'Effects of high hydrostatic pressure on milk', *Milchwiss,* 47, 760–763.

JOHNSTON, D E, AUSTIN, B A and MURPHY, R J (1993), 'Properties of acid-set gels prepared from high pressure treated skim milk', *Milchwiss,* 48, 206–209.

JOHNSTON, D E, MURPHY, R J and BIRKS, A W (1994), 'Stirred-style yoghourt type product prepared from pressure treated skim-milk', *High Pressure Res,* 12, 215–219.

JOHNSTON, D E, O'HAGAN, M and BALMER, D W (2002), 'Effects of high pressure treatment on the texture and cooking performance of half-fat Cheddar cheese', *Milchwiss,* 57(4), 198–201.

KHEADR, E E, VACHON, J F, PAQUIN, P and FLISS, I (2002), 'Effect of dynamic high pressure on microbiological, rheological and microstructural quality of Cheddar cheese', *Int Dairy J,* 12(5), 435–446.

KNORR, D (1999), 'Novel approaches in food-processing technology: new technologies for preserving foods and modifying function', *Curr Opin Biotechnol,* 10(5), 485–491.

KUMENO, K, NAKAHAMA, N, HONMA, K, MAKINO, T and WATANABE, M (1993), 'Production and characterization of a pressure-induced gel from freeze-concentrated milk', *Biosci Biotechnol Biochem,* 57, 750–752.

LADO, B H and YOUSEF, A E (2002), 'Alternative food-preservation technologies: efficacy and mechanisms', *Microbes Infect,* 4(4), 433–440.

LINTON, M and PATTERSON, M F (2000), 'High pressure processing of foods for microbiological safety and quality (a short review)', *Acta Microbiol Immunol Hung,* 47(2–3), 175–82.

LÓPEZ-FANDINO, R and OLANO, A (1998a), 'Cheese-making properties of ovine and caprine milks submitted to high pressures', *Lait,* 78(3), 341–350.

LÓPEZ-FANDINO, R and OLANO, A (1998b), 'Effects of high pressures combined with moderate temperatures on the rennet coagulation properties of milk', *Int Dairy J,* 8(7), 623–627.

LÓPEZ-FANDINO, R, CARRASCOSA, A V and OLANO, A (1996), 'The effects of high pressure on whey protein denaturation and cheese-making properties of raw milk', *J Dairy Sci,* 79(6), 923–936.

LÓPEZ-FANDINO, R, DE LA FUENTE, M A, RAMOS, M and OLANO, A (1998), 'Distribution of minerals and proteins between the soluble and colloidal phases of pressurized milks from different species', *J Dairy Res*, 65, 69–78.

LUDIKHUYZE, L R, CLAEYS, W L and HENDRICKX, M E (2001), 'Effect of temperature and/or pressure on lactoperoxidase activity in bovine milk and acid whey', *J Dairy Res*, 68(4), 625–637.

MCCLEMENTS, J M, PATTERSON, M F and LINTON, M (2001), 'The effect of growth stage and growth temperature on high hydrostatic pressure inactivation of some psychrotrophic bacteria in milk', *J Food Prot*, 64(4), 514–522.

MERTENS, B and DEPLACE, G (1993), 'Engineering aspects of high-pressure technology in the food industry', *Food Technol*, 47(6), 164–169.

MESSENS, W (2000), 'High-pressure-brining and ripening of hard and semi-hard cheeses', Faculty of Agricultural and Applied Biological Sciences, Ghent, Ghent University, 154.

MESSENS, W, VAN CAMP, J and HUYGHEBAERT, A (1997), 'Review article: the use of high pressure to modify the functionality of food proteins', *Trends Food Sci Technol*, 4(8), 107–112.

MESSENS, W, DEWETTINCK, K, VAN CAMP, J and HUYGHEBAERT, A (1998), 'High pressure brining of Gouda cheese and its effect on the cheese serum', *Food Sci Technol*, 31(6), 552–558.

MESSENS, W, DEWETTINCK, K and HUYGHEBAERT, A (1999a), 'Transport of sodium chloride and water in Gouda cheese as affected by high-pressure brining', *Int Dairy J*, 9(8), 569–576.

MESSENS, W, ESTEPAR-GARCIA, J, DEWETTINCK, K and HUYGHEBAERT, A (1999b), 'Proteolysis of high-pressure-treated Gouda cheese', *Int Dairy J*, 9(11), 775–782.

MESSENS, W, FOUBERT, I, DEWETTINCK, K and HUYGHEBAERT, A (2000a), 'Proteolysis of a high-pressure-treated smear-ripened cheese', *Milchwiss*, 55(6), 328–332.

MESSENS, W, VAN DE WALLE, D, AREVALO, J, DEWETTINCK, K and HUYGHEBAERT, A (2000b), 'Rheological properties of high-pressure-treated Goat cheese', *Int Dairy J*, 10(5–6), 359–367.

MESSENS, W, FOUBERT, I, DEWETTINCK, K and HUYGHEBAERT, A (2001), 'Proteolysis of a high-pressure-treated mould-ripen cheese', *Milchwiss*, 56(4), 201–204.

MOLINA, E, ALVAREZ, M D, RAMOS, M, OLANO, A and LÓPEZ-FANDINO, R (2000), 'Use of high-pressure-treated milk for the production of reduced-fat cheese', *Int Dairy J*, 10(7), 467–475.

MORGAN, S M, ROSS, R P, BERESFORD, T and HILL, C (2000), 'Combination of hydrostatic pressure and lacticin 3147 causes increased killing of *Staphylococcus* and *Listeria*', *J Appl Microbiol*, 88(3), 414–420.

MORRIS, H A, GUINEE, T P and FOX, P F (1985), 'Salt diffusion in Cheddar cheese', *J Dairy Sci*, 68, 1851–1858.

MUSSA, D M and RAMASWAMY, H S (1997), 'Ultra high pressure pasteurization of milk: kinetics of microbial destruction and changes in physico-chemical characteristics', *Food Sci Technol*, 30, 551–557.

MYLLYMÄKI, O (1996) 'High pressure food processors', in Ohlsson, T, *High Pressure Processing of Food and Food Components – a Literature Survey and Bibliography*, Göteborg, Kompendiet, 29–46.

NAKAMURA, T, SADO, H and SYUKUNOBE, Y (1993), 'Production of low antigenic whey protein hydrolysates by enzymatic hydrolysis and denaturation with high pressure', *Milchwiss*, 48(3), 141–145.

NEEDS, E C, CAPELLAS, M, BLAND, A P, MANOJ, P, MACDOUGAL, D and PAUL, G (2000a),

'Comparison of heat and pressure treatments of skim milk, fortified with whey protein concentrate, for set yogurt preparation: effects on milk proteins and gel structure', *J Dairy Res*, 67(3), 329–348.

NEEDS, E C, STENNING, R A, GILL, A L, FERRAGUT, V and RICH, G T (2000b), 'High-pressure treatment of milk: effects on casein micelle structure and on enzymic coagulation', *J Dairy Res*, 67(1), 31–42.

OHMIYA, K, FUKAMI, K, SHIMIZU, S and GEKKO, K (1987), 'Milk curdling by rennet under high pressure', *J Food Sci*, 52(1), 84–87.

OKAMOTO, M, HAYASHI, R, ENOMOTO, A, KAMINOGAWA, S and YAMAUCHI, K (1991), 'High-pressure proteolytic digestion of food proteins: Selective elimination of β-lactoglobulin in bovine milk whey concentrate', *Agr Biol Chem*, 55(5), 1253–1257.

O'REILLY, C E, O'CONNOR, P M, KELLY, A L, BERESFORD, T P and MURPHY, P M (2000a), 'Use of hydrostatic pressure for inactivation of microbial contaminants in cheese', *Appl Environ Microbiol*, 66(11), 4890–4896.

O'REILLY, C E, O'CONNOR, P M, MURPHY, P M, KELLY, A L and BERESFORD, T P (2000b), 'The effect of exposure to pressure of 50 MPa on Cheddar cheese ripening', *Inn Food Sci Emerg Technol*, 1, 109–117.

O'REILLY, C E, KELLY, A L, MURPHY, P M and BERESFORD, T P (2001), 'High pressure treatment: applications in cheese manufacture and ripening', *Trends Food Sci Technol*, 12(2), 51–59.

PANDEY, P K, RAMASWAMY, H S and ST-GELAIS, D (2000), 'Water-holding capacity and gel strength of rennet curd as affected by high-pressure treatment of milk', *Food Sci Technol*, 33(8), 655–663.

PATTERSON, M F and KILPATRICK, D J (1998), 'The combined effect of high hydrostatic pressure and mild heat on inactivation of pathogens in milk and poultry', *J Food Prot*, 61(4), 432–436.

PAVIA, M, TRUJILLO, A J, GUAMIS, B and FERRAGUT, V (2000), 'Effectiveness of high-pressure brining of Manchego-type cheese', *Food Sci Technol*, 33(5), 401–403.

REPS, A, KOLAKOWSKI, P and DAJNOWIEC, F (1998), 'The effect of high pressure on microorganisms and enzymes of ripening cheeses', in Isaacs, N S, *High Pressure Food Science, Bioscience and Chemistry*, Reading, Royal Society of Chemistry, Cambridge, UK, 265–270.

SALDO, J, SENDRA, E and GUAMIS, B (2000), 'High hydrostatic pressure for accelerating ripening of goat's milk cheese: proteolysis and texture', *J Food Sci*, 65(4), 636–640.

SALDO, J, SENDRA, E and GUAMIS, B (2001), 'Hard cheese structure after a high hydrostatic pressure treatment at 50 MPa for 72 h applied to cheese after brining', *Lait*, 81(5), 625–635.

SALDO, J, MCSWEENEY, P L H, SENDRA, E, KELLY, A L and GUAMIS, B (2002a), 'Proteolysis in caprine milk cheese treated by high pressure to accelerate cheese ripening', *Int Dairy J*, 12(1), 35–44.

SALDO, J, SENDRA, E and GUAMIS, B (2002b), 'Colour changes during ripening of high pressure treated hard caprine cheese', *High Pressure Res*, 22(3–4), 659–663.

SCHRADER, K and BUCHHEIM, W (1998), 'High pressure effects on the colloidal calcium phosphate and the structural integrity of micellar casein in milk. II. Kinetics of the casein micelle disintegration and protein interactions in milk', *Kieler Milchwirtsch Forsch*, 50, 79–88.

SCHRADER, K, BUCHHEIM, W and MORR, C V (1997), 'High pressure effects on the colloidal calcium phosphate and the structural integrity of micellar casein in milk. 1. High pressure dissolution of colloidal calcium phosphate in heated milk systems', *Nahrung*, 41, 133–138.

SCHWARZENBOLZ, U, KLOSTERMEYER, H and HENLE, T (2000), 'Maillard-type reactions under high hydrostatic pressure: formation of pentosidine', *Eur Food Res Technol*, 211, 208–210.

SCHWERTFEGER, M and BUCHHEIM, W (1999), 'Coagulation of skim milk under high hydrostatic pressure with acidification by glucono-δ-lactone', *Int Dairy J*, 9, 487–492.

SCOLLARD, P G, BERESFORD, T P, NEEDS, E C, MURPHY, P M and KELLY, A L (2000), 'Plasmin activity, beta-lactoglobulin denaturation and proteolysis in high pressure treated milk', *Int Dairy J*, 10(12), 835–841.

SENDRA, E, SALDO, J and GUAMIS, B (1999), 'Goat's milk cheese accelerated ripening. Compositional indexes', in Ludwig, H, *Advances in High Pressure Bioscience and Biotechnology*, Heidelberg, Springer, 465–468.

SHIBAUCHI, Y, YAMAMOTO, H and SAGARA, Y (1992), 'Conformational change of casein micelles by high pressure treatment', in Balny, C, Hayashi, R, Heremans, K and Masson, P, *High Pressure and Biotechnology, Colloque INSERM*, London, John Libbey, 239–242.

SIERRA, I, VIDAL-VALVERDE, C and LÓPEZ-FANDINO, R (2000), 'Effect of high pressure on the vitamin B1 and B6 content of milk', *Milchwiss*, 55(7), 365–367.

SMELT, J P P M (1998), 'Recent advances in the microbiology of high pressure processing', *Trends Food Sci Technol*, 9, 152–158.

STAPELFELDT, H, PETERSEN, P H, KRISTIANSEN, K R, QVIST, K B and SKIBSTED, L H (1996), 'Effect of high hydrostatic pressure on the enzymatic hydrolysis of β-lactoglobulin B by trypsin, thermolysin and pepsin', *J Dairy Res*, 63, 111–118.

STYLES, M F, HOOVER, D G and FARKAS, D F (1991), 'Response of *Listeria monocytogenes* and *Vibrio parahaemolyticus* to high hydrostatic pressure', *J Food Sci*, 56, 1404–1407.

SZCZAWINSKI, J, SZCZAWINSKA, M, STANCZAK, B, FONBERG-BROCZEK, M, ARABAS, J and SZCZEPEK, J (1997), 'Effect of high pressure on survival of *Listeria monocytogenes* in ripened, sliced cheeses at ambient temperature', in Heremans, K, *High Pressure Research in the Biosciences and Biotechnology*, Leuven, Belgium, Leuven University Press, 295–298.

TAUSCHER, B (1995), 'Pasteurization of food by hydrostatic high pressure: chemical aspects', *Z Lebensm Unters Forsch*, 200, 3–13.

TRUJILLO, A J, FERRAGUT, V, GERVILLA, R, CAPELLAS, M and GUAMIS, B (1997), 'High pressure effects on milk and milk products', *Rec Res Dev in Agric Food Chem*, 1, 137–159.

TRUJILLO, A J, ROYO, C, FERRAGUT, V and GUAMIS, B (1999a), 'Ripening profiles of goat cheese produced from milk treated with high pressure', *J Food Sci*, 64(5), 833–837.

TRUJILLO, A J, ROYO, C, GUAMIS, B and FERRAGUT, V (1999b), 'Influence of pressurization on goat milk and cheese composition and yield', *Milchwiss*, 54(4), 197–199.

TRUJILLO, A J, CAPELLAS, M, BUFFA, M, ROYO, C, GERVILLA, R, FELIPE, X, SENDRA, E, SALDO, J, FERRAGUT, V and GUAMIS, B (2000), 'Application of high pressure treatment for cheese production', *Food Sci Technol*, 33(3–4), 311–316.

VACHON, J F, KHEADR, E E, GIASSON, J, PAQUIN, P and FLISS, I (2002), 'Inactivation of foodborne pathogens in milk using dynamic high pressure', *J Food Prot*, 65(2), 345–352.

VAN WILLIGE, R W G and FITZGERALD, R J (1995), 'Tryptic and chymotryptic hydrolysis of β-lactoglobulin A, B and AB at ambient and high pressure', *Milchwiss*, 50(4), 183–186.

VARDAG, T, DIEKES, H and KÖRNER, P (1995), 'High pressure food processing', *Food Technol Europe* (Sept/Oct), 106–110.

VÉLEZ-RUIZ, J F, SWANSON, B G and BARBOSA-CANOVAS, G V (1998), 'Flow and viscoelastic properties of concentrated milk treated by high hydrostatic pressure', *Food Sci Technol*, 31, 182–195.

YOKOYAMA, H, SAWAMURA, N and MOTOBAYASHI, N (1992), 'Method for accelerating cheese ripening', *European Patent Application EP 0469857 A1*.

16

Optimising product quality and process control for powdered dairy products

R. E. M. Verdurmen and P. de Jong, NIZO Food Research, The Netherlands

16.1 Introduction: evaporation and drying processes

Fresh milk and dairy products have a high nutritional value, but as the products as such have a limited shelf-life they should be processed in order to become microbiologically stable. One of the widely used techniques for this is reducing the water content, and thereby the water activity, by concentration and drying. Another advantage of these water-removing techniques is the decrease in costs for storage and transportation by reduction of the product volume. The disadvantage, however, is that the energy consumption for drying is high; no other process in the dairy industry has such a high energy demand per tonne of finished product. This is due to the fact that approximately 90% of the milk is water, and practically all that water has to be removed by heat. The removal of water usually takes place in two stages. The first stage is concentration by vacuum evaporation and the second stage is drying; 90% of the water is removed in the evaporator and only 9–10% in the spray dryer when calculating the amount of water removal per dry mass. However, the energy required per kg water evaporated in the dryer is about 15 times the energy required per kg water removed in the evaporator (see also Table 16.1).

Besides the processing of the milk products, an important criterion for preservation by concentration and drying is the quality of the (recombined) product. Modern technologies are focused on minimising the loss of nutritive value, improving microbiological quality and improving the rehydration properties of the milk powder. Nowadays, optimal design by using predictive process and product models and advanced automation are the ingredients for producing high-quality products for the food market (De Jong and Verdurmen, 2001).

Table 16.1 Typical figures for the conversion from milk to milk powder

Product	Milk	Concentrated milk	Milk powder
Total solids (%)	10	50	96
kg water per kg total solids	11.1	1	0.04
Specific energy use for conversion (MJ/kg water evaporation)	0.3		4.4

16.1.1 Evaporation

In the dairy industry falling-film evaporators are commonly used and have practically replaced all other types. Falling-film evaporators operate as thin film evaporators, resulting in short retention times and gentle heat treatment. The heat exchange surface consists of a bundle of vertical tubes. In Fig. 16.1 a basic scheme is shown of a modern falling-film evaporator plant for concentration of milk products. In practice a large number of different evaporator configurations are used in the industry. For example, the number of evaporator effects (tube bundles) varies from one to seven. The actual configuration depends on the desired properties of the concentrate and the state of the art at the time of installation of the evaporation plant.

In order to obtain a high thermal efficiency in a number of cases the products are heated first in spiral tubes placed in the condenser and the evaporator effects. Before the product enters the evaporator effects, it is preheated to a temperature above the boiling temperature of the first effect. In general, the whole preheating trajectory has a great impact on the properties and quality of the concentrate and powder. To meet some quality standards, it can be necessary to use a direct heater (e.g. steam injection, steam infusion) to apply a short-time high-temperature treatment.

The product entering an effect of the falling-film evaporator is distributed (e.g. by distribution plate, see Fig. 16.2) over the bundle of evaporation tubes. The liquid is 'falling' as a film through the inner side of the tube. On the outer side of the evaporator tubes steam is condensing. The water evaporation, which usually takes place below 70–80°C, is based on the physical law that the boiling point of a liquid is lowered when the liquid is exposed to a pressure below atmospheric pressure (Bouman *et al.*, 1993). The vapour is separated from the product in a separator placed at the base of the effect and is used as the heating medium for the next effect. From the last effect, the vapour goes to the condenser. This can be an open condenser in which the product is condensed by direct contact with a water spray, but in modern evaporators the vapour is condensed using an indirect heat exchanger in order to reduce water usage. The boiling temperatures in the effects vary from 70–80°C in the first effect to 40–50°C in the last effect.

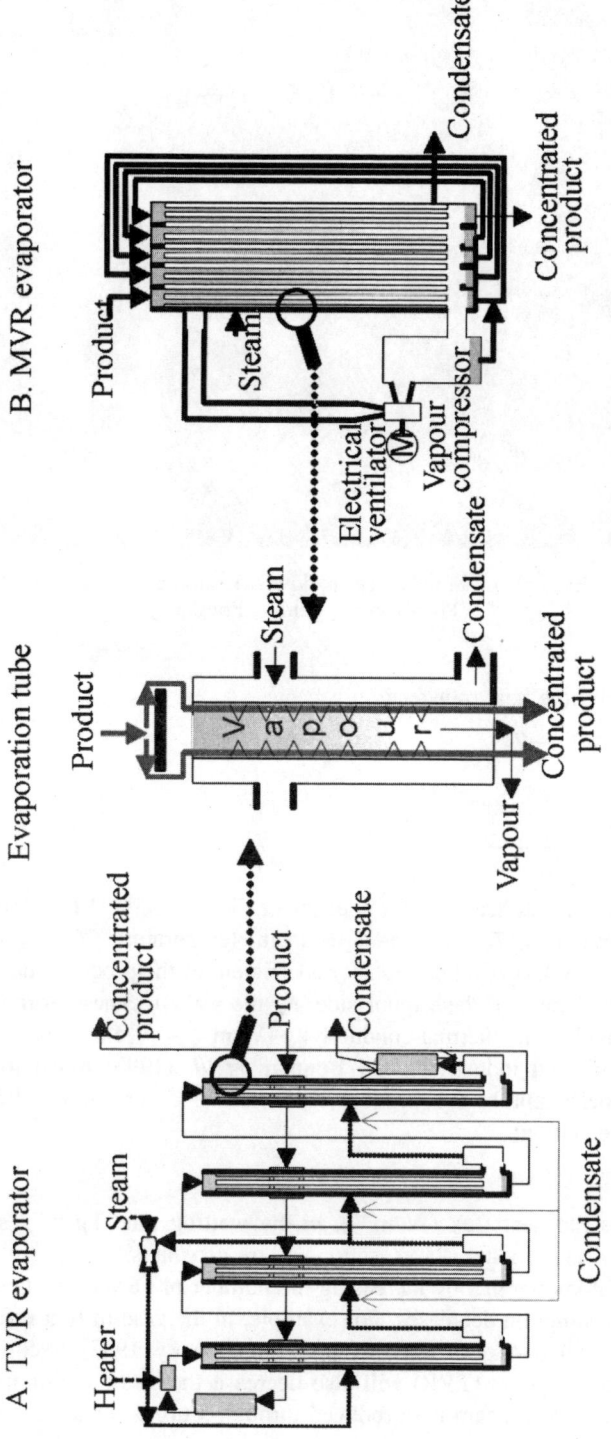

Fig. 16.1 Schematic representation of industrial configurations of falling-film evaporators.

Fig. 16.2   Example of an industrial liquid distribution device (courtesy of Carlisle
Processing Systems – Friesland).

Generally, the heat transfer is given by:

$$Q = kA(T_v - T_p) \qquad\qquad 16.1$$

where

$$\frac{1}{k} = \frac{1}{\alpha_p} + \frac{\delta_w}{\lambda_w} + \frac{1}{\alpha_v} \qquad\qquad 16.2$$

and k is the overall heat transfer coefficient (W m^{-2} s^{-1}), A the amount of heat
transfer area (m^2), T_v the vapour or steam temperature (°C), T_p the product
temperature (°C), α_p the heat transfer coefficient of the product side, α_v the heat
transfer coefficient of the vapour side, δ_w the wall thickness of the evaporator
tube (m), and λ_w its thermal conductivity (W m^{-2} s^{-1}). Based on a large set of
experimental and industrial data, Bouman *et al.* (1993) found that the heat
transfer coefficient at the product side can be described by the following
empirical equation:

$$\alpha_p = c_1 \cdot q^{c_2} \cdot m^{c_3} \cdot \eta_p^{c_4} \qquad\qquad 16.3$$

where q is the heat flux (W m^{-2}), m the wetting rate (kg m^{-1} s^{-1}), η_p the
viscosity of the product (Pa s), and c_1–c_4 are constants.

It is well known that by increasing the number of vacuum units (effects) the
energy consumption decreases. For example, in the case of four effects 1 kg of
steam results in 3–4 kg of water evaporation (Písecký, 1997). Recompression of
a part of the vapours (TVR) will also decrease the steam consumption. In the
thermocompressor steam is introduced through a nozzle creating a steam jet in

the mixing chamber, whereby vapour from the separator is sucked into the mixing chamber.

An indication of the energy consumption of a multi-stage falling-film evaporator with thermal vapour recompression can be calculated from:

$$E = \frac{\left(1 - \dfrac{DS_{in}}{DS_{out}}\right)\phi_{in}h_v}{N_{effects} + N_{effects,TVR}}$$ 16.4

where E is the energy consumption (J kg^{-1} raw material), DS the dry solids content of the raw material and the product (%), ϕ_{in} the flow of the raw material, h_v the heat evaporation (J kg^{-1}), $N_{effects}$ the total number of effects, and $N_{effects,TVR}$ the number of effects with thermal vapour recompression.

A more energy-efficient recompression method is the application of mechanical vapour recompression (MVR). In contrast to TVR, all the vapour is recompressed. Normally, the MVR evaporator consists of only one or two effects and the boiling temperature can be chosen depending on the desired product properties. Apart from the steam used for start-up, an MVR evaporator requires no steam and no cooling water. Modern MVR evaporators use a heavy-duty fan instead of a relatively complex compressor. This has resulted in diminishing investment costs and nowadays most of the new evaporators use MVR. In Table 16.2 compares the energy consumption of TVR evaporators and the latest generation of MVR evaporators (Vissers et al., 2002).

Depending on the desired product properties the concentrate from the last effect can be homogenised, heat-treated and/or crystallised. When the concentrated product is used for powder production the product is transported to a balance tank.

16.1.2   Drying
In the dairy industry drying of concentrate into powder is mainly done by spray drying. Spray drying is a relatively gentle drying process that has replaced the cheaper but also the more product-denaturing drum dryers. Moreover spray drying makes it possible to manufacture powder qualities for different applications and quality standards.

Table 16.2 Comparison between the energy consumption of TVR evaporators (six effects) and the latest generation of MVR evaporators. Figures based on 30–40 tonnes water evaporation per hour

Energy consumption (m^3 natural gas equivalents per tonne water evaporation)	TVR	MVR (new generation)
Specific steam consumption	10.8	0.5
Specific electricity consumption	0.8	3.0
Total specific energy consumption	11.6	3.5

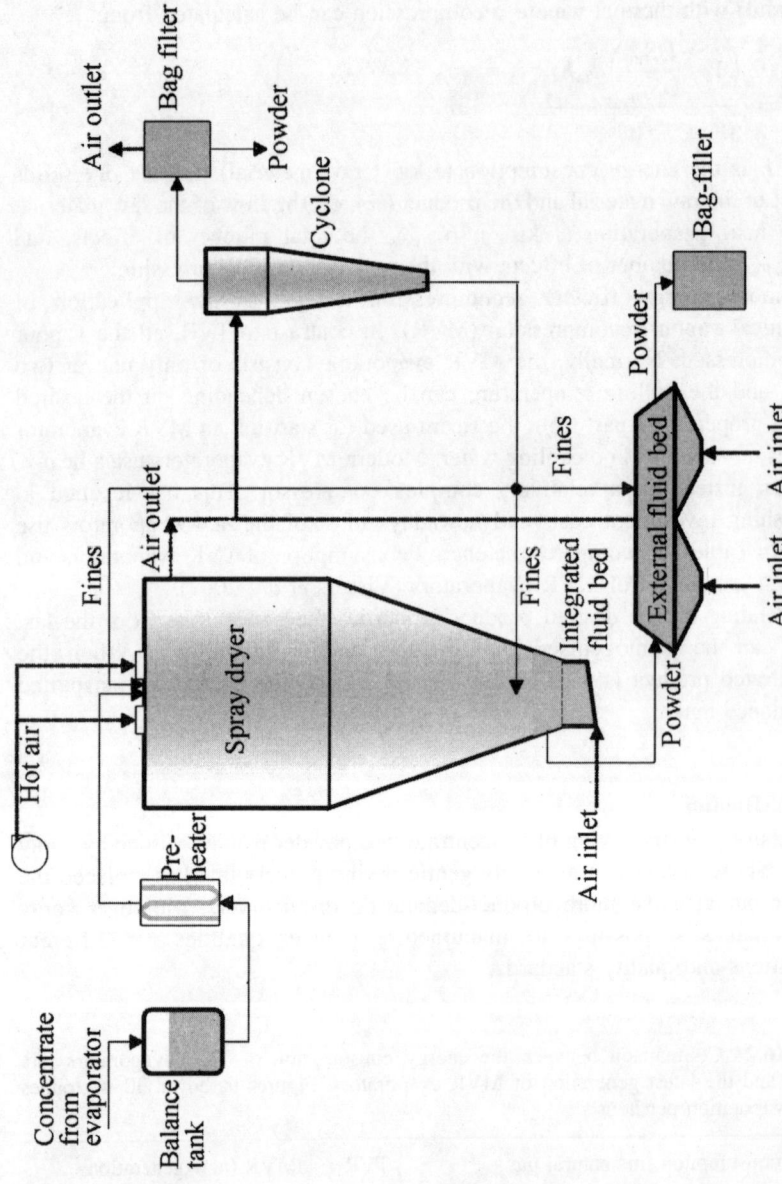

Fig. 16.3 Schematic representation of industrial configurations of spray dryers (single-, two- and three-stage).

In Fig. 16.3 the scheme of a multi-stage dryer is shown. In practice a spray dryer can consist of one, two or three stages. Multi-stage drying increases the thermal efficiency of the drying process (about 20% less energy, Filková and Mujumdar, 1995), produces agglomerated powder with good rehydration properties (see Section 16.2.2) and prevents overheating of powder particles (Písecký, 1997). In the first stage, the preheated product (<100°C) is sprayed by atomisation into a chamber filled with circulating hot air. The inlet temperature of the air is normally 150–250°C. By atomisation the concentrate is converted into droplets of 10–200 μm. In the industry two atomisation systems are used: stationary pressure nozzles and rotating atomisers. The droplets are flowing in the tower and adsorb heat necessary for evaporating the moisture. The moisture is removed by the hot air. Depending on the dimensions of the tower, the residence time of the powder particles is in the order of 5–30 seconds. The dried powder falls to the bottom of the dryer and is transported to the next drying stage

Fig. 16.4   The bottom of a spray chamber incorporating an internal fluid bed and an external fluid bed (courtesy of Anhydro A/S).

or to a packaging system. The exhaust air is removed through an outlet duct and passes through cyclones and filters where small powder particles (fines) are removed. The fines can be recycled to the top of the dryer or to other drying stages. The result is an agglomerated powder.

As said before, the first processing stage is done in the dryer chamber. For the next stages normally fluid-bed dryers are used, both internal in the drying chamber and external (see also Fig. 16.4). In the fluid bed a powder layer is formed of a defined height through which hot air (cooler than the tower hot air) is flowing. In certain cases the fluid bed is used to achieve some product trans-formations, for example lactose crystallisation in whey powder. Lecithination during drying in the external fluid bed is in some cases (e.g. whole milk powder) applied to improve instant properties. In the final part of the fluid bed the powder is cooled towards the packaging and storage temperature.

16.2　Quality criteria for dairy-based powders

Different aspects of the quality of dairy-based powders can be distinguished: microbiological quality, quality of physical properties and chemical quality.

16.2.1　Microbiological quality
The requirements for the microbiological quality of dairy-based powders depend partly on its intended use and partly on the manufacturing process. In this perspective it is of importance as to whether powder is an end-product and will be used for human consumption or whether it is an intermediate product that is subjected to heating after reconstitution (e.g. as an ingredient for other products). The reasons for milk powder to be microbiologically unacceptable or even a health risk can be of three kinds:

1.　The microbiological quality of the raw materials used. For example in fresh milk, heat resistant bacteria and bacterial spores can be present that are not inactivated by the heat treatments to which the milk is subjected before and after drying (Walstra *et al.*, 1999);
2.　Conditions during the various process steps before the formation of powder allow growth of some species. Especially thermophilic bacteria can grow in regenerative sections of heat exchangers and in evaporators (De Jong *et al.*, 2002a, 2002b);
3.　During powder manufacture, incidental contamination can occur at many places – in the spray dryer, in the fluid beds and during packaging. This can usually be avoided by taking appropriate hygienic measures.

16.2.2　Physical powder properties
Many physical powder properties can be influenced by certain pretreatment processes, by choosing the conditions for evaporation and spray drying and by

applying various post-drying treatments. The most important physical powder properties are listed below and how these properties can be influenced is briefly discussed.

Moisture content

The moisture content of a powder is often subject to (legal) product specifications defining the maximum moisture content. This is based on the fact that too high a moisture content may result in inferior shelf-life due to non-enzymatic browning (Maillard) reaction, creation of lumps and possibly microbiological problems. Too low a moisture content may in some cases result in an increased fat oxidation rate (Labuza, 1971; Van Mil and Jans, 1991). It is therefore very important to control the end moisture content of spray dried powder, not only in view of quality but also for manufacturing economics. When two- and multi-stage drying systems are used it is not just the end moisture content that must be strictly controlled; the moisture content of powder leaving the drying chamber (first stage of the drying process) is also important (Masters, 1991).

The moisture content of powder is influenced by a combination of factors involving feed properties (total solids content, temperature), atomisation conditions and most importantly the conditions of the drying air (inlet and outlet temperature of the drying chamber and fluid beds). The influence of the most important factors on the moisture content can be computed using heat and mass balances (Straatsma et al., 1991).

Insolubility index

When milk powders are reconstituted and centrifuged, some insoluble fraction can be observed. This is considered as a quality defect. Several methods have been developed to determine the insolubility of milk powders. The most well-defined method is the International Dairy Federation's method for the determination of the 'insolubility index' (IDF, 1988).

The mechanism by which insoluble material is formed is not yet fully understood. The current view is that the mechanism involves the unfolding of β-lactoglobulin, followed by aggregation with casein, but it appears that also other mechanisms play a role. The main factor controlling the insolubility index is the particle temperature during the drying stage when the moisture content is between 10% and 30%. Straatsma et al. (1999b) developed a kinetic model that predicts the insolubility index as a function of temperature and particle diameter.

Bulk density

Bulk density expresses the weight of a volume unit of powder and is expressed in kg/m^3. Bulk volume is also often used in the milk powder industry and is expressed as a volume in ml of 100 g of powder. Bulk density of dairy-based powders is a very important property from the point of view of economy, functionality and market requirements. High bulk densities save in packaging materials. Agglomeration may result in a low bulk density and is an important

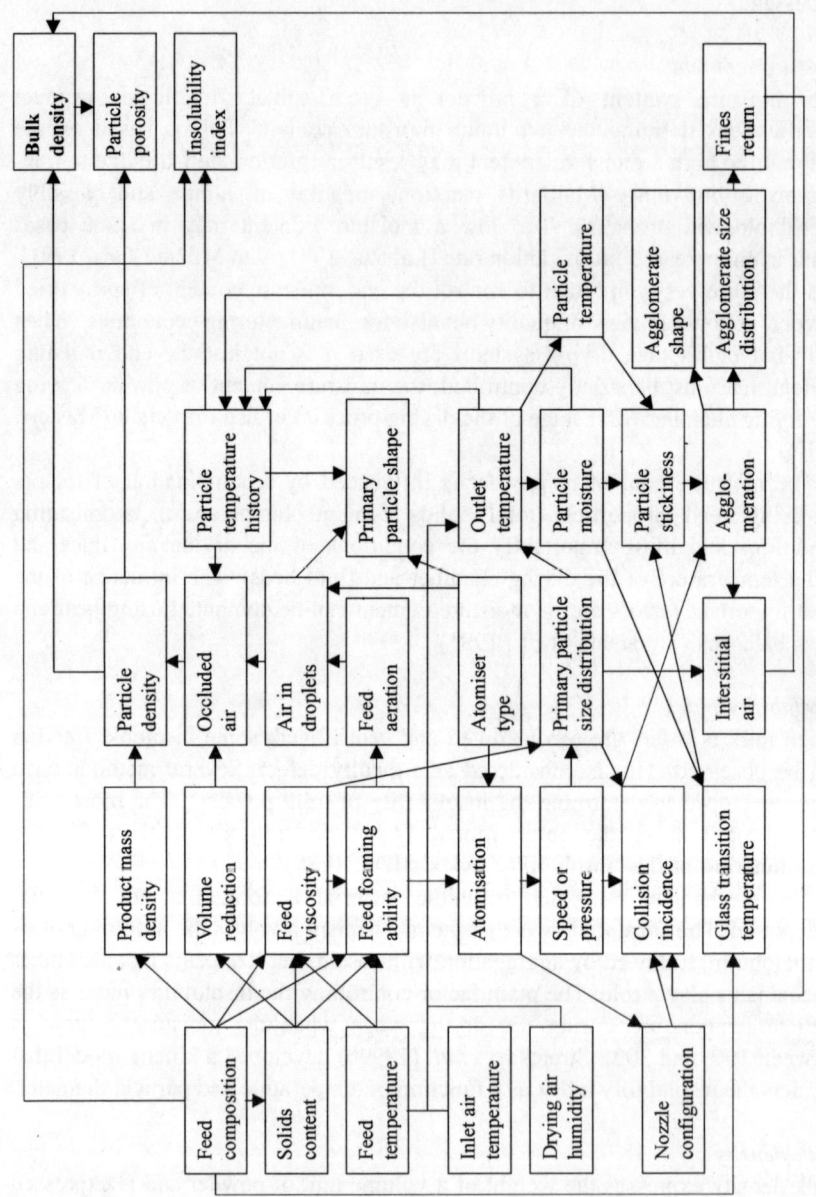

Fig. 16.5 The effect of various parameters on agglomeration and powder properties (adapted from Písecký, 1997).

factor influencing other product properties, such as flowability and instant properties. The bulk density is influenced by numerous factors as shown in Fig. 16.5. The primary factors determining bulk density are the density of the solids, the amount of air entrapped in the powder particles (occluded air) which is also reflected in the particle density and the interstitial air, i.e. the air between the particles or agglomerates (Písecký, 1997).

Agglomeration is a size enlargement process of powders, where small particles combine to form large relatively permanent masses, in which the original particles are still identifiable. In this way, the characteristics of a single particle are maintained while the bulk density is decreased by the creation of the larger agglomerates. The rehydration behaviour – the so-called instant properties – of the powder is improved because the open porous structure of the agglomerate allows water to penetrate to the particles it is originally constituted from, forcing the particle to sink. In this way, better dissolution behaviour is obtained compared to dissolving separate particles. For retention of the instant properties of the powder the mechanical strength of the agglomerate plays an important role. Low mechanical strength leads to falling apart of the agglomerate into its constituent particles when attrition forces during transport or storage are applied, thus deteriorating the instant and the flowability properties, whereas too high a mechanical strength gives a very limited dispersibility.

Agglomeration in spray dryers can be achieved by different methods. In the drying chamber agglomeration can take place within the spray of an atomiser, between sprays of various atomisers and between sprays and dry material being introduced into the drying chamber. Also agglomeration on a fluid bed, static bed or perforated belt (outside the spray chamber) is possible. Two types of agglomeration processes can be distinguished:

1. Primary agglomeration, caused by collision of primary spray particles with each other
2. Secondary agglomeration caused by collision of primary spray particles with fines.

Both processes can be either spontaneous (random unprovoked collisions) or forced. Forced primary agglomeration occurs when sprays from different nozzles collide. Forced secondary agglomeration takes place when fines from the spray dryer outlet are returned to the atomisation zone.

Several designs have been presented in order to establish the formation of ideal agglomerates by optimising the position of returning fines to the atomisation zone, by optimising the distance between the spray nozzles and the fluid bed for optimal stickiness of the particles in the fluid bed, or by adjusting the spray nozzles. In the latter case, the spray nozzles are adjusted in such a way that their spray patterns intersect at a location distant enough from the nozzles to prevent the formation of lumps, at the point where the particles are sticky enough to form agglomerates upon collision. In Fig. 16.6 a novel design is presented, where the pitch of the nozzle sticks can be changed to influence the degree of agglomeration.

Fig. 16.6 Nozzle set (three nozzle sticks and one central fines return) having the possibility to alter the pitch of the nozzles relative to the fines return. Narrow pitch (left) will lead to maximal primary and secondary agglomeration. Wide pitch and switching off fines return to the atomisation zone (right) will lead to minimal primary agglomeration and no secondary agglomeration (courtesy of Carlisle Processing Systems – Friesland, patent pending).

Flowability

Good flowability is especially important when the powder will be processed or used without mechanical handling and dosing devices. Examples of applications that require good flowability are powders to be used in coffee vending machines and milk replacers used by farmers for feeding calves. Flowability can be influenced by the following factors:

- Particle size distribution, amongst others influenced by agglomeration
- Free fat content of the powders
- Addition of free-flowing agents, e.g. silicates.

Free fat

Traditionally, the term 'free fat' has unfavourable associations in terms of shelf-life (oxidation), instant properties and deterioration of flowability. The term 'free-fat' actually means extractable fat; methods for the determination of free fat are based on contact extraction of powder by an organic solvent (e.g. carbon tetrachloride or petroleum ether). Many different methods are used for the determination of 'free-fat', which makes comparison difficult when the extraction method is not specified. Buma (1971) developed a physical model, dividing the extractable fat in four forms, which made the term 'free-fat' more comprehensible:

1. *Surface fat* present at pools or patches of fat on the powder surface.

2. *Outer layer fat*, consisting of fat globules in the surface layer of the powder particles, which can be released directly by fat solvents.
3. *Capillary fat*, consisting of fat globules inside the powder particles, which can be reached by fat solvents via capillary pores or cracks.
4. *Dissolution fat*, consisting of fat globules inside the powder particles, which can be reached by fat solvents via the holes left by dissolved fat globules in the outer particle layer or close to wide capillaries in the powder particles (also called 'second echelon fat').

Factors controlling the level of free fat are amongst others:

*   Total fat content of the powder. Below approximately 26% fat, the free fat content is low but above this level it increases rapidly (Kelly *et al.*, 2002).
*   Storage conditions of the powder. If lactose crystallises, due to moisture absorption from the surroundings, the free fat increases sharply (Buma, 1971).
*   Total solids content of feed to dryer. Snoeren *et al.* (1983) found that increasing the viscosity of the feed resulted in a reduction of free fat.
*   Homogenisation of the concentration before spray drying reduced the free fat content (De Vilder, 1979).

Instant properties
Instant properties (also called reconstitution properties) involve the ability of the powder to dissolve quickly and completely in water. This ability features a rather complicated mechanism. Each individual particle has initially to be wetted, then to sink into the liquid in order to be finally dissolved. The most important instant properties are wettability and dispersibility (IDF, 1979), but many other tests have also been developed, e.g. slowly dissolving particles, coffee test, white flecks number (IDF, 1995) and sludge. Instant properties can be improved by agglomeration, which alters the physical state of the powder to such an extent that the rates of wetting, sinking and dispersing increase. Whole milk can furthermore be 'instantised' by spraying lecithin on the agglomerated powder.

16.2.3   Chemical quality
Protein denaturation
Heat treatment of the original dairy liquid, concentrate or drying droplet can cause denaturation of serum (or whey) proteins, although the conditions during drying and concentration are rarely such as to cause extensive heat denaturation (Walstra *et al.*, 1999). This means that the main operation to adjust the required denaturation of whey proteins is the pasteurisation/heating process prior to concentration. The whey protein nitrogen (WPN) index is usually applied to classify milk powders according to the intensity of the heat treatment used in manufacturing the powder (ADMI, 1971).

The WPN index is an important quality mark in connection with the use of milk powder. If the reconstituted powder is used for cheese manufacture, the amount of denatured whey proteins should be as low as possible, i.e. low heat milk powder (WPN index $\geq$ 6) should be used. High heat milk powder (WPN index $\leq$ 1.5) is used, for example, for producing milk chocolate.

Fat oxidation
For diary products containing fat (e.g. whole milk powder) an important aspect of shelf-life is to prevent fat oxidation. Oxidation of fat will lead to the formation of degradation products, eventually leading to the development of various off-flavours. An important aspect of fat oxidation is that it is auto-catalytic. The rate of oxidation is usually slow at the beginning and increases as the reaction progresses (Labuza, 1971). The initial reaction rate is often so slow that there is an induction period at the beginning where the rate is too small to be measured. Factors controlling fat oxidation are amongst others:

- Presence of trace metals. Several metals that possess two or more valency states both decrease the induction period and increase the rate of oxidation. The metals include cobalt (Co), iron (Fe), copper (Cu), nickel (Ni) and manganese (Mn) as well as others of minor importance.
- Degree of unsaturation of fatty acids. In general it can be stated that the higher the degree of unsaturation of a fatty acid, the higher is its relative rate of oxidation. This is of special importance for dairy-based powders that contain vegetable fats or other added fats (e.g. with high amounts of polyunsaturated fatty acids).
- Oxygen concentration. Decreasing the oxygen concentration reduces the rate of fat oxidation. For this reason, oxidation sensitive dairy based powders (e.g. infant milk formulae) are packed in tins or pouches and are usually gassed with a mixture of nitrogen (N_2) and carbon dioxide (CO_2) to decrease the oxygen content below a level of 2–3%.
- Amount of anti-oxidants present in the powder. Anti-oxidants do not improve the quality of the product, but maintain it by preventing oxidation of labile lipid components. Examples of anti-oxidants are α-tocopherol, ascorbic acid and β-carotene. Free sulphydryl-groups (SH-groups) which are created in milk by high heat treatment (e.g. 30 seconds at 110°C) also seem to have anti-oxidative properties in the powder produced from it (McCluskey *et al.*, 1997).
- Water activity or moisture content. Dehydration of foods is a good method to enhance shelf-life. However, it has been found that if food is dried to too low a moisture content (less than 2–3%), it becomes very susceptible to oxidation (Labuza, 1971). Van Mil and Jans (1991) found that the peroxide value (an oxidation product) of whole milk powder increased more rapidly at a moisture content of 2.4% than at a moisture content of 3.0%.
- Temperature. Chemical reactions proceed faster when the temperature is increased. Van Mil and Jans (1991) found that an increase in storage temperature from 20°C to 35°C resulted in faster fat oxidation.

16.3   Modelling quality

16.3.1   General approaches

In the dairy industry the evaporator and the dryer are controlled separately. Both the control of the evaporator and the control of the dryer are directed mainly on moisture content. To obtain a high-quality powder, it is necessary to maintain a constant dry matter content in the concentrate produced in the evaporator preceding the drying process. Changes in dry matter content in the feed to the dryer are one of the major sources of disturbance in the drying process. It is also advantageous to remove as much water as possible at the evaporation stage from an energy-saving point of view. In practice, however, due to variations that occur in dry matter content of the concentrate as a consequence of variations in feed and process variables, the set-point for this dry matter content is often lower than theoretically possible, in order to reduce the risk of too high a viscosity of the concentrate. Less variation in dry matter content of the concentrate enables a higher set-point and thus also improves the energy efficiency of the powder production process. In closely coupled production lines the production rate of the evaporator and the dryer should be balanced. Most drying processes either are controlled by the feed rate or require a constant feed rate. The concentrate flow from the evaporator should closely match this rate in order to avoid the need for large buffers.

The control of evaporators is focused mainly on a constant flow rate and dry matter content of the concentrate. Where multiple-effect falling-film evaporators are to be controlled, evaporators should be viewed as complex interacting systems. The commonly used conventional control technology, such as single-loop proportional integral and derivative controllers, will therefore perform poorly compared to multivariable controllers. Modern multivariable robust control design methods make it possible to design compensators that optimise performance objectives under uncertainty about the exact plant behaviour. Central in this approach is the process model or predictive model, partly for the transfer of the control inputs to the process outputs and partly for the process transfer from the measured disturbance (dry matter content of the feed) to the process outputs (Schaafsma *et al.*, 1997).

16.3.2   State of the art of mathematical models used for control

Black box models

Black box models such as neural network and fuzzy logic models are data-driven. In principle, physical laws are ignored. These black box models have no mechanistic basis and are very specific for the process and product trained for. Training is performed by fitting the (numerous) model constants with a huge data set of measured process and product data. In the case of fuzzy logic models it is possible to translate qualitative relations (expert knowledge) into linguistic rules. These rules avoid the model producing unrealistic numbers just outside the model training area. For example, if *temperature* is *high* then *bacterial product load* is *high*.

The main advantage of black box models is the simplicity of developing them, even for complex phenomena such as taste development. Once there is enough data, the computer tools, with some expert help, can make a model within minutes. However, even one small change in the process equipment or the composition of the raw materials means that the model must be trained again. In most cases, this makes black box models interesting for the control only of those processes and bulk products that show no variation in requirements. The only known successful applications are the control of the total solids content of the concentrate leaving evaporators and of the moisture content of bulk powders from spray dryers.

Predictive models
Traditionally (food) science is focused on white box modelling, mostly represented as a hypothesis. In principle, only models based on chemical and physical phenomena and theories can be indicated as predictive. Although no model is a real white box model, it can be stated that predictive models have a more or less white box nature. With the increasing number of models becoming available to the industry, predictive models are being introduced more and more in the research and development of new products and processes. Examples are the fouling model for the design of heat exchangers and evaporators, the contamination model for the production of high-quality food products in a factory, the prediction of the formation of taste attributes in cheeses during ripening, etc.

Reaction kinetic approach
To describe the transformation of food products during processing, good results are obtained with reaction kinetic modelling techniques. The model consists of a set of reaction rate equations based on a reaction scheme that implies a mechanistic hypothesis. Depending on the application, this set might be very simple or very complex.

During processing, raw materials behave like a complex reaction system. A large number of chemical, physical and biochemical reactions take place. Some of these transformations are important because they change those product characteristics that are easily recognised by a consumer. Examples are inactivation of enzymes, denaturation of proteins, loss of nutrients and formation of new components. In general, most of these reactions can be described by nth-order reactions (single or consecutive):

$$\frac{dC_1}{dt} = k_n C_1^n, \quad \frac{dC_1}{dt} = k_n C_1^n - k_m C_2^m, \quad \text{etc.} \qquad 16.5$$

A large amount of kinetic data of several food components has been collected. Models available (De Jong, 1996) are the protein fouling model, models for bacterial spores (quality related), models for vitamin breakdown, models for enzyme inactivation (shelf-life related), models for protein denaturation and aggregation, and models for protein breakdown. Examples of more complex mechanistic models are the polymerisation model for prediction of heat-induced protein denaturation and viscosity changes in milk and milk concentrates (De Jong and Van der Linden, 1998) and reaction models of the non-enzymatic browning (Maillard) process (Brands, 2002).

Reaction kinetic modelling can also be used for product–process interaction such as fouling and biofouling in preheating equipment and falling-film evaporators upstream of the spray dryer. Figures 16.7 and 16.8 show the underlying mechanisms. For example, based on this reaction mechanism De Jong *et al.* (1992) developed a predictive fouling model based on the following reaction scheme:

$$[\text{native } \beta\text{-lg}] \xrightarrow{k_1} [\text{unfolded } \beta\text{-lg}] \xrightarrow{k_2} [\text{aggregated } \beta\text{-lg}]$$

$$[\text{unfolded } \beta\text{-lg}] \xrightarrow{k_3} [\text{aggregates of milk components}] \qquad 16.6$$

$$[\text{aggregates of milk components}] \xrightarrow{k_4} [\text{deposits}]$$

where β-lg stands for β-lactoglobulin, a reactive protein in milk, and k_1–k_4 are reaction rate constants depending on temperature. The protein denaturation affects the product texture while the amount of deposits affects the heat transfer and indirectly the process economics. This model has been used for optimising dairy production plants by relating the amount of deposits to operating costs (De Jong, 1996). The same approach was applied for biofouling and resulted in a model that predicts the contamination in powders as a result of adherence and growth of bacteria upstream of the spray dryer (De Jong *et al.*, 2002a). An example of contamination prediction in equipment upstream of the spray dryer is

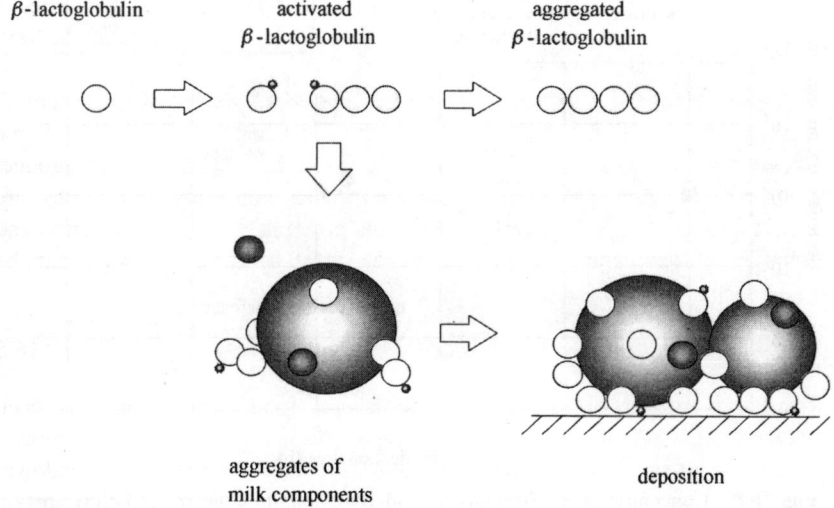

Fig. 16.7 Reaction kinetic representation of the fouling process in heating equipment.

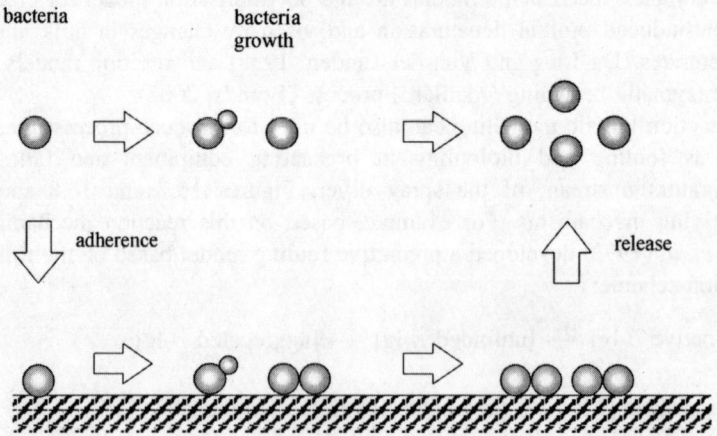

Fig. 16.8   Reaction kinetic representation of the biofouling and contamination process in heating equipment.

given in Fig. 16.9. White box models are excellent for modelling process and product development. The model constants have a physical meaning and are not dependent on process design. The main disadvantage of white box models is the time of development; however, an increasing number of white box models are becoming available.

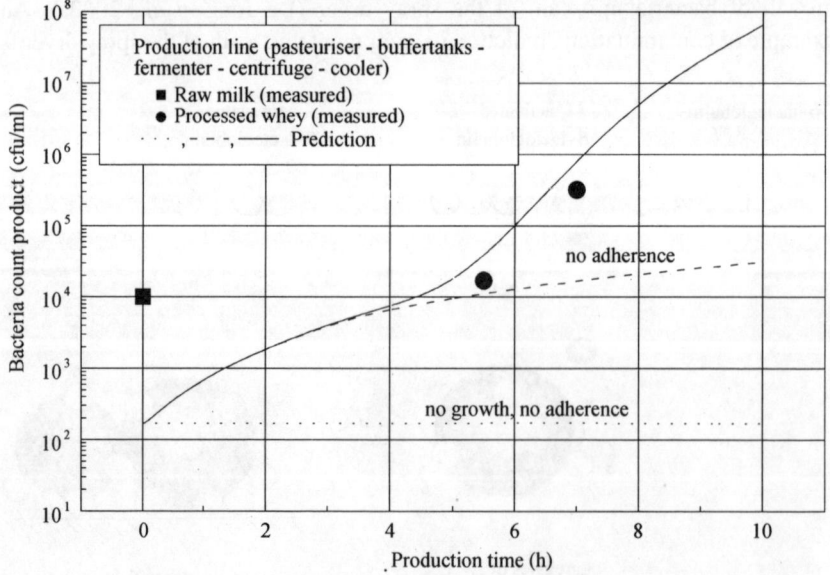

Fig. 16.9   Concentration of *Streptococcus thermophilus* in concentrate before spray drying related to the operating time: effect of local adherence and growth in the processing equipment.

Advanced models: Computational Fluid Dynamics

Computational Fluid Dynamics (CFD) has grown from a mathematical curiosity to become an essential tool in almost every branch of fluid dynamics. It allows for a deep analysis of the fluid mechanics and local effects in a lot of equipment. Most of the CFD results will give improved performance, better reliability, more confident scale-up, improved product consistency and higher plant productivity. However, it is only in recent years that CFD has been applied in the food processing area (Xia and Sun, 2002). CFD has been used to investigate the performance and design of dryers in the food industry. However, the design of spray dryers is heavily influenced by the complexity of air and spray flow patterns inside the dryers. Therefore, there is considerable scope for the application of CFD simulation, including optimum design of spray dryers and solutions for operational problems, such as wall deposition. Straatsma *et al.* (1999a, 1999b) developed a drying model utilising a turbulence model to calculate the gas flow field and showed that the drying model was an effective tool in giving indications how to adapt industrial dryers to obtain a better product quality or to optimise the drying performance of the unit.

During spray drying, agglomerates of powder particles are formed (see Fig. 16.10) which determine the instant properties of the powder (i.e. the ability to dissolve easily, quickly and completely). Agglomeration during spray drying is considered to be a difficult process to control. The main cause of this is the complex interaction of the process variables: the atomisation process, the mixing of spray and hot air and the collision of particles. As a consequence, agglomeration during spray drying is often regarded as a black box and is operated by trial-and-error.

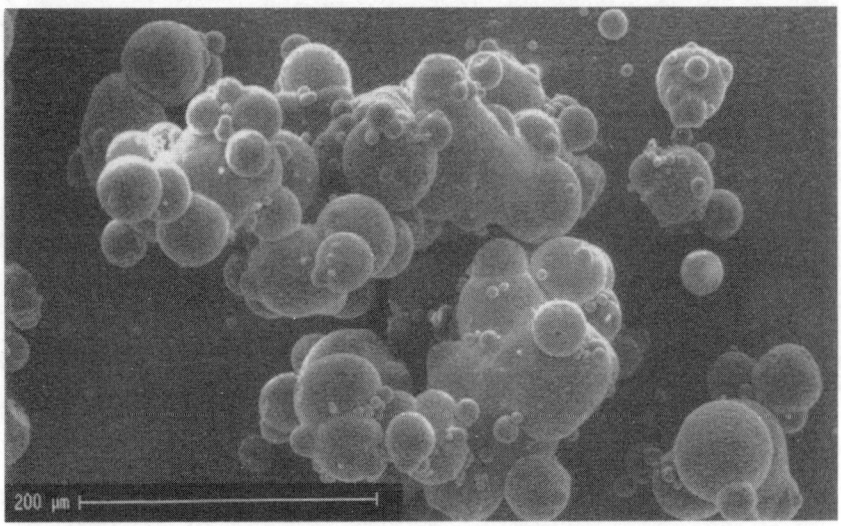

Fig. 16.10 SEM-photograph of spray dried and agglomerated powder.

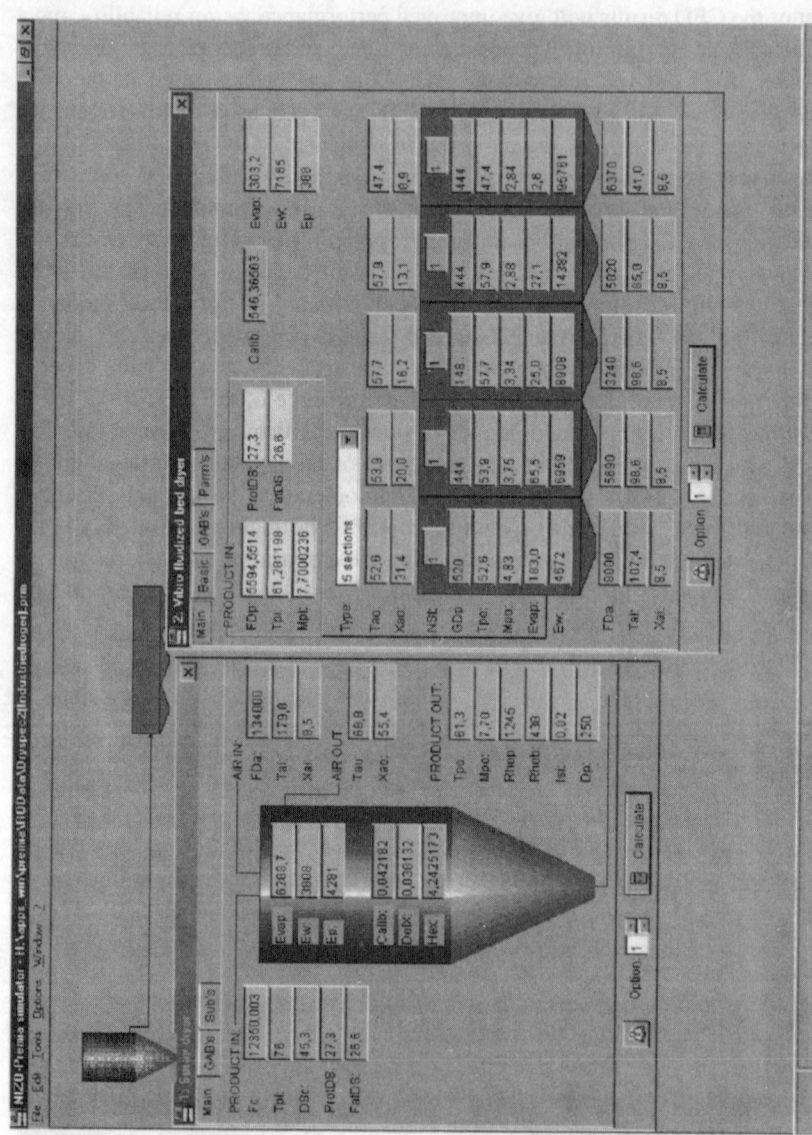

Fig. 16.11   The Premia flow sheeting system for parallel process and product evaluation (shown: DrySpec2).

It turns out that with CFD it is possible to predict agglomeration processes in spray drying machines (EDECAD, 2001). Based on the CFD model a second model is developed which establishes relations between the configuration of the drying installation (geometry, nozzle selection), process conditions, product composition and final powder properties. Important steps in the formation of agglomerated powders are atomisation, the mixing of spray and gas (collision of droplets, drying) and agglomeration of sticky particles. This second model can be used for control purposes.

Flow-sheeting and predictive models
The powder properties cannot be addressed to one mechanism or one unit-operation. This means that for the prediction of powder properties different models have to be coupled. For example, the production of milk powder is facilitated by a chain of unit-operations: standardisation, preheating, evaporation, etc. The composition of the raw materials and the applied preheating conditions affects the denaturation degree of the proteins. The denaturation degree affects the viscosity of the concentrate at the outlet of the evaporator and the solubility of the powder. The viscosity affects the droplet size distribution after atomisation in the spray dryer. The process operation also influences the operation costs.

For the dairy industry a (flow sheeting) system called Premia has been developed that enables the coupling of a variety of unit-operations generating a complete production chain (Smit *et al.*, 2001). In a library of product models (e.g. bacteria inactivation, enzyme inactivation, microbial spore inactivation, contamination, protein deposition, destruction of vitamins, formation of Maillard products, viscosity change, etc.) the connection is made between process operation and product properties. In Fig. 16.11 a screen shot of the Premia system is given, showing, for example, the spray dry module DrySpec2 (Straatsma *et al.*, 1991).

16.4   Process and product control

The main issue of the automatic control of spray dryers is a constant level of the moisture content of the powder. As illustrated in Fig. 16.12 a reduced standard deviation of the moisture content minimises the operating costs. Particularly in drying processing there is a trend to use more and more predictive models in the control strategy (see Fig. 16.13). In most cases these models are first-principle or neural network models (respectively the white and black box approaches). Only a few first-principle approaches have been described in the literature (Alderlieste *et al.*, 1984; Chen, 1994; Delemarre, 1994; Pérez-Correa and Farías, 1995). All these references are directed on moisture content only. Since more and more (predictive) models become available, it is possible to design control procedures focused on other powder properties such as insolubility and stickiness.

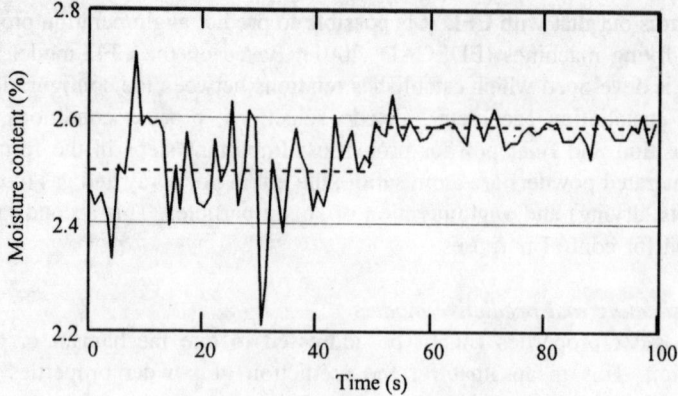

Fig 16.12   The effect of a well-defined automatic controller on the moisture content of powder, thereby reducing the operating costs.

Table 16.3 compares control approaches of predictive models and black box models. The predictive model approach is more flexible and robust to handle changes in the design and process operation. The advantage of the black box approach is that it needs less knowledge about the design and operation of the process equipment; an example for an evaporator is described by Verdurmen *et al.* (2002). Since the neural network approach is still considered as a special field of expertise, manufacturers of dryer installations have initiated cooperation with specialised software-houses.

16.4.1   On-line monitoring of moisture content of powder

The classical control strategy of spray dryers is based on the PID concept (Stapper, 1979). Modern dryers use the moisture content measured by infrared, resistive or capacitive measurements as a control variable. Manipulated variables are the thermal flux (air temperature, gas flow rate) or the concentrate flow rate. The choice of the product flow rate as the manipulated variable is

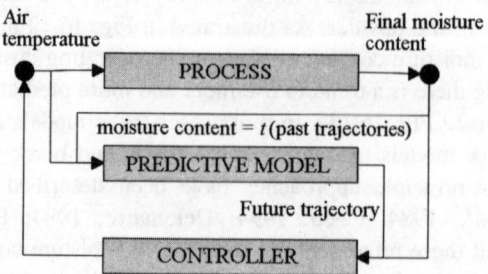

Fig 16.13   Example of a model-based control scheme.

Table 16.3 Comparison between two modelling approaches used for model-based control of dryers

Predictive model-based (first principle and reaction models)	Black box model-based (response and neural network models)
• Relatively high predictive power outside the operation point (location independent) • Process knowledge needed • Custom-made dryer models • Few measuring points needed	• Less predictive power outside the operation point (location dependent) • No process knowledge needed • Standard software tools available (process independent) • Many measuring points needed for model training • Training after every change in process configuration

generally cheaper but it should be avoided in case of continuous flow production because it modifies locally the production capacity and creates larger buffers. Continuous on-line monitoring allows a full realisation of process capability and operation of the spray dryer closer to the upper specification limits of the dryer. Over-drying, which can cause damage to the product, is avoided and both production yield and productivity are maximised. In addition, the optimum product shelf-life is achieved and avoidance of over-drying provides a saving on energy costs. Amongst others, NIR techniques provide continuous, high-speed measurements of the moisture content of milk and other powders (see also Chapter 21). In addition, measurement of protein and fat content in milk powder is also feasible. An example of an on-line NIR gauge mounted below an industrial fluid-bed dryer (part of a spray dryer for milk powder) is given in Fig. 16.14. The possibility of measuring the moisture content of powder on-line also enables a feedback signal to be given to the control system of the dryer.

16.4.2 Predictive model-based control

Predictive models as described turn out to be an effective tool to translate scientific knowledge to practical applications in the food factories. The most effective way to ensure the benefits of using predictive models would be to integrate them into process control systems. Based on actual process data and the composition of the raw materials, the models can predict the state of the process (e.g. amount of fouling, biofilm thickness, energy usage) and the state of product (degree of contamination, stability, texture). This means that the process can be controlled on product specifications instead of process conditions. By adding cost-related models the system can continuously optimise the production process with respect to the product quality and the production costs (De Jong *et al.*, 2002c).

Fig. 16.14   On-line NIR gauge mounted below a fluid bed (Courtesy of NDC Infrared Engineering).

In Fig. 16.15 this approach is shown in general terms. Based on process design (e.g. dimensions, apparatus configuration, in-line measured process conditions) the temperature–time history of the product is calculated with the process model. Together with the given composition this information is used to predict the product properties using the kinetic product models. In addition the operating costs per tonne of product are estimated based on the fouling and contamination models. The predicted product properties are compared with the given desired product properties. In the optimisation module the production process set-points are optimised to meet the desired product properties as closely as possible with minimum operating costs.

In the ideal situation the process is controlled based on the desired product specifications and minimum operating costs. The system corrects itself automatically when:

- Fouling changes the temperature–time history of the concentrate at the inlet of the spray dryer
- The product specifications change
- The composition of the raw materials changes
- Disturbances occur (e.g. temperature changes, flow instabilities).

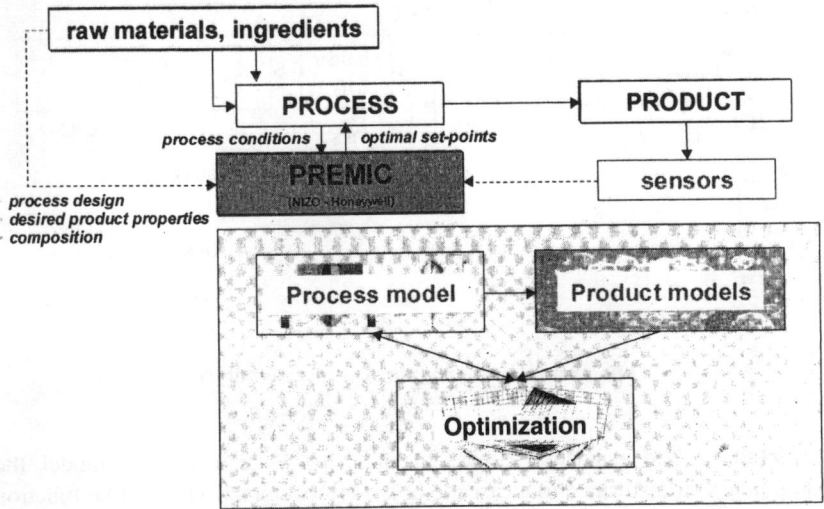

Fig. 16.15   Schematic representation of the PREMIC control system (PREdictive Models for Industrial Control).

Optimisation algorithm

An essential part of the control procedure based on predictive models is the optimisation module. The main control factors for product and process optimisation are the temperature–time relationship and the configuration of the processing equipment. In order to determine the optimal values of the control variables, a general objective function is used:

$$F(u,x) = \alpha c_{\text{quality}}(u,x) + \beta c_{\text{operation}}(u)$$ 16.7

where u is a vector of process control variables (e.g. temperature, flow) and x is a vector of desired product properties related to food quality and safety. The value of c_{quality} depends on the outcomes of the predictive models for contamination and transformation of food components, and $c_{\text{operation}}$ is related to the operating costs. The optimal configuration and operation of a production chain is achieved by minimisation of the objective function. To avoid trivial and undesired solutions, the weight factors α and β are introduced. These weight factors give the relative importance of each term of the objective function. For example, too high a value of β may result in a very clean and cheap production process but an inferior product quality.

Example of process and product optimisation

To illustrate the application of the procedure described for optimising food production chains, the following case study has been performed. A heating process with a capacity of 40 tonnes skim milk per hour consists of a regenerative section, a heating section and two holding sections and a cooler. In Fig. 16.16 the scheme of the process is shown with some preliminary

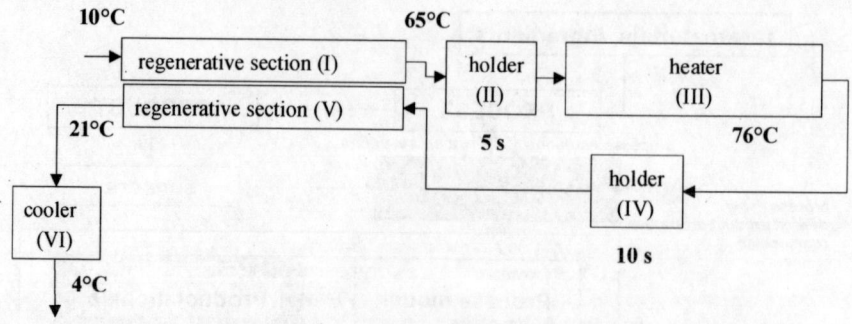

Fig. 16.16   Example process (upstream dryer).

temperatures and residence times. In order to have a process model the equipment is transformed to a cascade of model reactors. The objective function is defined as:

$$F(u, x) = \sum_{i=1}^{3} \alpha_i \left(\frac{x_{ides} x_i(\mathbf{u})}{x_{ides}} \right)^2 + F_{cost} \qquad 16.8$$

where

$$F_{cost} = \frac{c_{operation} \cdot t_{operation} + c_{solids} \cdot t_{production} \cdot \iint_{x,t} J_{x,t} \mathrm{d}t \ \mathrm{d}x}{t_{production} \cdot \phi} \qquad 16.9$$

where α_i is a weight factor for the relative importance of product property x_i, $x_{i,des}$ is the desired product property, $\mathbf{u}$ is the set of control variables, c are costs, t is time, the integral term is the total amount of deposits after 1 h of production, ϕ is the capacity of the process in tonnes per hour,

$$t_{production} = \frac{t_{operation} \cdot t_{run}}{t_{run} + t_{cleaning}} \qquad 16.10$$

and the production time per run:

$$t_{run} = t \quad \text{if } C_{s.thermophilus} > 0.0001 \text{ cfu ml}^{-1} \qquad 16.11$$

The weight factor α_i is introduced to avoid trivial and undesired solutions. The chosen values of the weight factors are determined by the relative importance of the different product properties. However, since the relationship between the weight factor values and the optimisation results are not clear in advance, the determination of the weight factor value is an iterative process in consultation with industrial experts.

In this case the control variables ($\mathbf{u}$) are limited to two: the heating temperature and the residence time at this temperature in the second holder section. With two control variables surface plots can present the results of the computer model simulations. Figure 16.17 shows the results of the objective function evaluations. The optimal set-points are a heating temperature of 78.7°C

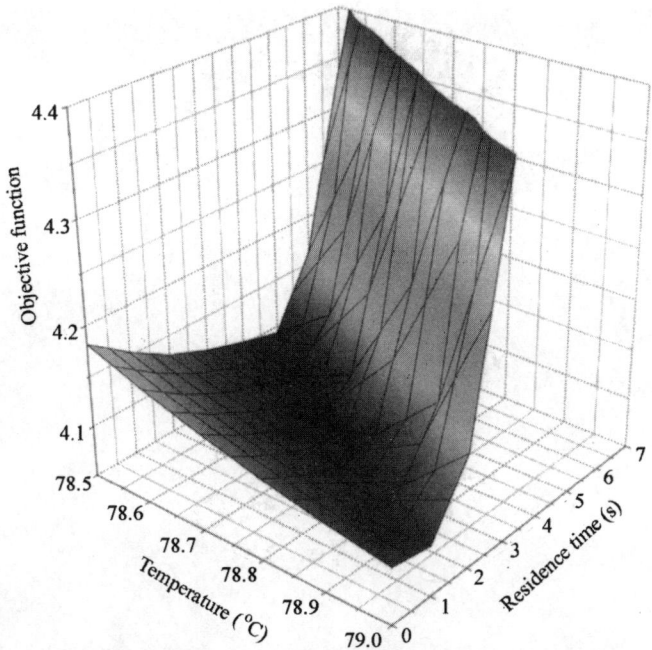

Fig. 16.17   Evaluation of the objective function.

and a residence time of 3 s. As compared to the initial preliminary design (10 s, 76°C) the operating costs could be decreased by 14%. At an annual production of 4700 h this means an estimated cost saving of Euro 58 000. More details are given by De Jong *et al.* (2002c). Detailed studies show that cost reductions of more than 50% are feasible (De Jong, 1996).

16.5   Ensuring process safety

One of the hazards in producing powders is fire in a drying installation. Fire and the resulting explosion risks can be reduced by taking technical and organisational measures (IDF, 1986). Fire and explosion protection can be obtained using relief venting, automatic suppression or inerting. Venting is the most frequently used method, see also Fig. 16.18. Protection by automatic suppression (see Fig. 16.19) is usually straightforward, although dryers of very large volume may present problems due to the airflow through the drying chamber removing the suppressant agent (Palmer, 1990). However, considerable damage may still result, because the available explosion or fire protection systems are only activated when the explosion or fire has actually started. About 80% of the recorded fires were preceded by smouldering of powder. Deposits of milk powder in spray dryers may undergo exothermic reactions between the milk constituents and this may lead to self-ignition and smouldering. Smouldering

Fig. 16.18 Inside of an industrial spray dryer with atomisation units at the top and explosion venting panels at the spray chamber wall (courtesy of Carlisle Processing Systems – Friesland).

deposits may, if the occasion arises, fall down and initiate an explosion in the lower part of the drying chamber (cone) where the dust concentration often considerably exceeds the lower explosion limit (Skov, 1986). Once the milk powder is smouldering it produces a significant amount of carbon monoxide (CO). It has been shown that this increase of CO can be detected by a sensitive CO analyser which makes it possible to detect a smouldering lump of powder before the powder actually takes fire (Steenbergen *et al.*, 1991). Figure 16.20 shows a part of the measuring system. The system comprises an air sample line from the inlet of the dryer, an air-treating unit for cleaning and drying the air issuing from the outlet of the dryer, a CO analyser and, if necessary, a control

Fig. 16.19 Commercial explosion suppression system mounted on top of a cyclone (courtesy of Anhydro A/S).

system for consecutive performance of the measuring cycle. Nowadays an increasing number of CO detection systems are operating on an industrial scale as early-warning systems for fire, and the CO detection system is linked to the control system of the dryer systems to perform automatic shutdown.

Requirements for the safety and health protection of workers potentially at risk from explosive atmospheres will become more strict from 1st July 2003 when the European Council Directive 1999/92/EC (also known as ATEX 137) will become operational. This directive, which makes area classification, documentation, inspection, verification, training and warning signs legal requirements, applies to all new hazardous area equipment from this date. Existing workplaces have a further three years before the full requirements of the directive are applied.

The employer is required to take all reasonable measures to prevent the formation of an explosive atmosphere in the workplace. Where this is not

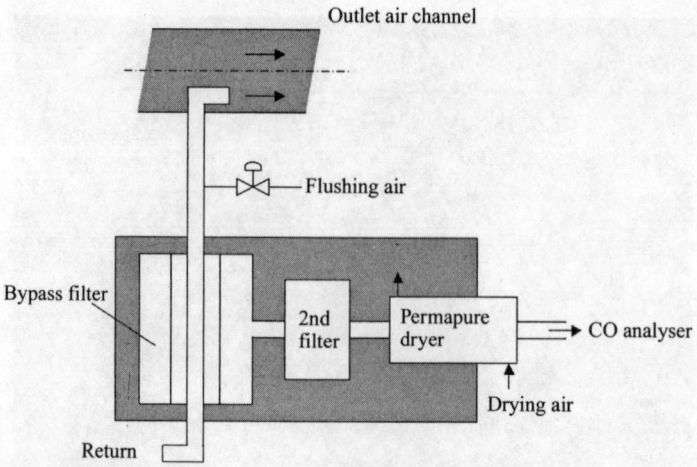

Fig.16.20   Set-up of a CO measuring system for dryers.

possible, measures must be taken to avoid the ignition of any potentially explosive atmosphere (prevention). Furthermore, the effects of any explosion must be minimised in such a way that workers are not put at risk (protection). The employer will be required to carry out an assessment of the likelihood that an explosive atmosphere will occur, likelihood of ignition and scale of effects. In carrying out this assessment the employer will be required to produce an Explosion Protection Document.

An EU-project group, 'Risk Assessment of Unit Operations and Equipment', reported on a risk assessment for spray dryers producing milk powder (RASE, 2000). They concluded that an explosive atmosphere in the form of a cloud of combustible milk powder in air is present continuously and cannot be eliminated. Consequently the prevention of ignition sources should have the highest priority and self-ignition of milk powder deposits is considered to be a major risk; other ignition sources are considered to be a minor risk. Reducing the risks caused by self-ignition focuses at eliminating fire events as much as possible by taking preventive fire and explosion measures, such as temperature monitoring, CO detection or fire suppression systems. These preventive measures should become part of the inherently safe design of the spray chamber, but should also be considered for the fluid beds and filters. In addition, protective systems should also be applied, for example pressure-relief systems or explosion suppression systems (RASE, 2000).

16.6   Sources of further information and advice

De Jong P and Verdurmen R E M (2001), 'Concentrated and dried dairy products', in Tamime A Y and Law B A, *Mechanisation and Automation in Dairy Technology*, Sheffield, Sheffield Academic Press, 95–118.

Masters K (1991), *Spray Drying Handbook,* New York, Longman Scientific & Technical.

Písecký J (1997), *Handbook of Milk Powder Manufacture*, Copenhagen, Niro A/S.

Walstra P, Geurts T J, Noomen A, Jellema A and Van Boekel M A J S (1999), *Dairy Technology,* New York, Marcel Dekker.

16.7   References

ADMI (1971), 'Standards for grades of dry milk including methods of analysis', Bulletin 916 (Revised), Chicago, American Dry Milk Institute.

ALDERLIESTE P J, FRANSEN J J and VAN BOXTEL A J B (1984), 'Control of moisture content of milk powder', *Voedingsmiddelentechnologie* 17(6), 21–23.

ALVES T L M, DA COSTA A C, DA SILVA-HENRIQUES A W and LIMA E L (1998), 'Adaptive optimal control of fed-batch alcoholic fermentation', *Appl, Biochem. Biotechnol.* 70–72, 463–478.

BELUHAN D and BELUHAN S (2000), 'Hybrid modeling approach to on-line estimation of yeast biomass concentration in industrial bioreactor', *Biotechnol. Lett.* 22, 631– 635.

BENNE M, GRONDIN-PEREZ B, CHABRIAT J P and HERVE P (2001), 'Artificial neural networks for modelling and predictive control of an industrial evaporation process', *J. Food Eng.* 46, 227–234.

BOUMAN S, LUND D B, DRIESSEN F M and SCHMIDT D G (1982), 'Growth of thermoresistant streptococci and deposition of milk constituents on plates of heat exchangers during long operating times', *J. Food Prot.* 45, 806–812.

BOUMAN S, WAALEWIJN R, DE JONG P and VAN DER LINDEN H J L J (1993), 'Design of falling-film evaporators in the dairy industry', *J. Soc. Dairy Techn.* 46, 100–106.

BRANDS C (2002), 'Kinetic modelling of the Maillard reaction between proteins and sugar', Ph.D. thesis, Wageningen University, The Netherlands.

BUMA T J (1971), 'Free fat and physical structure of spray-dried whole milk', Ph.D. thesis, Wageningen University, The Netherlands.

CHEN X D (1994), 'Towards a comprehensive model-based control of milk drying processes', *Drying Technology* 12, 1105–1130.

CORRIEU G, TRELEA I C and PERRET B (2001), 'On-line estimation and prediction of density and ethanol evolution in the brewery', *Technical Quarterly of Masters Brewers' Association of the Americas* 37, 173–181.

DE JONG P (1996), *Modelling and Optimization of Thermal Processes in the Dairy Industry,* Montfoort, The Netherlands.

DE JONG P and VAN DER LINDEN H J L J (1998), 'Polymerisation model for prediction of heat-induced protein denaturation and viscosity changes in milk', *J. Agric. Food Chem.* 46, 2136–2142.

DE JONG P and VERDURMEN R E M (2001), 'Concentrated and dried dairy products', in Tamime A Y and Law B A, *Mechanisation and Automation in Dairy Technology*, Sheffield, Sheffield Academic Press, 95–118.

DE JONG P, BOUMAN S and VAN DER LINDEN H J L J (1992), 'Fouling of heat treatment equipment in relation to the denaturation of β-lactoglobulin', *J. Soc. Dairy Techn.* 45, 3–8.

DE JONG P, VAN DER HORST H C and WAALEWIJN R (1999), 'Reduction of protein and mineral fouling', in Wilson D I, Fryer P J and Hasting A P M (eds), *Fouling and*

Cleaning in Food Processing '98, EUR 18804, Cambridge, 39–46.

DE JONG P, TE GIFFEL M C and KIEZEBRINK E A (2002a), 'Prediction of the adherence, growth and release of microorganisms in production chains', *Int. J. Food Microbiol.* 74, 13–25.

DE JONG P, TE GIFFEL M C, STRAATSMA H and VISSERS M M M (2002b), 'Reduction of fouling and contamination by predictive kinetic models', *Int. Dairy J.* 12, 285–292.

DE JONG P, SMIT F, VISSERS M M M, STRAATSMA J, VERSCHUEREN M and VAN DER WIEL J (2002c), 'A new process control system based on predictive kinetic models for food quality and operating costs', in *Proc. 2nd Int. Conf. on Simulation in Food and Bio Industries*, SCS Europe, 45–49.

DELEMARRE V (1994), 'New control strategy of spray dryers reduces operation costs', *Voedingsmiddelentechnologie* 17(3), 20–21.

DE VILDER J, MARTENS R and NAUDTS M (1979), 'The influence of the dry matter content, the homogenization and the heating of concentrate on physical characteristics of whole milk powder', *Milchwissenschaft* 34(2), 78–84.

EDECAD (2001), Efficient DEsign and Control of Agglomeration in spray Drying machines, EC Fifth Framework Programme within the research programme 'Competitive and Sustainable Growth' co-ordinated by NIZO Food Research (http://www.edecad.com).

EUROPEAN PARLIAMENT AND COUNCIL (2000), 'Directive 1999/92/EC of the European Parliament and of the Council of 16 December 1999 on minimum requirements for improving the safety and health protection of workers potentially at risk from explosive atmospheres', *Off. J. Eur. Comm.*, 28 January.

FILKOVÁ I and MUJUMDAR A S (1995), 'Industrial spray drying systems', in Mujumdar A S, *Handbook of Industrial Drying, Volume 1,* Second edition, New York, Marcel Dekker, 263–307.

HALEY T A and MULVANEY S J (2000), 'On-line system identification and control design of an extrusion cooking process', *Food Control* 11, 121–129.

IDF (1979), 'Determination of the dispersability and wettability of instant dried milk, standard 87', Brussels, International Dairy Federation.

IDF (1986), 'Recommendations for fire prevention in spray drying of milk powder, IDF Document B 128', Brussels, International Dairy Federation.

IDF (1988), 'Dried milk and dried milk products: determination of the insolubility index, standard 129A', Brussels, International Dairy Federation.

IDF (1995), 'Determination of white flecks number, provisional standard 174', Brussels, International Dairy Federation.

KELLY J, KELLY P M and HARRINGTON D (2002), 'Influence of processing variables on the physicochemical properties of spray dried fat-based milk powders', *Lait* 82(4) 401–412.

KURZ T, FELLNER M, BECKER T and DELGADO A (2002), 'Observation and control of the beer fermentation using cognitive methods', *J. Inst. Brewing* 107, 241–252.

LABUZA T P (1971), 'Kinetics of lipid oxidation in foods', *CRC Crit. Rev. Food Technol.*, 2(3), 355–405.

MASTERS K (1991), *Spray Drying Handbook*, New York, Longman Scientific & Technical.

MCCLUSKEY S, CONOLLY J F, DEVERY R, O'BRIEN B, KELLY J, HARRINGTON D and STANTON C (1997), 'Lipid and cholesterol oxidation in whole milk powder during processing and storage', *J. Food Sci.* 62(2), 331–337

NANTAWAN T (2002), 'Hybrid neural modeling', *Int. J. of Food Properties* 5, 49–61.

PALMER K N (1990), 'Explosion and fire hazards of powders', in Rhodes M J, *Principles of Powder Technology*, John Wiley & Sons.

PÉREZ-CORREA J R and FARÍAS F (1995), 'Modelling and control of a spray dryer: a simulation study', *Food Control* 6, 219–227.

PÍSECKÝ J (1997), *Handbook of Milk Powder Manufacture*, Copenhagen, Niro A/S.

RASE – EXPLOSIVE ATMOSPHERE: RISK ASSESSMENT OF UNIT OPERATIONS AND EQUIPMENT (2000), 'Report: Methodology for the Risk Assessment of Unit Operations and Equipment for Use in Potentially Explosive Atmospheres', EU project SMT4-CT97–2169.

SCHAAFSMA J, HAREN J J and STRAATSMA J (1997), 'Process control in the food/dairy industry', *Voedingsmiddelentechnologie* 30(14/15), 11–13.

SILVA-HENRIQUES A W, DA COSTA A C, ALVES T L M and LIMA E L (1999), 'A hybrid neural model of ethanol production by *Zymomonas mobilis*', *Appl. Biochem. Biotechnol.* 77–79, 277–291.

SKOV O (1986), 'Protection against fire and explosion in spray dryers', in Robinson R K, *Modern Dairy Technology. Volume 1. Advances in Milk Processing*, Second edition, London, Chapman & Hall.

SMIT F, DE JONG P, STRAATSMA J and VERSCHUEREN M (2001), 'Premia enables knowledge management. 1. Background and system application', *Voedingsmiddelentechnologie* 34(22), 23–26.

SNOEREN T H M, DAMMAN A J and KLOK H J (1983), 'De viscositeit van volle melk concentraat en de invloed ervan op de poedereigenschappen', *Zuivelzicht* 75, 847–849.

STAPPER H L (1979), 'Control of an evaporator and spray dryer using feedback and ratio feedforward controller', *N.Z. J. Dairy Sci. Technol.* 14, 241–257.

STEENBERGEN A E, VAN HOUWELINGEN G and STRAATSMA J (1991), 'System for early detection of fire in a spray dryer', *J. Soc. Diary Techn.* 44(3) 76–79.

STRAATSMA J, VAN HOUWELINGEN G, MEULMAN A P and STEENBERGEN A E (1991), 'DrySPEC2: a computer model of a two-stage dryer', *J. Soc. Dairy Techn.* 44, 107–111.

STRAATSMA J, VAN HOUWELINGEN G, STEENBERGEN A E and DE JONG P (1999a), 'Spray drying of food products: 1. Simulation model'. *J. Food Engineering*, 42, 67–72.

STRAATSMA J, VAN HOUWELINGEN G, STEENBERGEN A E and DE JONG P (1999b), 'Spray drying of food products: 2. Prediction of insolubility index', *J. Food Eng.* 42, 73–77.

TRELEA I C, ALVAREZ G and TRYSTRAM G (1998), 'Nonlinear predictive optimal control of a batch refrigeration process', *J. Food Process Eng.* 21, 1–32.

VAN MIL P J J M and JANS J A (1991), 'Storage stability of whole milk powder: effects of process and storage conditions on product properties', *Neth. Milk Dairy J.* 45(3) 145–167.

VERDURMEN R E M, STRAATSMA H, VERSCHUEREN M, VAN HAREN J J, SMIT E, BARGEMAN G and DE JONG P (2002), 'Modelling spray drying processes for dairy products', *Lait* 82 (4), 453–463.

VISSERS M, DE JONG P and DE WOLFF J (2002), 'New evaporator design results in 70% reduction of energy consumption', *Voedingsmiddelentechnologie*, 2002(6), 20–22.

WALSTRA P, GEURTS T J, NOOMEN A, JELLEMA A and VAN BOEKEL M A J S (1999), *Dairy Technology*, New York, Marcel Dekker.

XIA B and SUN D-W (2002), 'Application of computational fluid dynamics (CFD) in the food industry: a review', *Computers and Electronics in Agriculture* 34, 5–24.

17

Separation technologies to produce dairy ingredients

G. Bargeman, Akzo Nobel Chemicals bv, The Netherlands

17.1   Introduction

Milk, the first source of nutrition for newly born mammals, is rich in components essential for life-maintaining functions and growth. These components include fat, proteins, enzymes, lactose and minerals. During many centuries humans have used the nutritional value of bovine milk through the production and consumption of bulk products, such as fluid milk and cheese. Whey, produced in large quantities during cheese manufacturing, was originally discharged to the environment. In the course of the twentieth century, human behaviour with respect to feeding their newly born and regarding their perception of the discharge of waste streams changed drastically. Tightened environmental regulations and new economic threats, such as increased discharge costs, forced the dairy industry to look for alternative outlets for their waste streams. Whey was concentrated and spray-dried, and the whey powders produced were sold to the animal feed industry at relatively low prices. As the nutrition of human infants started to divert from human to bovine milk, gradually different bovine milk-based infant formulas were demanded for newly born humans.

The dairy industry realised the value of ingredients present in whey (see Table 17.1) in that respect. Processes to separate milk and especially whey into different fractions and to isolate specific components from milk or whey to produce speciality products with a higher value were developed and implemented in the industry.

The most important separation technologies that are currently used for the production of these speciality products – crystallisation, membrane filtration and chromatography – will be discussed in the following section. Since

Table 17.1 Examples of ingredients in whey and their (potential) application

Ingredient	(Potential) application
Lactose	Drug carrier in pharmaceutical applications. Component in infant formulas (de Wit, 2001). Feedstock for production of lactulose, galacto-oligosaccharides, lactitol and other health-improving ingredients (Strohmaier, 1998, Timmermans, 1998)
Sialyllactose/sialic acid	Nutraceutical, in medical and health products (Brian et al., 1994; Shimatani et al., 1990; Horton, 1998)
Proteins:	
α-Lactalbumin	Rich in essential amino acids for nutritional requirements of growing infants. Used for enriching current infant formulas (Chatterton, 2001)
β-Lactoglobulin	Stabilises emulsions and foams. Alternative for caseinate, egg-white and gelling agents in food products (Visser and Paulsson, 2001).
Glycomacropeptide (GMP)	Therapeutic uses (Coolbear et al., 1998)
Immunoglobulins (IgG1, IgG2, IgA, IgM)	Defence protein. Anti-microbial function and protection of neonates against infections (Mallée and Steijns, 2001)
Lactoferrin	Defence function. Anti-microbial, antiviral, iron absorption, anti-oxidant, anti-inflammatory immune modulation, anticancer (Mallée and Steijns, 2001; Li-Chan et al., 1995). Application in infant formula, cosmetics, oral care products, functional foods and as additive for the prevention of E. coli and Salmonella growth on fresh meat in the USA
Lactoperoxidase	Anti-microbial and anti-oxidant protein (Perraudin and Reiter, 1998). Application in toothpaste and mouthwash (Horton, 1998).
Growth factors (TGF-beta, IGF-1, IGF-2, FGF-1, FGF-2,PDGF-BB)	Growth-promoting proteins (Mallée et al., 2001)

chromatography is a relatively new technology in dairy processing, it will be outlined in slightly more detail. The production of whey protein concentrates (WPC) and isolates (WPI) and the separation of lactose, α-lactalbumin (α-lac), β-lactoglobulin (β-lg) and defence proteins will then be discussed. Many of these dairy proteins contain fragments (bioactive peptides and individual amino acids) with specific functional properties (Meisel and Schlimme, 1996). Enzymatic hydrolysis is used to produce these fragments. This has boosted their use in infant formula and sports drinks. Recently, the isolation of these fragments has received increasing attention. The last section of this chapter will deal with the isolation of these components and the development of alternative separation technologies.

17.2   Separation technologies

For the isolation of ingredients from milk or milk derivatives several technologies are applied commercially. The most important and generally applied ones are membrane filtration and chromatography. The principles of these technologies are outlined in this section. Crystallisation, which is used mainly for lactose production, is described briefly. Apart from these separation technologies other mature technologies, such as centrifugation, evaporation, spray-drying and precipitation, are frequently used. Examples of the use of these technologies for bulk processing in the dairy industry are:

- The removal of micro-organisms, fat and other solidified components by centrifugation
- The concentration of milk or whey and subsequent powder production using evaporation and spray-drying
- The production of cheese and the isolation and separation of proteins (e.g. α-lac or β-lg) by precipitation.

Since these technologies are common practice in dairy processing (Walstra et al., 1999), they will not be discussed in this chapter.

17.2.1   Crystallisation
Crystallisation features nucleation and growth of small crystals from a solution (Van der Heijden and Van Rosmalen, 1994). The formation of the crystals occurs as a consequence of supersaturation of the solution. The driving force for crystallisation is the difference in chemical potential between liquid (μ_l) and solid (μ_s) phase ($\Delta\mu_l - \mu_s$). The relative supersaturation σ gives an indication of the difference from the equilibrium state. It is defined as:

$$\sigma = \exp\left(\Delta\mu/kT\right) - 1$$

where k and T are Boltzmann's constant and absolute temperature, respectively.

In industrial crystallisation supersaturation of the isolated crystalline component is generally achieved via (flash) evaporation, salting-out, precipitation or cooling. For evaporation and flash evaporation, supersaturation is a consequence of the increase of the concentration as a result of evaporation of the solvent. During flash evaporation, the temperature drop further enhances the driving force for crystallisation and also contributes to the formation of the crystals. During salting-out crystallisation, the formation of crystals is achieved by adding an anti-solvent to the liquid, thereby creating supersaturation. Precipitation is usually achieved by mixing of two feeds containing the separate ingredients of the desired product. After mixing of these feeds the nucleation starts as a consequence of the high degree of supersaturation. During cooling crystallisation, the supersaturation is a result of the temperature reduction imposed.

Even when a situation is created where supersaturation of the liquid occurs, the formation of crystals can still be absent. In this case a metastable situation is reached. Higher supersaturation (for primary or spontaneous nucleation) or initiation of crystal nucleation due to external factors (for secondary nucleation, the addition of small product crystals) is required to enter the unstable region and initiate the crystallisation process. For (flash) evaporative and cooling crystallisation generally the secondary nucleation mechanism is used and the primary mechanism can be neglected completely (Van der Heijden and Van Rosmalen, 1994). In those situations, conditions just in excess of supersaturation are required to start the crystallisation process. For precipitation crystallisation, primary nucleation is the overriding mechanism. Consequently, a large number of very small particles with sizes between 1 and 10 μm are formed. Aggregation of these particles results in the formation of larger particles. The particle size distribution is hard to control for precipitation crystallisation.

The disadvantage of crystallisation is the slow growth rate of the crystals, leading to large residence times (typically between 0.5 and 5 hours) and consequently big crystallisation vessels. Usually one crystallisation step is sufficient for the required purity of the product, since contaminants, e.g. salt ions, are not easily incorporated in the crystals. The separation of the crystals from the mother liquid is usually achieved by sedimentation, centrifugation, filtration or using a washing column.

17.2.2 Membrane filtration

Membrane filtration was introduced in the dairy industry around 1970. At present it is considered to be a mature technology with an estimated installed total membrane surface area of more than 500 000 m^2 in the dairy industry worldwide. Approximately 70% of this area is being used for treatment of whey (Timmer and Van der Horst, 1998).

Membrane filtration is a separation process that makes use of semi-permeable polymeric or ceramic materials (membranes). During the separation process, part of the feedstock will be rejected or retained by the membrane (the concentrate or retentate), whereas the other part will flow through the membrane (the permeate). The main driving force in most dairy applications is the difference in operating pressure between the concentrate (retentate) and the permeate side of the membrane (ΔP) minus the difference in osmotic pressure ($\Delta \Pi$) between the solutions at the concentrate and permeate side of the membrane. The osmotic pressure difference is a result of the difference in chemical potential between the solutions on either side of the membrane. Important characteristics of the membranes are the flow per membrane surface area (the flux, J) or the permeability (the flux per unit pressure applied, $J/\Delta P$) and the retention, defined as $1 - c_p/c_r$ (c_p = concentration in the permeate; c_r = concentration in the retentate). The flux and the permeability play an important role in the required capital investment for the membrane filtration installation, whereas the retention describes the separation efficiency of the process.

For pressure-driven membrane filtration four categories are recognised. These categories are, going from tight to more open membranes (Van der Horst, 2000):

1. Reverse osmosis (RO, typical operating pressures 3–4 MPa)
2. Nanofiltration (NF, typical pore sizes around 1 nm and operating pressures 1.5–3 mPa)
3. Ultrafiltration (UF, typical operating pressures 0.3–0.8 MPa)
4. Microfiltration (MF, typical pore sizes 0.2–2 μm and operating pressures of 0.05–0.2 MPa).

The permeation of typical components from dairy liquids through RO, NF, UF and MF membranes is presented schematically in Fig. 17.1. Generally, the flux through the membrane decreases when the concentration factor (the ratio of the feed volume to the retentate volume) is increased. When the removal of certain components from the feed by concentration alone becomes uneconomic due to too low a flux, a combination of concentration and subsequent diafiltration (DF) is used. During DF, water is added to the feed of the membrane module and a similar amount of permeate is removed.

Mechanisms for the separation of components during membrane filtration are:

• Pore size exclusion
• Donnan exclusion (based on charge interactions between the charged surface layer of the membrane and the charged components)

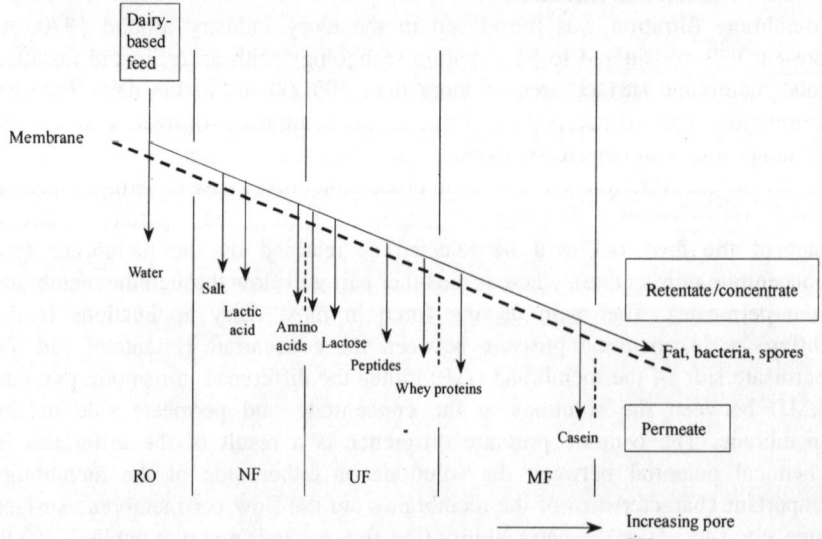

Fig. 17.1 Permeation of typical components from dairy or dairy-based liquids for RO, NF, UF and MF membranes (adapted from Van der Horst, 2000).

- Dielectric exclusion (due to a difference in static electric energy between the retentate and the liquid in membrane pores)
- Hydrophobicity/hydrophilicity of the membrane.

The membrane filtration process can be described by different models, e.g. the Extended Nernst-Planck (Schlögl, 1966) and Maxwell-Stefan (Straatsma *et al.*, 2002) transport models.

To avoid or limit concentration polarisation (formation of a layer at the membrane surface, where components accumulate and the concentrations are higher than in the bulk of the retentate) and fouling of the membranes, a considerable part of the retentate is recycled to the inlet of the membrane system. This type of operation, commonly used in the dairy industry, is called cross-flow operation. The following membrane module configurations are used commercially:

- Spiral-wound modules
- Tubular modules
- Capillary or hollow-fibre modules
- Plate and frame modules.

Further information on membrane filtration can amongst others be found in Walstra *et al.* (1999) and Van der Horst (2000).

17.2.3 Chromatography

Solid/liquid chromatography is based on the adsorption/desorption of components, present in a feedstock, to/from specific (functional) groups present on the pore surface of a resin. The component targeted for isolation in a so-called capture step should preferably have the highest adsorption and lowest desorption kinetics compared to the other components under the resin loading conditions used. The retardation time of the target component is thus much higher than that of the other components present in the feed solution. The operation mode and the adsorption mechanism used during chromatography determine the success of this process for component isolation.

Operation mode

During chromatography the following operation modes are applied:

- Stirred-tank operation
- Fixed-bed operation
- Expanded-bed operation
- Radial-flow operation
- Simulated moving-bed (SMB) operation.

During stirred-tank chromatography the feed solution is brought into contact with resin particles which are kept in suspension by mechanical mixing. An advantage of this type of operation is that relatively small resin particles can be (and have to be) used. This results in relatively low internal mass-transfer limitations in the resin particles and consequently a high particle utilisation. The main disadvantage compared to fixed-bed chromatography is the relatively low driving force for adsorption as a consequence of mixing of the liquid (ideally mixed versus plug-flow operation).

In most operation modes the resin particles are loaded into a cylindrical vessel, the chromatographic column. The feedstock is supplied to the column in a buffer solution to create optimal conditions for maximum adsorption of the target component. The column is usually operated in the traditional fixed-bed mode, where the particles are fixed between distinct borders. The column can be operated in up-flow (liquid supply at the bottom and withdrawal at the top) or in down-flow (liquid supply at the top and withdrawal at the bottom) mode. In both cases the column is operated liquid-full at relatively low liquid superficial velocity. The selection of the particle size is usually a compromise between a low pressure-drop (large particles) and a low mass-transfer limitation in the particle (small particles). The selection of the pore size of the particles is a compromise between sufficiently effective diffusion of the target component in the pores, sufficiently large pores, and a large uptake capacity of the resin, usually relatively small pores. The maximum uptake capacity of the resin, which is resin- and component-specific, can be determined by measuring a break-through curve (the amount of the target component which can be adsorbed before the concentration of the target component at the outlet starts to increase to the inlet concentration).

In industrial applications the feedstock is switched off or switched to another column (swing mode) when a certain fraction of the maximum uptake capacity is reached. The column is washed and subsequently a different buffer solution is supplied to the loaded column to desorb the components adsorbed to the resin (elution process) and to regenerate the bed. This change in buffer solution may be done stepwise or using a gradient going from the adsorption buffer to the final desorption buffer. The main advantage of chromatography is the high separation selectivity, especially compared to membrane filtration. Disadvantages of fixed-bed chromatography are the relatively high costs and possible plugging during processing of feeds with a high fouling tendency. To avoid plugging, often a pre-treatment step, e.g. MF, is required.

This latter disadvantage can be avoided by using expanded-bed operation, where the column is operated in up-flow mode. The superficial liquid velocity must be sufficiently high to exceed the minimum fluidisation velocity of the particles (the solid particles experience a drag force that exceeds the gravitational force and the interaction forces between the particles) to maintain bed expansion. Furthermore the liquid velocity should be sufficiently low to avoid strong mixing of the particles and liquid in the column, thus approaching plug-flow conditions for the liquid phase. The volume of the expanded bed may be two to three times the initial bed volume. In this operation mode generally relatively high-density resin particles are used to allow a sufficiently high superficial velocity and liquid throughput. This can be achieved by the use of an inert high-density core in the resin particle (Olander *et al.*, 2001). Desorption of the captured component takes place in fixed-bed mode.

Recently, radial-flow chromatography was introduced in the dairy industry as an alternative to fixed-bed columns (Nielsen, 2000). In this chromatographic process the resin particles are confined between two concentric cylindrical tubes 11–15 cm apart. The feed is supplied to the top of the outer tube and withdrawn from the column at the bottom of the inner tube. The main advantage of this patented Sepralac® technology is the high utilisation of the resin in combination with a low pressure-drop over the system.

SMB chromatography was also recently introduced (Horton, 1998) for the separation of valuable proteins from dairy streams. This technology features a series of chromatographic columns and a periodic change of the introduction points of feed, washing liquid and regenerate or a frequent rotation of the columns placed on a carousel (see Fig. 17.2) using fixed introduction points of feed, washing liquid and regenerate. For the latter operation type, the carousel is rotated such that each column changes one position (see Fig. 17.2). In both cases counter-current operation of the liquid and resin is obtained.

SMB chromatography allows for continuous operation and leads to the use of less resin and buffer volume. The main disadvantage of this system is the relatively high capital investment costs. However, for applications where resin

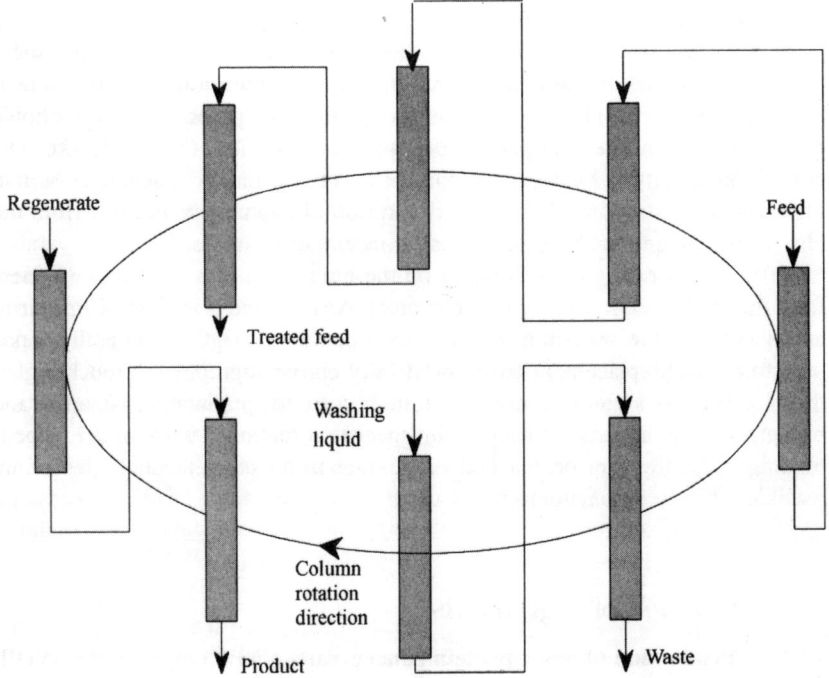

Fig. 17.2   Schematic representation of SMB operation.

replacement costs are the most important cost factor, this system may be an attractive alternative to the fixed-bed contactor.

Adsorption mechanisms
During chromatography the following types of adsorption can be applied:

- Ion-exchange chromatography (IEC)
- Hydrophobic interaction chromatography (HIC)
- Affinity chromatography.

IEC is the most widely applied within the dairy industry. The adsorbent is usually a polymeric resin with ionogenic functional groups. Anion-exchange resins contain positively charged surface groups such as NH_3^+ or NR_3^+, whereas in cation-exchange resins negatively charged surface groups such as CO_2^- or SO_3^- are present. The counter-ions of the charged surface groups present in fresh or regenerated resins to maintain electroneutrality are exchanged with the charged target components during the adsorption (capture) step. The charge of target proteins or protein fragments can be manipulated by adjusting the pH of the solution sufficiently in excess (for a negatively charged target component) or below (to obtain a positively charged target component) the iso-electric point (pI) of the target component. Desorption of the target component can be induced by changing the pH or the ionic strength of the buffer solution, thereby changing the net charge of the adsorbed component and the adsorption/desorption kinetics of the component to the surface of the resin.

In HIC, adsorption of the molecules to the resin matrix (usually sugar polymers) is based on the hydrophobic interaction between the functional (e.g. ethyl, octyl or phenyl) ligand on the surface of the resin pores and a hydrophobic group present in the component targeted for isolation (Marx, 1999). The adsorption activity of hydrophobic components to the matrix is generally high at high salt concentrations. To induce desorption of captured molecules from the HIC resins, eluents with decreased salt concentration are used.

Affinity chromatography is based on the interaction of a special component from the feed solution to a ligand (receptor). An example is the use of Protein A as ligand for the isolation of immunoglobulin G (IgG). Generally resin investment and replacement costs for affinity chromatography are much higher than for IEC, as a consequence of the high costs for production, isolation and binding of the ligands. However, in specific situations, when much higher binding capacities can be reached or binding using other technologies is not feasible, affinity chromatography is used.

17.3   Isolation of ingredients

17.3.1   Production of whey protein concentrates (WPC) and isolates (WPI)
Whey contains, apart from water, mostly lactose (72% of the total solids), minerals (8% of the total solids) and whey proteins, e.g. α-lac, β-lg, bovine

serum albumin (BSA), Ig and lactoferrin (LF). Whey powders produced through evaporation and spray-drying are, due to their unbalanced composition, not attractive for human consumption and are mainly used in animal feed (De Wit, 2001). The introduction of membrane filtration, especially UF, and in a later stage NF, has resulted in the production of whey powders with a higher value. The simultaneous concentration and demineralisation of acid, salty or sweet whey by NF creates products which are used in human foods, e.g. chocolate. More information about NF for the production of whey powders and advantages of NF over a process comprising concentration by RO and demineralisation by electrodialysis (ED) is described by Bargeman et al. (2003).

UF of whey results in simultaneous concentration, demineralisation and lactose removal from this feedstock (see Section 17.2.2) and consequently a whey concentrate with a protein/total solids ratio higher than originally present in whey. After further concentration and spray-drying whey powders with protein percentages, based on total solids, of 35 (WPC35), 50 (WPC50), 60 (WPC60), 70 (WPC70) or 80 (WPC80) are produced (Van der Horst, 2000). Functional properties and applications of these different WPCs have been reported by De Wit (2001). The quality and composition of the WPC powder produced depend on (Van der Horst, 2000):

- Whey quality and history
- Pre-treatment prior to UF
- UF process conditions
- Further processing of UF retentate
- Storage.

Usually, spiral-wound UF membranes with a molecular weight cut-off of around 10 000 daltons are used to minimise lactose and maximise the protein retention. It is crucial to avoid the loss of whey proteins as much as possible. The retentions for monovalent cations and anions during UF are close to zero. However, since the anions, e.g. phosphates and carbonates, present in whey are slightly larger than the cations, the retention for the latter is usually slightly lower. To maintain electroneutrality in the permeate, the lower anion salt transport is compensated for by a slightly higher OH^- transport. Consequently, the pH of the UF permeate is typically 0.04–0.10 higher than that of the feed (Walstra et al., 1999).

The concentration factor typically required for the production of different WPCs and the typical protein contents of these WPCs are shown in Fig. 17.3. The membrane flux during UF is reduced when the concentration factor is increased, as a consequence of the strongly increasing protein concentration in the retentate and consequently an increasing viscosity (Van der Horst et al., 1992; De Wit, 2001). For protein percentages in the retentate as high as 60%, the flux is reduced so much that DF operation becomes required to further increase the protein concentration if desired. Using DF, protein percentages as high as 80% can be obtained (De Wit, 2001).

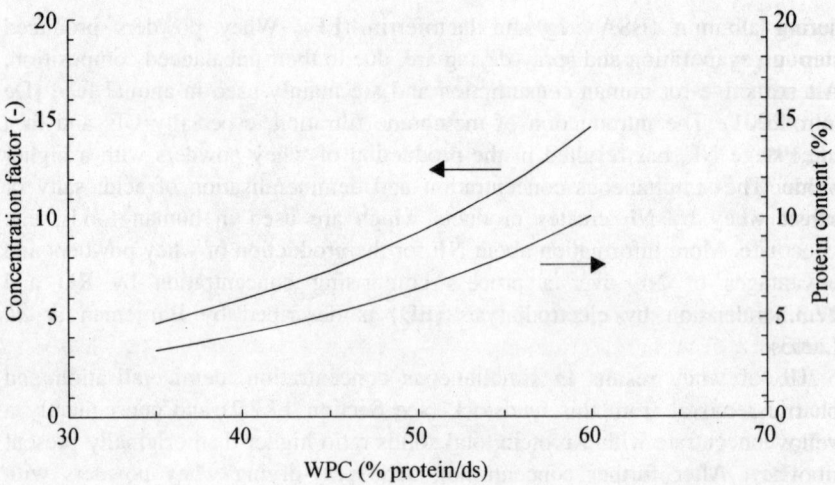

Fig. 17.3   Typical protein contents and required concentration factors for WPC.

Originally, UF was carried out at temperatures between 50°C and 60°C. During concentration at these temperatures precipitation of calcium phosphate in the pores and gel or concentration polarisation layer of the membrane may occur, resulting in membrane fouling and a strong flux reduction. This can be avoided when the whey is pre-treated prior to UF by one of the following methods (Walstra *et al.*, 1999):

- Increasing temperature or pH to allow precipitation and removal of calcium phosphate by dead-end filtration before UF
- Reducing pH to avoid precipitation during UF
- Selective removal of calcium before UF.

The solubility of calcium phosphate is much higher at lower operating temperatures. To avoid membrane fouling, more and more UF installations for WPC production are operated at temperatures between 10°C and 15°C. Thus the pre-treatment steps required for high temperature operation can be avoided. A disadvantage of low-temperature operation is the considerably higher viscosity of the permeate. A reduction of the temperature from 50°C to 10°C increases the permeate viscosity by a factor of 2, resulting in a 50% lower flux. However, due to the strongly reduced membrane prices, this is not regarded as an important drawback. Furthermore, microbial growth at temperatures below 15°C is substantially slower than at temperatures above 50°C and especially at temperatures between 15°C and 50°C. Low-temperature operation consequently results in a decreased cleaning frequency. It should be realised that the actual flux and retentions, and consequently the compositions of the permeate and retentate, strongly depend on the membrane used and the history of the whey treatment.

WPIs have a protein content of 90% or higher. The main non-protein component of WPC80 is fat (De Wit, 2001), which is retained in the concentrate during UF/DF. Consequently, for the production of WPI a separate fat-removal step using MF is required, prior to UF/DF and subsequent concentration. Alternative processes, featuring stirred or fixed-bed cation-exchange, were introduced for production of WPI from acid whey and acid casein whey (Etzel *et al.*, 1998; De Wit, 2001). The composition and functional properties of the WPIs produced from these different sources and using these different processes differ substantially (De Wit, 2001).

17.3.2 Separation of lactose and sialyllactose

Lactose, a disaccharide, is unique to milk. Its content in whey is typically 4.6–5.2%. Several grades of lactose, varying from industrial via edible to pharmaceutical grade, are produced commercially (see Table 17.2). The yellowish colour of some of the lactose grades is a result of the presence of riboflavin, also known as vitamin B2. Generally tomahawk-shaped α-lactose crystals are produced. However, for use in direct compression of pills, anhydrous lactose, β-lactose or spray-dried lactose (a combination of monohydrate and amorphous lactose) are manufactured (De Boer and Dijksterhuis, 1998).

The traditional industrial process for the isolation of lactose involves pasteurisation and subsequent concentration of whey, using conventional evaporation (Strohmaier, 1998). In some cases the whey is pre-concentrated using NF or RO. The degree of concentration that can be achieved is limited by the onset of salt precipitation, resulting in fouling of the evaporator tubes. When the salts in the concentrated whey are allowed to crystallise in a separate vessel prior to further concentration of the whey, this problem is largely avoided. Lactose ·crystallisation occurs at the same time (Walstra *et al.*, 1999). The required crystallisation time is reduced, and the fraction of lactose crystallised (the lactose yield) is increased, when higher concentration factors in the evaporator are used (see Table 17.3). Riboflavin is one of the crystal growth inhibitors present in whey. To avoid the production of very large lactose crystals as a consequence of slow nucleation and slow crystal growth, seed lactose crystals are supplied to the crystallisation vessel to enhance the secondary nucleation and the amount of crystals formed.

Table 17.2 Lactose grades

Lactose grade	Minimum lactose content (%)	Typical application	Colour
Industrial grade	98.0	Feed, fermentation, technical applications	Light yellow
Food grade	99.0	Bakery, confectionery, baby food, infant formula	White to pale yellow
Pharmaceutical grade	99.8	Excipient in pharmaceuticals	Pure white

Table 17.3 Effect of dry solids content and crystallisation time on lactose yield (based on Roetman, 1982)

Dry solids content in whey (%)	Fraction crystallised after 2 h	Fraction crystallised after 4 h
42.6	8	16
54.0	43	58
59.5	76	78
63.4	85	87

After the lactose crystallisation the crystals are separated and dried using a special lactose dryer (Strohmaier, 1998). Depending on the required lactose quality further refining may be required. During purification of the α-lactose hydrate crystals by recrystallisation, lower crystal growth rates are obtained as a consequence of the presence of a mixture of lactose monophosphates. These can be removed by ion exchange (Walstra *et al.*, 1999).

Since the introduction of the WPC processes, lactose is also separated from the whey proteins using UF (see Section 17.3.1). This is a process option widely used in the dairy industry with more than 160 000 m^2 UF membrane surface area implemented worldwide (Timmer and Van der Horst, 1998). The UF permeate contains, apart from lactose, significant amounts of minerals. NF is frequently used for the demineralisation of UF permeate prior to lactose crystallisation, to increase lactose yield and reduce crystallisation costs as a result of reduced washwater requirements. The NF installation is at present usually operated in cross-flow operation at temperatures below 15°C. This process is described in more detail by Bargeman *et al.* (2003).

Milk and whey furthermore contain minor amounts of sialyloligosaccharides such as 3′-sialyllactose, 6′-sialyllactose and sialyllactoseamine (Brian *et al.*, 1994). These sialic acid-containing lactose molecules are anti-adhesives and anti-infectives. These valuable components (typically $60 000–100 000/kg) are used for infant formulas and as effective ingredients for drugs and foods (Shimatani *et al.*, 1990). Snow Brand Milk Products Company (Shimatani *et al.*, 1990) and Neose Pharmaceuticals Inc. (Brian *et al.*, 1994), amongst others, have patented processes for the isolation of these components.

In the Snow Brand process (Shimatani *et al.*, 1990), ED or ion exchange using a cation and subsequently a strongly basic anion-exchange resin or a combination of these processes is used to remove remaining proteins and ions from deproteinised whey or skim milk. Seeding, e.g. by addition of α-lactose, and drying follow these process steps, to produce a sialic acid-containing lactose product. Products containing typically 50 mg sialic acid per 100 g lactose are thus obtained.

In the Neose process preferably mother liquid from lactose crystallisation is used as process feed. Positively charged proteins and ions are removed from the mother liquid using, e.g., cation-exchange chromatography, prior to the use of anion-exchange chromatography for the adsorption of the sialyloligo-saccharides. Typical superficial velocities used are in the range of 2–15 cm/min. Elution of the adsorbed sialyloligosaccharides is achieved using a lithium or sodium salt buffer. The elution procedure using lithium salts is claimed to be the key factor in the success of this process. The elute can be concentrated and dried. When sodium salts are used the elute has to be desalted, using, for instance, NF/DF prior to drying. Lithium salts can be removed from the lithium sialyloligosaccharides by washing the obtained solids using organic solvents at temperatures between 0°C and 5°C. Isolation of individual sialyloligosaccharides from the mixture of lithium sialyloligosaccharides obtained can be achieved using anion-exchange chromatography (Brian et al., 1994). Ion-exchange steps are performed at room temperature. An alternative to this isolation procedure is a solvent extraction process using, e.g., packed columns of lactose or using supercritical CO_2 (Brian et al., 1994).

17.3.3   Separation of α-lactalbumin and β-lactoglobulin

A further step in the separation of whey proteins is the isolation of individual whey proteins. Applications of purified α-lac and β-lg are listed in Table 17.1. Several processes have been developed and reported for the isolation of α-lac and β-lg. In some cases only one purified fraction is produced. This section focuses mainly on simultaneous production of purified α-lac and β-lg fractions.

Two production process categories can be distinguished. One uses a phase-transition step (precipitation of α-lac or β-lg), whereas the other is carried out without phase transition (Timmer and Van der Horst, 1998). An example of the first category, starting from a WPI, features the following steps (De Wit and Bronts, 1995):

1. Cation-exchange chromatography to capture calcium and to destabilise α-lac
2. Separation of the resin and the liquid phase
3. pH adjustment of the product solution to 4.3–4.8
4. Incubation of the product at a temperature between 10°C and 50°C to promote α-lac flocculation
5. Separation of an α-lac-rich fraction and a β-lg-rich fraction using, e.g., centrifugation or MF
6. Increasing the pH of the α-lac-rich fraction to redissolve the fraction.

α-Lac-rich (62% pure at 80% yield) and β-lg-rich (85% pure at 85% yield) fractions are thus produced simultaneously. The purity of the redissolved α-lac-rich fraction can be increased further to 74% at the expense of yield (reduced to 70%) using 0.1μm MF.

The process described by Stack et al. (1995) uses similar steps. However, in their process the demineralisation using ED and IEC is done on raw whey. Subsequently a heat treatment is carried out and lactose crystallisation is allowed before the pH is adjusted and precipitation of α-lac is induced. After the separation of the fractions, UF or MF and subsequent spray-drying is used to produce powders rich in α-lac and β-lg, the latter with 94.6% purity, respectively. The purity of the β-lg fraction is mainly limited by the presence of IgG and caseinomacropeptide (CMP), which do not precipitate (Timmer and Van der Horst, 1998). Consequently, the production of β-lg from acid casein whey results in higher purity as compared to sweet whey, as a result of the absence of CMP in this whey type (Gésan-Guiziou *et al.*, 1999).

The separation of α-lac and β-lg without phase transition has the advantage that the likelihood of protein denaturation is reduced considerably. The use of membrane filtration for this process has been studied extensively (Timmer and Van der Horst, 1998). However, membrane filtration alone does not result in production of very pure products. This is due to the relatively small difference in the apparent molecular weight between α-lac and β-lg (approximately 14.000 and 36.000 g/mol, respectively). Furthermore the difference in iso-electric points (pI) between α-lac and β-lg is small (4.2–4.5 and 5.1, respectively). Therefore the difference in size exclusion and Donnan exclusion for these components is too small to obtain sufficient separation efficiency and production of α-lac and β-lg fractions with sufficient purity simultaneously. Production of enriched α-lac fractions, with purity as high as 90%, using membrane filtration is reported by, e.g., Timmer and Van der Horst (1998). Furthermore, membrane filtration can be used as part of the separation process, sometimes in combination with a precipitation process (Timmer and Van der Horst, 1998; Van der Horst, 2000).

Several processes without phase transition use IEC for the purification of α-lac and β-lg. In these processes ion-exchange is not used for removal of calcium, leading to destabilisation and precipitation of α-lac, but to capture proteins and elute them selectively. Outinen *et al.* (1995) use anion-exchange chromatography for the separation between α-lac and β-lg. Their adsorption process is carried out at a pH between 6 and 7, where both components have a net negative charge. The majority of the α-lac flows through the anion-exchange column, whereas most of the β-lg is adsorbed to the resin, despite the higher pI of β-lg. The water used for washing the loaded column is added to the run-through material for production of a purified α-lac fraction. The adsorbed β-lg is eluted using a 2–5% wt NaCl solution. The ratio of α-lac over β-lg for the α-lac-rich and β-lg-rich fraction was typically 2.2 and 0.07, respectively, for Diaion HPA 75 (Resindion, Mitsubishi Kasei Corp., Japan), a strong anion-exchange resin. The reported yields for α-lac in the α-lac-rich fraction and for β-lg in the β-lg-rich fraction were typically 78% and 87%, respectively. Contaminants were Ig, BSA and orotic acid in the α-lac-rich, and Ig and BSA in the β-lg-rich fraction. Glycomacropeptides (GMP) were removed from the whey prior to the anion-exchange process through precipitation and removal of the precipitate. The flow rate used during this process was relatively low, 3–5 column volumes per hour.

Alternatively, Etzel (1999) proposes the use of a single cation-exchange step. Prior to ion-exchange the pH of the whey is reduced below 4.5. At this pH, α-lac and β-lg are captured by the cationic resin as a consequence of their net positive charge. The adsorbed α-lac and β-lg are eluted as different fractions using eluents with different pH. Although the pI for α-lac is lower than for β-lg, surprisingly a β-lg-rich fraction is obtained at pH 4.9. Subsequent elution at pH 6.5 produces an α-lac-rich fraction.

17.3.4   Isolation of defence proteins and growth factors

During the last decade special attention has been paid to the development and implementation of industrial production processes for purified defence proteins such as lactoferrin (LF), lactoperoxidase (LP), immunoglobulins (Ig) and growth factors. These valuable proteins are present in bovine milk and whey in low concentrations, e.g. 10–30 mg LP/l whey and 30–100 mg/l whey (Chiu and Etzel, 1997; Kussendrager *et al.*, 1997). LF, a salmon-coloured powder, is used to enrich infant formulas (Burling, 1994), since bovine milk is deficient in LF as compared to human milk. The latter has a 20-fold higher concentration (Chiu and Etzel, 1997). LP is used in toothpaste to reduce caries. Several other applications of these proteins are listed in Table 17.1.

The pI values of LF and LP are 7.8–8.0 and 9.2–9.9, respectively (Groves, 1971). Other proteins present in milk or whey have much lower pI. Consequently, LF and LP are positively charged at pH 6.5, whereas the other proteins are negatively charged. Industrial processes (see Fig. 17.4) to isolate these minor proteins from especially whey, a relatively low-cost feed, as developed by Burling (1989; 1994), Kussendrager *et al.* (1997) and Sato *et al.* (1996), consequently use cation- exchange chromatography. In these processes generally a pre-treatment step is used to remove micro-organisms, fat and protein aggregates and to avoid clogging the fixed-bed cation-exchange chromatography column. MF using 1.4 μm pore diameter membranes is often used, but also other technologies like bactofugation (centrifugation), UF or coarse filters can be applied (Kussendrager *et al.*, 1997). The use of pasteurisation is avoided to prevent inactivation of these very heat-sensitive defence proteins as a consequence of protein denaturation. Depending on the procedure used to elute the proteins adsorbed in the resin pores, LP and LF can be obtained as a mixture or as separate products (Kussendrager *et al.*, 1997). During elution LP is desorbed first, while LF remains adsorbed to the resin and is eluted later.

The Sato process also produces secretory immunoglobulin A (SIgA, secretory component associated with immunoglobulin), a component preventing

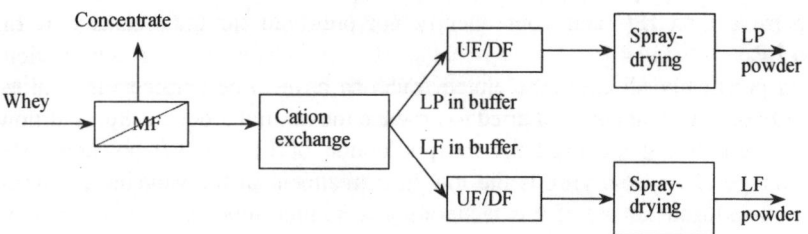

Fig. 17.4 Typical industrial process for the isolation of lactoferrin and lactoperoxidase.

infectious diseases for infants. The following elution procedure is used, after the adsorption and washing step, to obtain the components separately (Sato *et al.*, 1996):

1. Selective elution of LP using a buffer with an ionic strength between 0.2 and 0.5 and a pH ≤ 5
2. Selective elution of secretory component using a buffer with an ionic strength of 0.1–0.5 and pH > 5
3, Selective elution of LF using a buffer with an ionic strength in excess of 0.5 and pH > 5.

During the Sato process product purities of about 80% or higher are achieved in a single-stage cation-exchange process. Different types of adsorbers, e.g. fixed-bed and slurry adsorbers, can be used for the isolation of LP, SIgA and LF. A rotary-column adsorber is mentioned as the preferred option for efficient mass production (Sato *et al.*, 1996). A serious disadvantage of this adsorber compared to the other adsorber equipment mentioned is the presence of rotary parts.

The Burling and Kussendrager processes use similar ionic strength buffers for the elution of LP and LF, but no variation in pH is applied. The Burling process provides products with purities in excess of 95%, as commercially proven in the Kristianstad dairy plant (Burling, 1994). Furthermore, the cation-exchange step results in a more than 500-fold concentration of the product. In the process described by Burling and Sato for fixed-bed cation-exchange, low flow rates are used (typically 1.25 bed volumes/min) resulting in very long loading times (15–20 h). The low flow rates used are a consequence of the small particle size of the resins used in these processes and the pressure drop limitations of the system. The long loading times are clearly a disadvantage of these processes.

In the fixed-bed cation-exchange process of Kussendrager *et al.* (1997) the use of high superficial velocities (in excess of 500 cm/h) and high liquid loads (100–600 bed volumes/h) is achieved by the use of SP Sepharose Big Beads. This resin has particle sizes in excess of 100 μm. Pressure-drops in excess of 10 bar/m and even as high as 40 bar/m can be applied. More than 80% of the LF and LP present in the whey feedstock is captured in this process.

Apart from conventional fixed-bed chromatography, SMB chromatography is also used for the isolation of LF from whey, e.g. at Agri-mark Vermont. As an alternative capture step, affinity chromatography is mentioned in several publications and patents. However, this capture step is usually much more expensive than IEC and consequently not preferred for the isolation of LF and LP.

In practically all cases the eluted fractions have to be demineralised using UF/DF or ion exchange, and dried to produce the desired products. Spray-drying and freeze-drying are used for the production of LP and LF powders. The advantage of freeze-drying is the low heat treatment of the valuable products. The main disadvantage of this technology is its high process costs. Especially, the investment, energy and operating costs for spray-drying are lower than for freeze drying.

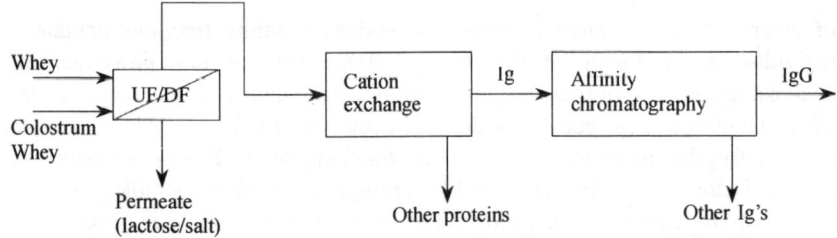

Fig. 17.5 Isolation of Ig and IgG (adapted from Mallée and Steijns, 2001).

Immunoglobulins are the best-known antimicrobial proteins (Mallée and Steijns, 2001). Bovine milk, but especially colostrum, contains significant amounts of immunoglobulins (especially IgG). Obviously, colostrum is a good source of Ig, but the availability of this feed is limited. Furthermore, the concentration of Ig in colostrum drops relatively fast during the first days after the birth of the calf. Commercial processes use whey from colostrum and milk, to produce enriched fractions, which may contain 80% Ig after UF/DF. Further purified Ig and IgG products may be obtained by the use of IEC and affinity chromatography (Mallée and Steijns, 2001). The isolation of Ig and IgG is schematically shown in Fig. 17.5.

Apart from the traditional fixed-bed chromatography process, expanded-bed chromatography can also be used for the simultaneous isolation of LP, LF and IgG from whey and subsequent production of WPC or WPI from the remaining proteins in the whey (Olander *et al.*, 2001). For the use of this expanded-bed adsorption pre-filtration is not required.

An alternative process for the isolation of Ig from whey or whey derivatives features precipitation of other proteins by supplying a cationic polymer (e.g. chitosan) and fatty acids to the feedstock simultaneously. The precipitate can be removed by low-speed centrifugation. The remaining supernatant contains more than 60% Ig. This supernatant can be further concentrated, diafiltered and dried (Acker *et al.*, 1997).

During the mid-1990s, the isolation of growth factors from whey received more attention. Goddard *et al.* (1998) describe the production of whey growth factor extract (WGFE) using:

1. MF for de-fatting and clarification of whey
2. Cation-exchange chromatography of MF permeate to capture the growth factors
3. Concentration and desalting of the elute containing the growth factors using UF
4. Sterilising and packaging of the WGFE.

The WGFE contains a mixture of the growth factors IGF-1 (22 μg/l), IGF-2 (24 μg/l), PDGF-BB (4 μg/l), TGF-beta (3 μg/l), FGF-1 (0.2 μg/l) and FGF-2 (0.2 μg/l). Since some growth factors can have a negative effect on the activity of others, there is a clear incentive to produce separate fractions containing individual growth factors (Mallée *et al.*, 2001). Several of these processes have been patented. Most of these require many downstream processing steps or use a LP denaturation step, both of which are economically undesirable. A simpler process for the isolation of individual fractions of TGF-beta (transforming growth factor) and IGF-1 (insulin-like growth factor) from a milk product is presented by Mallée *et al.* (2001). This process resembles that proposed by Goddard *et al.* (1998) but has a second adsorption step for the isolation of the individual growth factor fractions. The process features the following steps:

1. Minimal heat treatment for sufficient reduction of the micro-organism content of the feed and minimum protein denaturation
2. MF for fat removal
3. Capture of growth factors from feed using a cation-exchange column
4. Elution
5. Capture of growth factors from elute using a hydroxyapatite column
6. Elution.

After the elution step, the following fractions are obtained:

- IGF-1 (between 50 and 500 μg/g peptide) practically free of TGF-beta
- TGF-beta (more than 200 pg/g peptide) practically free of IGF-1
- Optionally LP.

The IGF-1 and TGF-beta fractions furthermore contain approximately 30–50% Ig on a protein basis.

17.3.5 Production and isolation of bioactive peptides and amino acids from dairy proteins

Apart from the isolation of ingredients with high value like α-lac and β-lg and defence proteins, the production and isolation of active fragments from these and other dairy-based proteins such as amino acids, e.g. tryptophan and arginine, and functional peptides, e.g. phosphopeptides, antimicrobial peptides and opioid peptides, are becoming increasingly important. The active fragments are usually produced through enzymatic hydrolysis of the proteins (Visser and Floris, 2000). The hydrolysates are used directly in infant formula, and skin care and hair conditioning products. The active fragments are attractive alternatives to ingredients produced from non-natural sources using fermentation with genetically modified or pathogenic micro-organisms. Isolation of ingredients can be done using chromatography, in some cases preceded by membrane filtration as first separation step. Due to the variety of ingredients and consequently the variety in production processes, these are not discussed in further detail here.

17.4   Developments in separation technology

17.4.1   Membrane adsorbers

To overcome the long adsorption cycles and low liquid velocities required for most fixed-bed chromatography processes, membrane adsorbers using microporous ion-exchange and affinity membranes have been and are being developed. Several studies report the isolation of LF and LP using commercially available cation-exchange membranes (e.g. Sartobind^{TM} Membrane Adsorber). Chiu and Etzel (1997) used a microporous membrane with a pore size of 3–5 μm in laboratory-scale tests. This membrane contained R–CH$_2$–SO$_3^-$ groups covalently bonded to the internal pore surface. LF and LP recoveries were 50% and 73%, respectively. Loading times with respect to traditional ion-exchange chromatography could be reduced significantly. Pilot-scale experiments using modules of 1 m^2 confirmed the feasibility of membrane adsorbers for the isolation of LF and LP (Ulber *et al.*, 2001). A loading capacity of 2 g LF/m^2 was reported. A product purity of 85% and 95% was achieved for LP and LF, respectively. On the basis of the results a process for the isolation of LF and LP from whey is proposed similar to the traditional process proposed for ion-exchange, but replacing the fixed-bed resin column by a membrane absorber. Recently, production of lactoferrin using cation-exchange membranes was started on a commercial scale.

Etzel (1999) reported the feasibility of the isolation of enriched α-lac and β-lg fractions from whey using cation-exchange membrane adsorbers. For the isolation of IgG, affinity membranes with immobilised Protein A are being developed. These membranes are based on, e.g., composite chitosan–cellulose membranes (Yang *et al.*, 2002) or nylon membranes coated with dextrans–polyvinyl alcohol (Castilho *et al.*, 2000).

Since the production and isolation of biologically active peptide fragments from proteins (e.g. antimicrobial peptides) is becoming more and more important, membrane adsorbers provide new opportunities for the industry. Apart from the isolation of peptides from hydrolysates produced after enzymatic hydrolysis in stirred vessels, this technology can also be used in a different way (Recio and Visser, 1999). Prior to enzymatic hydrolysis the target protein is adsorbed by the membrane (see Fig. 17.6). Following the loading procedure, the feed is switched to a different membrane adsorber and an enzyme solution is supplied to the loaded membrane to perform the enzymatic hydrolyses of the adsorbed protein. After this hydrolysis procedure the bioactive peptides are eluted at high purity. Very pure lactoferricin, a proven bioactive peptide originating from LF, could be produced by feeding whey directly to the adsorber, following the procedure described. Furthermore the feasibility of the process for several other applications was proven. The main advantage of this procedure over the traditional one is that the entire feed is not hydrolysed, but only the adsorbed protein. The feed can therefore practically retain its initial value.

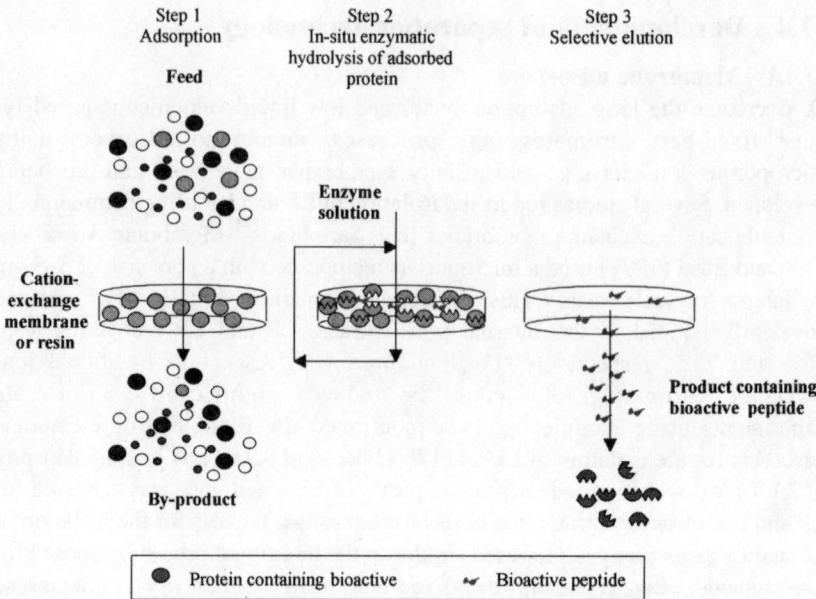

Fig. 17.6   Production of bioactive peptides by adsorption of milk proteins followed by in-situ hydrolysis of the adsorbed protein (adapted from Recio and Visser, 1999).

17.4.2   Electro-membrane filtration

Electro-membrane filtration (EMF) is currently being developed for the isolation of valuable charged ingredients such as proteins or protein fragments. This technology combines electrophoresis and conventional membrane filtration. A conventional MF, UF or NF membrane separates the feedstock from the permeate (see Fig. 17.7). The selection of this membrane depends on the size of the component to be isolated. Ion-exchange membranes are used to shield the feedstock and the permeate from the electrodes, thereby preventing degradation of these solutions and fouling of the electrodes. To obtain a selective isolation of the charged target components, the electrical field strength in the feedstock compartment is maximised in relation to convection (a function of the transmembrane pressure) and diffusion. Examples of successful separations are the isolation of lysine from casein hydrolysate (Bargeman et al., 2000), of antimicrobial peptides from a LF hydrolysate (Bargeman et al., 2000) and an α_{s2}-casein hydrolysate (Bargeman et al., 2002a, 2002b). EMF is very selective in the isolation of a mixture of charged components, but less selective in the isolation of individual charged components. However, for many applications in the food industry the product purities are sufficiently high. On the basis of first cost evaluations, the processing costs of EMF will be considerably lower than those for chromatography (Bargeman et al., 2002c). Further technology development and scale-up of EMF will be required before this technology can be implemented in the industry.

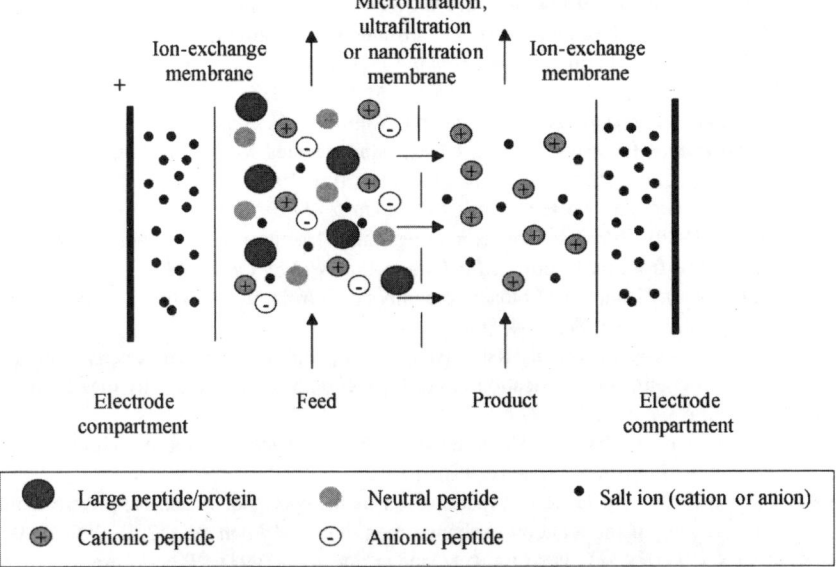

Fig. 17.7   Principle of electro-membrane filtration (EMF).

17.5   Sources of further information and advice

More information about crystallisation, membrane filtration and chromatography for protein separation can be found in the book *Basic Principles of Membrane Technology* (Mulder, 1991), in the chapter on 'Industrial mass crystallisation' in Van der Heijden and Van Rosmalen (1994) and in the book *Protein Purification, Principles, High-Resolution Methods, and Applications* (Janson and Rydén, 1998), respectively.

17.6   References

ACKER E A, FREEDMAN D J, CRABB J H and RUCK F E (1997), 'Process for isolating immunoglobulins in whey', *Int Patent WO 97 12901*.

BARGEMAN G, DOHMEN-SPEELMANS M, RECIO I, TIMMER M and VAN DER HORST H C (2000), 'Selective isolation of cationic amino acids and peptides by electro-membrane filtration', *Lait*, 80, 175–185.

BARGEMAN G, HOUWING J, RECIO I, KOOPS G H and VAN DER HORST H C (2002a), 'Electro-membrane filtration for the selective isolation of bio-active peptides from an α_{s2}-casein hydrolysate', *Biotechnol Bioeng*, 80(6), 599–609.

BARGEMAN G, KOOPS G H, HOUWING J, BREEBAART I, VAN DER HORST H C and WESSLING M. (2002b), 'The development of electro-membrane filtration for the isolation of bio-active peptides. The effect of membrane selection and operating parameters on the transport rate', *Desalination*, 149, 369–374.

BARGEMAN G, KOOPS G H, HOUWING J, BREEBAART I, VAN DER HORST H C and WESSLING M (2002c), 'The development of electro-membrane filtration for the isolation of valuable charged components', *Chemie Ingenieur Technik*, 74(5), 639–640.

BARGEMAN G, TIMMER M J K and VAN DER HORST H C (2003), 'Applications in the food industry', in Schaefer A, Fane A G and Waite T D, *Nanofiltration – Principles and Applications*, Elsevier Science, Amsterdam, accepted for publication.

BRIAN B, ZOPF D A, LU L, MCCAULEY J P JR and PARTSCH M (1994), 'Methods of processing a cheese processing waste stream', *US Patent 5,714,075*.

BURLING H (1989), 'Process for extracting pure fractions of lactoperoxidase and lactoferrin from milk serum', *Int Patent Appl WO 89 04608 A1*.

BURLING H (1994), 'Isolation of bioactive components from cheese whey', *Scandinavian Dairy Information*, 8(3), 54–56.

CASTILHO L R, DECKWER W-D and ANSPACH F B (2000), 'Influence of matrix activation and polymer coating on purification of human IgG with protein A affinity membranes', *J Membr Sci*, 172, 269–277.

CHATTERTON D E W (2001), 'Alpha-lactalbumin: an ingredient for enriching infant formulas', *Industrial Proteins*, 9(3), 13–15.

CHIU C K and ETZEL M R (1997), 'Fractionation of lactoperoxidase and lactoferrin from bovine whey using a cation exchange membrane', *J Food Sci*, 62(5), 996–1000.

COOLBEAR K P, ELGAR D F, PRITCHARD M and AYERS J S (1998), 'Process for isolating glycomacropeptide from dairy products with phenylalanine impurity of 0.5%w/w', *Int Patent WO 98 14071*.

DE BOER R and DIJKSTERHUIS J (1998), 'Permeate, milk sugar, and derivatives – an overview', *Proc 2nd Int Whey Conf, Chicago, 27–29 October 1997, IDF Special Issue 9804*, IDF Brussels, 220–226.

DE WIT J N (2001), 'Whey protein concentrates: manufacture, composition and applications', *Industrial Proteins*, 9(3), 3–5.

DE WIT J N and BRONTS H (1995), 'Process for the recovery of α-lactalbumin and β-lactoglobulin from a whey protein product', *US Patent 5,420,249*.

ETZEL M R (1999), 'Isolating α-lactoglobulin and β-lactalbumin by eluting from a cation exchanger without sodium chloride', *US Patent 5,986,063*.

ETZEL M R, DERMAWAN S, BUDIMAN M N, HENDRIADI V V and ROSALINA I (1998), 'Protein separation by ion exchange in columns', *Proc 2nd Int Whey Conf, Chicago, 27–29 October 1997, IDF Special Issue 9804,* IDF Brussels, 66–72.

GÉSAN-GUIZIOU G, DAUFIN G, TIMMER M, ALLERSMA D and VAN DER HORST H C (1999), 'Process steps for the preparation of purified fractions of α-lactalbumin and β-lactoglobulin from whey protein concentrates', *J Dairy Res*, 66, 225–236.

GODDARD C, FRANCIS G L, BELFORD D A, REGESTER G O, COPELAND A C, DE SILVA K S, SMITHERS G W, TONEMAN L Z and BALLARD F J (1998), 'A growth factor supplement for cell culture purified from whey', *Proc 2nd Int Whey Conf, Chicago, 27–29 October 1997, IDF Special Issue 9804*, IDF Brussels, 365–367.

GROVES M L (1971), 'Minor milk proteins and enzymes', in McKenzie H A, *Milk Proteins, Chemistry and Molecular Biology Vol. 2*, Academic Press, New York, 367–418.

HORTON B (1998), 'The whey processing industry into the 21st century', *Proc 2nd Int Whey Conf, Chicago, 27–29 October 1997, IDF Special Issue 9804*, IDF Brussels, 12–25.

JANSON J-C and RYDÉN L (1998), *Protein Purification, Principles, High-Resolution Methods, and Applications*, 2nd edition, Wiley-VCH, Weinheim, Germany.

KUSSENDRAGER K D, KIVITS M G C and VERVER A B (1997), 'Process for isolating lactoferrin and lactoperoxidase from milk and milk products, and products obtained by such process', *US Patent 5,596,082*.

LI-CHAN E, KUMMER A, LOSSO J N, KITTS D D and NAKAI S (1995), 'Stability of bovine immunoglobulins to thermal treatment and processing', *Food Res Int*, 28 (1), 9–16.

MALLÉE L F and STEIJNS J M (2001), 'Defence proteins in milk', *Industrial Proteins*, 9(3), 16–19.

MALLÉE L F, HENDRICKS A W J and KIVITS M G C (2001), 'Process for obtaining growth factor preparations (TGF-beta and IGF-1) from milk products having low mutual cross-contamination', *Int Patent WO 01 25,276*.

MARX P (1999), 'Proceschromatografie: Zuiveren op grote schaal', *Chemisch2Weekblad* 11, 8–9.

MEISEL H and SCHLIMME E (1996), 'Bioactive peptides derived from milk proteins: ingredients for functional foods?', *Kieler Milchwissenschaftliche Forschungs-berichte*, 48, 343–357.

MULDER M (1991), *Basic Principles of Membrane Technology*, Kluwer Academic Publishers.

NIELSEN W K (2000), 'Cost effective recovery of whey proteins', *Scandinavian Dairy Information* 3/00, 24–27.

OLANDER M A, JAKOBSEN A L, HANSEN M B and LIHME A (2001), 'Fractionation of high-value whey proteins', *Scandinavian Dairy Information*, 2/01, 22–25.

OUTINEN M, HARJU M, TOSSAVAINEN O and ANTILA P (1995), 'Process for fractionating whey proteins and the components so obtained', *Int Patent WO 95 19,714*.

PERRAUDIN J P and REITER B (1998), 'The role of lactoperoxidase in reducing the activity of free radicals', *Proc 2nd Int Whey Conf, Chicago, 27–29 October 1997, IDF Special Issue 9804*, IDF Brussels, 326–332.

RECIO I and VISSER S (1999), 'Two ion-exchange chromatographic methods for the isolation of antibacterial peptides from lactoferrin. In-situ enzymatic hydrolyses on an ion-exchange membrane', *J Chrom A*, 831, 191–201.

ROETMAN K (1982), Ph.D. thesis, Wageningen University, The Netherlands.

SATO K, UCHIDA T, DOSAKO S I and KAWASAKI Y (1996), 'Separation of lactoperoxidase, secretory component and lactoferrin from milk or whey with cation exchange resin', *US Patent 5,516,675*.

SCHLÖGL R (1966), 'Membrane permeation in systems far from equilibrium', *Ber Bunsenges Phys Chem*, 70, 400.

SHIMATANI M, MURAKAMI Y, IDOTA T and IDO K (1990), 'Production process of sialic acid-containing lactose', *US Patent 5,118,516*.

STACK F M, HENNESSY M, MULVIHILL D and O'KENNEDY B T (1995), 'Process for the fractionation of whey constituents', *Int Patent WO 95 34,216*.

STRAATSMA J, BARGEMAN G, VAN DER HORST H C and WESSLINGH J A (2002), 'Can nanofiltration be fully predicted by a model?', *J Membr Sci*, 198, 273–284.

STROHMAIER W (1998), 'Lactulose: status of health-related applications', *Proc 2nd Int Whey Conf, Chicago, 27–29 October 1997, IDF Special Issue 9804*, IDF Special Issue 9804, IDF Brussels, 262–271.

TIMMER J M K and VAN DER HORST H C (1998), 'Whey processing and separation technology: state-of-the-art and new developments', *Proc 2nd Int Whey Conf, Chicago, 27–29 October 1997, IDF Special Issue 9804*, IDF Brussels, 40–65.

TIMMERMANS E (1998), 'Lactose derivatives: functions and applications', *Proc 2nd Int Whey Conf, Chicago 27–29, October 1997, IDF Special Issue 9804*, IDF Brussels, 233–250.

ULBER R, PLATE K, WEISS T, DEMMER W, BUCHHOLZ H and SCHEPER T (2001), 'Downstream processing of bovine lactoferrin from sweet whey', *Acta Biotechnol*, 21(1), 27–34.

VAN DER HEIJDEN A E D M and VAN ROSMALEN G M (1994), 'Industrial mass crystallisation', in Hurle D T J, *Handbook of Crystal Growth, Vol. 2 Bulk Crystal Growth, Part A. Basic Techniques,* Chapter 7, Elsevier Science Publishers Amsterdam.

VAN DER HORST H C (2000), 'Membrane processing', in Tamime A Y and Law B A, *Mechanisation and Automation in Dairy Technology*, Sheffield Academic Press, Sheffield, UK.

VAN DER HORST H C, HOLS G and TEERINK S (1992), 'Bereiding van wei-concentraten', *Voedingsmiddelentechnologie*, 25(19), 13–15.

VISSER H and PAULSSON M (2001), 'Beta-lactoglobulin: a whey protein with unique properties', *Industrial Proteins*, 9(3), 9–12.

VISSER S and FLORIS R (2000), 'Valorisation of milk proteins by proteolysis', *Industrial Proteins*, 8(2), 8–10.

WALSTRA P, GEURTS T J, NOOMEN A, JELEMA A and VAN BOEKEL M A J S (1999), *Dairy Technology (Principles of Milk Properties and Processes)*, Marcel Dekker, New York.

YANG L, HSIAO W W and CHEN P (2002), 'Chitosan-cellulose composite membrane for affinity purification of biopolymers and immunoadsorption', *J Membr Sci*, 197, 185–197.

18

The use of dissolved carbon dioxide to extend the shelf-life of dairy products

C. R. Loss and J. H. Hotchkiss, Cornell University, USA

18.1 Introduction: factors limiting the shelf-life of dairy products

The shelf-life of refrigerated dairy products is limited to 1 to 3 weeks (Muir, 1996). A number of factors contribute to this limited shelf-life: microbial quality of the raw milk (Muir, 1996), bacterial enzymes (Champagne et al., 1994), thermal processing conditions (Lewis, 1999), and distribution/storage temperatures (Henyon, 1999). Carbon dioxide (CO_2) can be used to influence these factors and improve the quality of a variety of dairy products. Growth and metabolism of a wide range of bacteria (Dixon and Kell, 1989), particularly those found in the dairy processing environment (Roberts and Torrey, 1988; Ruas-Madiedo et al., 1996), are inhibited in the presence of added CO_2. Combined inhibitory effects of CO_2 and other preservation techniques (refrigeration, pasteurisation or high barrier packaging) on bacterial growth and survival have been demonstrated.

18.2 The effects of CO_2 on bacterial growth

When CO_2 is dissolved in an aqueous medium it can retard the growth of Gram-positive and Gram-negative organisms. The magnitude of the effect on the different phases of growth depends upon the organism (see Table 18.1). For example, the lag phase of growth for Pseudomonas fluorescens increases with increasing concentrations of CO_2 (Fig. 18.1) (Hendricks and Hotchkiss, 1997). Other organisms are similarly affected but to different degrees: Listeria monocytogenes (Hendricks and Hotchkiss, 1997; Fernandez et al., 1997),

Table 18.1 Effects of CO_2 on bacterial growth (measured by conductance) described with the Gompertz model (adapted from Martin et al., 2003)

Organism(s)	$[CO_2]$ (mM)	R^2	Growth rate (μS/h)	Time to max. growth rate (h)	Max. change in conductance (μS)	Doubling time (h)	Lag time (h)
Raw milk microflora	0.6	1.0	0.200[a]	26.0[a]	88.9[a]	1.8	20.0
	15.4	1.0	0.132[b]	33.0[b]	92.2[b]	2.3	25.4
	27.9	1.0	0.135[c]	40.2[c]	98.0[c]	2.2	32.8
	38.6	0.99	0.133[d]	44.3[d]	80.5[d]	2.3	37.7
	44.5	1.0	0.113[e]	52.9[e]	87.9[e]	2.7	44.1
P. fluorescens	0.4	0.99	0.112[a]	11.7[a]	78.2[a]	2.7	3.3
	11.2	0.99	0.128[b]	21.1[b]	69.2[b]	2.4	13.3
	27.1	0.99	0.130[b]	22.7[c]	59.9[c]	2.3	15.0
	33.6	0.99	0.088[c]	27.3[d]	61.9[d]	3.4	16.0
	46.3	0.99	0.088[c]	37.5[e]	65.6[e]	3.4	26.1
E. coli	0.5	0.99	0.064[a]	47.6[a]	56.0[a]	4.7	29.4
	49.4	0.97	0.055[b]	53.8[b]	22.0[b]	5.5	38.1
L. monocytogenes	0.5	0.98	0.136[a]	22.6[a]	118.0[a]	2.2	15.2
	48.9	0.99	0.100[b]	44.4[b]	71.5[b]	3.0	34.4
Enterococcus faecalis	0.5	0.99	0.055[a]	51.8[a]	69.0[a]	5.5	33.6
	51	0.98	0.076[b]	50.7[b]	40.7[b]	4.0	37.6
B. cereus	0.5	1.00	0.128[a]	33.9[a]	79.3[a]	2.4	26.1
	47.1	0.99	0.105[b]	37.6[b]	77.9[b]	2.9	28.1
	61.4	0.99	0.057[c]	44.4[c]	74.8[c]	5.3	26.7
B. licheniformis	0.5	0.99	0.057[a]	48.4[a]	51.4[a]	5.3	30.9
	49.4	0.96	0.057[a]	54.1[b]	31.2[b]	5.2	36.7

[a-e] For each organism, different superscript letters denote that parameters are statistically different from each other ($\alpha = 0.05$).

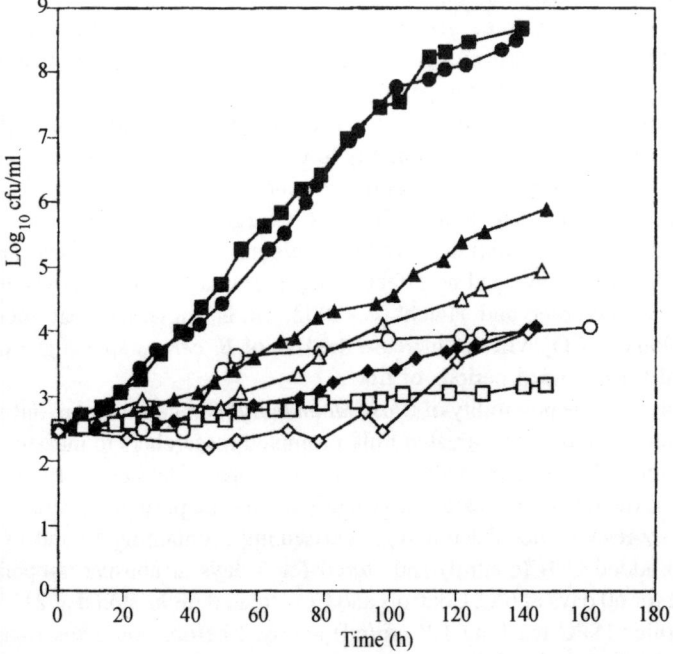

Fig. 18.1   Effects of CO_2 concentrations in modified atmospheres on growth of
Pseudomonas fluorescens in media at 7.5°C. $O_2/CO_2/N_2$: 20/0/80 ■; 20/5/75 ●; 20/20/60
▲; 20/40/40 ◆; 20/80/0 ▯; 10/30/60 ○; 20/30/50 △; 40/30/30 ◇ (Hendricks and
Hotchkiss, 1997, with permission).

Escherichia coli (Martin *et al.*, 2003), *Bacillus licheniformis* (Martin *et al.*,
2003), SPC, and milk-borne psychrotrophs (Roberts and Torrey, 1988).

The log phase of growth is also altered by CO_2. An atmosphere containing
70% CO_2 doubled the generation time of *Pseudomonas aeruginosa* when grown
in defined media at 24°C compared to controls grown in the presence of air
(King and Nagel, 1967). The maximum specific growth rate (per hour) of
Bacillus cereus, in broth, decreased from 0.46 at 0.0 atm CO_2 pressure to 0.37,
0.13, and 0.0 (no growth) at 0.5, 2.0, and 3.0 atm CO_2 respectively (Enfors and
Molin, 1980). A simultaneous increase in the lag phase and decrease in the
growth rate due to CO_2 has been demonstrated in experimental growth medium
for *P. fluorescens* (Devlieghere *et al.*, 1998a) and in UHT milk for *L.
monocytogenes* (Martin *et al.*, 2003).

The growth of fungi is also inhibited by CO_2 (McIntyre and McNeil, 1998).
Inhibitory effects of CO_2 on the growth of yeast and moulds in dairy products
have been demonstrated (Alves *et al.*, 1996; Choi and Kosikowski, 1985; Eliot *et
al.*, 1998). The growth of anaerobes in media (Reilly, 1980) and milk (Roberts
and Torrey, 1988) are inhibited in the presence of CO_2.

18.2.1 Effects of CO_2 on spores

Carbon dioxide affects spore germination in laboratory media (Hambleton and Rigby, 1970). *Clostridia* species germinate at a faster rate in the presence of CO_2 (Foegeding and Busta, 1983) in peptone yeast extract broth, but germination of *B. cereus* spores in phosphate buffer is inhibited (Enfors and Molin, 1978b). Even different strains respond differently to CO_2. In milk treated with CO_2 to a pH of 5.86 activation of *B. cereus* spores was increased by 26% while *B. cereus* var. *mycoides* was not activated by the CO_2 (Guirguis *et al.*, 1984).

Carbon dioxide (11.9 mM) dissolved in sterile milk packaged in glass jars and stored at 6°C for 35 days had no effect on the germination and outgrowth of *B. cereus* spores (Werner and Hotchkiss, 2002). It is suggested that moderate concentrations of CO_2 will not increase the risk of *B. cereus* spores growing in milk stored for extended periods of time.

Concerns with the possibility of *Clostridium botulinum* germination, outgrowth and toxin production in CO_2-treated milk prompted researchers to measure toxin production in milk inoculated with *C. botulinum* spores (Glass *et al.*, 1999). After a heat shock treatment, a cocktail of proteolytic and nonproteolytic strains of *C. botulinum* spores was inoculated into pasteurised milk containing 9.1 and 18.2 mM CO_2 or no added CO_2 (control) and stored for 6 days at abusive temperatures (21°C) and for 60 days at 6°C. Controls and CO_2-treated milks stored at 21°C were grossly spoiled (SPC reaching 10^7 cfu/ml) at day 2 before *botulinum* toxin was detectable. Milk stored at 6°C, regardless of treatment, did not contain toxin over the 60-day storage period, leading to the conclusion that dissolved CO_2 as high as 18.2 mM in milk does not increase the risk of botulism.

18.2.2 Effects of CO_2 on enzyme production and activity in milk

The effects of CO_2 on extracellular enzyme production by *P. fluorescens* in a simulated milk medium have been reported (Rowe, 1988). Carbon dioxide dissolved at 30 mM resulted in a 50% reduction in protease production at 7°C. After 5 days, lipase production was 85% greater in controls than in CO_2-treated milk. This may have something to do with the increased solubility of CO_2 in lipids. More recently Habulin and Knez demonstrated that supercritical CO_2 (100 bar) can also significantly decrease the activity of a *P. fluorescens* lipase by 50% (Habulin and Knez, 2001).

18.2.3 Inhibitory mechanisms of CO_2

The direct and indirect mechanisms by which CO_2 affects microbial growth and metabolism are not entirely clear even though the topic has been studied in detail (Daniels *et al.*, 1985; Dixon and Kell, 1989; McIntyre and McNeil, 1998; Stretton and Goodman, 1998). Four major theories on the inhibitory mechanism of CO_2 have been proposed:

1. Solubility of CO_2 in lipids may adversely affect membrane stability (Nilsson *et al.*, 2000; Ballestra *et al.*, 1996).

2. Hydration reactions of CO_2 result in reduced pH creating intracellular and environmental stress (Wolfe, 1980).
3. As a metabolite in many biochemical pathways, CO_2 can cause futile expenditure of cell energy (Dixon *et al.*, 1987).
4. CO_2 can cause physiochemical alteration and regulation of enzymes (King and Nagel, 1975; Pichard *et al.*, 1984).

Depending upon the growth medium, the organism, and its physiological state, a combination of these mechanisms is probably responsible for the observed effects.

It has been demonstrated that O_2 displacement is not the only inhibitory mechanism affecting growth (Enfors and Molin, 1980; King and Nagel, 1967). For example, when O_2 concentrations are kept constant the lag phase for *P. fluorescens* increases as CO_2 concentration increases (Hendricks and Hotchkiss, 1997) (Fig. 18.1). The inhibitory effect of CO_2 on anaerobes (Reilly, 1980) supports these conclusions.

The significance of solubility
Carbon dioxide must first dissolve to have an inhibitory effect on microorganisms. When the gas dissolves into an aqueous environment a series of hydration reactions occur (equation 18.1):

$$CO_2 + H_2O \longleftrightarrow H_2CO_3 \longleftrightarrow HCO_3^- + H^+ \longleftrightarrow CO_3^{2-} + 2H^+ \qquad 18.1$$

Upon solvating, CO_2 forms carbonic acid, which dissociates to form the bicarbonate anion and H^+. Carbon dioxide and the H^+ ions are largely responsible for the inhibitory mechanisms mentioned above; however, bicarbonate and carbonate ions have also been shown to have an inhibitory effect (Diez-Gonzalez *et al.*, 2000; Corral *et al.*, 1988).

The equilibrium of the reaction (equation 18.1) will be determined by the pH of the aqueous phase. At lower pH, the reaction will be pushed to the left. Therefore the pH of the medium in which the CO_2 is dissolved or its buffering capacity may affect the mechanism that is at work.

Carbon dioxide molecules are nonpolar and therefore more soluble in lipids than in water. When CO_2 comes into contact with a bacterial membrane it will prefer to dissolve into the lipid bilayer. In doing this, CO_2 increases the fluidity of the membrane (Sears and Eisenberg, 1961; Nilsson *et al.*, 2000) and exposes the cytoplasm of the cell to its toxic environment. Depending upon concentration and pressures, some CO_2 will eventually solubilise in the cytoplasm, which is an aqueous environment with a neutral pH. These conditions will permit the reduction in the pH of the cytoplasm and a change in the pH gradient that will stress the cell.

The mechanism by which CO_2 affects spores is not clear. Spores have a thin membrane embedded beneath a series of protein coats. These coats are porous (Setlow and Johnson, 1997) and it may be that CO_2 solubilises within the spore membrane, rendering the spore more sensitive to environmental stress such as heat either by triggering germination or by increasing the fluidity of the membrane (Enfors and Molin, 1978a).

The effects of CO_2 on phenotypic characteristics of microorganisms suggest that there are changes in gene expression due to CO_2 levels in the environment. Stretton and Goodman (1998) have reviewed the literature describing the effects of CO_2 on gene expression in a wide range of microorganisms. It is proposed that CO_2 as a ubiquitous environmental signal is part of a global regulatory system.

The inhibitory effect of CO_2 is also dependent upon temperature, as it is more soluble at lower temperatures (Tomasula and Boswell, 1999). The effect of temperature on CO_2 solubility and its inhibitory effect on the growth rate of *Lactobacillus sake* demonstrated that growth rates in laboratory media are inversely correlated with CO_2 solubility (Devlieghere *et al.*, 1998b). Carbon dioxide is soluble in milk even at temperatures of 38°C (Ma *et al.*, 2001) and therefore can be added and retained in refrigerated products during storage and distribution.

18.3   The effects of CO_2 on raw milk quality

The inhibitory effect of dissolved CO_2 and storage temperature on total plate counts (TPC), psychrotrophic plate counts (PPC), coliforms, anaerobic plate counts, lactobacilli and *Bacillus* spp. have been demonstrated. The effects of CO_2 on spores and their outgrowth have been studied to a lesser extent. Different species and strains have varying resistance to CO_2. Physiochemical changes in the raw milk resulting from dissolved CO_2 have been observed to be minimal or reversible depending upon the concentrations added.

18.3.1   Standard plate counts

Carbon dioxide dissolved in refrigerated (4–7°C) raw milk can reduce the growth of TPC organisms by 1–1.5 log compared to untreated controls that do not contain added CO_2 (Ruas-Madiedo *et al.*, 1996, 1998b). The growth of spoilage organisms in raw milk of both good and poor quality can be slowed with the addition of CO_2 (Espie and Madden, 1997; Roberts and Torrey, 1988). For example, raw milk stored at 4°C with high (1.6×10^5 cfu/ml) and low (7.8×10^3 cfu/ml) initial TPC prior to CO_2 addition (30 mM) remained below 10^6 cfu/ml for an additional 2.2 days and >3 days respectively compared to controls (King and Mabbitt, 1982). Aerobic plate count organisms in raw milk stored at 7°C had an increased lag phase (72 h) in the presence of 25–27 mM CO_2 compared to controls (24 h) (Roberts and Torrey, 1988).

18.3.2   Psychrotrophs

Psychrotrophs in raw milk are sensitive to CO_2 (King and Mabbitt, 1982; Sierra *et al.*, 1996). For example, after 6 days of storage at 7°C raw milk containing 25 mM CO_2 had 3.4 log cfu/ml fewer psychrotrophs compared to controls (Roberts and Torrey, 1988). The lag phase of psychrotrophs in raw milk stored at 4°C was 6 days in the presence of 30 mM CO_2 compared to 2 days in untreated milk (King and Mabbitt, 1982).

Some researchers have not measured CO_2 concentrations directly but instead have looked at the effects of pH reduction due to CO_2 addition on PPC. Reducing the pH from 6.8 to 6.0 held the PPC to 5.89 log cfu/ml after 4 days' storage at 7°C, compared to controls that had 7.30 log cfu/ml (Sierra et al., 1996). The same pH reduction reduced lipolytic PPC by approx 1 log cfu/ml after 4 days at 4°C compared to controls that had reached 3.5 log cfu/ml (Ruas-Madiedo et al., 1996). This bactericidal effect of CO_2 on lipolytic psychrotrophs was not discussed. Nonpolar characteristics of CO_2 allow it to be more soluble in the lipid fraction. It is possible that higher concentrations in the milk fat rendered this particular carbon source inaccessible to the lipolytic psychrotrophs, putting them at a disadvantage compared to the other microbial populations.

18.3.3   Coliforms

Growth of coliforms in raw milk is inhibited by CO_2. After 4 days' storage at 4°C raw milk acidified to pH 6.0 with CO_2 had coliform counts of 2.5 log cfu/ml compared to untreated controls that had 3.5 log cfu/ml (Ruas-Madiedo et al., 1996). The greater the amount of CO_2 dissolved in raw milk the greater the magnitude of inhibition. For example, raw milk containing 45 mM CO_2 stored at 6°C for 6 days had 4.7 log cfu/ml coliforms compared to controls that had 7 log cfu/ml (Espie and Madden, 1997). Milk containing lower levels of CO_2 (25–28 mM) and stored at a slightly higher temperature (7°C) for 6 days inhibited coliform growth by 1–1.5 log cfu/ml compared to controls (Roberts and Torrey, 1988).

18.3.4   Anaerobes

Carbon dioxide has an inhibitory effect on anaerobically grown microorganisms (Enfors and Molin, 1980). Raw milk containing 26.5 mM CO_2 stored at 7°C for 6 days had 5.7 log cfu/ml anaerobic counts compared to 8.5 cfu/ml in controls (Roberts and Torrey, 1988).

18.3.5   *Pseudomonas* species

Pseudomonas species, in general, are significantly inhibited by CO_2 (Roberts and Torrey, 1988; King and Mabbitt, 1982). Counts of pseudomonads were 3 log cycles lower in raw milk containing 30 mM CO_2 stored at 4°C for 4 days compared to controls (Espie and Madden, 1997).

18.3.6   Biochemical and physical changes in raw milk due to CO_2 addition

The biochemical effects of CO_2 on raw milk have been studied. Carbon dioxide does not alter the stability of fat-soluble vitamins in raw milk stored at 7°C for seven days (Sierra et al., 1996). Organic acid profiles and the casein and whey protein ratios in refrigerated (4°C) raw milk were unaltered by CO_2 addition that reduced the pH to 6.0 (Ruas-Madiedo *et al.*, 1996). High-temperature short-time (HTST) treatments of raw milk, post-CO_2 removal, did not alter the protein ratios or composition of volatile compounds (Ruas-Madiedo *et al.*, 1996) compared to untreated controls. Standard analytical tests such as alkaline phosphatase detection, freezing point, pH, antibiotic tests, and FTIR to measure fat, protein, and lactose, were performed in raw milk with and without CO_2 (Ma *et al.*, 2001). Alkaline phosphatase and antibiotic tests were unaltered due to CO_2 addition. Fat and protein content as measured by FTIR were also unaltered. An absorbance increase in the lactose wavelengths due to CO_2 was measured. The reduction of pH due to CO_2 (Fig. 18.2) was noted to be the likely cause of the concurrent reduction in freezing point of raw milk with added CO_2. Reductions in pH cause a dissociation of casein micelles, resulting in a release of calcium and phosphate salts into the aqueous portion (Gevaudan *et al.*, 1996). This increase in solutes likely causes the linear decrease in freezing point (FP) from 0.55°Hortvet (°H) in raw milk without added CO_2 to 0.59°H in milk containing 1000 ppm CO_2 (FP = $-0.5434 - 0.0000510 \times [CO_2]$ (ppm); $R^2 =$ 0.98) (Ma *et al.*, 2001).

Destabilisation of the casein micelle due to CO_2 addition may be of concern with respect to increased fouling on plate heat exchangers during thermal processing. It is known that decreasing the pH of milk during thermal treatment can increase the amount of fouling (Patil and Reuter, 1988; Skudder *et al.*, 1986) and CO_2 acidification of milk could cause an increase in scaling on the heat

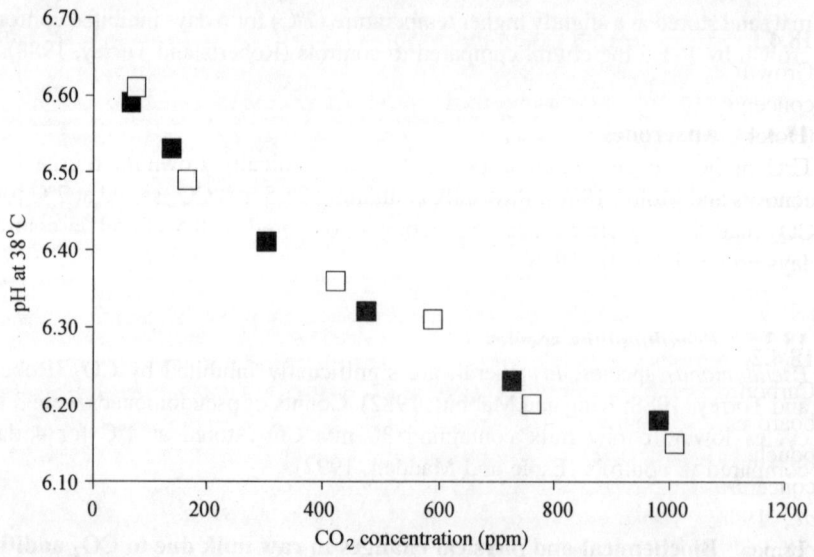

Fig. 18.2 Effect of dissolved CO_2 on pH of raw milk (38°C) from two different farms (distinguished by open and closed symbols) (Ma *et al.*, 2001, with permission).

exchangers (Calvo and de Rafael, 1995). Twenty litres of raw milk treated with CO_2 sufficient to reduce the pH to 6.0 and heated for 20 s at 80°C formed deposits of mostly protein and minerals on pasteuriser plates. The lipid content of the deposits on heat exchanger plates exposed to the CO_2-treated milk was dramatically lower (45 ± 0.72 g/kg dry matter) than in untreated controls (234 ± 0.79 g/kg dry matter). The concentration of CO_2 dissolved in the milk was not measured. Milk acidified to the same pH with hydrochloric acid completely clogged the pasteuriser (Calvo and de Rafael, 1995).

Recent work (Guillaume *et al.*, 2002) concluded that the effects of acidification of reconstituted milk to pH 5.8 were completely reversible after CO_2 was removed by vacuum treatment. Both the composition and structure of the micellar calcium phosphate were unaltered by CO_2 addition and removal.

18.4   The effects of CO_2 on dairy product quality

Carbon dioxide is 'Generally Recognized As Safe' (GRAS; FDA, 2000). It can be used to extend the shelf-life of a variety of dairy products including concentrated raw milk, pasteurised milk, yogurt, cottage cheese, ice cream mixes, and aged cheeses. For fluid products CO_2 can be directly sparged in-line (DAC) but for cheeses CO_2 is incorporated into a modified atmosphere surrounding the product. Important to both of these approaches is a low CO_2/O_2 permeability of the package barrier.

18.4.1   Concentrated raw milk

Growth of Gram-negative and TPC can be reduced in raw milk that has been concentrated by reverse osmosis (RO) or ultrafiltration (UF) techniques (Hotchkiss, unpublished data). UF whole milk containing 25.3 mM CO_2 had TPC of 10^5 cfu/ml after 14 days of storage at 7°C, compared to untreated controls that had 10^8 cfu/ml. RO concentrated whole milk containing 25 mM CO_2 had 10^3 and 10^5 cfu/ml of Gram-negatives and TPC respectively after 7 days compared to 10^6 cfu/ml for both Gram-negative and TPC in controls.

18.4.2   Fluid milk

Carbon dioxide can improve the microbial quality of milk packaged in paper-board cartons (Duthie, 1985), glass containers (Glass *et al.*, 1999), and plastic pouches (Hotchkiss *et al.*, 1999). Depending upon packaging material and CO_2 concentration, the shelf-life can be increased by as much as 200% (Hotchkiss *et al.*, 1999). Table 18.2 describes the relationship between package barrier permeability, CO_2 concentration in the milk, and microbial growth. Shelf-life, defined as the days to reach 10^6 cfu/ml, increases as CO_2 concentration increases and package barrier permeability to CO_2 decreases. Shelf-life of milk packaged in a low-barrier film increased by 65% from 9.6 days without added CO_2 to 15.9

Table 18.2   Combined effects of dissolved CO_2 and packaging permeability on shelf-life of milk (adapted from Hotchkiss et al., 1999)

Film permeability[a]	Days at 6.1°C for SPC to reach 10^6 cfu/ml[b] [CO$_2$] (mM)			
	0	8.7	14.2	21.5
3801	9.6	11.8	12.5	15.9
2040	–	9.9	14.0	14.6
110	–	13.4	18.4	19.6
<0.5	–	13.3	19.1	19.1

[a] ($cm^3/m^2/24$ h at 7°C).
[b] Initial counts = 1 cfu/ml.

days at 21.5 mM CO_2. Milk packaged in higher-barrier films had a shelf-life of 19 days (Hotchkiss et al., 1999).

The growth of psychrotrophs (Duthie, 1985), pseudomonads (Hotchkiss et al., 1999; King and Mabbitt, 1982; Shipe et al., 1982), and SPC (Glass et al., 1999) is inhibited in pasteurised milk that has been treated with CO_2. Safety issues associated with the effect of CO_2 on toxin-producing anaerobes, such as *Clostridium botulinum* (Glass et al., 1999) and pathogenic spore formers such as *Bacillus cereus* (Werner and Hotchkiss, 2002) have been addressed. Carbon dioxide does not appear to increase the risk of toxin production by *C. botulinum* or the outgrowth of *B. cereus* in inoculated refrigerated milks.

The sensory threshold, as determined by a trained panel, for CO_2 in 2% pasteurised milk is approximately 9.0 mM. At levels just below the threshold (8.7 mM) a high-barrier package increased the shelf-life by nearly 40% (Table 18.2). The organoleptic properties of CO_2-treated milk are improved after 14 days (Duthie, 1985) and 21 days (Glass et al., 1999) of refrigerated storage compared to controls not containing CO_2.

Recently, conductance, which correlates with plate counts, has been used to monitor the growth at 15°C of inoculated spoilage organisms (in mixed and pure cultures) and pathogens in milk containing dissolved CO_2 at levels ranging from 0.4 to 61.4 mM (Martin et al., 2003). Conductance data accurately fit the Gompertz model with R^2 ranging from 0.96 to 1.00, permitting a quantifiable effect of CO_2 on the lag, exponential and stationary phases of growth (Table 18.1). The doubling time for native microflora in raw milk was 1.8 h in controls containing 0.6 mM CO_2 and increased to 2.3 and 2.7 h in milk containing 15.4 and 44.5 mM CO_2 respectively. Lag times (h) for raw milk microflora were 20, 25.4 and 44.1 respectively for the same CO_2 concentrations mentioned above. The doubling time for *B. cereus* increased from 2.4 to 2.9 and 5.3 h as the CO_2 concentration (mM) increased from 0.5 to 47.1 and 61.4 respectively. The doubling time for *Listeria monocytogenes* increased from 2.2 to 3.0 h and the lag time more than doubled from 15.2 to 34.4 h in milk containing 0.5 and 48.9 mM CO_2 respectively (Martin et al., 2003).

18.4.3   Effects of CO_2 on the microbial quality of cottage cheese

Several commercial cottage cheese manufacturers in the United States use CO_2 to improve the quality of their product (DMI, 1998) as well as in other parts of the world. When CO_2 is flushed into the headspace (Kosikowski and Brown, 1972; Maniar *et al.*, 1994), bubbled into the cream dressing (Lee, 1996; Chen and Hotchkiss, 1991, 1993), or bubbled directly through the finished product (Moir *et al.*, 1993), the lag phase of spoilage organisms increases and product quality improves.

A simple and effective approach to incorporating CO_2 into cottage cheese is to add it to the cream dressing prior to mixing with the curds. An inline sparging apparatus and flow diagram for this process has been described (Hotchkiss and Lee, 1996). Cottage cheese prepared in this way can have a shelf-life as long as 80 days (Fig. 18.3). A mixture of three Gram-negative psychrotrophic spoilage organisms inoculated at a level of 10^3 cfu/ml did not grow in CO_2-treated (40% in head space) cottage cheese over a 70-day period when stored at 4°C in glass jars (Chen and Hotchkiss, 1991). In controls not containing CO_2 bacterial levels reached 10^6 cfu/ml within 15 days. A storage temperature of 7°C combined with CO_2 addition held counts below 10^4 cfu/ml for 30 days, and in controls, SPC reached 10^6 cfu/ml within 5 days.

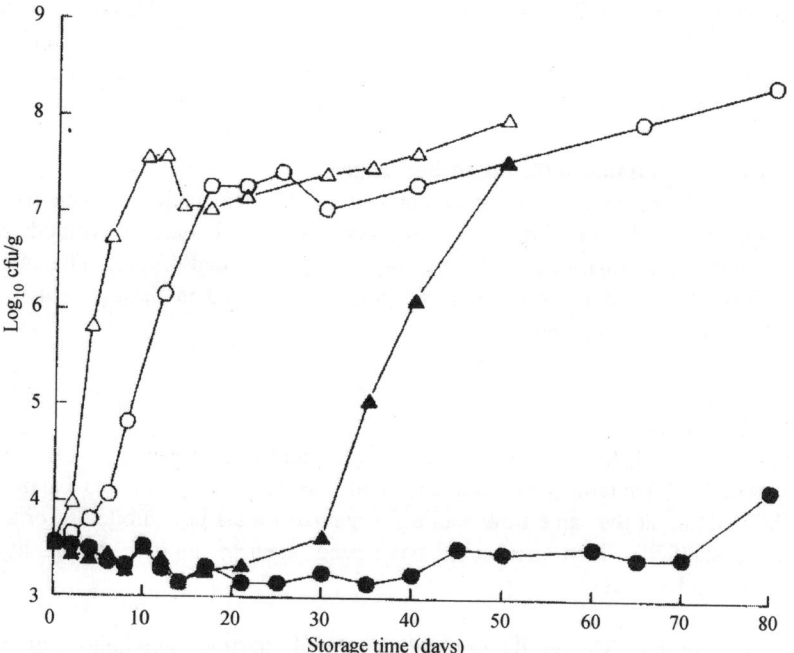

Fig. 18.3 Standard plate counts in cottage cheese packaged with (solid symbols) and without (open symbols) added dissolved CO_2 and stored at 4°C ($\bullet$, $\circ$) and 7°C ($\blacktriangle$, $\triangle$) (Chen and Hotchkiss, 1991, with permission).

Gram-negative organisms, particularly *Pseudomonas* spp. (Moir *et al.*, 1993), psychrotrophs (Maniar *et al.*, 1994), yeasts and moulds (Kosikowski and Brown, 1972; Chen and Hotchkiss, 1991) and lactic acid bacteria (Maniar *et al.*, 1994), are inhibited by CO_2 in cottage cheese. Microscopic examination of CO_2-treated cottage cheese showed that Gram-positive bacilli and cocci predominated compared to controls (Chen and Hotchkiss, 1991). Carbon dioxide seemed to have an inhibitory effect on the yeast and mould populations in cottage cheese, as they were undetectable in CO_2-treated samples but found in the controls at levels of 10 cfu/g (colony forming units per gram). These effects are not attributed to the pH-reducing effect of CO_2 as the controls and treated samples had similar pH (5.2–5.25) (Chen and Hotchkiss, 1991).

Improved flavour scores for cottage cheese parallel the improved microbial quality in CO_2-treated samples (Maniar *et al.*, 1994; Kosikowski and Brown, 1972; Lee, 1996). The amount of CO_2 added is below the taste threshold and cannot be detected by the consumer.

Concerns with outgrowth of facultative and obligate anaerobes, such as *L. monocytogenes* and *C. sporogenes* have been addressed (Chen and Hotchkiss, 1993). Over a 63-day storage period at 4°C and 7°C, *C. sporogenes* did not grow in either CO_2-treated (35% of the volume in the headspace) or control cottage cheeses. *Listeria monocytogenes* inoculated at 10^4 cfu/ml in CO_2-treated cottage cheese did not increase during 63 days of storage at 4°C, but did increase by 1 log when stored at 7°C. In the control products without added CO_2, counts reached 10^7 cfu/ml in 28 days and 7 days when stored at 4°C and 7°C respectively.

18.4.4   Carbonated milk-based beverages

Milk-based beverages with sufficient CO_2 to be detectable by taste have a refrigerated shelf-life of more than 6 weeks. Such carbonated flavoured dairy beverages have equal or better nutritional quality than that of milk. The amount of CO_2 added and the type of flavouring system used in these products are critical to their acceptance.

18.4.5   Yogurt

When using CO_2 to improve the quality of fermented dairy products, the growth of beneficial bacteria such as lactic acid producers or probiotics cannot be inhibited and at the same time spoilage organisms must be inhibited in order to extend shelf-life. Two approaches have been taken to improve the quality of yogurts and cheeses:

1. Incorporate CO_2 into the raw milk to provide starting ingredients with good microbial quality.
2. Incorporate CO_2 into the final product or atmosphere surrounding the product to inhibit spoilage.

To evaluate these strategies, researchers have monitored the growth and metabolism of fermentative bacteria in CO_2-treated products and evaluated their quality compared to controls made by conventional methods.

Yogurt made from CO_2-treated raw milk (to a pH of either 6.0, 6.2, or 6.4) had similar sensory properties and viscosity as control yogurt but lower pH values after 7 days of storage at 7°C (Calvo et al., 1999). In a different study growth and metabolism of two combinations of yogurt starter cultures in carbonated milk were monitored over a 49-day storage period at 4°C (Vinderola et al., 2000). Carbon dioxide was added to the milk after the heat treatment of the raw milk and prior to inoculation with either of two starter culture blends:

- *Lactobacillus acidophilus* and *Streptococcus thermophilus*
- *L. acidophilus*, *S. thermophilus* and *Bifidobacteria bifidum*.

The growth of the first culture mixture was unaltered by the addition of CO_2 which reduced the pH from 6.84 to 6.31. In the presence of *B. bifidum* and CO_2 the counts of *L. acidophilus* were lower towards the latter part of the storage period. Concentrations of organic acids (pyruvic, lactic, and acetic) were the same in both CO_2-treated and control milks for both culture combinations at the end of the storage period. However, acetic acid was lower in the CO_2-treated milk containing *B. bifidum* during the first 4 weeks of storage, which may have been related to the lower counts of *L. acidophilus* in these samples later on. After 24 days the sensory properties of the yogurts, including mouthfeel, odour, acidity, and overall acceptability, were slightly improved in the CO_2-treated yogurts, but statistically indistinguishable from controls. Carbon dioxide-treated milks reached the break point pH of 5.0 sooner than untreated milk (Vinderola et al., 2000). Gueimonde et al. (2002) found that CO_2 dissolved in milk did not have a negative effect on the growth of probiotic bacteria.

When CO_2 was dissolved directly into finished Swiss-style yogurt, the growth and viability of inoculated pathogens (*L. monocytogenes*, *E. coli*) and typical starter cultures were unaltered (Karagul-Yuceer et al., 2001). In this study the CO_2 content was not measured directly so the actual amount dissolved is unclear.

A consumer acceptance test demonstrated that the shelf-life of a yogurt beverage could be extended to 4 months with the addition of CO_2 (5 kg/cm^2 at 4°C) compared to uncarbonated controls that were spoiled at 30 days (Kosikowski and Choi, 1985). The yogurt beverages (fermented with *L. bulgaricus* and *S. thermophilus*) were packaged in glass containers and stored at 4.4°C and 10°C. After 40 days yeast and mould counts increased from 10 cfu/g to 100 and 200 cfu/g in uncarbonated yogurt beverages stored at 4.4 and 10°C respectively, whereas in the carbonated product they remained below 10 cfu/g over an 80-day period at both storage temperatures. The soluble protein and volatile fatty acid content of the control yogurts increased at a faster rate than the carbonated samples, an indication that spoilage was occurring more rapidly, though unfortunately SPC were not measured. The noncarbonated yogurt pH dropped faster than the carbonated yogurt pH, indicating slowed metabolism of the lactic acid bacteria (LAB), but their growth was not measured in the different treatments.

18.4.6   Ice cream and unfrozen mixes

Early attempts to incorporate CO_2 into ice-cream processing did not demonstrate a significant effect on microbial growth in the frozen product (Prucha et al., 1922; Rettger et al., 1922; Valley and Rettger, 1927). Extending the shelf-life of the unfrozen mix using dissolved CO_2 may be more useful and feasible. Total aerobic plate and Gram-negative counts were measured in chocolate ice-cream mix containing 0, 690, and 1080 ppm CO_2, packaged in high-barrier pouches and stored at 6.1°C for 43 days (Hotchkiss, unpublished data). Total aerobic plate counts reached 6.0 log cfu/ml at 20, 35 and 41 days in mixes containing 0, 690 and 1080 ppm CO_2 respectively. Gram-negative counts reached 6.0 log cfu/ml in control mix at 30 days, whereas the CO_2-treated samples took longer than 40 days to reach this level. Sensory tests on soft-serve ice cream made from treated mixes indicated that the threshold for CO_2 was 800 to 1400 ppm.

18.4.7   Aged cheeses

Carbon dioxide added to raw milk to be used for cheese production can decrease the processing time (Montilla et al., 1995; McCarney et al., 1995; Ruas-Madiedo et al., 2002), reduce the amount of rennet necessary for coagulation (Montilla et al., 1995; McCarney et al., 1995; Calvo et al., 1993), and increase yields (Ruas-Madiedo et al., 1998a, 2002). Organoleptic properties of cheese made from CO_2-treated milk are as good as (Ruas-Madiedo et al., 2002) or better than (McCarney et al., 1995) controls made from untreated milk.

The amount of rennet necessary to make Cheddar cheese can be decreased by 50% when added to milk that has been treated with CO_2 to a concentration of 30.6 mM (McCarney et al., 1995). Lipolysis and proteolysis in cheese made from CO_2-treated milk was significantly lower compared to controls after 3 months of storage at 7°C. The cheese made from CO_2-treated milk received a higher sensory score than control cheese as determined by a commercial grader (McCarney et al., 1995).

When raw milk with high TPC (5×10^5 cfu/ml) was sparged with CO_2 (to pH 6.2) and refrigerated (4°C) prior to being used for production of a short ripened cheese, the resulting cheese had a higher yield compared to cheese made from uncarbonated milk (Ruas-Madiedo et al., 1998a). After 7 days of ripening at 17°C the CO_2-treated cheese had a yield of 10.4% compared to 5.9% in the control. After 3 and 7 days of ripening the non-casein nitrogen fraction of the cheese made from CO_2-treated milk was significantly lower than in the untreated controls, an indication of reduced proteolysis. Alpha, beta, and gamma casein fractions were not affected by the CO_2 treatment, and at 15 days of ripening the proteolytic activity in both cheeses was the same. Treating milk with CO_2 did not alter the sensory properties of the cheeses compared to controls (Ruas-Madiedo et al., 1998a).

Carbon dioxide dissolved in milk does not affect the growth and metabolism of cheese starter cultures (Van Hekken et al., 2000; Ruas-Madiedo et al., 1998a; Calvo et al., 1993). The growth of individual strains and mixed cultures of Lactococcus ssp. and Leuconostoc citreum at 22°C over an 18 h period was the same in pasteurised milk treated with CO_2 (to a pH of 6.2) and untreated controls (pH 6.7). After 8 hours of incubation the concentrations of organic acids (citric, pyruvic, lactic, formic, acetic, and hippuric) were identical in both CO_2-treated and control milks (Ruas-Madiedo et al., 1998a).

Once cheese has been manufactured, modified atmospheres containing CO_2 can be used to extend shelf-life (Alves et al., 1996; Eliot et al., 1998; Piergiovanni et al., 1993; Pintado and Malcata, 2000; Gonzalez-Fandos et al., 2000; Olarte et al., 2001, 2002). Fluorescent light exposure may need to be considered in order to prevent defects in colour that are enhanced by high CO_2 concentrations (Colchin et al., 2001).

Pintado and Malcata (2000) compared the growth of psychrotrophs, mesophiles, lactococci, lactobacilli, Bacillus, and spore-forming clostridia, amongst others, in Requeijão, a whey cheese, packaged under 100% CO_2 to that packaged under 100% N_2. After 15 days at 4°C storage under CO_2, none of the populations tested had reached 10^6 log cfu/g, whereas under N_2 most had exceeded this level. For example, PPC reached 5.97 and 8.08 log cfu/g under CO_2 and N_2 atmospheres respectively. Pseudomonas spp. reached 4.32 log cfu/g under 100% CO_2 compared to 8.81 log cfu/g under N_2-packaged cheese. At 18°C the two packaging configurations had less effect on the outgrowth of the microbial populations tested, emphasising the need for refrigerated storage together with MAP to hinder microbial growth. Yeasts and moulds were not detected in cheeses stored in 100% CO_2 at day 15 (at 4°C) compared to 4 log cfu/g in 100% N_2. Bacillus spp. were not detected at days 2 and 4 in CO_2-packaged cheese but reached 5.6 log cfu/g by day 15, the same as that found in N_2-packaged cheese (Pintado and Malcata, 2000).

Atmospheres containing 20–100% CO_2 reduced proteolysis and lipolysis in Cameros, a fresh goat's milk cheese, and inhibited the growth of psychrotrophs, mesophiles, Enterobacteriaceae, and coliforms. After 28 days of storage at 4°C control cheeses, packaged in the presence of air, had psychrotrophic levels reaching eight log cfu/g whereas in an atmosphere containing 100% CO_2 counts had not exceeded 2.7 log cfu/g (Gonzalez-Fandos et al., 2000). Yeasts were undetectable in the CO_2-stored cheese, but in controls counts reached 3.34 log cfu/g in 28 days. Packaging Taleggio cheese in an atmosphere containing 10% CO_2 resulted in a 1 log reduction in moulds compared to controls packaged in the presence of air (Piergiovanni et al., 1993). Anaerobes decreased in Cameros cheese packaged in 100% CO_2 atmospheres from 3 log cfu/g to 1 log cfu/g after 28 days. In controls (air), 20 and 40% CO_2 atmospheres (balance N_2) there was a 4 log cfu/g increase over the same time period (Olarte et al., 2002). Sensory analysis of Cameros cheeses suggests that 100% CO_2 atmospheres can be deleterious to quality but that a 50/50 (CO_2/N_2) atmosphere is optimal for improving flavour and reducing microbial growth (Gonzalez-Fandos et al., 2000; Olarte et al., 2001).

The microbial quality of Mozzarella shreds (Eliot et al., 1998) and slices (Alves et al., 1996) stored under modified atmospheres containing CO_2 was improved over those packaged under air or N_2, and 100% CO_2 atmospheres inhibited the growth of yeast and moulds in both products. Over a 58-day storage period at 7°C no growth of yeast and moulds was detected on Mozzarella slices packaged in 100% CO_2 compared to greater than 10^6 cfu/ml in controls after only 10 days.

Shredded Cheddar cheese stored at 4°C under 100% CO_2 (barrier permeability: O_2 transmission of 2 cm^3/m^2/day forming layer; 4 cm^3/m^2/day – non-forming layer) contained lower levels of volatiles associated with mould growth (Colchin et al., 2001). L^*, a^* and b^* colour-values for N_2- and CO_2-packaged cheeses stored under fluorescent lighting were measured. L^* values were significantly higher, and a^* and b^* values were significantly lower, in cheeses stored under CO_2 compared to N_2. It is suggested that CO_2 generates free radicals in the presence of fluorescent light, oxidising bixin (the carotenoid compound in anatto responsible for the orange colour) and resulting in a bleached appearance. Perhaps opaque packaging material could hinder this defect.

18.5   Bactericidal and sporicidal effects of dissolved CO_2 during thermal processing

Bacteria and their spores are more sensitive to thermal treatments under acidic conditions (Jay, 1992). When CO_2 is dissolved in an aqueous solution, such as milk, the pH decreases (equation 18.1, Fig. 18.2). The effects of CO_2 on the thermal resistance of vegetative cells and spores have been studied. The majority of work has been conducted in media at high pressures or near-supercritical conditions and at moderate to ambient temperatures.

D-values (min) for L. monocytogenes in a solution of physiological saline and media (1%) under 15 atm CO_2 pressure were 35.8, 22.3 and 14.3 at 25°C, 35°C and 45°C respectively (Erkmen, 2000). At 60 atm CO_2 the D-values at these temperatures decreased to 13.4, 8.8 and 7.3 respectively, demonstrating that increased CO_2 pressures can increase the thermal sensitivity of a common facultative pathogen. A similar pattern was observed for the inactivation of E. coli in ringer solution (Ballestra et al., 1996). The $D_{35°C}$-values (min) were 496, 30.3 and 1.9 at 1.2, 2.5 and 5 MPa CO_2 respectively.

At 45°C in the absence of CO_2 the viability of E. coli cells was unchanged over a 1 h period. As the CO_2 pressure was increased from 1.2 to 5 MPa the inactivation curves became biphasic. An initial shoulder portion during the first 30 min of exposure became shorter and the slope of the second phase became more negative as CO_2 pressure increased (Ballestra et al., 1996). Similar patterns were observed for L. monocytogenes (Erkmen, 2000). It is hypothesised that during the initial phase CO_2 penetrates the cell, and that the second phase represents the point at which a critical amount of CO_2 has collected in the cell, resulting in a more dramatic drop in viability. Scanning electron micrographs (SEM) of CO_2-treated cells revealed deformed cell walls of some cells but the percentage of damaged cells did not correlate with the loss in viability. The activity of seven of eight enzymes assayed was reduced in the CO_2-treated cells compared to untreated (Ballestra et al., 1996). It is hypothesised that CO_2 passes through the cell membrane and acidifies the cell cytoplasm below the isoelectric point of the enzymes, rendering them inactive. It has also been proposed that the chemical composition of the bacterial cell wall and the surface-to-volume ratio of the cell may be important factors determining the sensitivity of a particular bacterial strain (Dillow et al., 1999).

The amount of heat and the concentration of CO_2 influence the degree of increased thermal sensitivity of bacteria in milk. Microbial survivors (enumerated by SPC) in heat-treated raw milk were significantly lower in milk containing 44–58 mM CO_2 compared to controls that had natural levels of CO_2 ranging from 2 to 4 mM (Loss and Hotchkiss, 2002). For example, CO_2-treated milk heated for 5 min at 67°C, 72°C and 90°C had 257, 89 and 25 cfu/ml respectively compared to controls that had 338, 282 and 44 cfu/ml in untreated milk heated for the same time and temperatures (Loss and Hotchkiss, 2002). Aerobic plate counts and L. monocytogenes in whole milk heated to 45°C under 60 atm of CO_2 both decreased by 3 log cycles after 12 hours (Erkmen, 2000). Unfortunately, reductions in control milks without added CO_2 are not mentioned in this study.

Thermal inactivation rates of P. fluorescens in whole milk treated with CO_2 (0–35 mM) increase as concentration of CO_2 increases (Fig. 18.4). There is a negative linear correlation between $D_{50°C}$-value (min) and CO_2 concentration ($D_{50°C} = -0.20x + 13.74$; $r^2 = 0.90$). $D_{50°C}$-values in the untreated control, 15 and 35 mM CO_2-treated milk were 13.4, 10.5 and 7.2 min respectively, representing reductions of 22% and 46% (Loss and Hotchkiss, 2002). Although this organism is sensitive to HTST treatments, its lipolytic and proteolytic enzymes are not (Champagne et al., 1994). Perhaps on-farm thermisation combined with CO_2 treatments could reduce the numbers of psychrotrophs that can proliferate during bulk milk collection and transportation.

Carbon dioxide added to fluid foods in the form of carbonate can reduce the pH of the food and increase the thermal sensitivity of spores (Alderton, 1969). Unlike vegetative cells, spores are essentially metabolically inactive and support little enzyme activity. It has been proposed that the increased acidity results in a desorption of cations from the spore causing an increase in hydration of the core of the spore (Lynch, 1988). Dehydration of the spore is its main defence against thermal treatments as wet heat is more severe than dry heat (Setlow and Johnson, 1997).

Carbon dioxide at 5 MPa can increase the thermal sensitivity of bacterial and fungal spores in Ringer solution (Ballestra and Cuq, 1998). Bacillus subtilis spores heated at 80°C under 5 MPa CO_2 for 1 h were reduced by 3 logs, but in

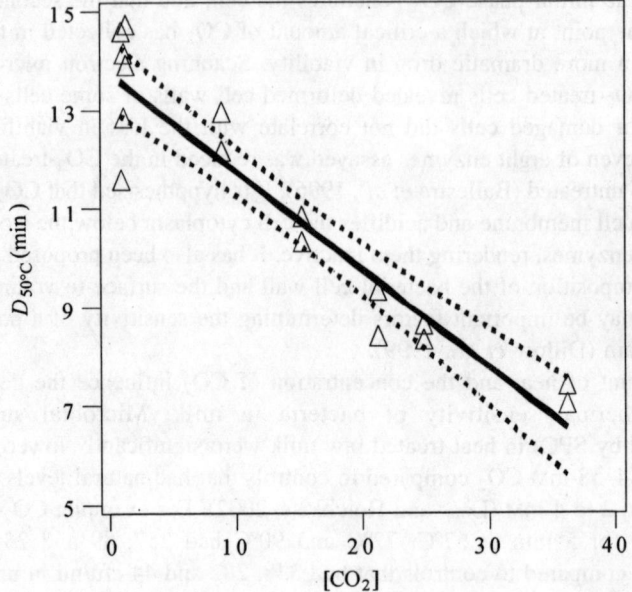

Fig. 18.4 Effect of dissolved CO_2 on $D_{50°C}$-values for *P. fluorescens* R1-232 in milk ($y = -0.20x + 13.74, R^2 = 0.90$). Dotted lines represent 95% confidence bands ($n = 1$).

the absence of CO_2 no reduction in viability was observed at this temperature. $D_{90°C}$-values for *B. subtilis* spores were 14 min at 5 MPa CO_2 and 66 min in the absence of CO_2. $D_{80°C}$-values for *Byssochlamys fulva* ascospores decreased from 350 min in controls to 85.5 min in the presence of 5 MPa CO_2. $D_{50°C}$-values for *Aspergillus niger* conidia decreased from >200 min in controls to 11 min under 5 MPa CO_2. At 60°C and 85°C 5 MPa CO_2 had no effect on the thermal sensitivity of *A. niger* conidia and *B. fulva* ascopores, suggesting that the lethal effects of the heat treatment are masking the sporicidal effects of the CO_2 (Ballestra and Cuq, 1998).

The $D_{89°C}$-value for *Bacillus cereus* spores was significantly decreased from 5.56 min in control milks (no added CO_2) to 5.24 min in milk containing 33 mM CO_2 (Loss and Hotchkiss, 2002). A higher concentration of dissolved CO_2 (37 mM) in milk containing an initial inoculum of 8.7 log cfu/ml also resulted in fewer survivors (4.25 log cfu/ml) after a 15-minute treatment at 89°C compared to controls that had 4.73 log cfu/ml survivors (Loss, 2001). After a 40-second treatment at 105°C, CO_2-treated TSB (pH reduced to 6.3) had 1 log fewer survivors of *B. cereus* spores compared to untreated (pH 7.2) media heated for the same amount of time (Loss, unpublished data).

The effect of CO_2 on spore germination at higher heat treatments for shorter durations depends upon species and strain (Guirguis *et al.*, 1984). For example, 100% of spores of *B. subtilis* in reconstituted milk with pH adjusted to 5.86 with CO_2, heated at 120°C for 2 s, survived compared to 0.1% survival of spores

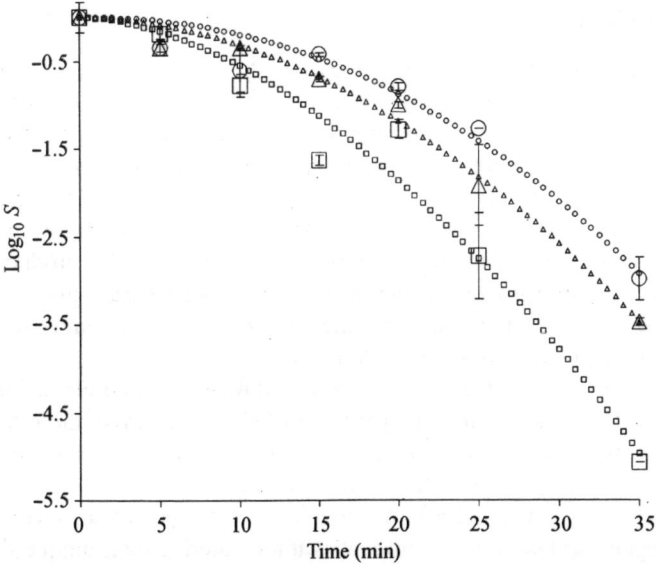

Fig. 18.5 Nonlinear modelling of thermal death rate of *P. fluorescens* R1-232 at 50°C in milk. Curves represent nonlinear regressions of the survival data in milk containing 1 (○ actual, ○ predicted), 15 (△ actual, △ predicted) and 36 mM (□ actual, □ predicted) dissolved CO_2, respectively. $R^2 = 0.96$, 0.99 and 0.97 respectively ($n = 2$, ±1 s.d.).

suspended in control milk that had no CO_2. On the other hand, 2% of *B. cereus* spores heated at 125°C for 2 s in the CO_2-treated milk survived compared to 100% survival in control milk.

The combined effects of dissolved CO_2 and thermal treatment on inactivation of spores and vegetative cells have been modelled using the Weibull function (Loss and Hotchkiss, 2002) (Fig. 18.5). Thermal inactivation curves for *P. fluorescens* at 50°C in the presence and absence of CO_2 are distinctly biphasic in nature, as is the case for *B. subtilis* spores (Ballestra and Cuq, 1998) and *E. coli* (Ballestra *et al.*, 1996). The Weibull model more accurately describes the combined effects of dissolved CO_2 and thermal treatments on survival of common milk spoilage organisms ($R^2 = 0.96$, 0.99 and 0.97 for 1, 15 and 36 mM CO_2 treatments respectively) than does the linear model ($R^2 = 0.83$, 0.89 and 0.90 respectively). Given a useful model like the Weibull, nonthermal treatments such as CO_2 combined with thermal processing can be used to optimise hurdle preservation approaches.

Two major obstacles to producing raw milk cheese on a large scale are the potential for survival of pathogens (such as *L. monocytogenes*) and the deleterious effects of psychrotrophic spoilage organisms. Current data suggest that CO_2 combined with heat treatments may decrease the number of pathogens in the cheese at the beginning of the ageing process and also improve sensory quality by reducing the number of surviving spoilage organisms.

18.6   Conclusions

Carbon dioxide is a unique natural antimicrobial and processing aid that has several potential uses in the dairy industry. It is unique because it can be added to and removed from dairy products with no deleterious effects. It is GRAS, and at the present time does not need to be declared on an ingredient label. The physiochemical properties of CO_2, i.e. ease of solubility in aqueous and lipid phases, its ability to reduce pH, and temperature-dependent solubility, make it ideal for use in dairy products. It can be dissolved into fluid dairy products as a preservative to inhibit growth of pathogens and spoilage organisms and/or to alter the functionality of the casein micelle, and then it can be removed with a simple vacuum or by agitation and mild heating.

The benefits of CO_2 to the cottage cheese industry are quite clear. There is also an abundance of data supporting the use of CO_2 to improve the microbial quality of raw milk, but the benefits of this technology have not transferred to the farm and milk collection sector of the industry. Safe raw milk cheeses are highly desirable in the US and Europe, and CO_2 has the potential to reduce the risk of pathogen survival in these products without altering their unique flavour characteristics.

Quantifying the effects of CO_2 on growth of spoilage organisms and pathogens through the use of statistical modelling will be critical for optimising its use and ensuring safe and wholesome products. Work in this area is just beginning but thus far has demonstrated that the effects of CO_2 can be accurately described using the Gompertz growth model (Martin *et al*, 2003). All preservation technologies from refrigeration to pasteurisation have altered the microbial ecology of dairy products. Refrigeration has selected for Gram-negative psychrotrophs, and pasteurisation has created a niche for psychrotrophic spore formers. Undoubtedly, CO_2 will also effect the microbial ecological balance in dairy foods. Modelling the effects of CO_2 on a wide spectrum of bacteria in pure and mixed cultures, in a variety of dairy products, will give us a better understanding of the changes due to CO_2 and allow us to protect and preserve our nutritious supply of dairy foods.

18.7   References

ALDERTON G (1969), 'Process for sterilizing foods and other materials', United States Patent Office, Patent No. 3454406.

ALVES R M V, ISABEL C, SARANTOPOULOS G L, VANDENDER A G F and FARIA J A F (1996), 'Stability of sliced mozzarella cheese in modified-atmosphere packaging', *J Food Prot*, 59, 838–844.

BALLESTRA P and CUQ J L (1998), 'Influence of pressurized carbon dioxide on the thermal inactivation of bacterial and fungal spores', *Lebens- Wiss- und -Technol*, 31(1), 84–88.

BALLESTRA P, DASILVA A A and CUQ J L (1996), 'Inactivation of *Escherichia coli* by carbon dioxide under pressure' *J Food Sci*, 61(4), 829–831, 836.

CALVO M M and DE RAFAEL D (1995), 'Deposit formation in a heat exchanger during pasteurization of CO_2 acidified milk', *J Dairy Res*, 62, 641–644.

CALVO M M, MONTILLA M M and OLANO A (1993), 'Rennet-clotting properties and starter activity on milk acidified with carbon doixide', *J Food Prot,* 56, 1073–1076.

CALVO M M, MONTILLA A and COBOS A (1999), 'Lactic acid production and rheological properties of yogurt made from milk acidified with carbon dioxide', *J Sci Food Agric,* 79, 1208–1212.

CHAMPAGNE C P, LAING R R, MAFU R D, AKIER A and GRIFFITHS, W (1994), 'Psychrotrophs in dairy products: their effects and their control', *Crit Rev Food Sci Nutr,* 34(1), 1–30.

CHEN J H and HOTCHKISS J H (1991), 'Effect of dissolved carbon dioxide on the growth of psychrotrophic organisms in cottage cheese', *J Dairy Sci* 74(9), 2941–2945.

CHEN J H and HOTCHKISS J H (1993), 'Growth of *Listeria monocytogenes* and *Clostridium sporogenes* in cottage cheese in modified atmosphere packaging', *J Dairy Sci,* 76(4), 972–977.

CHOI H S and KOSIKOWSKI F V (1985), 'Sweetened plain and flavored carbonated yogurt beverage', *J Dairy Sci,* 68, 613–619.

COLCHIN L M, OWENS S L, LYUBACHEVSKAYA G, BOYLE-RODEN E, RUSSEK-COHEN E and RANKIN S A (2001), 'Modified atmosphere packaged cheddar cheese shreds: influence of fluorescent light exposure and gas type on the color and production of volatile compounds', *J Agric Food Chem,* 49, 2277–2282.

CORRAL L G, POST L S and MONTVILLE T J (1988), 'Antimicrobial activity of sodium-bicarbonate', *J Food Sci,* 53, 981–982.

DANIELS J A, KRISHNAMURTHI R and RIZVI S S (1985), 'A review of the effects of carbon dioxide on microbial growth and food quality', *J Food Prot,* 48, 532–537.

DEVLIEGHERE F, DEBEVERE J and VAN IMPE J (1998a), 'Concentration of carbon dioxide in the water-phase as a parameter to model the effect of modified atmosphere on microorganisms', *Int J Food Microbiol,* 43(1–2), 105–113.

DEVLIEGHERE F, DEBEVERE J and VAN IMPE J (1998b), 'Effect of dissolved carbon dioxide and temperature on the growth of *Lactobacillus sake* in modified atmospheres', *Int J Food Microbiol* 41(3), 231–238.

DIEZ-GONZALEZ F, JARVIS G N, ADAMOVICH D A and RUSSELL J B (2000), 'Use of carbonate and alkali to eliminate *Escherichia coli* from dairy cattle manure', *Env Sci Technol,* 34, 1275–1279.

DILLOW A K, DEHGHANI F, HRKACH J S, FOSTER N R and LANGER R (1999), 'Bacterial inactivation by using near and supercritical carbon dioxide', *Proc Nat Acad Sci,* 96, 10344–10348.

DILLOW A K, LANGER R S, FOSTER N and HRKACH J S (2000), 'Supercritical fluid sterilization method', Massachusetts Institute of Technology, USA, Patent No. 6149864.

DIXON N M and KELL D B (1989), 'A review – the inhibition by CO_2 of the growth and metabolism of microorganisms', *J Appl Bacteriol,* 67(10), 109–136.

DIXON N M, LOVITT R W, KELL D B AND MORRIS J G (1987), 'Effects of pCO_2 on the growth and metabolism of *Clostridium sporogenes* NCIB 8053 in defined media', *J Appl Bacteriol,* 63(2), 171–182.

DMI (1998), 'Extending shelf life of dairy foods', *Innovations in Dairy Technology Review,* April, 1–6.

DUTHIE C M (1985), 'Effect of low-level carbonation on the keeping quality of processed milk', Masters Thesis Department of Food Science, Cornell University, Ithaca, NY.

ELIOT S C, VUILLEMARD J C and EMOND J P (1998), 'Stability of shredded mozzarella cheese under modified atmospheres', *J Food Sci*, 63, 1075–1079.

ENFORS S and MOLIN G (1978a), 'Mechanisms of the inhibition of spore germination by inert gases and carbon dioxide', in Chambliss G and Vary J C, *Spores VII*, Madison, American Society for Microbiology, 80–84.

ENFORS S O and MOLIN G (1978b), 'The influence of high concentrations of carbon dioxide on the germination of bacterial spores', *J Appl Bacteriol*, 45(2), 279–285.

ENFORS S O and MOLIN G (1980), 'Effect of high concentrations of carbon dioxide on growth rate of *Pseudomonas fragi*, *Bacillus cereus*, and *Streptococcus cremoris*', *J Appl Bacteriol*, 48, 409–416.

ERKMEN O (2000), 'Effect of carbon dioxide pressure on *Listeria monocytogenes* in physiological saline and foods', *Food Microbiol*, 17, 589–596.

ESPIE W E and MADDEN R H (1997), 'The carbonation of chilled bulk milk', *Milchwissenschaft*, 52(5), 249–253.

FDA (2000), 'Code of Federal Regulations', National Archives and Record Administration, Washington DC.

FERNANDEZ P S, GEORGE S M, SILLS C C and PECK M W (1997), 'Predictive model of the effect of CO_2, pH, temperature, and NaCl on the growth of *Listeria monocytogenes*', *Int J Food Microbiol*, 37, 37–45.

FOEGEDING P M and BUSTA F F (1983), 'Effect of carbon dioxide, nitrogen and hydrogen on germination of *Clostridium botulinum* spores', *J Food Prot*, 46, 987–989.

GEVAUDAN S, LAGAUDE A, DE LA FUENTE T and CUQ J L (1996), 'Effect of treatment by gaseous carbon dioxide on the colloidal phase of skim milk', *J Dairy Sci*, 79, 1713–1721.

GLASS K A, KAUFMAN K M, SMITH A L, JOHNSON E A, CHEN J H and HOTCHKISS J (1999), 'Toxin production by *Clostridium botulinum* in pasteurized milk treated with carbon dioxide', *J Food Prot*, 62(8), 872–876.

GONZALEZ-FANDOS E, SANZ S and OLARTE C (2000), 'Microbiological, physiochemical and sensory characteristics of Cameros cheese packaged under modified atmospheres', *Food Microbiol*, 17, 407–414.

GUEIMONDE M, CORZO N, VINDEROLA G, REINHEIMER J and DE LOS REYES-GAVILAN C G (2002), 'Evolution of carbohydrate fraction in carbonated fermented milks as affected by beta-galactosidase activity of starter strains', *J Dairy Res*, 69, 125–137.

GUILLAUME C, MARCHESSEAU S, LAGAUDE A and CUQ J L (2002), 'Effect of salt addition on the micellar composition of milk subjected to pH reversible CO_2 acidification', *J Dairy Sci*, 85, 2098–2105.

GUIRGUIS A H, GRIFFITHS M W and MUIR D D (1984), 'Spore forming bacteria in milk. II. Effect of carbon dioxide addition on heat activation of spores of *Bacillus* species', *Milchwissenschaft*, 39(3), 144–146.

HABULIN M and KNEZ Z (2001), 'Activity and stability of lipases from different sources in supercritical carbon dioxide and near-critical propane', *J Chem Technol Biotechnol*, 76, 1260–1266.

HAMBLETON R and RIGBY G J (1970), 'A study on the effect of carbon dioxide on the germination and outgrowth of spores of *Clostridium butyricum* using a slide culture technique', *J Appl Bacteriol*, 33, 664–673.

HENDRICKS M T and HOTCHKISS J H (1997), 'Effect of carbon dioxide on *Pseudomonas fluorescens* and *Listeria monocytogenes* growth in aerobic atmospheres', *J Food Prot*, 60, 1548–1552.

HENYON D K (1999), 'Extended shelf-life milks in North America: a perspective', *Int J Dairy Technol*, 52(3): 95–101.

HOTCHKISS J H and LEE E (1996), 'Extending shelf-life of dairy products with dissolved carbon dioxide', *Euro Dairy Mag*, 3, 16–19.

HOTCHKISS J H, CHEN J H and LAWLESS H T (1999), 'Combined effects of carbon dioxide addition and barrier films on microbial and sensory changes in pasteurized milk', *J Dairy Sci*, 82, 690–695.

JAY J M (1992), *Modern Food Microbiology*, 4th edn. London, Chapman & Hall.

KARAGUL-YUCEER Y, WILSON J C and WHITE C H (2001), 'Formulations and processing of yogurt affect the microbial quality of carbonated yogurt', *J Dairy Sci*, 84, 543–550.

KING A D and NAGEL C W (1967), 'Growth inhibition of a *Pseudomonas* by carbon dioxide', *J Food Sci*, 32(5), 575–579.

KING A D and NAGEL C W (1975), 'Influence of carbon dioxide upon the metabolism of *Pseudomonas aeruginosa*', *J Food Sci*, 40(2), 362–366.

KING J S and MABBITT L A (1982), 'Preservation of raw milk by the addition of carbon dioxide', *J Dairy Res*, 49(3), 439–447.

KOSIKOWSKI F V and BROWN D P (1972), 'Influence of carbon dioxide and nitrogen on microbial populations and shelf life of cottage cheese and sour cream', *J Dairy Sci*, 56, 12–18.

KOSIKOWSKI F V and CHOI H S (1985), 'Sweetened plain and flavored yogurt beverages', *J Dairy Sci*, 68, 613–619.

LEE E (1996), 'Carbon dioxide gas analysis and applications in the determination of the shelf-life of modified atmosphere packaged dairy products', Masters Thesis, Department of Food Science, Cornell University, Ithaca, NY.

LEWIS M (1999), 'Microbiological issues associated with heat treated milks', *Int J Dairy Technol*, 52(4) 121–125.

LOSS C R (2001), 'Effect of dissolved carbon dioxide on the thermal resistance of microorganisms in milk', Masters Thesis, Department of Food Science, Cornell University, Ithaca, NY.

LOSS C R and HOTCHKISS J H (2002), 'The effect of dissolved carbon dioxide on thermal resistance of milk borne microorganisms', *J Food Prot*, 65, 1924–1929.

LYNCH D J (1988), 'Effects of organic acids and processing variables on thermal inactivation of *Bacillus* spores in meat slurries and particulates', PhD Thesis, Department of Food Science, Cornell University, Ithaca NY.

MA Y, BARBANO D M, HOTCHKISS J H, MURPHY S and LYNCH J M (2001), 'Impact of CO_2 addition to milk on selected analytical testing methods', *J Dairy Sci*, 84, 1959–1968.

MANIAR A B, MARCY J E, BISHOP J R and DUNCAN S E (1994), 'Modified atmosphere packaging to maintain direct-set cottage cheese quality', *J Food Sci* 59, 1305–1308, 1327.

MARTIN J D, WERNER B G, HOTCHKISS J H (2003), 'Effects of carbon dioxide on bacterial growth parameters in milk as measured by conductivity', *J Dairy Sci*. 86: 1932–1940.

MCCARNEY T, MULLAN W M A and ROWE M T (1995), 'Effect of carbonation of milk on cheddar cheese yield and quality', *Milchwissenschaft*, 50, 670–674.

MCINTYRE M and MCNEIL B (1998), 'Morphogenetic and biochemical effects of dissolved carbon dioxide on filamentous fungi in submerged cultivation', *Appl Microbiol Biotechnol*, 50(3), 291–298.

MOIR C J, EYLES M J and DAVEY J A (1993), 'Inhibition of pseudomonads in cottage cheese by packaging in atmospheres containing carbon dioxide', *Food Microbiol*, 10(4), 1–7.

MONTILLA A, CALVO M M and OLANO A (1995), 'Manufacture of cheese made from CO_2-treated milk', *Z Lebensm-Unters und -Försch A*, 200, 289–292.

MUIR D D (1996), 'The shelf-life of dairy products. 1. Factors influencing raw milk and fresh products', *J Soc Dairy Technol*, 49: 24–32

NILSSON L, CHEN Y, CHIKINDAS M L, HUSS H H, GRAM L and MONTVILLE J (2000), 'Carbon dioxide and nisin act synergistically on *Listeria monocytogenes*', *Appl Env Microbiol*, 66(2), 769–774.

OLARTE C, GONZALEZ-FANDOS E and SANZ S (2001), 'A proposed methodology to determine the sensory quality of a fresh goat's cheese (Cameros cheese): application to cheeses packaged under modified atmospheres', *Food Qual Pref*, 12, 163–170.

OLARTE C, GONZALEZ-FERNANDEZ E, GIMINEZ M, SANZ S and PORTU J (2002), 'The growth of *Listeria monocytogenes* in fresh goat cheese (Cameros cheese) packaged under modified atmospheres', *Food Microbiol*, 19, 75–82.

PATIL G R and REUTER H (1988), 'Deposit formation in UHT plants. III. Effect of pH of milk in directly and indirectly heated plants', *Milchwissenschaft*, 43, 360–362.

PICHARD B, SIMARD R E and BONCHARD C (1984), 'Effect of nitrogen, carbon monoxide, and carbon dioxide on the activity of proteases of *Pseudomonas fragi* and *Streptomyces caespitosus*', *Sci Aliment*, 4(4), 595–608.

PIERGIOVANNI L, FAVA P and MORO M (1993), 'Shelf-life extension of Taleggio cheese by modified atmosphere packaging', *Ital J Food Sci*, 2, 115–127.

PINTADO M E and MALCATA F X (2000), 'The effect of modified atmosphere packaging on the microbial ecology in Requeijao, a Portuguese whey cheese', *J Food Process Preserv*, 24, 107–124.

PRUCHA M J, BRANNON J M and AMBROSE A S (1922), 'Does carbon dioxide in carbonated milk and milk products destroy bacteria?', *University of Illinois Agricultural College and Experimental Station Circular*, 256, 1–8.

REILLY S (1980), 'The carbon dioxide requirements of anaerobic bacteria', *J Med Microbiol*, 13, 573–579.

RETTGER L F, WINSLOW C E A and SMITH A H (1922), 'Report of an investigation into the effect of freezing ice cream in an atmosphere of carbon dioxide', National Association of Ice Cream Dealers, New York.

ROBERTS R F and TORREY G S (1988), 'Inhibition of psychrotrophic bacterial growth in refrigerated milk by addition of carbon dioxide', *J Dairy Sci*, 71(1), 52–60.

ROWE M T (1988), 'Effect of carbon dioxide on growth and extracellular enzyme production by *Pseudomonas fluorescens*', *Int J Food Microbiol*, 6, 51–56.

RUAS-MADIEDO P, BADA-GANCEDO J C, FERNANDEZ-GARCIA E, DELLANO D G and REYES-GAVILAN C G (1996), 'Preservation of the microbiological and biochemical quality of raw milk by carbon dioxide addition: a pilot-scale study', *J Food Prot*, 59(5), 502–508.

RUAS-MADIEDO P, ALONSO L, DELLANO D G and DEREYES-GAVILAN C G (1998a), 'Growth and metabolic activity of a cheese starter in CO_2-acidified and non-acidified refrigerated milk', *Z Lebens-Unter und -Forsch A*, 206, 179–183.

RUAS-MADIEDO P, BASCARAN V, BRANA A, BADA-GANCEDO J C and DE LOS REYES-GAVILAN C G (1998b), 'Influence of carbon dioxide addition to raw milk on microbial levels and some fat-soluble vitamin contents of raw and pasteurized milk', *J Agric Food Chem*, 46(7), 1552–1555.

RUAS-MADIEDO P, BADA-GANCEDO C, ALONSO L and REYES-GAVILAN D (1998c), 'Afuega'l pitu cheese quality: carbon dioxide addition to refrigerated milk in acid-coagulated cheese making', *Int Dairy J,* 8, 951–958.

RUAS-MADIEDO P, ALONSO L, DELGADO T, BADA-GANCEDO J C and REYES-GAVILAN C G (2002), 'Manufacture of Spanish hard cheese from CO_2-treated milk', *Food Res Int,* 35, 681–691.

SEARS D F and EISENBERG R M (1961), 'A model representing a physiological role of CO_2 at the cell membrane', *J Gen Physiol,* 44(5), 869–887.

SETLOW P and JOHNSON E A (1997), 'Spores and their significance', in Doyle M P, Beauchat L R and Montville T J, *Food Microbiology Fundamentals and Frontiers,* Washington DC, ASM Press, 30–65.

SHIPE W F, SENYK G F, ADLER E J and LEDFORD R A (1982), 'Effect of infusion of carbon dioxide on the bacterial growth in fluid milk', *J Dairy Sci,* 65 (Suppl), 77.

SIERRA I, PRODONAV M, CALVO M, OLANO A and VIDAL-VALVERDE C (1996), 'Vitamin stability and growth of psychrotrophic bacteria in refrigerated raw milk acidified with carbon dioxide', *J Food Prot,* 59(12), 1305–1310.

SKUDDER P J, BROOKER B E, BONSEY A D and ALVAREZ-GUERRERO N R (1986), 'Effect of pH on the formation of deposit from milk on heated surfaces during ultrahigh-temperature processing', *J Dairy Res,* 53, 75–87.

STRETTON S and GOODMAN A (1998), 'Carbon dioxide as a regulator of gene expression in microorganisms', *Antonie van Leeuwenhoek,* 73, 79–85.

TOMASULA P M and BOSWELL R T (1999), 'Measurement of the solubility of carbon dioxide in milk at high pressures', *J Supercrit Fluids,* 16, 21–26.

VALLEY G and RETTGER L F (1927), 'The influence of carbon dioxide on bacteria', *J Bacteriol,* 14, 101.

VAN HEKKEN D L, RAJKOWSKI K T, TOMASULA P M, TUNICK M H and HOLSINGER V H (2000), 'Effect of carbon dioxide under high presssure on the survival of cheese starter cultures', *J Food Prot,* 63, 758–762.

VINDEROLA C G, GUEIMONDE M, DELGADO T, REINHEIMER J A and DE LOS REYES-GAVILAN C G (2000), 'Characteristics of carbonated fermented milk and survival of probiotic bacteria', *Int Dairy J,* 10, 213–220.

WERNER B G and HOTCHKISS J H (2002) 'Effect of carbon dioxide on the growth of *Bacillus cereus* spores in milk during storage', *J Dairy Sci,* 85, 15–18.

WOLFE S K (1980), 'Use of CO- and CO_2-enriched atmospheres for meats, fish, and produce', *Food Technol,* 34(3), 55–58.

Part III

Cheese manufacture

19

Acceleration of cheese ripening

V. K. Upadhyay and P. L. H. McSweeney, University College Cork, Ireland

19.1 Introduction

Most rennet-coagulated cheeses are ripened after manufacture for periods ranging from *ca.* two weeks (e.g., Mozzarella) to more than two years (e.g., Parmigiano-Reggiano or extra-mature Cheddar). Cheese ripening involves a complex series of microbiological and biochemical events which result in the development of the flavour and texture characteristic of each variety. Biochemical changes which occur during ripening include metabolism of residual lactose and of lactate and citrate (often, although incorrectly, referred to as 'glycolysis'), lipolysis and metabolism of free fatty acids and proteolysis and metabolism of free amino acids. The biochemistry of cheese ripening, which has been reviewed by Fox *et al.* (1993, 1996a), Fox and McSweeney (1997) and McSweeney and Sousa (2000), is summarized below.

Cheese ripening is a slow, and consequently an expensive, process. The expense of cheese ripening originates principally from the inventory cost associated with holding a large amount of cheese in storage and the capital cost of providing a ripening facility adequate to hold sufficient cheese for its ripening time. The temperature and, in certain cases, the relative humidity of ripening rooms must also be controlled, adding to the cost of cheese ripening. Ripening costs have been estimated at approximately €500–800 per tonne of cheese matured for nine months. Thus, acceleration of cheese ripening has received considerable attention in the scientific literature. This topic has been reviewed by Fox (1988/89), El Soda and Pandian (1991), Wilkinson (1993) and Fox *et al.* (1996b).

Overview of cheese ripening

Most of the lactose in milk is lost in the whey during cheesemaking. Residual lactose is metabolized quickly to lactate early in ripening by the action of the starter or non-starter flora of the cheese. Lactate is an important precursor compound for certain reactions which occur during ripening. Lactate metabolism is most significant in surface mould-ripened cheeses (e.g., Brie and Camembert) where oxidative metabolism of lactate at the surface by *Penicillium camemberti* causes pH gradients across the cheese mass, migration of Ca^{2+} and lactate to the surface with a concomitant softening of the cheese (see McSweeney and Sousa, 2000). Lactate metabolism is also of great importance to Swiss cheese where *Propionibacterium freudenreichii* ssp. *shermanii* metabolizes it to propionate, acetate, H_2O and CO_2, contributing to the flavour of the cheese and causing its characteristic eyes. Other pathways for lactate metabolism include racemization of L- to DL-lactate, resulting in white crystals of calcium-D-lactate on many mature cheeses. Late gas blowing is a defect resulting from the anaerobic metabolism of lactate to butyrate and H_2 gas by *Clostridium* spp.

Milk contains low levels of citrate (*ca.* 8 mmol L^{-1}) most of which is lost in the whey. However, the low level of citrate in cheese curd is an important substrate for citrate-positive (Cit^+) microorganisms (*Leuconostoc* spp. and Cit^+ strains of *Lactococcus*), the metabolism of which produces important flavour compounds (e.g., diacetyl, 2,3-butanediol, acetoin) in Dutch-type cheese.

The fat fraction of cheese also acts as an important source of flavour compounds; cheeses made with a reduced fat level or in which milk fat has been replaced with other lipids do not develop satisfactory flavour (see McSweeney and Sousa, 2000). In foods in general, fats can undergo degradation by either oxidative or hydrolytic mechanisms; the former is not important in cheese due to its low oxidation–reduction potential. Milk fat is hydrolysed in cheese during ripening by lipases originating from the milk, the coagulant or the cheese microflora. Indigenous lipoprotein lipase is of particular importance for lipolysis in raw milk cheese. Lactic acid bacteria are weakly lipolytic, but secondary starters (particularly *Penicillium* spp. in mould-ripened cheeses and coryneform bacteria in smear cheeses) may cause extensive lipolysis in certain varieties. Free fatty acids, particularly short chain acids, contribute directly to cheese flavour. In addition, they also act as precursor compounds for a range of catabolic reactions, including the formation of lactones by intramolecular esterification of hydroxyacids. Esters (principally ethyl esters) are important flavour compounds, imparting a fruity note to cheese. Recent research has indicated that esters may be formed during cheese ripening by transesterification of partial glycerides (Holland *et al.*, 2002). Free fatty acids can form thioesters by reaction with sulphydryl compounds. However, the most important example of fatty acid catabolism occurs in blue cheese where the mould *P. roqueforti* converts fatty acids via incomplete β-oxidation to alkan-2-ones (*n*-methyl ketones), which are the characteristic flavour compounds of these varieties.

Proteolysis is the principal biochemical event which occurs during the ripening of most hard cheese varieties. The initial breakdown of the caseins is catalysed by residual coagulant (usually chymosin) and the principal indigenous proteinase in milk, plasmin. A range of enzymes from the starter bacteria degrades the resulting peptides. The cell envelope-associated proteinase (lactocepin, PrtP) of lactic acid bacteria (LAB) is particularly important in degrading intermediate-sized peptides produced by chymosin and plasmin to a range of shorter peptides. Short peptides are substrates for a range of intracellular exopeptidases produced by LAB and released into the cheese curd on lysis of the cells, which occurs after cell death. The action of peptidases from the starter and non-starter microflora of the cheese results in the production of free amino acids which, in addition to being important flavour compounds *per se*, act as precursors for a wide range of catabolic reactions which produce volatile compounds characteristic of the flavour of many cheese varieties.

Various approaches have been used to accelerate the ripening process of cheese including:

- Use of elevated ripening temperatures
- Addition of exogenous enzymes or attenuated starters
- Use of adjunct cultures
- Genetic modification of starter bacteria
- High-pressure treatment.

Certain approaches (in particular the use of attenuated starters and adjunct cultures) are also used commercially in hard cheese to modify flavour, without necessarily reducing ripening time. Although not strictly acceleration of cheese ripening, the technology of enzyme-modified cheeses, products which rapidly develop a cheese-like flavour, is also discussed briefly.

19.2 Accelerating cheese ripening: elevated temperature

Cheese ripening at an elevated temperature is technically the simplest method for accelerating ripening and the lower refrigeration costs may provide overall savings to the producer. The drawbacks of this approach are an increased risk of microbial spoilage and non-specific increases in ripening reactions, possibly leading to unbalanced flavour or off-flavours (Wilkinson, 1993).

Although ripening temperature is the most important single factor determining flavour intensity (Law *et al.*, 1979), relatively few studies have been conducted on the effect of elevated temperatures on cheese ripening (El Soda, 1993). Studies in which the effects of different time–temperature combinations on cheese ripening were used to accelerate ripening were reviewed by Wilkinson (1993). Ripening temperature influences the rate of proteolysis (Aston *et al.*, 1983a, b; Fedrick *et al.*, 1983; Folkertsma *et al.*, 1996), lipolysis (Folkertsma *et al.*, 1996; O'Mahony and McSweeney, unpublished), cheese microflora (Cromie *et al.*, 1987; Folkertsma *et al.*, 1996), texture (Fedrick and Dulley, 1984) and quality (Aston *et al.*, 1985) of cheese. Ripening at elevated temperature to 15°C has been recommended to accelerate the ripening of cheese of good chemical and microbiological quality (Fedrick, 1987; Folkertsma *et al.*, 1996).

El Soda and Pandian (1991) concluded that the use of elevated temperature to accelerate ripening was likely to be limited to large cheese factories where very hygienic procedures are adopted during manufacture and ripening. Cheddar and certain other hard cheeses are now generally produced from pasteurized milk in large, highly automated plants with high hygienic standards and thus ripening of Cheddar and other cheeses at elevated temperatures is feasible and is practised in industry, particularly for cheese intended for ingredient use. However, successful ripening at elevated temperatures requires careful control of cheese composition and microflora.

19.3   Addition of exogenous enzymes or attenuated starters

Rennet and plasmin are mainly responsible for primary proteolysis while proteinases and peptidases from starter and non-starter bacteria convert the larger peptides, produced by action of rennet on caseins to intermediate and smaller peptides, which are precursors for flavour compounds. Addition of exogenous enzymes to cheese increases the enzyme pool, which eventually helps to accelerate the rate of certain reactions in cheese in contrast to elevated temperature, which results in the increase in rate of all reactions, some of which may impart an off-flavour to the cheese. However, there are certain limitations to enzyme addition as a method for accelerating ripening. Legal barriers in many countries restrict the use of exogenous enzymes in cheesemaking

Addition to cheesemilk appears to be the best stage for enzyme incorporation due to the homogeneous mixing of the enzyme with the milk and its subsequent transfer to cheese curd. However, most of the enzyme added to the milk (~95%) is lost in the whey and proteolytic enzymes degrade caseins to peptides, which are lost in the whey, resulting in a reduction in cheese yield. Moreover, early breakdown of the caseins results in disruption of the casein matrix, leading to poor gel strength and difficulty in working the curd at later stages of the cheese manufacture (Law, 2001). Due to loss of expensive enzyme preparations in cheese whey and an additional cost to inactivate enzymes in whey before its use as an ingredient in food preparations, alternative stages or techniques of addition of enzyme during the cheesemaking process need to be explored. Figure 19.1 indicates stages at which enzymes may be added during cheesemaking

Microencapsulation of the enzyme before addition to cheesemilk helps to protect casein from degradation and facilitate more enzyme to be entrapped physically in the curd, hence reducing the loss of the enzyme in the whey (El Soda *et al.*, 1989). Law and King (1985) and Kirby *et al.* (1987) developed a type of phospholipid liposome, which degraded in the cheese matrix after the whey separation. Due to the high cost of pure phospholipids to prepare high capacity and stable liposomes, application of this technique on a large scale is not feasible.

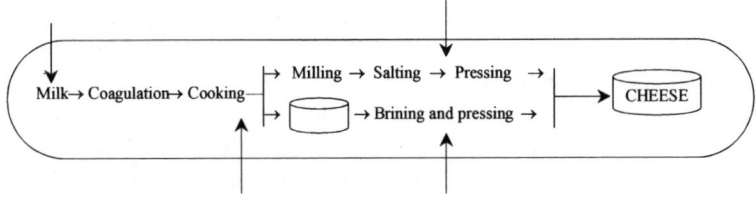

Fig. 19.1   Possible points for addition of enzymes to cheese curd (modified from Law, 2001). Arrows indicate the possible points of enzyme addition.

Certain semi-hard cheeses such as Edam and Gouda have a characteristic 'curd washing' step in the manufacturing protocol, where part of cheese whey is replaced by hot water in an attempt to reduce the acidity. This is another stage where addition of enzyme to soft curd is a possibility, although the flux of whey from the curd would impede uptake of enzymes, which in any case diffuse only very slowly through the protein matrix of curd. Thus, enzyme addition at this stage of manufacture is not usually practised. Likewise, addition of the enzyme at the brining stage is difficult due to the close texture of the cheese block. Kosikowski (1976) first suggested the addition of enzymes to dry-salted cheese varieties by mixing enzymes with salt. Addition of granulated enzyme with salt after milling in Cheddar-type cheeses is also an option for enzyme addition but is difficult to adopt at an industrial level. Also, since diffusion of enzymes through curd is extremely slow, localized high concentrations of enzymes can lead to uneven ripening throughout the cheese ('hot spots').

The proteinase(s) from the coagulant cause primary proteolysis in most cheese varieties (Fox and McSweeney, 1997); hence, increasing the level of coagulant might be expected to accelerate proteolysis. Research indicates that chymosin is the limiting proteolytic agent in the initial hydrolysis of the caseins during ripening. However, increasing the levels of chymosin often results in bitter cheese (Fox and Tobin, 1999).

Plasmin plays an important role in proteolysis in many cheese varieties, especially in high-cooked cheese varieties where the high cooking temperature during cheese manufacture results in increased plasmin activity and in extensive denaturation of chymosin. Since casein in milk can bind at least 10 times the amount of plasmin normally present, plasmin added to cheesemilk is retained in the curd. Plasmin, when added to cheesemilk, accelerated proteolysis in Cheddar cheese (Farkye and Fox, 1992). However, exogenous plasmin is expensive and, due to its scarce availability on the market, activation of its zymogen, plasminogen, by means of various plasminogen activators (PA) could provide an alternative to adding exogenous plasmin to accelerate the ripening of cheese. This approach was used by Barrett *et al.* (1999) using exogenous urokinase for plasminogen activation to accelerate proteolysis in Cheddar cheese. A similar concept, using a semi-purified preparation of streptokinase, a bacterial PA secreted by *S. uberis*, was used by Upadhyay *et al.* (unpublished) to accelerate proteolysis in Cheddar cheese. Streptokinase from *S. uberis* is able to activate bovine plasminogen to plasmin, whereas streptokinases from Lancefield C or Lancefield E streptococci do not activate bovine plasminogen (Leigh, 1993). In both studies, plasmin activity in cheese was increased, levels of plasminogen decreased, and proteolysis, as determined by levels of water-soluble N and peptide profiles by urea-polyacrylamide gel electrophoresis and reversed-phase HPLC, increased. Increased plasmin activity had little effect on levels of free amino acids in the latter study while individual free amino acids increased with increasing levels of urokinase in the former.

Use of enzyme mixtures has an advantage over the use of a single enzyme as they enhance the rates of multiple reactions aimed at enhancing or modifying particular aspects of cheese ripening. Since proteolysis is the major biochemical process occurring during the ripening of Cheddar, Gouda and Italian-type cheeses, most enzyme preparations used to accelerate ripening contain proteinases and peptidases; lipases may also be present in certain preparations. Some commercially available enzymes or enzyme preparations are listed in Table 19.1.

Accelase™, an enzyme preparation developed based on research on the role of starter enzymes and cell lysis in flavour development (Law et al., 1974; Law and Wigmore, 1983) by IBT Ltd (now Rhodia Foods, UK), has been evaluated for acceleration of cheese ripening. Experimental results on cheeses made with Accelase™ suggest that cheeses reach the equivalent of 9 months' maturity after 5 months of ripening. It is also claimed that Accelase™ reduces the bitterness in cheese and there is an increase in flavour notes including 'sulphur', 'acid' and 'Cheddar' (Law, 2001). A number of studies have used Neutrase®, a neutral proteinase from Bacillus subtilis, as exogenous enzyme to accelerate ripening in cheese (see Wilkinson, 1993). Guinee et al. (1991) added Neutrase®, FlavorAge™-FR (a lipase proteinase preparation from Aspergillus oryzae) and extra rennet to Cheddar cheese curd at salting. Addition of these enzymes accelerated the ripening in Cheddar cheeses, when ripened at 5°C for 4–5 months. Longer storage of the cheeses resulted in excessive proteolysis and flavour defects in cheeses. When using FlavorAge™-FR and DCA 50 (a proteinase–peptidase blend; IBT, London), these authors reported acceleration of flavour development.

Since lipases play a role in the ripening of Cheddar cheese, many researchers have focused work on accelerating lipolysis in Cheddar cheese by the use of exogenous lipases or lipase preparations. FlavorAge™ is a commercially available enzyme preparation containing a lipase, which has very high specificity for C_6–C_8 acids. Arbige et al. (1986) used FlavorAge™ in Cheddar cheese manufacture and found increased formation of short-chain fatty acids and acceleration in the development of flavour intensity. O'Connell (2002), when investigating the effects of addition of low levels of two commercially available enzyme preparations (Lipase M 'Amano' 10, Amano Enzymes and Palatase® 20000L, NOVO) on ripening and sensory characteristics of Cheddar cheese, found higher lipolysis in cheeses with added enzymes as indicated by increased levels of free fatty acids. Enzyme addition had a profound effect on the sensory characteristics of cheese; the highest level of addition gave attributes (pungent,

Table 19.1 Enzyme preparations, other than rennets, commercially available for cheese or enzyme-modified cheese (modified from Wilkinson and Kilcawley, 2002)

Principal enzymatic activity	Trade name	Host organism/source	Company
Aminopeptidase	Accelase[TMa], Savorase®, Debitrase®	*Lactococcus lactis* *Rhizopus oryzae*	Rhodia Food
Aminopeptidase	Acid Protease A	*Aspergillus niger*	Amano Enzymes
Prote(in)ase	Acid Protease II	*Rhizomucor niveus*	Amano Enzymes
	Bioprotease A conc	*Aspergillus niger*	Quest International
	Bioprotease N 100	*Bacillus subtilis*	Quest International
	Bioprotease P conc	*Aspergillus oryzae*	Quest International
	Fermizyme® B 500	*Bacillus subtilis*	DSM
	FlavorAge[b]	*Aspergillus* sp.	Chr Hansen
	Flavorpro 192	*Aspergillus* var. strains	Biocatalysts
	Flavourzyme	*Aspergillus oryzae*	NOVO
	Neutrase	*Bacillus subtilis*	NOVO
	Peptidase 'R' Amano	*Rhizomucor oryzae*	Amano Enzymes
	Promod 24L	*Bacillus subtilis*	Biocatalysts
	Promod 215P	*Aspergillus sojae*	Biocatalysts
	Protease 'A' Amano 2	*Aspergillus oryzae*	Amano Enzymes
	Protease M	*Aspergillus oryzae*	Amano Enzymes
	Protease N	*Bacillus subtilis*	Amano Enzymes
	Prozyme 6	*Aspergillus melleus*	Amano Enzymes
	Sternzyme B5021	*Aspergillus niger*	Stern-Enzyme
	Sternzyme B5026	*Aspergillus oryzae*	Stern-Enzyme
Lipase	Capalase®	Animal	Degussa Bioactives
	Italase®	Animal	Degussa Bioactives
	Kid Lipase	Animal	Chr Hansen
	Lipase M 'Amano' 10	*Rhizomucor javanicus*	Amano Enzymes
	Palatase® 20000 L	*Rhizomucor miehei*	NOVO

[a] Can also be mixed with enzymes from other sources.
[b] Proteinase-lipase preparation.

rancid, sweaty, vomit) that are used to describe enzyme-modified cheeses (EMCs) or mould-ripened cheese.

19.3.1   Attenuated starters

As discussed above, enzymes play very important roles in the ripening of cheese. The use of attenuated starters provides an alternative means of increasing the enzyme pool in the cheese curd without the drawbacks of exogenous enzyme addition (enzyme loss in cheese whey, additional cost of processing the whey, legal barriers in many countries and difficulties of incorporation of enzymes with cheese curd in combination with high cost). An advantage of the use of attenuated starters compared with exogenous enzymes is that the former are largely trapped within the curd on whey drainage and release their enzymes directly into the curd on lysis of the cells. In addition to accelerating ripening, recent work has shown the potential of attenuated starters in modifying flavour.

Attenuated starters can be defined as LAB which are unable to produce significant levels of acid during cheesemaking, but which provide active starter enzymes that are important for cheese ripening and flavour development. Attenuated starter is added to cheesemilk together with the primary starter. Attenuation can be achieved by heat treatment, freezing and thawing, freeze or spray-drying, lysozyme treatment, use of solvents, and natural and induced genetic modification. The use of attenuated starters and methods of attenuation were discussed by Klein and Lortal (1999).

Petterson and Sjöström (1975) proposed the use of attenuated starters in cheesemaking to accelerate proteolysis and reduce ripening time. They attenuated the cells by heat treatment, which is the most widely studied method of attenuation. Heat treatment of LAB retards acid production but excessively severe treatment results in denaturation of starter enzymes. Hence, the temperature–time combination of heat treatment is critical; combinations are chosen to ensure greatest reduction of acid production by LAB but with least denaturation of starter enzymes. Petterson and Sjöström (1975) suggested treatment at 59°C for 15 s for mesophilic starters and at 69°C for 15 s for thermophilic starters. However, the treatment parameters vary between studies (see Klein and Lortal, 1999). Attenuated preparations of various LAB strains (e.g., mixed lactococcal strains; Exterkate *et al.*, 1987) have been studied, but the most studied species is *Lb. helveticus* owing to its high peptidase activity compared to other LAB. Inoculation level for heat-shocked cells varies; an estimated 5×10^6 to 5×10^7 cells ml^{-1} were added to milk in most trials. Retention of the added cells in the curd varies depending on cell morphology; retention of rods is higher than that of cocci (Petterson and Sjöström, 1975). Retention of cells in curd (as a percentage of cells added to milk) decreases with increasing addition of attenuated cells to the milk. Many of the studies conducted on attenuated starter using heat treatment have shown acceleration in proteolysis of cheese, improvement of flavour and reduction in levels of bitterness (Petterson and Sjöström, 1975; Skeie *et al.*, 1997; Salomskiene, 1998).

Development of flavour is a challenge in low-fat cheese, cheese made from ultrafiltered milk and cheeses made on a large industrial scale from pasteurized milk. Based on the research of Ardö and Petterson (1988), a commercial preparation, ENZOBACT™ (composed of heat-shocked Lb. helveticus), is available from Medipharm, Sweden, which has been shown to accelerate the ripening in reduced-fat Swedish hard cheese.

Attenuation by freezing and thawing was first proposed by Petterson and Sjöström (1975), and was studied in cheese trials by Bartels et al. (1987). The authors subjected concentrated bacterial cells to freezing at −20°C overnight or longer and rapidly thawing the cells to 40°C, resulting in attenuation of LAB. During the process of freezing and thawing, physical, chemical and biochemical changes occur within the cell. Attenuation is achieved more easily by this method than by heat treatment, where accurate time–temperature control is essential to minimize denaturation of starter enzymes. Freeze-drying of the attenuated starter can be used to reduce the storage volume and facilitate its use. A comparative study on the effectiveness of freezing, freeze-drying and spray-drying treatments for the production of attenuated Lb. helveticus CNRZ 32 by Johnson and Etzel (1995) indicated that spray-drying at an outlet temperature of 120°C delayed acid production but decreased enzyme activity substantially, while cells spray-dried at an outlet temperature of 82°C had higher enzyme activity compared to cells treated by other methods, but acid production was not delayed. El Soda et al. (2000a) studied the effects of heat-shocking and freeze-shocking on cell viability, autolytic properties, aminopeptidase and esterase activities and acid production of Lb. helveticus and Lb. casei in buffer and cheese slurry systems. Heat-shocking was very effective in reducing cell viability but at the cost of enzymatic activity.

Treatment of bacterial cells with lysozyme results in greater reduction in acid production while preserving more enzyme activity than heat treatment and hence can be used as a means to attenuate LAB. However, the high cost of lysozyme treatment limits its application for attenuation. Use of solvents such as n-butanol has been attempted to prepare LAB for use as attenuated starters. However, legal barriers and risk of health hazards has hampered the use of solvents to achieve attenuation. A method for attenuation using the surfactant sodium dodecyl sulphate has been patented by Smith et al. (2000).

Use of lactase-negative (Lac⁻), proteinase-negative (Prt⁻) or Lac⁻ proteinase positive (Prt⁺) mutants has added a new dimension to use of attenuated starter cultures in cheesemaking. Culture variants that spontaneously lose their ability to ferment lactose (Lac⁻) can be classified as attenuated cultures as they can no longer produce acid in milk and hence do not acidify milk or curds during manufacture. Dulley et al. (1978) isolated Lac⁻ and Prt⁻ variants from Lc. lactis ssp. lactis C2 which were used by Grieve and Dulley (1983) to accelerate proteolysis in Cheddar cheese. They added concentrated cells (approximately $10^{11}\,g^{-1}$) to the cheesemilk, and ripening of the cheese made from this milk at 20°C for 1 month resulted in increased proteolysis and flavour development. Besides deriving these mutants naturally, chemicals have been used to induce modifications to obtain Lac⁻ Prt⁺ mutants. Nakajima *et al.* (1991) used nitroguanidine while Birkeland *et al.* (1992) used ethidium bromide to induce Lac⁻ Prt⁺ mutants. A commercially available system based on natural genetic variants of lactococci, named Flavour Control (FC™) CR cultures, is available from Chr Hansen A/S, Hørsholm, Denmark. These cultures are effective in flavour enhancement of full-fat hard and semi-hard cheeses and improving flavour in reduced-fat Cheddar (Banks *et al.*, 1993). Tobin (1999) assessed a selection of Lac⁻ cultures from Chr Hansen's Laboratories (Reading, UK) in Cheddar cheese. Inoculation of these cultures individually or in combination increased the flavour of experimental Cheddar cheeses and resulted in higher production of amino acids. All the studies done so far with Lac⁻ mutants have used mutants of lactococci; use of similar mutants from other genera may be interesting.

19.3.2   Increased rate of lysis of starter cells

Immediately after manufacture, cheese curd generally contains *ca.* 10^8–10^9 viable starter cells g^{-1} cheese. As ripening progresses, the starter cells die and lyse. Starter lactococci contain proteinases and peptidases, which degrade large peptides derived from casein to small peptides and amino acids (Fox *et al.*, 1996a). Acceleration of autolysis of starter bacteria is seen as a possible mechanism to accelerate cheese ripening, owing to the fact that lysis of the starter cells releases intracellular peptidases into the matrix of the cheese. Release of these intracellular enzymes into the cheese matrix results in higher levels of free amino acids and a reduction in bitterness due to the breakdown of hydrophobic peptides by peptidases.

Autolysins are involved in breaking the peptidoglycan structure during the growth of the cell, in order to separate cells during division. The rate of lysis of cells in the cheese matrix is strain-dependent and factors such as difference in cell wall structure and autolysins affect lysis of cells. In Gram-positive bacteria, five types of enzymes with lytic activity against peptidoglycan have been identified. Figure 19.2 illustrates the structure of the peptidoglycan in *Lc. lactis* together with the action of peptidoglycan-degrading enzymes. Among these peptidoglycan-degrading enzymes, only endo-β-N-acetylmuramidase (AcmA) has been isolated biochemically from *Lc. lactis* ssp. *cremoris* AM2 (Mou *et al.*, 1976). The gene for AcmA was cloned and studied at molecular level by Buist *et al.* (1995), which is the only autolysin gene cloned to date from *Lactococcus*. However, recent findings suggest that AcmA is not solely responsible for autolysis in *Lc. lactis* (Pillidge *et al.*, 1998, 2002).

Autolysis can be monitored in cheese by electron microscopy or measurement of the release of intracellular enzymes (Crow *et al.*, 1995a). Measurement of starter cell numbers by viable cell count does not give an accurate indication of the extent of autolysis, as cells which have died may not have lysed. Measurement of intracellular enzymes gives a good indication of lysis as they are released into the curd upon lysis. Wilkinson *et al.* (1994a)

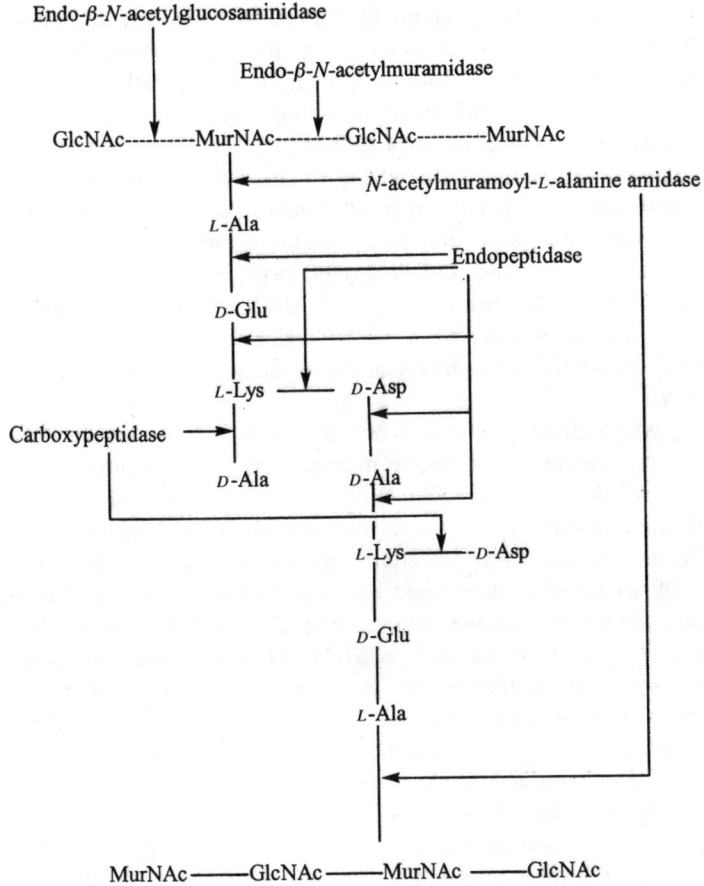

Fig. 19.2   A representation of the lactococcal peptidoglycan structure showing specificities of the different peptidoglycan hydrolases (adapted from Crow *et al.*, 1995a).

studied autolysis of starter bacteria in Cheddar cheese by monitoring the release of lactate dehydrogenase (LDH), glucose-6–phosphate dehydrogenase (G6PDH) and X-prolyl dipeptidylaminopeptidase (PepX) over time. Precisely monitoring autolysis in cheese is difficult due to possible instability of marker enzymes. Wilkinson *et al.* (1994b), when evaluating factors that influence the determination of autolysis, found that, under cheese-like conditions, LDH activity appeared to be the most stable (40% of the original activity survived after 500 h at 4°C) compared to G6PDH and PepX, the activity of which disappeared after 72 and 24 h, respectively. The extraction method (hypertonic extraction) influences marker activity. The authors prepared cheese juice by subjecting the cheese to high pressure to extract the aqueous phase and analysing the activity of the marker in cheese juice. However, the effect of pressure treatment on the stability of these marker enzymes needs further research.

Autolysis varies greatly among strains of starters. Wilkinson *et al.* (1994a) monitored autolysis in cheese made using *Lc. lactis* ssp. *cremoris* G11/C25 (non-bitter), HP (bitter) or AM2 (non-bitter). Viability of the cells was in the order G11/C25 > HP > AM2, while autolysis in the cheeses, measured by the activity of the above markers, was in the order AM2 > G11/C25 > HP. Levels of free amino acids in the cheeses were related to the rate of lysis of strains. Bitterness in cheeses made using HP may be attributed to slow lysis of the starter cells, making the substrate inaccessible to the peptidases and resulting in slow degradation of some of the bitter casein-derived peptides. O'Donovan *et al.* (1996) showed similar trends when using starters AM2, HP and 303, where the trend for viability was in the order 303 > HP > AM2 and autolysis in the order AM2 > 303 > HP. Strain 303 is a commercial starter that maintains high viability and lyses slowly.

Other factors which affect the autolysis of starter cells include environmental factors such as temperature during cheese manufacture, salt concentration and lactose depletion (El Soda *et al.*, 2000b). Wilkinson *et al.* (1994b) showed that increasing salt concentration results in an increase in the activity of marker enzymes. Differences in the salting procedure may affect autolysis of the starter. Crow *et al.* (1995a) found a more rapid decrease in starter cell densities in Cheddar cheeses when using trummel salting, compared to a normal salting belt.

'Thermolytic' *Lc. lactis* strains such as SK11 and US3 contain temperate phage, inducible by UV light, mitomycin C or temperature shock (Pillidge *et al.*, 2002). A higher cooking temperature (38–39°C) induces the temperature-sensitive prophage in *Lc. lactis* ssp. *cremoris* SK11 (Feirtag and McKay, 1987), resulting in cell lysis. Controlled infection of starter cells with bacteriophage is also a means for lysing cells. Crow *et al.* (1995b) found increased lysis of *Lc. lactis* ssp. *lactis* ML8 in Cheddar cheese when a homologous phage was added with increased rennet levels compared to *Lc. lactis* ssp. *lactis* ML8 alone, resulting in increased levels of free amino acids (FAAs). However, the use of phage in cheesemaking is not advisable (Morgan *et al.*, 1995).

The use of bacteriocins or bacteriocin-producing starters in cheesemaking is a novel approach for accelerating lysis. Plasmids encoding genes for bacteriocin production isolated from strains of LAB can be cloned into other LAB which can then be used as adjuncts. The use of bacteriocins in cheesemaking carries the risk of delay in acid production, hence affecting the cheesemaking schedule. However, the use of a bacteriocin-producing starter immune to the bacteriocin (Imm$^+$) provides a remedy for any delay in acidification during cheesemaking (Martínez-Cuesta *et al.*, 2001). These authors transferred a 46 kb plasmid, encoding the production of lacticin 3147 from *Lc. lactis* IFPL105 to *Lc. lactis* IFPL359, which was used for the manufacture of goats' milk cheese. Cheesemaking with *Lc. lactis* IFPL3593 (Lac$^+$ Imm$^+$) allowed proper acidification without any delay, and increased lysis was observed, resulting in increased levels of amino nitrogen. O'Sullivan *et al.* (2002) isolated a lantibiotic (lacticin 481)-producing strain, *Lc. lactis* DPC5552, from raw milk. Lacticin 481 resulted in a slower growth rate of the target strain along with release of intracellular enzymes such as LDH or PepX, unlike lacticin 3147 or lactococcins A, B and M which kill the target strain. Use of the strain *Lc. lactis* DPC5552 in laboratory-scale cheesemaking resulted in increased release of LDH from starter *Lc. lactis* HP strain, without severely delaying acid production. Morgan *et al.* (1997) used a citrate-utilizing *Lc. lactis* ssp. *lactis* DPC3286 modified to contain a plasmid that encodes production of lactococcins A, B and M which have a lytic effect against the lactococcal starter cultures, as an adjunct with a cheesemaking strain *Lc. lactis* ssp. *cremoris* HP for manufacture of Cheddar cheese. Cheddar cheese manufactured with the adjunct bacteriocin-producing strain had increased cell lysis, higher levels of free amino acids and higher sensory score compared to the cheeses manufactured either by starter culture alone or with adjunct that did not produce bacteriocin.

19.4   Use of adjunct cultures

Several studies have shown that non-starter lactic acid bacteria (NSLAB) play an important role in cheese flavour development (Fox *et al.*, 1998; Shakeel-Ur-Rehman *et al.*, 1999, 2000). The NSLAB, which are present in numbers below $100\,cfu\,g^{-1}$ cheese at day 1, grow rapidly in the hostile environment of cheese (low pH, low E_h, low a_w, low lactose concentration, anaerobic) to reach counts of $10^7–10^8\,cfu\,g^{-1}$ cheese within 2 months, the rate of growth depending on temperature. NSLAB gain entry to milk from various sources. Post-processing contamination of pasteurized milk results in an increase in NSLAB numbers in milk. NSLAB include facultatively heterofermentative (mesophilic) lactobacilli, micrococci, pediococci and enterococci; mesophilic lactobacilli (e.g., *Lactobacillus casei*, *Lb. paracasei*, *Lb. plantarum*, *Lb. curvatus*) usually dominate the NSLAB microflora. Cheeses manufactured from raw milk develop a more intense flavour than cheeses manufactured from pasteurized milk, which may be attributed to killing of the indigenous microflora by pasteurization. The role of the indigenous microflora in cheese ripening was investigated by McSweeney *et al.* (1993), who manufactured Cheddar cheese from raw, pasteurized or microfiltered milk. Cheeses made from raw milk had a more intense flavour than cheese produced from pasteurized or microfiltered milk. Cheeses made from pasteurized milk or microfiltered milk were similar in terms of proteolysis, lipolysis and microflora. Similar observations on the difference in flavour of raw and pasteurized milk cheeses were reported by Bouton and Grappin (1995) and Beuvier *et al.* (1997). A study by Ryan *et al.* (1996) also demonstrated the importance of NSLAB in cheese ripening and flavour development.

Several cheese varieties contain a secondary microflora which does not produce acid during manufacture but is responsible for development of a particular characteristic of the cheese, e.g., eye formation in Swiss cheese caused by *Pr. freudenreichii* ssp. *shermanii*, blue veins in Blue cheese (*P. roqueforti*) or the red smear in smear-ripened cheese (a complex Gram-positive microflora).

Cheddar cheese generally does not contain a deliberately added secondary flora. However, owing to the importance of NSLAB in flavour development, the use of NSLAB as adjuncts has opened a new area of research as a means for manipulating chemical and sensory characteristics of Cheddar cheese.

Many studies have used mesophilic lactobacilli to accelerate cheese ripening. The inoculation level of mesophilic lactobacilli in cheesemilk varies from 10^2 to 10^5 cfu ml^{-1}. A higher inoculation level ($\sim 10^5$ ml^{-1}) has been used for pasteurized cheesemilk in many studies to resemble the count of NSLAB in raw cheesemilk. Mesophilic lactobacilli, which have been studied as adjuncts either singly or in combination, include strains of *Lb. casei*, *Lb. paracasei*, *Lb. plantarum*, *Lb. brevis*, *Lb. curvatus* and *Lb. rhamnosus*. Lynch *et al.* (1996) studied the effects of added mesophilic lactobacilli on proteolysis and flavour development in Cheddar cheese made under controlled microbiological conditions. The *Lactobacillus* counts in experimental cheeses ranged from 10^4 to 10^5 cfu g^{-1} cheese at milling, which increased to 5×10^7 cfu g^{-1} after 4 weeks. The control cheese remained free from lactobacilli for up to 100 days and did not exceed 5×10^5 cfu g^{-1}. Addition of adjuncts to the cheesemilk increased the levels of free amino acids in experimental cheeses compared to control cheeses. However, little differences were observed in other indices of proteolysis. Lane and Fox (1996) found that addition of adjunct lactobacilli increased proteolysis in starter-free cheese (acidified using gluconic acid-δ-lactone), but this increase was not apparent when a starter was used together with the adjunct.

Recently, many investigations have reported use of adjuncts for improving flavour in low fat cheese varieties. Katsiari *et al.* (2002) investigated the effect of two commercial adjuncts, LBC 80 (*Lb. casei* ssp. *rhamnosus*) and CR-213 (containing *Lc. lactis* ssp. *cremoris* and *Lc. lactis* ssp. *lactis*), on the compositional, sensory and textural characteristics of low-fat Kefalograviera-type cheese. Low-fat cheese with adjuncts received higher scores for flavour intensity, texture and body than low-fat cheese without adjuncts. The aminopeptidase activity of the adjunct culture can reduce bitterness, which is a defect encountered commonly in low-fat cheese.

Thermophilic lactobacilli such as *Lb. helveticus* do not constitute part of NSLAB of Cheddar-type cheeses but are commonly used in the production of high-cooked cheese varieties and yogurt. Compared to mesophilic lactobacilli, few studies have been done on the use of thermophilic lactobacilli as adjunct, although our experience is that they improve quality substantially. Tobin (1999) found beneficial effects of the use of *S. thermophilus* TS3 and *Lb. helveticus* HL3 as adjuncts on the quality of Cheddar cheese. Hannon *et al.* (2003) manufactured Cheddar cheese using blends of two *Lc. lactis* strains (223, 227) as a starter with or without *Lb. helveticus* DPC4571 as adjunct or using *Lb. helveticus* DPC4571 as the only starter. *Lb. helveticus* DPC4571 lysed rapidly and cheeses made using *Lb. helveticus* DPC4571 as starter contained greater levels of free LDH than the other cheeses. Higher levels of proteolysis and flavour scores were obtained in cheeses made using *Lb. helveticus* DPC4571 as starter or as adjunct compared to cheese made only using *Lc. lactis* strains 223 and 227.

19.5   Genetic modification of starter bacteria

In recent years, attention has been focused on genetic engineering as a means of producing starters expressing proteinases and many intracellular enzymes (e.g., PepC, PepI, PepN, PepO, PepW, PepX) which play an important role in secondary proteolysis in cheese during ripening.

Due to their commercial significance, intensive research has been carried out to understand the genetics of LAB. The complete genomic sequence of *Lc. lactis* ssp. *lactis* IL1403 (Bolotin *et al.*, 2001) is now known and those of a number of other LABs are expected in the near future. Hence, targeted modifications to starter *Lactococci* used in cheesemaking are possible.

McKay and Baldwin (1976) found that lactococci contain extrachromosomal elements called plasmids. Most lactococcal strains contain multiple copies of four to seven plasmids with molecular masses of 2 to 100 kDa. The importance of plasmids can be highlighted from the fact that many important industrial traits such as proteinase production and lactose metabolism (and hence the ability to grow in milk), citrate metabolism, phage resistance and bacteriocin production are encoded on plasmids. The information that needs to be expressed is coded on a plasmid vector and then inserted into a plasmid-free host. When the host multiplies, the inserted plasmid vector also multiplies and expresses the characteristics encoded on the plasmid. Plasmids, and thus the traits they encode, can be lost easily on subculturing.

Based on the huge potential of genetic engineering in the area of cheese ripening, efforts have been made to accelerate ripening of cheeses by cloning and inserting genes for certain enzymes into starter bacteria. McGarry *et al.* (1995) made Cheddar cheese using a strain of *Lactococcus* containing the cloned gene for the neutral proteinase from *Bacillus subtilis* (Neutrase). Cheeses manufactured with the modified starter showed extensive proteolysis and their texture became very soft after 2 weeks of ripening at 8°C. A blend of Neutrase-producing lactococci and wild-type strains was used as a starter for Cheddar cheese manufacture by McGarry *et al.* (1994); a blend of 80:20 gave the best results and controlled and accelerated proteolysis was observed. Upadhyay *et al.* (unpublished) observed an increase in plasmin activity and increased proteolysis in miniature Cheddar-type cheese made using a strain of *Lactococcus* modified to express the plasminogen activator streptokinase from *S. uberis*. The production of streptokinase during cheesemaking resulted in activation of plasminogen to active plasmin as indicated by increased degradation of β-casein and concomitant increase in the concentration of γ_1-, γ_2- and γ_3-caseins.

Owing to the importance of starter peptidases in secondary proteolysis, peptidases from LAB have been characterized biochemically and genetically. Among LAB, *Lc. lactis* and *Lb. delbruechi* ssp. *bulgaricus* are the most extensively studied organisms (Christensen *et al.*, 1999). Several investigations have attempted to clone various peptidases into *Lactococcus*. Courtin *et al.* (2002) cloned five different peptidases of *Lactobacillus* into strains of *Lc. lactis* in order to assess their effect on ripening in a model cheese system. The authors found an increase in the levels of PepQ, PepX and PepW, which led to a threefold increase in production of amino acids in a model curd system. Joutsjoki *et al.* (2002) cloned genes for PepN, PepC, PepX and PepI from the proteolytic *Lb. helveticus* into *Lc. lactis* using a food grade cloning system. Peptidase activity, assayed under conditions similar to that of cheese, was higher in the recombinant strain than in the control strain. Similarly Anastasiou *et al.* (2002) cloned the gene for PepX from *S. thermophilus* ACA-DC4 into a lactococcal strain, while Christensson *et al.* (2002) cloned the gene for an oligopeptidase, PepO, from *Lb. rhamnosus* HN001 (DR 20) and over-expressed it into *Lc. lactis* ssp. *cremoris* NZ9000. The purified PepO enzyme demonstrated specificity for cleavage of α_{s1}-casein fragment 1-23.

Genetic modification (GM) of starter cultures seems a very promising method for accelerating cheese ripening by increasing the pool of enzymes with uniform distribution through the cheese curd matrix. This approach for accelerating cheese ripening is relatively novel and attention to date has focused primarily on the proteolytic system of *Lactococcus*. Recent work on cheese ripening has suggested that the proteinases and peptidases of *Lactococcus*, while very important for proteolysis in cheese during ripening, play only an indirect role in flavour development. Much attention has been paid recently to the importance of amino acid catabolic enzymes to flavour (Yvon and Rijnen, 2001) and exciting developments are expected in the form of starter cultures genetically modified to enhance their amino acid catabolic abilities. However, besides legal barriers to the use of GM starters in industrial cheesemaking, consumer concerns and lack of knowledge of the importance of key or limiting lactococcal enzymes in cheese ripening are stumbling blocks to the successful adoption of GM starters in industrial cheesemaking.

19.6   High-pressure technology

The application of high-pressure treatment (HPT) of milk dates back to the end of the nineteenth century when it was first investigated by Hite (1899). Since then, research in the area of HPT at the industrial level was limited until the advances in ceramics and metallurgy made the utilization of HPT techniques practical in 1970s and 1980s. The success of HPT at an industrial level has drawn the attention of many researchers to the application of HPT to the dairy and other food sectors. A range of pressure-treated food products, including fruit preparations, fruit juices, oysters, raw squid and rice cakes, are available on the French, Japanese and US markets (Trujillo *et al.*, 2000).

According to Le Chatelier's principle, when a disturbance is imposed on a system at equilibrium, the equilibrium shifts in such a way as to minimize the effect of the disturbance. In the case of HPT, an increase in pressure tends to result in a decrease in volume, which enhances chemical reactions, phase transitions and changes in molecular configuration. Irrespective of size and geometry, the pressure is instantaneously and uniformly distributed throughout the food. The increased pressure affects the environment of bacterial cell and many biochemical reactions in cells. HPT can cause conformational change in proteins but small macromolecules (such as those responsible for flavour and odour) and vitamins are not affected.

The application of HPT to cheese is limited. Studies have been carried out to evaluate the effect of HPT on rennet coagulation time (RCT), curd firmness, acid production by starter cultures, salt uptake, proteolysis, lipolysis and the rheological characteristics of cheese, in addition to the growth and survival of spoilage and pathogenic bacteria. The effects and application of HPT to milk and cheese were reviewed by Trujillo *et al.* (2000), O'Reilly *et al.* (2001) and Huppertz *et al.* (2002).

HPT of cheesemilk affects the coagulation process and its cheesemaking properties. Many studies have shown that HPT of cheesemilk results in improvement of RCT and gel strength. In most studies, pressure up to 200 MPa reduces the RCT compared to untreated milk, while treatment at a pressure in the range 200 to 400 MPa results in reduction in RCT compared to untreated milk but RCT values are higher than those of milk treated at 200 MPa (O'Reilly *et al,* 2001). HPT gives better curd firmness compared to untreated milk. Needs *et al.* (2000) reported that treatment of milk at 200–600 MPa yielded curd with a higher firmness than untreated milk, while López-Fandino *et al.* (1996, 1997) found the pressure treatment below 200 MPa increased curd firming rate, but that this parameter decreased following treatment at 200–400 MPa, though in all cases the rates were higher than in untreated milk. When cheesemilk is treated at a high pressure (above 100 MPa), whey proteins, particularly β-lactoglobulin, are denatured and interact with κ-casein, which leads to smaller losses of whey protein in the whey and increase in moisture retention, hence concomitant increase in the cheese yield.

Similar to thermal treatment, HPT causes destruction of microorganisms but, unlike thermal treatment, it does not inactivate certain enzymes that play an important role in cheese ripening, e.g. indigenous lipoprotein lipase. This characteristic of HPT may allow use of milk without thermal treatment in cheese manufacture. Trujillo *et al.* (1999) found higher production of free fatty acids in HP-treated goats' milk compared to pasteurized milk, indicating higher lipoprotein lipase activity in HP-treated milk than in pasteurized milk. Buffa *et al.* (2001) found that the levels of free fatty acids were higher in cheeses made from HP-treated goats' milk than in cheeses made from pasteurized milk; levels were similar to those in cheeses made from raw milk.

The application of HPT to cheese results in an increase in moisture content and pH and causes changes to the cheese matrix and lysis of cells, which contribute to ripening. HPT of cheeses affects the pattern of proteolysis during ripening, the effect of which is dependent on the type of cheese, magnitude, duration and temperature of pressure treatment and the age of the cheese. Yokoyama *et al.* (1992) applied pressure of 10 to 250 MPa at 25°C for 3 days to Cheddar cheese, made using a 10-fold higher level of a proteolytic starter. The authors claimed that the flavour of the treated cheese was equivalent to that of six-month-old Cheddar. The treated cheese had higher levels of free amino acids than control cheeses, but this may have been due to the use of a more proteolytic starter in cheese manufacture. The authors also treated cheese at 50 MPa at 25°C for 3 days in combination with addition of lipase and protease at salting and claimed that the resultant cheese developed a Parmesan-type flavour equivalent to a commercial control in terms of flavour scores and levels of FAA. O'Reilly *et al.* (2000) studied the effect of 50 MPa at 25°C for 3 days on Cheddar cheese ripening. Results indicated an immediate increase in the levels of pH 4.6-soluble nitrogen and free amino acids at 2 days of ripening, although the effect decreased with cheese age. Higher breakdown of α_{s1}-casein was observed by urea-polyacrylamide gel electrophoresis in the pressure-treated cheese compared to the untreated cheese. The effect of HPT on the degradation of α_{s1}-casein observed by O'Reilly *et al.* (2000) may have been due to pressure-induced modification of the substrate or to the high temperature (25°C) used for HPT. These authors also suggested that HPT is more effective in increasing proteolysis if applied to young cheese than to cheese that had been ripened for a few months. Plasmin activity remained unaffected by the above HPT and no differences were observed in the levels of α_{s2}-caseins and β-caseins between HPT cheeses and controls.

Goats' milk cheese was pressure treated at 50 MPa for 72 h or at 400 MPa for 5 min by Saldo *et al.* (2000). Treatment at 400 MPa for 5 min reduced starter counts by ~3 log cycles, while treatment at 50 MPa for 72 h decreased the starter counts slightly. As the ripening progressed (after 3 weeks), the starter population recovered. Lysis of starter by HPT is important in cheese ripening, as it releases intracellular enzymes into the cheese matrix, which play an important role in the breakdown of large and intermediate size peptides to small peptides and amino acids. The treatment resulted in an increase in pH and in levels of proteolysis. Saldo *et al.* (2002) pressure treated hard caprine milk cheese at 50 MPa for 72 h or at 400 MPa for 5 min. Pressure treatment at 50 MPa for 72 h resulted in slight differences compared to the control which became less apparent at the end of the ripening, while pressure treatment at 400 MPa for 5 min resulted in qualitative and quantitative differences that persisted throughout the ripening.

Messens *et al.* (1999) found no increases in indices of proteolysis when Gouda cheese was HP treated. However, a pH shift was observed between pressurized and non-pressurized cheese. HPT at 50 MPa for 8 h of Père Joseph, a French semi-hard smear-ripened cheese, resulted in a higher pH, which enhanced the proteolytic activity of the enzymes of *Brevibacterium linens* and peptidases of the starter bacteria (Messens *et al.*, 2000). Similar effects on proteolysis were observed when Paillardin, a white-mould ripened cheese, was HP treated at 50 MPa for 8 h by Messens *et al.* (2001).

19.7   Enzyme-modified cheeses as flavourings

The use of cheese flavours in various food preparations has increased significantly in recent times. Natural cheese can be used to obtain a characteristic cheese flavour in food products. However, variations in the flavour of natural cheeses due to variations in milk composition, degree of ripening, cost and other factors have led to the development of alternative sources of cheese flavours

Table 19.2   Differences between enzyme-modified cheeses (EMC) and natural cheeses (modified from Wilkinson and Kilcawley, 2002)

Parameter	EMC	Natural cheese variety (Cheddar, Gouda, Swiss, blue)
Raw material	Cheese curd, natural cheese, caseinate, butterfat	Milk, cream (standardized to protein to fat ratio)
Additives	Water, emulsifiers, enzymes (proteinases/peptidases, lipases/esterases or combination thereof), potentiators (monosodium glutamate, yeast extract, diacetyl)	Starter culture, adjuncts, CaCl$_2$, rennet, salt
Fermentation	Time 24–72 h Temperature 30–45°C	Acidification during manufacture (5–24 h) or shortly thereafter
Heat treatments	Pasteurization of curd-water slurry to inactivate bacteria or other contaminants. Heat treatment of enzyme treated slurry at high temperatures (~85°C for 30 min) to terminate enzymatic reactions	Cooking treatment of curd–whey mixture Up to 36°C for Gouda, 39°C for Cheddar, 55°C for Swiss
Ripening	Not deliberately ripened after manufacture	Ripening time 0.5 to >48 months Ripening temperature 4–23°C
Flavour genesis	Exogenous enzymes (contribute to extensive proteolytic and lipolytic changes)	Proteolysis, lipolysis, 'glycolysis' (metabolism of residual lactose and of lactate and citrate) by agents from the milk and coagulant, and from starter and non-starter microorganisms
Final product	In paste or powder form; high in flavour intensity with long shelf-life	Solid; lower flavour intensity with relatively short shelf-life after ripening
Legal parameters	Undefined legal parameters	Often defined legal parameters for cheese (pH, salt levels, fat-in-dry-matter, moisture, manufacturing technology)

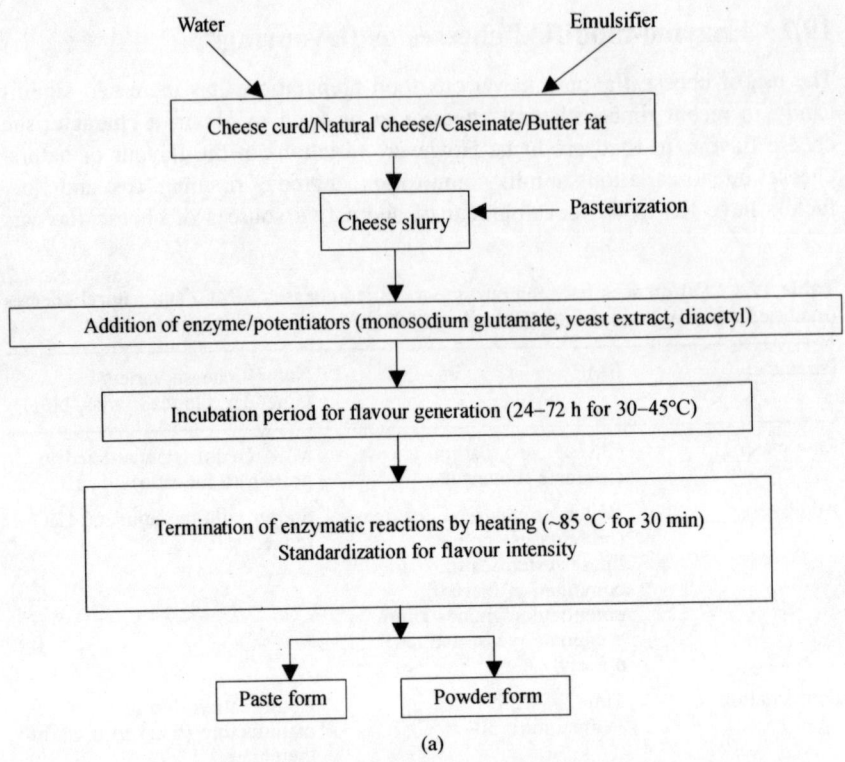

Fig. 19.3   Manufacture of EMC (modified from Wilkinson and Kilcawley, 2002): (a) one-step approach; (b) component approach.

(Kilcawley *et al.*, 1998). One such source is enzyme-modified cheeses (EMCs). EMCs are categorized as flavour preparations (EU, 1988) and have GRAS (generally regarded as safe) status under US regulations. EMCs have the advantage of cost effectiveness, ease of production, enhanced product stability, consistency in flavour and ease of handling over natural cheeses made by traditional processes (Kilcawley *et al.*, 1998). EMCs differ from traditional natural cheese in many different aspects. A comparison of EMC and natural cheeses is given in Table 19.2.

EMCs have approximately 5–25 times the flavour intensity of natural cheese (Moskowitz and Noelck, 1987). EMC flavours that are commercially available include Blue, Brick, Cheddar, Colby, Emmental, Feta, Gouda, Gruyère, Mozzarella, Parmesan, Provolone and Romano. EMCs have a wide range of application in various food preparations and are generally added to these preparations at levels of 0.1–2.0%, although they can be used up to 5% (Moskowitz and Noelck, 1987). The use of EMCs is ideal for frozen cheese-type products in which the proteins of natural cheese tend to produce a grainy texture (Kilcawley *et al.*, 1998). Because of their high flavour intensity, a given cheese flavour intensity can be obtained in a product using lower levels

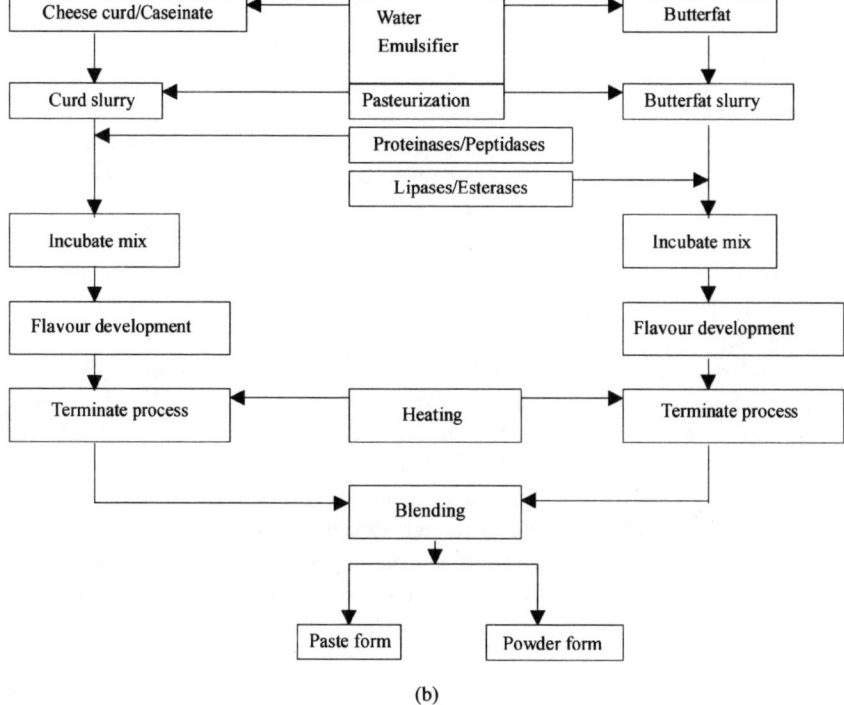

(b)

Fig. 19.3   continued

of EMCs than with natural cheese. Thus, low-fat cheese flavoured food products can be made using EMCs which are attractive to health-conscious consumers.

EMCs can be manufactured in two different ways, namely a one-step process (Fig. 19.3a) or a component approach process (Fig. 19.3b). The one-step process involves simultaneous hydrolysis of fat and protein, while in the component approach process, several flavour components are created separately and, at the end of hydrolysis, components are blended to give the final EMC product.

Companies that produce EMCs usually use different starting materials and enzyme preparations. The base material for the manufacture of EMC is usually immature cheese curd, although caseinates are used occasionally. In order to obtain the most authentic flavour, immature cheese curd of the target cheese may be used as the starting material. Small amounts of mature cheese may also be included in the blend (Wilkinson and Kilcawley, 2002).

Emulsifying agents, usually calcium sequestrants, are used in the production of EMCs. These salts solubilize protein by chelating Ca^{2+} and the solubilized proteins act as emulsifiers for the fat. The emulsified state of fat facilitates lipase action. The fat fraction is freely emulsified in EMC, increasing the area of the oil/water interface and providing improved conditions for the action of lipases (Villeneuve and Foglia, 1997).

Flavour enhancers (potentiators) such as monosodium glutamate, yeast extract or diacetyl can be used in the production of EMCs to enhance the flavour perception and savoury attributes of the product. The use of natural, nature-identical or artificial flavours is permitted for a specific flavour note but has to be declared on the label of the final product into which the EMC is added.

Selection of the enzyme or enzyme blend is very important in the production of EMC as it influences the flavour development directly. Generally, use of broad specificity proteinases ensures rapid proteolysis for flavour development. Most of the proteinases used in EMCs are derived from *Bacillus* spp. or *Aspergillus* spp. and often result in the production of bitter peptides from the caseins. Hence, it becomes necessary to include peptidases in the enzyme mix to break down these bitter peptides. Generally, the peptidases used are aminopeptidases from *Aspergillus oryzae* or from LAB. Use of lipases, which cause intense flavour development, in the enzyme mix can reduce reliance on proteinases and peptidases (Godfrey and Hawkins, 1991). Lipases in the enzyme mix are very important when producing Romano and blue cheese-type flavours as lipolysis contributes strongly to flavour development in these varieties.

After the preparation of the cheese slurry, it is necessary to pasteurize it so as to kill pathogenic or spoilage bacteria, as the incubation conditions used in EMC manufacture are favourable for their growth. Care should be taken to avoid subsequent contamination, and sterility of the equipment must be ensured. Heat treatment also inactivates many enzymes in the base material (e.g., residual coagulant and starter proteinases and peptidases) and thus helps to standardize the starting material. During the incubation period, efficient control of time, temperature, stirring and pH is necessary in order to obtain consistency in the final product. When the desired flavour is achieved, the enzymes are inactivated by heat treatment. The extent of heat treatment is very critical so as to inactivate enzyme without affecting the developed flavour. It is necessary to inactivate the enzymes, as continued activity would lead to instability in the EMC product, or residual enzyme activity may lead to the development of off-flavours in the food preparations in which EMCs are used. Hence, it is necessary to check EMCs for the residual proteinase and lipase activity after manufacture. Some processes used industrially in EMC manufacture were discussed by Kilcawley *et al.* (1998).

19.8   Future trends

Because of the cost of ripening hard cheeses, research into acceleration of ripening will continue in the future. Of the approaches discussed above, some have been restricted to date to academic research (e.g., high-pressure treatment) while others are used commercially to a lesser or greater extent (e.g., elevated temperatures and attenuated or adjunct cultures). As novel processing technologies become available, it is likely that they will find application in the area of acceleration of cheese ripening. The simplest and most successful approach to accelerate ripening studied to date is elevated temperature. Modification of the ripening temperature is used to control the rate of flavour development in hard cheese, and high temperature ripening (e.g., *ca.* 16°C) results in the rapid development of flavour, although problems can occur with texture but this is not a serious drawback if the cheese is to be used in certain ingredient applications. Finally, recent advances in the genetics of LAB and a greater understanding of the role of specific enzymes in the generation of volatile flavour compounds in cheese during ripening will facilitate the development of starter strains genetically modified to enhance flavour development.

19.9 Acknowledgement

The authors wish to thank Professor P. F. Fox for valuable comments and suggestions.

19.10 Sources of further information and advice

EL SODA M and PANDIAN S (1991), 'Recent developments in accelerated cheese ripening', *J Dairy Sci*, 74, 2317–2335.

FOX P F (1988/9), 'Acceleration of cheese ripening', *Food Biotechnol*, 2, 133–185.

FOX P F and TOBIN J (1999), 'Acceleration and modification of cheese ripening', *Proc 36th Annual Marschall Cheese Seminars*, 3, Santa Clara, CA.

FOX P F, WALLACE J M, MORGAN S, LYNCH C M, NILAND E J and TOBIN J (1996), 'Acceleration of cheese ripening', *Antonie van Leeuwenhoek*, 70, 271–297.

KLEIN N and LORTAL S (1999), 'Attenuated starters: an efficient means to influence cheese ripening – a review', *Int Dairy J*, 9, 751–762.

LAW B A (2001), 'Controlled and accelerated cheese ripening: the research base for new technologies', *Int Dairy J*, 11, 383–398.

WILKINSON M G (1993), 'Acceleration of cheese ripening', in Fox P F (ed.), *Cheese: Chemistry, Physics and Microbiology*, 2nd edn, Vol. 1, London, Chapman & Hall, pp. 523–555.

19.11 References

ANASTASIOU R, PAPADELLI M, GEORGALAKI M D, KALANTZOPOULOS G and TSAKALIDOU E (2002), 'Cloning and sequencing of the gene encoding X-prolyl-dipeptidyl aminopeptidase (Pep X) from *Streptococcus thermophilus* strain ACA-DC 4', *J Appl Microbiol*, 93, 52–59.

ARBIGE M V, FREUND P R, SILVER S C and ZELRO J T (1986), 'Novel lipase for Cheddar cheese flavor development', *Food Technol*, 40, 91–98.

ARDÖ Y and PETTERSON H E (1988), 'Accelerated ripening with heat-shocked *Lb. helveticus* and a commercial proteinase', *J Dairy Res*, 55, 239–245.

ASTON J W, FEDRICK I A, DURWARD I G and DULLEY J R (1983a), 'The effect of elevated ripening temperatures on proteolysis and flavour development in Cheddar cheese. 1. Higher initial storage temperatures', *NZ J Dairy Sci Technol*, 18, 143–151.

ASTON J W, GRIEVE P A, DURWARD I G and DULLEY J R (1983b), 'Proteolysis and flavour development in Cheddar cheeses subjected to accelerated ripening treatments', *Aust J Dairy Technol*, 38, 59–65.

ASTON J W, GILES J E, DURWARD I G and DULLEY J R (1985), 'Effect of elevated ripening temperatures on proteolysis and flavour development in Cheddar cheese', *J Dairy Res*, 52, 565–572.

BANKS J, HUNTER E and MUIR D (1993), 'Sensory properties of low-fat Cheddar cheese: effects of salt content and adjunct culture', *J Soc Dairy Technol*, 46, 119–123.

BARRETT F M, KELLY A L, MCSWEENEY P L H and FOX P F (1999), 'Use of exogenous urokinase to accelerate proteolysis in Cheddar cheese during ripening', *Int Dairy J*, 9, 421–427.

BARTELS H J, JOHNSON M E and OLSON N F (1987), 'Accelerated ripening of Gouda cheese. II. Effect of freeze shocked *Lb. helveticus* on proteolysis and flavour development', *Milchwissenschaft*, 42, 139–144.

BEUVIER E, BERTHAUD K, CEGARRA S, DASEN A, POCHET S, BUCHIN S and DUBOZ G (1997), 'Ripening and quality of Swiss-type cheese made from raw, pasteurized or microfiltered milk', *Int Dairy J*, 7, 311–323.

BIRKELAND S E, ABRAHAMSEN R K and LANGSRUD T (1992), 'Accelerated cheese ripening: use of a Lac⁻ mutants of lactococci', *J Dairy Res*, 59, 389–400.

BOLOTIN A, WINCKER P, MAUGER S, JAILLON O, MALARME K, WEISSENBACH J, EHRLICH S D and SOROKIN A (2001), 'The complete genome sequence of the lactic acid bacterium *Lactococcus lactis* ssp. *lactis* IL1403', *Genome Res*, 11, 731–753.

BOUTON Y and GRAPPIN R (1995), 'Comparaison de la qualité de fromages à pâte pressée cuite fabriqués à partir de lait cru ou microfiltré', *Lait*, 75, 31–44.

BUFFA M, GUAMIS B, PAVIA M and TRUJILLO A J (2001), 'Lipolysis in cheese made from raw, pasteurized or high-pressure treated goats' milk', *Int Dairy J*, 11, 175–179.

BUIST G, KOK J, LEENHOUTS K J, DABROWSKA M, VENEMA G and HAANDRIKMAN A J (1995), 'Molecular cloning and nucleotide sequence of the gene encoding the major peptidoglycan hydrolase of *Lactococcus lactis*, a muramidase needed for cell separation', *J Bacteriol*, 177, 1554–1563.

CHRISTENSEN J E, DUDLEY E G, PEDERSON J A and STEELE J L (1999), 'Peptidases and amino acid catabolism in lactic acid bacteria', *Antonie van Leeuwenhoek*, 76, 217–246.

CHRISTENSSON C, HENRIK B, COLLINS L J, COOLBEAR T, HOLLAND R, LUBBERS M W, O'TOOLE P W and REID J R (2002), 'Cloning and expression of an oligopeptidase, Pep O, with novel specificity from *Lactobacillus rhamnosus* HN001 (DR20)', *Appl Environ Microbiol*, 68, 254–262.

COURTIN P, NARDI M, WEGMANN U, JOUTSJOKI V, OGIER J C, GRIPON J C, PALVA A, HENRICH B and MONNET V (2002), 'Accelerating cheese proteolysis by enriching *Lactococcus lactis* proteolytic system with lactobacilli peptidases', *Int Dairy J*, 12, 447–454.

CROMIE S J, GILES J E and DULLEY J R (1987), 'Effect of elevated ripening temperatures on the microflora of Cheddar cheese', *J Dairy Res*, 54, 69–76.

CROW V L, COOLBEAR T, GOPAL P K, MARTLEY F, MCKAY L L and RIEPE H (1995a), 'The role of autolysis of lactic acid bacteria in the ripening of cheese', *Int Dairy J*, 5, 855–875.

CROW V L, MARTLEY G M, COOLBEAR T and ROUNDHILL S J (1995b), 'The influence of phage assisted-lysis of *Lactococcus lactis* ssp. *lactis* ML8 on Cheddar cheese ripening', *Int Dairy J*, 5, 451–472.

DULLEY J R, BROOKS D E J and GRIEVE P A (1978), 'The possible use of Lac⁻ starter strains to accelerate cheese ripening and a method for their detection in cheese', *Proc XX International Dairy Congress,* Paris, p 485.

EL SODA M (1993), 'Accelerated maturation of cheese', *Int Dairy J*, 3, 531–544.

EL SODA M and PANDIAN S (1991), 'Recent developments in accelerated cheese ripening', *J Dairy Sci*, 74, 2317–2335.

EL SODA M, PANNELL L and OLSON N (1989), 'Microencapsulated enzyme systems for the acceleration of cheese ripening', *J Microencapsul*, 6, 319–326

EL SODA M, MADKOR S A and TONG P S (2000a), 'Evaluation of commercial adjuncts for the use in cheese ripening: 4. Comparision between attenuated and non attenuated lactobacilli', *Milchwissenschaft*, 55, 260–263.

EL SODA M, MADKOR S A and TONG P S (2000b), 'Adjunct cultures: recent developments and potential significance to the cheese industry', *J Dairy Sci*, 83, 609–619.

EUROPEAN UNION (1988), *Official Journal of the European Communities*, 31 (L184), 61–66. Completed by Directive No. 91/71/EEC of 16 January 1991, 34 (L42), 25.

EXTERKATE F A, DE VEER G J and STADHOUDERS J (1987), 'Acceleration of the ripening process of Gouda cheese by using heat-treated mixed-strain starter cells', *Neth Milk Dairy J*, 41, 307–320.

FARKYE N Y and FOX P F (1992), 'Contribution of plasmin to Cheddar cheese ripening: effect of added plasmin', *J Dairy Res*, 59, 209–216.

FEDRICK I A (1987), 'Technology and economics of the accelerated ripening of Cheddar cheese', *Proc Ann Conf Victorian Div Dairy Ind Assoc Aust*, Melbourne.

FEDRICK I A and DULLEY J R (1984), 'The effect of elevated storage temperatures on the rheology of Cheddar cheese', *NZ J Dairy Sci Technol*, 19, 141–150.

FEDRICK I A, ASTON J W, DURWARD I F and DULLEY J R (1983), 'The effect of elevated ripening temperatures on proteolysis and flavour development in Cheddar cheese. I. High temperature storage midway during ripening', *NZ J Dairy Sci Technol*, 18, 253–260.

FEIRTAG M J and McKAY L L (1987), 'Thermoinducible lysis of temperature-sensitive *Streptococcus cremoris* strains', *J Dairy Sci*, 70, 1779–1784.

FOLKERTSMA B, FOX P F and McSWEENEY P L H (1996), 'Accelerated ripening of Cheddar cheese at elevated temperatures', *Int Dairy J*, 6, 1117–1134.

FOX P F (1988/9), 'Acceleration of cheese ripening', *Food Biotechnol*, 2, 133–185.

FOX P F and McSWEENEY P L H (1997), 'Rennets: their role in milk coagulation and cheese ripening', in Law B A (ed.), *The Microbiology and Biochemistry of Cheese and Fermented Milk,* 2nd edn, London, Chapman & Hall, pp 1–49.

FOX P F and TOBIN J (1999), 'Acceleration and modification of cheese ripening', *Proc 36th Annual Marschall Cheese Seminars*, 3, Santa Clara, USA.

FOX P F, LAW J, McSWEENEY P L H and WALLACE J (1993), 'Biochemistry of cheese ripening', in Fox P F (ed.), *Cheese: Chemistry, Physics and Microbiology*, Vol 1, London, Chapman & Hall, pp 389–438.

FOX P F, O'CONNOR T P, McSWEENEY P L H, GUINEE T P and O'BRIEN N M (1996a), 'Cheese: physical, chemical, biochemical and nutritional aspects', *Adv Food Nutr Res*, 39, 163–328.

FOX P F, WALLACE J M, MORGAN S, LYNCH C M, NILAND E J and TOBIN J (1996b), 'Acceleration of cheese ripening', *Antonie van Leeuwenhoek*, 70, 271–297.

FOX P F, McSWEENEY P L H and LYNCH C M (1998), 'Significance of non-starter lactic acid bacteria in Cheddar cheese', *Aust J Dairy Technol*, 53, 83–89.

GODFREY T and HAWKINS D (1991), 'Enzymatic modification of fats for flavour', *Eur.Food*

Drink Rev, Autumn, 103–107.

GRIEVE P A and DULLEY J R (1983), 'Use of *Streptococcus lactis* Lac⁻ mutants for accelerating Cheddar cheese ripening. 2. Their effect on rate of proteolysis and flavour development', *Aust J Dairy Tech*, 38, 49–54.

GUINEE T P, WILKINSON M G, MULLHOLLAND E and FOX P F (1991), 'Influence of ripening temperature, added commercial enzyme preparations and attenuated, mutant (lac⁻) *Lactococcus lactis* starter on the proteolysis and maturation of Cheddar cheese', *Ir J Food Sci Technol*, 15, 27–51.

HANNON J, WILKINSON M G, DELAHUNTY C M, WALLACE J M, MORRISSEY P A and BERESFORD T P (2003), 'The use of autolytic starter systems to accelerate ripening of Cheddar cheese', *Int Dairy J*, 13, 313–323.

HITE B H (1899), 'The effect of pressure in the preservation of milk', *West Virginia Agric Exp Stat Bull*, 58, 15–35.

HOLLAND R, LIU S Q, WANG T, BENNETT M, NORRIS G, DELABRE M L, LUBBERS M W, DEKKER J W and CROW V L (2002), 'Esterases of lactic acid bacteria', *Aust J Dairy Technol*, 57, 116.

HUPPERTZ T, KELLY A L and FOX P F (2002), 'Effects of high pressure on constituents and properties of milk', *Int Dairy J*, 12, 561–572.

JOHNSON J A C and ETZEL M R (1995), 'Properties of *Lb. helveticus* CNRZ-32 attenuated by spray-drying, freeze drying or freezing', *J Dairy Sci*, 78, 761–768.

JOUTSJOKI V, LOUMA S, TAMMINEN M, KILPI M, JOHANSEN E and PALVA A (2002), 'Recombinant *Lactococcus* starters as a potential source of additional peptidolytic activity in cheese ripening', *J Appl Microbiol*, 92, 1159–1166.

KATSIARI M C, VOUTSINAS L P and KONDYLI E (2002), 'Improvement of sensory quality of low-fat Kefalograviera-type cheese with commercial adjunct cultures', *Int Dairy J*, 12, 757–764.

KILCAWLEY K N, WILKINSON M G and FOX P F (1998), 'Enzyme-modified cheese', *Int Dairy J*, 8, 1–10.

KIRBY C J, BROOKER B E and LAW B A (1987), 'Accelerated ripening of cheese using liposome-encapsulated enzyme', *Int J Food Sci Technol*, 22, 355–375.

KLEIN N and LORTAL S (1999), 'Attenuated starters: an efficient means to influence cheese ripening – a review', *Int Dairy J*, 9, 751–762.

KOSIKOWSKI F V (1976), 'Flavour development by enzyme preparations in natural and processed cheese', US Patent 3, 975,544.

LANE C N and FOX P F (1996), 'Contribution of starter and adjunct lactobacilli to proteolysis in Cheddar cheese during ripening', *Int Dairy J*, 6, 715–728.

LAW B A (2001), 'Controlled and accelerated cheese ripening: the research base for new technologies', *Int Dairy J*, 11, 383–398.

LAW B A and KING J C (1985), 'The use of liposomes for the addition of enzymes to cheese', *J Dairy Res*, 52, 183–188.

LAW B A and WIGMORE A S (1983), 'Accelerated cheese ripening of Cheddar cheese with commercial proteinase and intracellular enzymes from starter streptococci', *J Dairy Res*, 50, 519–525.

LAW B A, SHARPE M E and REITER B (1974), 'The release of intracellular dipeptidases from starter streptococci during Cheddar cheese ripening', *J Dairy Res*, 41, 137–146.

LAW B A, HOSKING Z D and CHAPMAN H R (1979), 'The effect of some manufacturing conditions on the development of flavour in Cheddar cheese', *J Soc Dairy Technol*, 32, 87–90.

LEIGH J A (1993), 'Activation of bovine plasminogen by *S. uberis*', *FEMS Microbiol Lett*,

114, 67–72.

LÓPEZ-FANDINO R, CARRASCOSA A V and OLANO A (1996), 'The effects of high pressure on whey protein denaturation and cheese-making properties of raw milk', *J Dairy Sci*, 79, 929–936.

LÓPEZ-FANDINO R, RAMOS M and OLANO A (1997), 'Rennet coagulation of milk subjected to high pressures', *J Agric Food Chem*, 45, 3233–3237.

LYNCH C M, McSWEENEY P L H, FOX P F, COGAN T M and DRINAN F D (1996), 'Manufacture of Cheddar cheese with and without adjunct lactobacilli under controlled microbiological conditions', *Int Dairy J*, 6, 851–867.

MARTÍNEZ-CUESTA M C, REQUENA T and PELÁEZ C (2001), 'Use of a bacteriocin producing transconjugant as starter in acceleration of cheese ripening', *Int J Food Microbiol*, 70, 79–88.

McGARRY A, EL-KHOLI A, LAW J, COFFEY A, DALY C, FOX P F and FITZGERALD G F (1994), 'Impact of manipulating the lactococcal proteolytic system on ripening and flavour development in Cheddar cheese', *Proc 4th Meeting BRIDGE T-Project*, Oviedo, Spain, p 32 (abstr.).

McGARRY A, LAW J, COFFEY A, DALY C, FOX P F and FITZGERALD G F (1995), 'Effect of genetically modifying the lactococcal proteolytic system on ripening and flavour development in Cheddar cheese', *Appl Environ Microbiol*, 60, 4226–4233.

McKAY L L and BALDWIN K A (1976), 'Plasmid distribution and evidence for a proteinase plasmid in *S. lactis*', *Appl Microbiol*, 29, 546–548.

McSWEENEY P L H and SOUSA M J (2000), 'Biochemical pathways for the production of flavour compounds in cheese during ripening', *Lait*, 80, 293–324.

McSWEENEY P L H, FOX P F, LUCEY J A, JORDAN K N and COGAN T M (1993), 'Contribution of the indigenous microflora to the maturation of Cheddar cheese', *Int Dairy J*, 3, 613–634.

MESSENS W, ESTEPAR-GARCIA J, DEWETTINCK K and HUYGHEBAERT A (1999), 'Proteolysis of high-pressure treated Gouda cheese', *Int Dairy J*, 9, 775–782.

MESSENS W, FOUBERT I, DEWETTINCK K and HUYGHEBAERT A (2000), 'Proteolysis of a high-pressure treated smear ripened cheese', *Milchwissenschaft*, 55, 328–332.

MESSENS W, FOUBERT I, DEWETTINCK K and HUYGHEBAERT A (2001), 'Proteolysis of a high-pressure treated mould ripened cheese', *Milchwissenschaft*, 56, 201–204.

MORGAN S, O'DONOVAN C, ROSS R P, HILL C and FOX P F (1995), 'Significance of autolysis and bacteriocin-induced lysis of starter cultures in Cheddar cheese ripening', *Proc 4th Cheese Symp*, Moorepark, Fermoy, Co. Cork, Ireland, pp. 51–60.

MORGAN S, ROSS R P and HILL C (1997), 'Increasing starter cell lysis in Cheddar cheese using a bacteriocin-producing adjunct', *J Dairy Sci*, 80, 1–10.

MOSKOWITZ G J and NOELCK S S (1987), 'Enzyme modified cheese technology', *J Dairy Sci*, 70, 1761–1769.

MOU L, SULLIVAN J J and JAGO G R (1976), 'Autolysis of *Streptococcus cremoris*', *J Dairy Res*, 43, 275–282.

NAKAJIMA H, TOYODA S, KITAMURA K and AHOKI K (1991), 'Accelerated ripening of Gouda cheese: direct inoculation of a lactose-negative mutant of *Lactococcus lactis* subsp. *cremoris* into cheesemilk', *Milchwissenschaft*, 46, 8–10.

NEEDS E C, STENNING R A, GILL A L, FERRAGUT V and RICH G T (2000), 'High-pressure treatment of milk: effects of casein micelle structure and on enzymatic coagulation', *J Dairy Res*, 67, 31–42.

O'CONNELL P B (2002), 'Studies in lipolysis in cheese during ripening', MSc thesis, National University of Ireland, Cork.

O'DONOVAN C M, WILKINSON M G, GUINEE T P and FOX P F (1996), 'An investigation of the autolytic properties of three lactococcal strains during cheese ripening', *Int Dairy J*, 6, 1149–1165.

O'REILLY C E, O'CONNOR P M, MURPHY P M, KELLY A L and BERESFORD T P (2000), 'The effect of exposure to pressure of 50 MPa on Cheddar cheese ripening', *Innov Food Sci Emer Technol*, 1, 109–117.

O'REILLY C E, KELLY A L, MURPHY P M and BERESFORD T P (2001), 'High pressure treatment: application in cheese manufacture and ripening', *Trends Food Sci Tech*, 12, 51–59.

O'SULLIVAN L, MORGAN S M, ROSS R P and HILL C (2002), 'Elevated enzyme release from lactococcal starter cultures on exposure to the lantibiotic lacticin 481, produced by *Lactococcus lactis* DPC5552', *J Dairy Sci*, 85, 2130–2140.

PETTERSON H E and SJÖSTRÖM G (1975), 'Accelerated cheese ripening: a method for increasing the number of lactic starter bacteria in cheese without detrimental effect to the cheese-making process, and its effect on the cheese ripening', *J Dairy Res*, 42, 313–326.

PILLIDGE C J, GOVINDASAMY-LUCEY R, GOPAL P K and CROW V L (1998), 'The major lactococcal cell wall autolysin AcmA does not detemine the rate of autolysis of *Lactococcus lactis* ssp. *cremoris* 2250 in Cheddar cheese', *Int Dairy J*, 8, 843–850.

PILLIDGE C J, RALLABHANDI P S V, TONG X, GOPAL P K, FARLEY P C and SULLIVAN P A (2002), 'Autolysis of *Lactococcus lactis*', *Int Dairy J*, 12, 133–140.

RYAN M P, REA M C, HILL C and ROSS R P (1996), 'An application in Cheddar cheese manufacture for a strain of *Lactococcus lactis* producing a novel broad-spectrum bacteriocin, Lacticin 3147', *Appl Environ Microbiol*, 62, 612–619.

SALDO J, MCSWEENEY P L H, SENDRA E, KELLY A L and GUAMIS B (2000), 'Changes in curd acidification caused by high pressure treatment', *Ir J Agric Food Res*, 39, 169.

SALDO J, MCSWEENEY P L H, SENDRA E, KELLY A L and GUAMIS B (2002), 'Proteolysis in caprine milk cheese treated by high pressure to accelerate cheese ripening', *Int Dairy J*, 12, 35–44.

SALOMSKIENE J (1998), 'Use of heat-treated starter for the intensification of cheese ripening', *Milchwissenschaft*, 53, 28–30.

SHAKEEL-UR-REHMAN, MCSWEENEY P L H and FOX P F (1999), 'A study on the role of the indigenous microflora of raw milk on the ripening of Cheddar cheese', *Milchwissenschaft*, 54, 388–392.

SHAKEEL-UR-REHMAN, BANKS J M, MCSWEENEY P L H and FOX P F (2000), 'Effect of ripening temperature on the growth and significance of non-starter lactic acid bacteria in Cheddar cheese made from raw or pasteurized milk', *Int Dairy J*, 10, 45–53.

SKEIE S, NARVHUS J A, ARDÖ Y, THORVALDSEN K and ABRAHAMSEN R K (1997), 'The effect of reduced salt content on the function of liposome-encapsulated neutrase and heat-treated lactobacilli in rindless low-fat cheese', *Lait*, 77, 575–585.

SMITH M R, BROWNING P D and PAWLETT D (2000), 'Cheese ripening process', World Patent 00000037.

TOBIN J (1999), 'Effects of adjunct cultures and starter blends on the quality of Cheddar cheese', PhD thesis, National University of Ireland, Cork.

TRUJILLO A J, ROYO C, GUAMIS B and FERRAGUT V (1999), 'Influence of pressurization on goat milk and cheese composition and yield', *Milchwissenschaft*, 54, 197–199.

TRUJILLO A J, CAPELLAS M, BUFFA M, ROYO C, GERVILLA R, FELIPE X, SENDRA E, SALDO J, FERRAGUT V and GUAMIS B (2000), 'Application of high pressure treatment for cheese production', *Food Res Int*, 33, 311–316.

VILLENEUVE P and FOGLIA T A (1997), 'Lipase specificities: potential application in lipid bioconversions', *INFORM*, 8, 640–650.

WILKINSON M G (1993), 'Acceleration of cheese ripening', in Fox P F (ed.), *Cheese: Chemistry, Physics and Microbiology*, 2nd edn, Vol 1, London, Chapman & Hall, pp 523–555.

WILKINSON M G and KILCAWLEY K N (2002), 'Technology of enzyme-modified cheese and natural cheese', Bulletin 371, Brussels, International Dairy Federation, pp 10–15.

WILKINSON M G, GUINEE T P, O'CALLAGHAN D M and FOX P F (1994a), 'Autolysis and proteolysis in different strains of starter bacteria during Cheddar cheese ripening', *J Dairy Res*, 61, 249–262.

WILKINSON M G, GUINEE T P and FOX P F (1994b), 'Factors which may influence the determination of autolysis of starter bacteria during Cheddar cheese ripening', *Int Dairy J*, 4, 141–160.

YOKOYAMA H, SAWAMURA N and MOTOBAYASHI N (1992), 'Method for accelerating cheese ripening', *Eur Patent* 0 469 587 A1.

YVON M and RIJNEN L (2001), 'Cheese flavour formation by amino acid catabolism', *Int Dairy J*, 11, 185–201.

20

Non-starter lactic acid bacteria (NSLAB) and cheese quality

T. P. Beresford, Dairy Products Research Centre, Ireland

20.1 Introduction

A wide diversity of microorganisms is associated with cheese and they are critical to the development of quality products. They contribute during both manufacture and ripening and are often responsible for the unique characteristics of flavour, aroma, appearance and texture associated with particular cheese varieties. Cheese microflora may be conveniently divided into two main groups, consisting of (a) starter and (b) secondary flora, on the basis that starters produce lactic acid during cheese manufacture while secondary flora do not. Secondary flora in turn may be considered to consist of four groups including:

- Propionic acid bacteria
- Moulds
- Smear flora
- Non-starter lactic acid bacteria (NSLAB).

NSLAB are unique among cheese flora in that they are adventitious microorganisms that grow in all cheese types studied to date. The best studied members of the NSLAB complex are mesophilic lactobacilli; however, *Pediococcus*, *Enterococcus* and *Leuconostoc* should also be considered part of the complex on the basis that they are members of the lactic acid group of bacteria and generally do not produce significant amounts of lactic acid during manufacture. With the exception of *Leuconostoc* species, which are responsible for 'eye' formation ensuing from CO_2 production and flavour development resulting from production of diacetyl and acetate, the contribution of NSLAB to cheese quality is not clearly defined. However, there is mounting evidence, in particular for mesophilic lactobacilli and to a lesser extent enterococci, that they do influence cheese quality. The application of molecular techniques and systematic approaches to strain selection is resulting in greater knowledge of NSLAB populations in cheese and identification of adjuncts with the potential to influence cheese quality.

20.1.1 Cheese microflora

The microflora of most natural cheese varieties is complex and consists of a wide range of microorganisms including bacteria, moulds and yeast. They form an essential component of the cheese and are required during both cheese manufacture and ripening. The microflora may be conveniently divided into two main groups, starters and secondary flora. These two groups are distinguished on the basis that starter flora are responsible for fermentation of the milk sugar lactose, primarily to lactic acid, during cheese manufacture, while both groups contribute to the development of flavour and texture during the ripening process, either directly due to their metabolic activity or through release of their enzymes into the cheese matrix (Cogan, 2000).

Lactococcus lactis, Streptococcus thermophilus, Lactobacillus helveticus and *Lactobacillus delbruckii* are the primary species of starter bacteria used in cheese manufacture. Depending on the cheese variety, individual species or blends of two or more species either are added to the cheese milk at the beginning of manufacture or may be naturally present in the milk.

The secondary flora is composed of mixtures of bacteria, yeast and moulds. Specific mixtures are often, though not exclusively, associated with particular cheese varieties, where their action contributes to the specific characteristics of that variety. The secondary flora may be added in the form of defined cultures, but in many situations are composed of adventitious microorganisms gaining access to the cheese either from ingredients or from the environment. They can be divided into four primary groups which include:

- Propionic acid bacteria such as *Propionibacterium freundenreichii* which grow internally in Swiss-type cheeses, for example Emmentaler, Gruyère and Comté, where they are responsible for 'eye' formation
- Moulds such as *Penicillium roqueforti* which grows internally in blue-veined cheeses, for example Roquefort, Gorgonzola and Stilton, or *Penicillium camembertia* which grow externally on Camembert and Brie type cheeses
- Bacteria and yeast which grow on the surface of smear ripened cheeses such as Tilsiter, Munster or Saint Paulin
- NSLAB which grow internally in many cheese varieties during ripening and consist primarily of mesophilic lactobacilli, though *Pediococcus, Enterococcus* and *Leuconostoc* may also be considered to form part of the NSLAB complex.

20.2   Bacteria comprising the NSLAB complex

A useful definition of NSLAB is 'lactic acid bacteria found in cheese which do not form part of the starter culture, i.e. do not contribute to acid production during the cheese manufacturing process'. Thus, as outlined above, the NSLAB complex is comprised of four main groups of bacteria:

• Mesophilic lactobacilli
• Pediococci
• Enterococci
• *Leuconostoc*.

Mesophilic lactobacilli are probably the most commonly encountered and best studied members of this complex. Lactobacilli are a genetically diverse group of organisms. They are Gram-positive, catalase-negative and generally non-motile, with complex nutritional requirements. Their cell shape can vary from long and slender, sometimes bent rods, to short, often coryneform coccobacilli; chain formation is common. They can grow in the temperature range 2–53°C and are aciduric with an optimal pH usually 5.5–6.2. They have been traditionally divided into three groups on the basis of being either (I) obligatory homofermentative, (II) facultatively heterofermentative, or (III) obligatory heterofermentative (Kandler and Weiss, 1986). Members of the facultatively heterofermentative lactobacilli (Group II) are most often encountered in cheese as part of the NSLAB flora and are sometimes referred to as facultatively heterofermentative lactobacilli (FHL). Most Group II isolates do not grow well in milk (Cogan *et al.*, 1997) and thus do not contribute to acid production during the manufacturing process. They can, however, grow in cheese during ripening and form a significant portion of the microbial flora of most cheese varieties. Many species of mesophilic lactobacilli have been isolated from cheese, but those most frequently encountered are *Lb. casei/Lb. paracasei*, *Lb. plantarum*, *Lb. rhamnosus* and *Lb. curvatus* (Jordan and Cogan, 1993; Coppola *et al.*, 1997; Fitzsimons *et al.*, 1999). Members of group III are occasionally encountered, in particular *Lb. brevis* and *Lb. fermentum*. Group I contains the lactobacilli that are normally considered part of the starter flora.

Pediococci are Gram-positive, catalase-negative, spherical cells found in pairs or tetrads. They are unusual among lactic acid bacteria as they can divide in two perpendicular directions to form tetrads, although this formation may not always be present. Single cells are rarely found and pediococci do not form chains. They are non-motile and generally facultatively anaerobic (Schleifer, 1986). They can grow in the temperature range 25–50°C. They ferment glucose to produce lactic acid but gas is not formed, lactose is not readily fermented and this limits their growth in milk. Species of pediococci vary in their tolerance to salt, with some able to grow in media containing 6.5% NaCl. These bacteria grow at pH 4.5 to 8.2. Pediococci are commonly found in fermenting vegetables, hay, silage, alcoholic beverages and soft drinks (Schleifer, 1986; Simpson and Taguchi, 1995). *Pediococcus pentosaceus* and *P. acidilactici* are the dominant species isolated from dairy products (Garvie, 1984).

While many enterococci will grow in milk, most strains isolated from cheese do not produce sufficient lactic acid to reduce milk to pH 5.3 in 6 hours at 30°C (Cogan *et al.*, 1997). Thus, they conform more to the definition of NSLAB rather than that of a starter and will be considered part of the NSLAB flora in this review. The genus *Enterococcus* consists of Gram-positive, catalase-negative, spherical or ovoid cells, which are typically arranged in pairs or chains. Enterococci are facultative anaerobes and most species within the genus will grow in the temperature range 10–45°C. Most are capable of growth in media containing 6.5% NaCl, at pH 9.6 and can hydrolyse aesculin in the presence of 40% bile salts (Schleifer, 1986). Traditionally two species, *Streptococcus faecalis* and *S. faecium*, were considered part of the genus *Streptococcus* and were termed faecal group D streptococci (Deibel *et al.*, 1963; Facklam and Moody, 1970; Facklam, 1973). Subsequently, molecular characterisation indicated that these two species were distinct from the majority of the species in the genus *Streptococcus* (Collins *et al.*, 1984). Thus, Schleifer and Kilpper-Bälz (1984) proposed their transfer to the genus *Enterococcus*. In the intervening years a further 17 species have been added to the genus on the basis of phylogenetic evidence provided by 16S rRNA sequencing studies. Enterococci have been isolated from a variety of dairy products where they often co-exist with lactococci. Lactococci and enterococci share many phenotypic characteristics; however, traditionally they have been separated on the basis that all species of enterococci were capable of growth at 45°C and in 6.5% NaCl, while lactococci were not. However, isolates have been identified which do not conform to these criteria; these include salt and/or temperature tolerant lactococci (Facklam and Collins, 1989; Teixeira *et al.*, 1996) along with salt and/or temperature sensitive enterococci (Collins *et al.*, 1984; Devriese *et al.*, 1990). Genotypic methods are likely to provide more reliable identification and a genus-specific RCR based method was recently developed which can reliably differentiate lactococci from enterococci (Deasy *et al.*, 2000). The dominant species isolated from cheese include *E. faecium, E. faecalis* and *E. durans*.

While *Leuconostoc* form a component of mixed starter cultures, as they grow and produce acid very slowly in milk they do not conform to the definition of 'starter culture' given above and thus should be considered part of the NSLAB flora. The genus *Leuconostoc* consists of Gram-positive, catalase-negative cells with irregular coccoid morphology. Their optimum growth temperature is in the range 20–30°C. Their distinction from gas-forming heterofermentative lactobacilli has long been controversial and the two genera are now considered to be phylogenetically intermixed (Stackebrandt and Teuber, 1988). They are also often confused with lactococci, but they can be distinguished on the basis of three fundamental characteristics:

1. They ferment sugars heterofermentatively rather than homofermentatively.
2. They produce the D rather than the L isomer of lactate.
3. With the exception of *Leuconostoc lactis*, they show no visual evidence of growth in litmus milk unless yeast extract (0.3 g per 100 ml) is added.

The taxonomy of dairy leuconostocs was recently reviewed in detail (Thunell, 1995). The leuconostocs are traditionally associated with plant material, fermented dairy products and wines. While they are found in mixed-strain starter cultures used in cheese manufacture, the exact species have not been clearly identified; however, both *L. mesenteroides* ssp. *cremoris* and *L. lactis* are involved.

20.3   NSLAB in different cheese varieties

While, with the exception of leuconostocs, NSLAB are not traditionally deliberately added to cheese, most cheeses studied to date contain bacteria from at least one group within the NSLAB complex. The mesophilic lactobacilli flora of Cheddar cheese has been extensively investigated in recent years using both phenotypic and molecular methods of characterisation. A study of 8-week-old commercial Irish Cheddar revealed that the flora consisted of 55% *Lb. paracasei*, 28% *Lb. plantarum* and 14% *Lb. curvatus* (Jordan and Cogan, 1993). A subsequent study on mature Irish Cheddar by Fitzsimons *et al.* (1999) which involved characterisation of 331 isolates from 14 premium quality and three sensorially defective cheeses indicated that 96.4% of the isolates were *Lb. paracasei*, 2.1% *Lb. plantarum*, 0.3% *Lb. curvatus*, 0.3% *Lb. brevis* and 0.9% were unidentified. A study of UK Cheddar ripened 6–9 months indicated that *Lb. paracasei* and *Lb. plantarum* were the dominant species; however, *Lb. curvatus*, *Lb. brevis*, *Lb. helveticus*, *Lb. fermentum*, *Lb. bifermentans*, *Lb. buchneri*, *Lb. parabuchneri*, *Lb. farciminis* and *Lb. kefir* were also isolated (Williams and Banks, 1997). In New Zealand Cheddar, manufactured in six factories, *Lb. paracasei* and *Lb. rhamnosus* were the dominant species isolated (Crow *et al.*, 2001).

The mesophilic lactobacilli flora from a range of European traditional cheeses was recently reviewed (Beresford *et al.*, 2001). While there appears to be some variation in the *Lactobacillus* populations depending on the cheese variety and the duration of ripening, the dominant species identified throughout the range of cheeses reported include *Lb. paracasei*, *Lb. rhamnosus* and *Lb. plantarum*. *Lactobacillus curvatus* was identified in some of the cheeses reviewed. Studies on Fossa (pit) cheese, which is ripened in flask-shaped pits dug in the tufa ground in the Emilia-Romagna region of Italy, indicated that *Lb. plantarum*, *Lb. curvatus* and *Lb. paracasei* dominated the mesophilic lactobacillus flora (Gobbetti *et al.*, 1999). Characterisation of mesophilic lactobacilli from Fiore Sardo cheese demonstrated that *Lb. plantarum* and *Lb. paracasei* were the dominant species and that the population attained maximum numbers of $\sim 10^8$ cfu g^{-1} at 15 days of ripening and then slowly decreased to $\sim 10^4$ cfu g^{-1} after 7 months' ripening (Mannu *et al.*, 2000). In a study of 12 Italian ewes' milk cheeses (de Angelis *et al.*, 2001) 32% of the isolated mesophilic lactobacilli were phenotypically identified as *Lb. plantarum*, 15% *Lb. brevis*, 12% *Lb. paracasei*, 9% *Lb. curvatus*, 6% *Lb. fermentum*, 6% *Lb.*

casei, 5% *Lb. pentosus*, 3% *Lb. casei* ssp. *pseudoplantarum*, and 1% *Lb. rhamnosus. Lactobacillus paracasei* was identified as the predominant species of mesophilic lactobacilli in Caciocavallo Pugliese, a pasta-filata type cheese that is generally aged prior to consumption (Gobbetti *et al.*, 2002).

Pediococci were first reported in experimental New Zealand Cheddar cheese by Dacre (1958a, 1958b). A number of subsequent studies on Cheddar from the UK also reported the presence of pediococci in the NSLAB flora (Franklin and Sharpe, 1963; Fryer and Sharpe, 1966; Law *et al.*, 1976). In young Canadian Cheddar pediococci were observed to constitute approximately 1% of the NSLAB flora (Elliott and Mulligan, 1968). They have also been isolated from Cheddar cheese manufactured in the USA (Litopoulou-Tzanetaki *et al.*, 1989). In varieties other than Cheddar strains of *P. pentosaceus* have been isolated from Manchego cheese (Nunez, 1976) and from a raw goats' milk cheese, Feta and Kaseri (Tzanetakis and Litopoulou-Tzanetaki, 1989), while *P. acidilactici* were reported in Parmigiano Reggiano cheese (Coppola *et al.*, 1997).

Enterococci occur in a variety of artisanal cheeses made from raw or pasteurised goat, ewe, water buffalo or bovine milk in southern Europe (Cogan *et al.*, 1997). Enterococci were identified in 96% of samples in a survey of 48 Italian fresh, soft and ripened semihard cheeses by Giraffa *et al.* (1997). Enterococci have been detected as a significant portion of the bacterial flora of a range of cheeses such as Manchego (Ordoñez *et al.*, 1978), Le Serena (Del Pozo *et al.*, 1988), Mozzarella (Coppola *et al.*, 1988), Kefalotyri (Litopoulou-Tzanetaki, 1990), Feta and Teleme (Tzanetaki and Litopoulou-Tzanetaki, 1992), Picante de Beira Baixa (Freitas *et al.*, 1995), Serra (Macedo *et al.*, 1995), Cebreiro (Centeno *et al.*, 1996), Comté (Bouton *et al.*, 1998) and in a farmhouse Cheddar type cheese (Gelsomino *et al.*, 2001). Enterococcal numbers vary with cheese type and production season and ranged from 10^4 to 10^6 cfu/g for Emmental cheese during a 15-year survey to 10^4 to 10^7 cfu g^{-1} for Appenzeller cheese (see Franz *et al.*, 1999). The dominant species isolated were *E. faecium, E. faecalis* and *E. durans*.

Cultures containing leuconostocs are used in the manufacture of Dutch varieties such as Gouda and Edam, Danish varieties such as Danbo, Havarti, Maribo and Danish Blue, Swedish cheeses such as Herrgård, Drabantost, Wästerbottensost, Prästost and Svecia, and Finnish cheeses such as Turunmaa and Karelia. *Leuconostoc mesenteroides* and *Leuc. citreum* have also been isolated from cheeses made using traditional technology in France (Cibik *et al.*, 2000). They have been isolated from Casar de Cáceres (Poullet *et al.*, 1993), Manchego (Garcia *et al.*, 1995), Cebreiro (Centeno *et al.*, 1996), Roncal and Idiazabal (Arizcun *et al.*, 1997), San Simon (Fontan *et al.*, 2001), Tetilla (Menendez *et al.*, 2001) and Tenerife cheese (Pérez *et al.*, 2002) from Spain, and Serra de Estrela cheese from Portugal (Dahl *et al.*, 2000). *Leuconostoc lactis* was reported in the Greek cheese Kefalotyri (Litopoulou-Tzanetaki, 1990) while *Leuc. lactis* and *Leuc. mesenteroides* were isolated from Teleme cheese (Tzanetakis and Litopoulou-Tzanetaki, 1992). Mozzarella cheese made from water-buffalo milk in Italy is traditionally produced using a natural whey starter culture. The composition of these cultures is complex and while lactococci and thermophilic lactobacilli were dominant, relatively high numbers of *Leuconostoc* were also isolated (Coppola *et al.*, 1988). A more recent study (Morea *et al.*, 1999) demonstrated that *Leuc. lactis* and *Leuc. mesenteroides* were present in raw cows' milk Mozzarella post-manufacture.

20.4   The source of NSLAB in cheese

With the exception of leuconostocs which in some situations are added as part of the mixed-strain starter culture, NSLAB are adventitious bacteria which gain access to the cheese either from the ingredients used in its manufacture or from the environment. Mesophilic lactobacilli are found in all natural cheeses investigated to date. For cheeses made from raw milk the likely source of these bacteria is the cheese milk. A study using molecular techniques to type strains of mesophilic lactobacilli in Comté cheese made from raw milk indicated that a large number of the strains investigated could have originated from the milk (Berthier *et al.*, 2001). A number of studies have reported on the heat sensitivity of mesophilic lactobacilli but the findings have been equivocal. In one study, which involved 21 cultures and included typical Cheddar cheese isolates, the most heat-resistant strain *Lb. casei* NCDO161 suffered a 3.5 log reduction when heated to 72°C for 15 s, while the majority of the other cultures were reduced by 6 log cycles, suggesting that mesophilic lactobacilli would be inactivated by pasteurisation (Turner *et al.*, 1986). However, a subsequent study indicated that small numbers of mesophilic lactobacilli may survive pasteurisation in an injured state, revive during cheese ripening and subsequently grow in the cheese (Jordan and Cogan, 1999). This hypothesis was supported by the data of McSweeney *et al.* (1994) who detected no mesophilic lactobacilli in pasteurised cheese milk, but noted that the resulting cheese manufactured under aseptic conditions supported a low population of mesophilic lactobacilli from the beginning of ripening.

Mesophilic lactobacilli that survive pasteurisation or gain access to the cheese plant from other cheese-making ingredients or the environment may survive within the plant in the form of biofilms. This was demonstrated in pilot plant studies where Cheddar cheese manufactured in the presence of biofilms of *Lb. curvatus* and *Lb. fermentum* was found to be contaminated with the *Lb. curvatus* strain used to make the biofilm (Somers *et al.*, 2001). The biofilm made with the *Lb. curvatus* was also able to survive the cleaning process used. In Cheddar cheese manufactured under commercial conditions the mesophilic *Lactobacillus* flora varied between factories in studies conducted in Ireland and New Zealand (Fitzsimons *et al.*, 1999; Crow *et al.*, 2001). Similar observations were reported for Herrgård cheese (Antonsson *et al.*, 2001) and a range of Italian ewe cheeses (de Angelis *et al.*, 2001). In three Irish Cheddar cheeses manufactured over a three-week period it was observed that the majority of the most prevalent strains were common (Fitzsimons *et al.*, 2001); however, seasonal variation was observed in the mesophilic lactobacillus flora of New Zealand Cheddar (Crow et al., 2001). These data imply that a unique and persistent flora is not associated with particular factories, though this topic demands further investigation. Pediococci have been reported in only a limited number of cheeses as outlined above and no reports on the manner in which they gain access to the cheese have been published.

The source of enterococci in cheese is not clearly defined; however, it is generally assumed that their presence in milk is the primary source. It has been considered that they contaminate milk during production and processing since they are present in bovine faeces (Devriese et al., 1992), animal hides and dairy equipment. In a set of recent studies (Gelsomino et al., 2001, 2002) enterococci were isolated from a Cheddar type cheese during manufacture and ripening, the milk used in its manufacture, the faeces of the personnel involved in cheese making, and the faeces of the dairy cows present on the farm. In addition, strains were isolated from the environment, the tap water, the milking machine and the cows' teats. Isolates were typed using pulse field gel electrophoresis. The key finding was that the same three clones, one of E. faecalis and two of E. casseliflavus, dominated almost all of the milk, cheese and human faecal samples. The two E. casseliflavus clones were also found in the bulk tank and the milking machine even after chlorination, suggesting that contamination of milk with enterococci is a result of contaminated milking equipment. Cows' faeces were not considered the source of enterococci in the cheese, as E. faecium and Streptococcus bovis, which largely dominated the cows' intestinal tracts, were not found in either the milk or the cheese.

20.5   The growth of NSLAB in cheese

Environmental parameters within cheese which influence bacterial growth and survival such as pH, level of salt, water activity and temperature were reviewed recently (Beresford et al., 2001). These parameters combine to inhibit the growth of most microorganisms, including starter bacteria. However, many NSLAB will survive in cheese and in some cases grow during ripening. Cheese is a nutritious food and contains high levels of protein and fat but would appear to be lacking in carbohydrates.

Mesophilic lactobacilli grow in all cheese types studied to date and in Cheddar cheese ripened at 6°C they have a generation time of 8.5 days (Jordan and Cogan, 1993). In Cheddar cheese manufactured from pasteurised milk the initial numbers of mesophilic lactobacilli in the cheese are low, sometimes below the detectable limit; however, they grow to levels of at least 10^7 cfu g^{-1} over the first 10–20 weeks of ripening, after which their population remains relatively constant for the duration of ripening (Fig. 20.1).

The energy source used by mesophilic lactobacilli for growth in cheese has not been clearly defined but a range of suggested sources have been identified (for review see Beresford et al., 2001). It is likely that mesophilic lactobacilli do

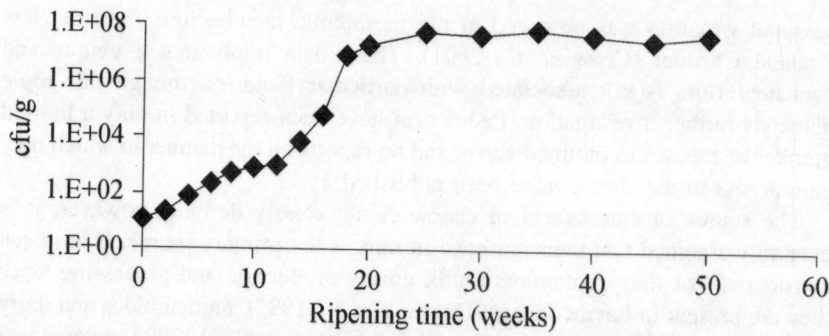

Fig. 20.1 Development of mesophilic lactobacilli in Cheddar cheese during ripening.

not depend on a single energy source to support their growth in cheese, and a recent study indicated that individual species and strains were apparently non-demanding and able to metabolise several different substrates potentially available in cheese (Williams *et al.*, 2000). This metabolic characteristic would assist their establishment and survival in cheese.

Substrate availability in cheese will vary throughout ripening; this will affect the heterogeneity of the mesophilic lactobacillus population and will thus influence population dynamics during ripening. In a study of Irish Cheddar over 39 weeks of ripening a mixture of *Lb. paracasei*, *Lb. plantarum*, *Lb. rhamnosus* and unidentified isolates was found up to 6 weeks' maturation; thereafter only *Lb. paracasei* was isolated (Fitzsimons *et al.*, 2001). Similar species dynamics were reported in New Zealand Cheddar except that the dominant species were *Lb. paracasei* and *Lb. rhamnosus* (Crow *et al.*, 2001). Evidence that strain dynamics occurs in Cheddar cheese was also reported (Fitzsimons *et al.*, 2001; Crow *et al.*, 2001). Species dynamics during ripening have also been reported for cheeses such as Fiore Sardo (Mannu *et al.*, 2000), Tenerife goats' cheese (Zarate *et al.*, 1997) and a Swiss type cheese (Demarigny *et al.*, 1996).

Few studies have reported on the growth of pediococci in cheese. Dacre (1958b) indicated that pediococci were not detected in Cheddar cheese in the first days post-manufacture but appeared within 18 days. They subsequently grew and comprised about one-fourth of the NSLAB population in 6-month-old cheese. The growth substrates for pediococci in cheese have not been studied; however, one report indicated that in buffer systems they could grow on the products released due to autolysis of starter cultures (Thomas, 1987).

As indicated above, enterococci occur in both raw and pasteurised milk cheeses. In Cheddar cheese produced in modern processing plants from pasteurised milk the numbers of enterococci in the cheese are very low or non-detectable. The sanitary methods of milk handling and refrigerated storage prior to processing contribute to such low levels. In Cheddar cheese manufactured with raw milk, enterococci are detected at levels in the range 10^2–10^3 cfu g^{-1} at day 1 of ripening and they maintain these levels during ripening (Gelsomino *et*

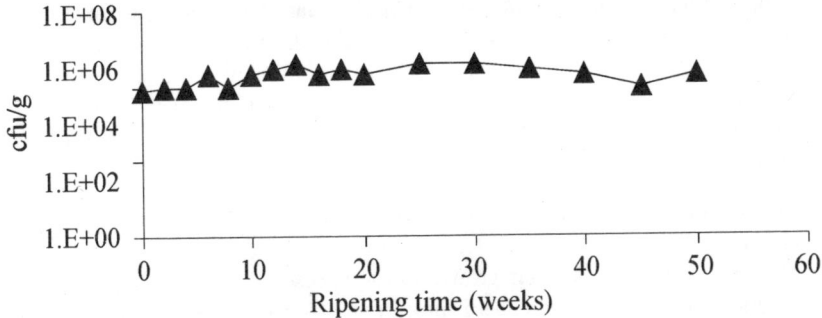

Fig. 20.2   Development of enterococci in a raw milk Cheddar cheese during ripening.

al., 2001). Typical growth of enterococci in raw milk Cheddar is illustrated in Fig. 20.2. Similar growth patterns have been reported for other cheese varieties (Del Pozo *et al.*, 1988; Litopoulou-Tzanetaki, 1990; Bouton *et al.*, 1998).

While a number of studies have indicated that leuconostocs are present in cheese, few reports on their growth dynamics during ripening have been published. Turner (1988) investigated the behaviour of two strains in experimental Gouda. One of the strains increased from ~10^5 to 5×10^5 cfu g^{-1} during the period from moulding of the curd to day 1 of ripening but thereafter decreased to ~10^4 cfu g^{-1} at 35 days of ripening. The other strain grew during the moulding period from ~5×10^5 cfu g^{-1} to 10^7 cfu g^{-1} and maintained this level in the cheese throughout the 35 days of ripening. These data suggest that growth and survival are strain dependent. In Serra da Estrela cheese, manufactured using traditional technology, the *Leuconostoc* population was ~10^7 cfu g^{-1} throughout the ripening period of 180 days (Dahl *et al.*, 2000).

20.6   The influence of NSLAB on cheese quality

Most research to date on the influence of various NSLAB on cheese quality and flavour has used Cheddar as a model. This is due in part to the 'relative' lack of complexity of the microflora associated with this cheese variety and the ability of the researcher to manipulate the flora to at least a limited extent. It should be noted, however, that in most experiments reported there are few, if any, examples where total control of the flora was achieved. This makes interpretation of the data difficult and definitive statements regarding the role of NSLAB problematic.

As demonstrated in Fig. 20.1, mesophilic lactobacilli are present in Cheddar at levels of >10^7 cfu g^{-1} from early in ripening. This represents a significant biocatalytic potential that would be expected to exert some impact on cheese quality. Traditionally Cheddar was manufactured from raw milk using undefined strain starter cultures. Since the introduction of pasteurisation, more hygienic milk handling practices and the defined strain starter system a perception has developed among many commentators that Cheddar cheese does not develop as mature a flavour as when it was manufactured using traditional methods.

Mesophilic lactobacilli as discussed above are adventitious microorganisms, which are ubiquitous in Cheddar. Attempts to investigate their influence on cheese quality have centred on approaches involving one or more of the following:

- Manufacture of cheese under conditions which hinder their access to the cheese
- Methods which inhibit their growth in the cheese
- Addition of strains to the cheese milk in an effort to ensure that the specific strains dominate the NSLAB flora during ripening.

The technology for the manufacture of cheese under controlled micro-biological conditions was developed by Mabbitt et al. (1959) who used a combination of pasteurisation (78°C for 17 s) and hygienic cheese manufacture in enclosed vats. This technology was later modified and the conclusion was that mesophilic lactobacilli did not have a significant effect on flavour development (Chapman et al., 1966). McSweeney et al. (1994) and Lynch et al. (1996) subsequently used this approach to study the effect of adjunct lactobacilli, which they reported to have a positive effect on cheese flavour and quality. Micro-filtration is a technology that facilitates the removal of indigenous micro-organisms from milk without the concomitant heat-induced changes resulting from pasteurisation. A study comparing Cheddar manufactured from either raw, pasteurised or microfiltered milks indicated that the flavour of the raw milk cheese was substantially more intense than that of the cheeses manufactured from either pasteurised or microfiltered milk, suggesting that the indigenous lactobacilli play a role in flavour development (McSweeney et al., 1993). It should be noted, however, that growth of lactobacilli in the microfiltered milk cheese was similar to growth in the pasteurised milk cheese, indicating that microfiltration in that series of experiments was no more efficient than pasteurisation at removal of lactobacilli.

The metabolic activity of the starter bacteria is essentially finished at the milling stage in Cheddar cheese. Thus it was proposed that the mesophilic lactobacillus population which develop during ripening could be controlled through the addition of antibiotics to the curd at salting without any deleterious impact on starter activity. A suitable combination of antibiotics was developed and applied during Cheddar manufacture (Walsh et al., 1996; Shakeel-Ur-Rehman et al., 1999). In both studies growth of mesophilic lactobacilli was greatly reduced, though not totally inhibited. While the overall pattern of proteolysis in the cheese was not impacted upon by the antibiotic treatment, higher levels of amino acids were reported in cheese containing antibiotic. It was not clear why this should be the case but it was speculated that the antibiotics might have induced autolysis of the starter culture.

Bacteriocins, which may be produced by the starter culture within the cheese, are an alternative to antibiotics to control growth of secondary flora in cheese.

Ryan *et al.* (1996) reported on the use of starter cultures capable of producing the broad-spectrum bacteriocin, lacticin 3147, to inhibit growth of mesophilic lactobacilli. In trials using a combination of three strains which naturally produced lacticin 3147, no mesophilic lactobacilli were detected in the cheese up to 6 months of ripening. In trials using a single transconjugant strain capable of producing lacticin 3147, mesophilic lactobacilli did grow in the cheese but at significantly lower levels (~100-fold) than the mesophilic population in the control cheese. Application of this technology to reduced-fat Cheddar also resulted in growth inhibition of mesophilic lactobacilli, and it was concluded that the differences in the rate of growth and the final population of mesophilic lactobacilli had no significant effect on proteolysis, or flavour and aroma, or body and texture of the resulting cheese (Fenelon *et al.*, 1999). Manipulation of temperature during ripening has been used extensively to control the rate of cheese ripening and the growth of mesophilic lactobacilli and has been reviewed recently by Shakeel-Ur-Rehman *et al.* (2000c). In all such studies to date, while reducing the ripening temperature inhibits growth of mesophilic lactobacilli, no cheese was maintained free of lactobacilli using this technology, even when the temperature was reduced to 1°C (Shakeel-Ur-Rehman *et al.*, 2000b).

The effect of adding adjunct cultures of mesophilic lactobacilli, isolated from cheese, to milk for cheesemaking has been researched for several decades. The results of these studies are equivocal, with some studies showing positive effects while others report negative effects on flavour formation (Peterson and Marshall, 1990; Fox *et al.*, 1998). The reason for the equivocal nature of the findings probably results from the flavouring potential of the isolates selected, combined with growth of adventitious strains during ripening. Most of the more recent studies on this topic have indicated that mesophilic adjuncts exert a positive effect on flavour (Puchades *et al.*, 1989; Broome *et al.*, 1990; Trépanier *et al.*, 1991, 1992; McSweeney *et al.*, 1993; Lynch *et al.*, 1996; Swearingen *et al.*, 2001). Gas production, which may result from growth of heterofermentative lactobacilli during ripening, is undesirable in Cheddar cheese. This defect could be controlled by addition of homofermentative lactobacilli to Cheddar during production (Laleye *et al.*, 1990). Direct comparison of the results from the various studies on the influence of mesophilic lactobacilli on cheese quality is difficult, as many differences exist in the experimental design and the level at which the adjunct lactobacilli were added.

Puchades *et al.* (1989) demonstrated that *Lb. casei* L2A when used as an adjunct resulted in a strong Cheddar flavour after 7 months of ripening at 6°C; however, growth of mesophilic lactobacilli was not monitored during this study. In a subsequent study the effect on flavour was confirmed (Trépanier *et al.*, 1992) and maximum counts of lactobacilli were obtained at two weeks. Interpretation is further complicated by the fact that adventitious lactobacilli almost invariably gain access to the 'control' cheese and eventually reach similar, and in some cases higher (e.g. Trépanier *et al.*, 1991), numbers in comparison to those in the experimental cheeses. In studies by Broome *et al.* (1990) two strains of *Lb. casei* were investigated as potential adjunct strains.

Neither had an effect on flavour after 6 months' ripening at 8°C, but cheese containing the adjunct had more pronounced Cheddar flavours after 9 and 12 months' ripening. Initial numbers of mesophilic lactobacilli were ~10^2 cfu g^{-1} and 10^8 cfu g^{-1} in the control and experimental cheeses respectively; however, the counts in the control cheese were ~10^8 cfu g^{-1} by 3 months of ripening. Improved flavour and reduced bitterness were obtained in American Cheddar using two strains of *Lb. paracasei* (Swearingen *et al.*, 2001); in these cheeses the counts for mesophilic lactobacilli were similar to those reported by Broome *et al.* (1990).

In another series of experiments (McSweeney *et al.*, 1993; Lynch *et al.*, 1996) adjuncts of *Lb. casei* ssp. *casei*, *Lb. casei* ssp. *pseudoplantarum*, *Lb. curvatus* and *Lb. plantarum* were added during the manufacture of Cheddar under controlled microbiological conditions. Mesophilic lactobacilli were detected in the control vats at initial levels of ~10^2 cfu g^{-1} and their population increased to ~10^6 cfu g^{-1} after 5 months' ripening at 8°C. In contrast, mesophilic lactobacilli in the experimental cheeses were ~10^8 cfu g^{-1} from the beginning of ripening. The cheeses containing the mesophilic lactobacillus adjuncts were generally reported to have better flavour intensities and flavour acceptabilities than the control cheeses. Thus, mounting evidence appears to support the hypothesis that mesophilic lactobacilli do exert an influence on cheese quality.

Although pediococci are recognised as part of the non-starter flora of cheese, their impact on cheese quality has not been well studied, due primarily to the infrequency with which they have been encountered (for review, see Bhowmik and Marth, 1990). A number of enzymes with potential to promote cheese ripening have been identified in various strains and include protease, peptidase and lipase activities. Acetate and diacetyl production by pediococci may contribute to flavour development. Further investigation regarding the prevalence of pediococci and their growth and survival during cheese ripening is required prior to defining their role in flavour development.

While enterococci occur in a variety of dairy products made from raw or pasteurised milk (Cogan *et al.*, 1997) their impact on cheese quality is unclear. Indeed their presence in cheese may be considered an indicator of insufficient sanitary conditions during the production and processing of milk. A study of 129 strains of food, human and veterinary origin indicated that the majority of the isolates exhibited low milk acidifying ability and extracellular proteolytic activity (Sarantinopoulos *et al.*, 2001). However, relatively high lipolytic activities were reported and many of the strains utilized citrate and pyruvate. Some studies have concluded that high levels of enterococci result in deterioration in the sensory properties of cheese (Thompson and Marth, 1986; López-Diaz *et al.*, 1995). However, others have reported improved characteristics (Jensen *et al.*, 1975a, 1975b; Ordoñez *et al.*, 1978; Trovatelli and Schiesser, 1987; Centeno *et al.*, 1999). The perceived beneficial impact of enterococci on cheese quality has resulted in their proposed inclusion as adjuncts for the production of a range of cheeses including Mozzarella (Coppola *et al.*, 1988; Parente *et al.*, 1989), Feta (Litopoulou-Tzanetaki *et al.*, 1993), Cebreiro

(Centeno *et al.*, 1996) and Venaco (Casalta and Zennaro, 1997). The British Advisory Committee on Novel Foods and Processes (ACNFP) recently approved the use of *E. faecium* K77D (Coppola *et al.*, 1988; Parente *et al.*, 1989) for use in the manufacture of Mozzarella cheese (ACNFP, 1996).

As part of the non-starter flora *Leuconostoc* differ from the other members of the group in that their primary role in the production of acetate, CO_2, diacetyl, acetoin and 2,3-butanediol resulting from citrate metabolism is well documented. The CO_2 produced is responsible for small eye formation in Dutch cheeses such as Edam and Gouda, while diacetyl and acetate contribute to the flavour of products such as Quark, Fromage Frais and Cottage Cheese. *Leuconostoc* are also rich in intercellular proteolytic enzymes (El-Shafei *et al.*, 1990) and esterase activities were reported from wild strains of leuconostocs from Greek cheese (Vafopoulou-Mastrojiannaki *et al.*, 1996). Thus, they may have a secondary impact on cheese quality through proteolysis and lipolysis but this requires clarification.

20.7   Selection of NSLAB adjuncts for quality improvement of cheese

Identification of suitable strains of NSLAB for use as starter adjunct for quality improvement of cheese offers considerable financial benefit to cheese manufacturers. Suitable strains would improve cheese flavour through production of key flavour compounds in the cheese and by inhibiting growth of deleterious adventitious strains. An important characteristic of NSLAB and mesophilic lactobacilli in particular is their ability to grow in the cheese during ripening, thus enabling the cheesemaker to add them at very low levels to the cheese milk at the beginning of manufacture and still obtain a positive impact in the cheese. However, correct selection of the adjunct strain is crucial, as it was demonstrated that some strains of *Lb. casei* ssp. *casei* and *Lb. casei* ssp. *pseudoplantarum* produced high quality Cheddar, while other strains of these species resulted in cheese with acid and bitter flavour defects (Lawrence and Gilles, 1987).

As the perceived deterioration in Cheddar flavour has been associated with the introduction of pasteurisation by some commentators, selection of non-starter bacteria from raw milk for use as adjuncts during commercial manufacture of Cheddar was proposed (Reiter *et al.*, 1967). This approach involved the development of a 'reference flora' whereby bacteria isolated from raw milk or fresh cheese curd by selective plating techniques were used as an adjunct blend during Cheddar manufacture. These experiments indicated that such an approach could result in cheese of improved flavour, but that off-flavours may also occur. This approach assumes that all the relevant microflora in the raw milk can be recovered by the selective plating techniques used and that the resulting reference flora is representative of the raw milk. This assumption may not be correct as it is recognised that many strains of particular species may be unable to grow on selective media designed for that particular species.

A similar approach was adopted by Beuvier *et al.* (1997) who added microfiltration retentate from raw milk to pasteurised milk to study the influence of the raw milk microflora on the quality of Swiss cheese. The cheese made using the retentate was reported to have a better flavour than the control cheeses. A further modification of this approach was used by Shakeel-Ur-Rehman *et al.* (2000a) who used blends of raw and pasteurised milk for Cheddar cheese manufacture. They reported that cheese made from a blend containing as little as 1% raw milk had a significantly higher population of mesophilic lactobacilli and graded better than cheeses made from pasteurised milk. The approaches outlined above use the milk as the source of mesophilic lactobacilli. Folkertsma (1999) suggested that if mesophilic lactobacilli have an impact on cheese quality, suitable strains should be present in mature high quality cheese. To test this hypothesis cheese milk was inoculated with slurries of mature Cheddar prior to cheese manufacture. Unfortunately the quality of the cheese made from the inoculated milk was not significantly better than that of the control cheese. Recent studies have indicated that the populations of mesophilic lactobacilli in Cheddar cheese are dynamic and that few cheeses are dominated by single strains or groups of strains during ripening (Crow *et al.*, 2001; Fitzsimons *et al.*, 2001). These findings may explain why the hypothesis proposed by Folkertsma (1999) was not verified.

The growing knowledge of mesophilic *Lactobacillus* populations in Cheddar cheese led Crow *et al.* (2001) to apply molecular and biochemical techniques to the selection of strains from cheese during ripening. Use of pulse field gel electrophoresis and fermentation patterns on 22 carbohydrates resulted in the identification of 140 strains. This bank of strains was further screened for their responses to salt, temperature and pH, their ability to metabolise citrate, produce biogenic amines and their proteolytic and lipolytic activities. This reduced the number of potential strains to 60, which were screened in a model cheese system for flavour development and biochemical changes (excess fermentation of glutamate, lactate racemisation). This resulted in 24 potential strains being selected and 20 adjunct combinations (made up of 2–4 strains each) were tested in Cheddar cheese trials. Twelve of the adjunct blends showed some flavour improvement over the control cheeses and seven of the blends resulted in significant improvement and accelerated flavour development. This demonstrated that a systematic approach to strain selection based on the available knowledge of cheese microbiology and biochemistry of flavour development can lead to the selection of strains of mesophilic lactobacilli with the potential to improve the quality of Cheddar cheese.

Studies on the selection of other NSLAB for use as starter adjuncts are limited but in general similar approaches to those for selection of adjuncts of mesophilic lactobacilli are used. Pediococci have been selected from raw milk by selective plating (Robertson and Perry, 1961) or from cheese (Law *et al.*, 1976), while enterococci have been isolated from natural whey cultures (Coppola *et al.*, 1988; Parente *et al.*, 1989) and cheese (Centeno *et al.*, 1999).

20.8   Conclusions

In summary, the NSLAB population of most cheese varieties is complex, composed of a number of species and strains, which are in a dynamic state during ripening. Significant progress has been made in understanding the behaviour of NSLAB in cheese and this has been greatly aided by the application of suitable molecular techniques. The potential of members of the NSLAB complex, in particular mesophilic lactobacilli and enterococci, to function as probiotics and the capacity of cheese to act as a suitable delivery system for such strains to the human gastrointestinal tract has been demonstrated (Gardiner *et al.*, 1998, 1999). Genomic sequencing of members of the NSLAB complex is either recently completed or underway (for review, see Klaenhammer *et al.*, 2002), and the information generated will provide opportunities for further exploitation. There is mounting evidence to support the hypothesis that NSLAB have the potential to influence cheese quality. Thus, selection of suitable strains for use as starter adjuncts is crucial if the economic potential of these bacteria is to be realised, and such selections will be aided by the expanding scientific understanding of NSLAB.

20.9   References

ACNFP (1996), 'Report on *Enterococcus faecium*, strain K77D', MAFF Advisory Committee on Novel Foods and Processes, Report, Ergon House, c/o Nobel House, 17 Smith Square, London SW1 3JR.

ANTONSSON, M., ARDO, Y. and MOLIN, G. (2001), 'A comparison between the microflora of Herrgård cheese from three different dairies', *Int. Dairy J.* 11(4–7), 285–291.

ARIZCUN, C., BARCINA, Y. and TORRE, P. (1997), 'Identification of lactic acid bacteria isolated from Roncal and Idiazabal cheeses', *Lait* 77(6), 729–736.

BERESFORD, T.P., FITZSIMONS, N.A., BRENNAN, N.L. and COGAN, T.M. (2001), 'Recent advances in cheese microbiology', *Int. Dairy J.* 11, 259–274.

BERTHIER, F., BEUVIER, E., DASEN, A. and GRAPPIN, R. (2001), 'Origin and diversity of mesophilic lactobacilli in Comté cheese, as revealed by PCR with repetitive and species-specific primers', *Int. Dairy J.* 11(4/7), 293–305.

BEUVIER, E., BERTHAUD, K., CEGARRA, S., DASEN, A., POCHET, S., BUCHIN, S. and DUBOZ, G. (1997), 'Ripening and quality of Swiss-type cheese made from raw, pasteurized or microfiltered milk', *Int. Dairy J.* 7, 311–323.

BHOWMIK, T. and MARTH, E.H. (1990), 'Role of *Micrococcus* and *Pediococcus* species in cheese ripening: a review', *J. Dairy Sci.* 73, 859–866.

BOUTON, Y., GUYOT, P. and GRAPPIN, P. (1998), 'Preliminary characterization of microflora of Comté cheese', *J. Appl. Microbiol.* 85, 123–131.

BROOME, M.C., KRAUSE, D.A. and HICKEY, M.W. (1990), 'The isolation and characterization of lactobacilli from Cheddar cheese', *Australian J. Dairy Technol.* 45, 60–66.

CASALTA, E. and ZENNARO, R. (1997), 'Effect of specific starters on microbiological, biochemical and sensory characteristics of Venaco, a Corsican soft cheese', *Sciences des Aliments* 17, 79–94.

CENTENO, J.A., MENÉNDEZ, S. and RODRIGUEZ-OTERO, J.L. (1996), 'Main microflora present in natural starters in Cebreiro raw cow's milk cheese (Northwest Spain)', *Int. J. Food Microbiol.* 33, 307–313.

CENTENO, J.A., MENÉNDEZ, S., HERMIDA, M.A. and RODRIGUEZ-OTERO, J.L. (1999), 'Effects of addition of *Enterococcus faecalis* in Cebreiro cheese manufacture', *Int. J. Food Microbiol.* 48, 97–101.

CHAPMAN, H.R., MABITT, L.A. and SHARPE, M.E. (1966), 'Apparatus and techniques for the manufacture of Cheddar cheese under controlled bacteriological conditions', *Proceedings of the 17th International Dairy Congress,* Munich, D, 774–775.

CIBIK, R., LEPAGE, E. and TAILLIEZ, P. (2000), 'Molecular diversity of *Leuconostoc mesenteroides* and *Leuconostoc citreum* isolated from traditional French cheeses as revealed by RAPD fingerprinting, 16S rDNA sequencing and 16S rDNA fragment amplification', *Syst. Appl. Microbiol.* 23, 267–278.

COGAN, T.M. (2000), 'Microbiology of cheese ripening', in Fox, P.F., Guinee, T.P., Cogan, T.M. and McSweeney, P.L.H., *Fundamentals of Cheese Science*, Maryland, Aspen, 206–232.

COGAN, T.M., BARBOSA, M., BEUVIER, E., BIANCHI-SALVADORI, B., COCCONCELLI, P.S., FERNANDES, I., GOMEZ, J., GOMEZ, R., KALANTZOPOULOS, G., LEDDA, A., MEDINA, M., REA, M.C. and RODRIGUEZ, V. (1997), 'Characterisation of the lactic acid bacteria in artisanal dairy products', *J. Dairy Res.* 64, 409–421.

COLLINS, M.D., JONES, D., FARROW, J.A.E., KILPPER-BÄLZ, R. and SCHLEIFER, K.H. (1984), '*Enterococcus avium* nom. rev., comb. nov.; *E. casseliflavus* nom. rev., comb. nov.; *E. durans* nom. rev., comb. nov.; *E. gallinarum* comb nov.; and *E. malodoratus* sp. nov.', *Int. J. Syst. Bacteriol.* 34(2), 220–223.

COPPOLA, R., NANNI, M., IORIZZO, M., SORRENTINO, A., SORRENTINO, E. and GRAZIA, L. (1997), 'Survey of lactic acid bacteria isolated during the advanced stages of the ripening of Parmigiano Reggiano cheese', *J. Dairy Res.* 64, 305–310.

COPPOLA, T.M., PARENTE, J.E., DUMONTET, S. and LA PECCRELLA, A. (1988), 'The microflora of natural whey cultures utilized as starters in the manufacture of Mozzarella cheese from water buffalo milk', *Lait* 68, 295–310.

CROW, V., CURRY, B. and HAYES, M. (2001), 'The ecology of non-starter lactic acid bacteria (NSLAB) and their use as adjuncts in New Zealand Cheddar', *Int. Dairy J.* 11, 275–283.

DACRE, J.C. (1958a), 'Characteristics of a presumptive *Pediococcus* occurring in New Zealand Cheddar cheese', *J. Dairy Res.* 25, 409–413.

DACRE, J.C. (1958b), 'A note on pediococci in New Zealand Cheddar cheese', *J. Dairy Res.* 25, 414–417.

DAHL, S., TAVARIA, F.K. and MALCATA, F.X. (2000), 'Relationships between flavour and microbiological profiles in Serra da Estrela cheese throughout ripening', *Int. Dairy J.* 10(4), 255–262.

DE ANGELIS, M., CORSETTI, A., TOSTI, N., ROSSI, J., CORBO, M.R. and GOBBETTI, M. (2001), 'Characterization of non-starter lactic acid bacteria from Italian ewe cheeses based on phenotypic, genotypic, and cell wall protein analyses', *Appl. Environ. Microbiol.* 67, 2011–2020.

DEASY, B.M., REA, M.C., FITZGERALD, G.F., COGAN, T.M. and BERESFORD, T. (2000), 'A rapid PCR based method to distinguish between *Lactococcus* and *Enterococcus*', *Syst. Appl. Microbiol.* 23, 510–522.

DEIBEL, R.H., LAKE, D.E. and NIVEN JR, C.F. (1963), 'Physiology of the enterococci as related to their taxonomy', *J. Bacteriol*, 86(6), 1275–1282.

DEL POZO, B.F., GAYA, P., MEDINA, M., RODRIGUEZ-MARIN, M.S. and NUNEZ, M. (1988),

'Changes in the microflora of la Serena ewes' milk cheese during ripening', *J. Dairy Res.* 55(3), 449–455.

DEMARIGNY, Y., BEUVIER, E., DASEN, A. and DUBOZ, G. (1996), 'Influence of raw milk microflora on the characteristics of Swiss-type cheeses. I. Evolution of microflora during ripening and characterisation of facultatively heterofermentative lactobacilli', *Lait* 76, 371–387.

DEVRIESE, L.A., CEYSSENS, K., RODRIGUES, U.M. and COLLINS, M.D. (1990), '*Enterococcus columbae*, a species from pigeon intestines', *FEMS Microbiol. Lett.* 71, 247–252.

DEVRIESE L.A., LAURIER, L., DE HERDT, P. and HAESEBROUCK, F. (1992), 'Enterococcal and streptococcal species isolated from faeces of calves, young cattle and dairy cows', *J. Appl. Bacteriol.* 72, 29–31.

ELLIOTT, J.A. and MULLIGAN, H.T. (1968), 'Pediococci in Canadian Cheddar cheese', *Can. Inst. Food Technol. J.* 1, 61.

EL-SHAFEI, H., EL-SODA, M. and EZZAT, N. (1990), 'The peptidase hydrolyase system of the *Leuconostoc*', *J. Food Prot.* 53, 165–169.

FACKLAM, R.R. (1973), 'Comparison of several laboratory media for presumptive identification of enterococci and group D streptococci', *Appl. Microbiol.* 26(2), 138–145.

FACKLAM, R.R. and COLLINS, M.D. (1989), 'Identification of *Enterococcus* species isolated from human infections by a conventional test scheme', *J. Clin. Microbiol.* 27(4), 731–734

FACKLAM, R.R. and MOODY, M.D. (1970), 'Presumptive identification of group D streptococci: the bile aesculin test', *Appl. Microbiol.* 20(2), 245–250.

FENELON, M.A., RYAN, M.P., RAE, M.C., GUINEE, T.P., ROSS, R.P., HILL, C. and HARRINGTON, D. (1999), 'Elevated temperature ripening of reduced fat Cheddar cheese made with or without lacticin 3147-producing starter culture', *J. Dairy Sci.* 82, 10–22.

FITZSIMONS, N.A., COGAN, T.M., CONDON, S. and BERESFORD, T. (1999), 'Phenotypic and genotypic characterisation of non-starter lactic acid bacteria in mature Cheddar cheese', *Appl. Environ. Microbiol.* 65, 3418–3426.

FITZSIMONS, N.A., COGAN, T.M., CONDON, S. and BERESFORD, T. (2001), 'Spatial and temporal distribution of non-starter lactic acid bacteria in Cheddar cheese', *J. Appl. Microbiol.* 90, 600–608.

FOLKERTSMA, B. (1999), 'Studies on ripening of Cheddar cheese', MSc dissertation, Department of Food Science and Technology, National University of Ireland, Cork.

FONTAN, M.C.G., FRANCO, I., PRIETO, B., TORNADIJO, M.E. and CARBALLO, J. (2001), 'Microbiological changes in "San Simon" cheese throughout ripening and its relationship with physico-chemical parameters', *Food Microbiol.* 18(1), 25–33.

FOX, P.F., MCSWEENEY, P.L.H. and LYNCH, C.M. (1998), 'Significance of non-starter lactic acid bacteria in Cheddar cheese', *Australian J. Dairy Technol.* 53, 83–89.

FRANKLIN, J.G. and SHARPE, M.F. (1963), 'The incidence of bacteria in cheese milk and Cheddar cheese and their association with flavour', *J. Dairy Res.* 30, 87–99.

FRANZ, C.M.A.P., HOLZAPFEL, W.H. and STILES, M.F. (1999), 'Enterococci at the crossroads of food safety?', *Int. J. Food Microbiol.* 47, 1–24.

FREITAS, A.C., PAIS, C., MALCATA, F.X. and HOGG, T.A. (1995), 'Microbiological characterization of Picante de Baixa cheese', *J. Food Prot.* 59, 155–160.

FRYER, T.F. and SHARPE, M.F. (1966), 'Pediococci in Cheddar cheese', *J. Dairy Res.* 33, 325–331.

GARCIA, A., CABEZAS, L. and PALOP, M.L. (1995), 'Identification of the lactic acid bacteria from origin labelled "Manchego" cheeses', *Microbiologie Aliments Nutrition* 13(3), 275–280.

GARDINER, G., ROSS, R.P., COLLINS, J.K., FITZGERALD, G. and STANTON, C. (1998), 'Development of a probiotic Cheddar cheese containing human-derived *Lactobacillus paracasei* strains', *Appl. Environ. Microbiol.* 64(6), 2192–2199.

GARDINER, G., ROSS, R.P., WALLACE, J.M., SCANLAN, F.P., JÄGERS, P.P.J.M., FITZGERALD, G.F., COLLINS, J.K. and STANTON, C. (1999), 'Influence of a probiotic adjunct culture of *Enterococcus faecium* on the quality of Cheddar cheese', *J. Agric. Food Chem.* 47, 4907–4916.

GARVIE, E. (1984), 'Taxonomy and identification of bacteria important in cheese and fermented dairy products', in Davis, F.L. and Law, B.A., *Advances in the Microbiology and Biochemistry of Cheese and Fermented Milk*, London and New York, Elsevier.

GELSOMINO, R., VANCANNEYT, M., CONDON, S., SWINGS, J. and COGAN, T.M. (2001), 'Enterococcal diversity in the environment of an Irish Cheddar-type cheesemaking factory', *Int. J. Food Microbiol.* 71, 177–188.

GELSOMINO, R., VANCANNEYT, M., COGAN, T.M., CONDON, S. and SWINGS, J. (2002), 'Source of enterococci in a farmhouse raw-milk cheese', *Appl. Environ. Microbiol.* 68(7), 3560–3565.

GIRAFFA, G., CARMINATI, D. and NEVIANI, F. (1997), 'Enterococci isolated from dairy products: a review of risks and potential technological use', *J. Food Prot.* 60(6), 732–738.

GOBBETTI, M., FOLKERTSMA, B., FOX, P.F., CORSETTI, A., SMACCHI, E., DE ANGELIS, M., ROSSI, J., KILCAWLEY, K. and CORTINI, M. (1999), 'Microbiology and biochemistry of Fossa (pit) cheese', *Int. Dairy J.* 9(11), 763–773.

GOBBETTI, M., MOREA, M., BARUZZI, F., CORBO, M.R., MATARANTE, A., CONSIDINE, T., DI CAGNO, R., GUINEE, T. and FOX, P.F. (2002), 'Microbiological, compositional, biochemical and textural characterisation of Caciocavallo Pugliese cheese during ripening', *Int. Dairy J.* 12(6), 511–523.

JENSEN, J.P., REINBOLD, G.W., WASHAM, J.C. and VEDAMUTHU, E.R. (1975a), 'Role of enterococci in Cheddar cheese: proteolytic activity and lactic acid development', *J. Milk Food Technol.* 38, 3–7.

JENSEN, J.P., REINBOLD, G.W., WASHAM, J.C. and VEDAMUTHU, E.R. (1975b), 'Role of enterococci in Cheddar cheese: free fatty acid appearance and citric acid utilization', *J. Milk Food Technol.* 38, 78–83.

JORDAN, K.N. and COGAN, T.M. (1993). Identification and growth of non-starter lactic acid bacteria in Irish Cheddar cheese. *Irish J. Agric. Food Res.* 32, 47–55.

JORDAN, K.N. and COGAN, T.M. (1999), 'Heat resistance of *Lactobacillus* spp. isolated from Cheddar cheese', *Lett. Appl. Microbiol.* 29, 136–140.

KANDLER, O. and WEISS, N. (1986), 'Regular, non-sporing, Gram positive rods', in Sneath, P.H.A., Mair, N.S., Sharpe, M.E. and Holt, J.G., *Bergey's Manual of Systematic Bacteriology*, Baltimore, Williams and Wilkins, Vol. 2, 1208–1234.

KLAENHAMMER, T., ALTERMANN, E., ARIGONI, F., BOLOTIN, A., BREIDT, F., BROADBENT, J., CANO, R., CHAILLOU, S., DEUTSCHER, J., GASSON, M., VAN DE GUCHTE, M., GUZZO, J., HARTKE, A., HAWKINS, T., HOLS, P., HUTKINS, R., KLEEREBEZEM, M., KOK, J., KUIPERS, O., LUBBERS, M., MAGUIN, E., MCKAY, L., MILLS, D., NAUTA, A., OVERBEEK, R., PEL, H., PRIDMORE, D., SAIER, M., VAN SINDEREN, D., SOROKIN, A., STEELE, J., O'SULLIVAN, D., DE VOS, W., WEIMER, B., ZAGOREC, M. and SIEZEN, R. (2002), 'Discovering lactic acid bacteria by genomics', in Siezen, R.J., Kok, J., Abee, T. and Schaafsma, G.,

Proceedings of the Seventh Symposium on Lactic Acid Bacteria: Genetics, Metabolism and Applications, The Netherlands, *Antonie van Leeuwenhoek*, Kluwer Academic Publishers, 29–58.

LALEYE, L.C., SIMARD, R.E., LEE, B.H. and HOLLEY, R.A. (1990), 'Quality attributes of Cheddar cheese containing added lactobacilli', *J. Food Sci.* 55, 114–118.

LAW, B.A., CASTANON, M. and SHARPE, M.E. (1976), 'The effect of nonstarter bacteria on the chemical composition and the flavour of Cheddar cheese', *J. Dairy Res.* 43, 117–125.

LAWRENCE, R.C. and GILLES, J. (1987), 'Cheddar cheese and related dry-salted varieties', in Fox, P.F., *Cheese: Chemistry, Physics and Microbiology*, London, Elsevier Applied *Science*, Vol. 2, 1–44.

LITOPOULOU-TZANETAKI, E. (1990), 'Changes in numbers and kinds of lactic acid bacteria during ripening of Kefalotyri cheese', *J. Food Sci.* 73, 111–113.

LITOPOULOU-TZANETAKI, E., GRAHAM, D.C. and BEYATLI, Y. (1989), 'Detection of pediococci and other non-starter organisms in American Cheddar cheese', *J. Dairy Sci.* 72(4), 854–858.

LITOPOULOU-TZANETAKI, E., TZANETAKIS, N. and VAFOPOULOU-MASTROJIANNAKI, A. (1993), 'Effect of type of lactic starter on microbiological, chemical and sensory characteristics of Feta cheese', *Food Microbiol.* 10, 31–41.

LÓPEZ-DIAZ, T.M., SANTOS, J.A., GONZALEZ, C.J., MORENO, B. and GARCIA, M.L. (1995), 'Bacteriological quality of a traditional Spanish blue cheese', *Milchwissenschaft* 50(9), 503–505.

LYNCH, C.M., MCSWEENEY, P.L.H., FOX, P.F., COGAN, T.M. and DRINAN, F.D. (1996), 'Manufacture of Cheddar cheese with and without adjunct lactobacilli under controlled microbiological conditions', *Int. Dairy J.* 6, 851–867.

MABBITT, L.A., CHAPMAN, H.R. and SHARPE, M.E. (1959), 'Making Cheddar cheese under controlled bacteriological conditions', *J. Dairy Res.* 26, 105–112.

MACEDO, A.C., MALCATA, F.X. and HOGG, T.A. (1995), 'Microbiological profile in Serra ewe's cheese during ripening', *J. Appl. Bacteriol.* 79, 1–11.

MANNU, L., COMUNIAN, R. and SCINTU, M.F. (2000), 'Mesophilic lactobacilli in Fiore Sardo cheese: PCR-identification and evolution during cheese ripening', *Int. Dairy J.* (5-6), 383–389.

MCSWEENEY, P.L.H., FOX, P.F., LUCEY, J.A., JORDAN, K.N. and COGAN, T.M. (1993), 'Contribution of indigenous microflora to the maturation of Cheddar cheese', *Int. Dairy J.* 3, 613–614.

MCSWEENEY, P.L.H., WALSH, E.M., FOX, P.F., COGAN, T.M., DRINAN, F.D. and CASTELO-GONZALEZ, M. (1994), 'A procedure for the manufacture of Cheddar cheese under controlled bacteriological conditions and the effect of adjunct lactobacilli on cheese quality', *Irish J. Agric. Food Res.* 33, 183–192.

MENENDEZ, S., GODINEZ, R., CENTENO, J.A. and RODRIGUEZ-OTERO, J.L. (2001), 'Identification and characterization of lactic acid bacteria isolated from Tetilla cows' milk cheese', *Alimentaria* 320, 77–83.

MOREA, M., BARUZZI, F. and COCCONCELLI, P.S. (1999), 'Molecular and physiological characterization of dominant bacterial populations in traditional Mozzarella cheese processing', *J. Appl. Microbiol.* 87, 574–582.

NUNEZ, M. (1976), 'Microflora of Manchego cheese, VI. Pediococci', *An. Inst. Nac. Invest. Agrarias, General*, No 4: 75 (in *Dairy Sci. Abstr.* 1978: 458).

ORDOÑEZ, J.A., BARNETO, R. and RAMOS, M. (1978), 'Studies on Manchego cheese ripened in olive oil', *Milchwissenschaft* 33(10), 609–613.

PARENTE, V., VILLANI, F., COPPOLA, R. and COPPOLA, S. (1989), 'A multiple strain starter for water-buffalo mozzarella cheese manufacture', *Lait* 69, 271–279.

PÉREZ, G., CARDELL, E. and ZÁRATE, V. (2002), 'Random amplified polymorphic DNA analysis for differentiation of *Leuconostoc mesenteroides* subspecies isolated from Tenerife cheese', *Lett. Appl. Microbiol.* 34, 82–85.

PETERSON, S.D. and MARSHALL, R.T. (1990), 'Non starter lactobacilli in Cheddar cheese: a review', *J. Dairy Sci.* 73, 1395–1410.

POULLET, B., HUERTAS, M., SÁNCHEZ, A., CÁCERES, P. and LARRIBA, G. (1993), 'Main lactic acid bacteria isolated during ripening of Casar de Cáceres cheese', *J. Dairy Res.* 60, 123–127.

PUCHADES, R., LEMIEUX, L. and SIMARD, R.E. (1989), 'Evolution of free amino acids during the ripening of Cheddar cheese containing added lactobacilli strains', *J. Food Sci.* 54, 885–888.

REITER, B., FRYER, T.F., PICKERING, A., CHAPMAN, H.R., LAWRENCE, R.B. and SHARPE, M.E. (1967), 'The effect of microbial flora on the flavour and free fatty acid composition of Cheddar cheese', *J. Dairy Res.* 26, 105–112.

ROBERTSON, P.S. and PERRY, K.D. (1961), 'Enhancement of flavour of Cheddar cheese by adding a strain of *Micrococcus* to the milk', *J. Dairy Res.* 28, 245–253.

RYAN, M.P., RAE, M.C., HILL, C. and ROSS, R.P. (1996), 'An application in Cheddar cheese manufacture for a strain of *Lactococcus lactis* producing a novel broad-spectrum bacteriocin, lacticin 3147', *Appl. Environ. Microbiol.* 62, 612–619.

SARANTINOPOULOS, P., ANDRIGHETTO, C., GEORGALAKI, M.D., REA, M.C., LOMBARDI, A., COGAN, T.M., KALANTZOPOULOS, G. and TSAKALIDOU, E. (2001), 'Biochemical properties of enterococci relevant to their technological performance', *Int. Dairy J.* 11(8), 621–647.

SCHLEIFER, K.H. (1986). 'Gram-positive cocci', in Sneath, P.H.A., Mair, N.S., Sharpe, M.E. and Holt, J.G., *Bergey's Manual of Systematic Bacteriology,* Baltimore, Williams and Wilkins, 999–1103.

SCHLEIFER, K.H. and KILPPER-BÄLZ, R. (1984), 'Transfer of *Streptococcus faecalis* and *Streptococcus faecium* to the genus *Enterococcus* nom. rev. as *Enterococcus faecalis* comb. nov. and *Enterococcus faecium* comb. nov.', *Int. J. Syst. Bacteriol.* 34(1), 31–34.

SHAKEEL-UR-REHMAN, MCSWEENEY, P.H.L. and FOX, P.F. (1999), 'A study on the role of indigenous microflora of raw milk on the ripening of Cheddar cheese', *Milchwissenschaft* 54(7), 388–392.

SHAKEEL-UR-REHMAN, BANKS, J.M., BRECHANY, E.Y., MUIR, D.D., MCSWEENEY, P.H.L. and FOX, P.F. (2000a), 'Studies on the ripening of Cheddar cheese made from blends of raw and pasteurized milk', *Int. Dairy J.* 10, 33–44.

SHAKEEL-UR-REHMAN, BANKS, J.M., MCSWEENEY, P.H.L. and FOX, P.F. (2000b), 'Effect of ripening temperature on the growth and significance of non-starter lactic acid bacteria in Cheddar cheese made from raw or pasteurized milk', *Int. Dairy J.* 10, 45–53.

SHAKEEL-UR-REHMAN, FOX, P.F. and MCSWEENEY, P.H.L. (2000c), 'Methods used to study non-starter micro-organisms in cheese: a review', *Int. J. Dairy Technol.* 53, 113–119.

SIMPSON, W.J. and TAGUCHI, H. (1995), 'The genus *Pediococcus* with notes on the genera *Tetragenococcus* and *Aerococcus*', in Wood, B.J.B. and Holzapfel, W.H., *The Genera of Lactic Acid Bacteria,* Blackie Academic & Professional, 125–172.

SOMERS, E.B., JOHNSON, M.E. and WONG, A.C.L. (2001), 'Biofilm formation and contamination of cheese by nonstarter lactic acid bacteria in the dairy environment', *J. Dairy Sci.* 84, 1926–1936.

STACKEBRANDT, E. and TEUBER, M. (1988), 'Molecular taxonomy and phylogenetic position of lactic acid bacteria', *Biochimie* 70(3), 317–324.

SWEARINGEN, P.A., O'SULLIVAN, D.J. and WORTHESON, J.J. (2001), 'Isolation, characterization and influence of native non-starter lactic acid bacteria on Cheddar cheese quality', *J. Dairy Sci.* 84, 50–59.

TEIXEIRA, L.M., MERQUIOR, V.L.C., DA CONCEIÇÃO, M., VIANNI, M. DA C.E., CARVALHO, M. DA G.S., FRACALANZZA, S.E.L., STEIGERWALT, A.G., BRENNER, D.J. and FACKLAM, R.R. (1996), 'Phenotypic and genotypic characterisation of atypical *Lactococcus garvieae* strains isolated from water buffalos with subclinical mastitis and confirmation of *L. garvieae* as a senior subjective synonym of *Enterococcus seriolicida*', *Int. J. Syst. Bacteriol.* 46(3), 664–668.

THOMAS, T.D. (1987), 'Cannibalism among bacteria found in cheese', *NZ J. Dairy Sci. Technol.* 22, 215–219.

THOMPSON, T.L. and MARTH, E.H. (1986), 'Changes in Parmesan cheese during ripening: icroflora – coliforms, enterococci, anaerobes, propionibacteria and staphylococci', *Milchwissenschaft* 41(4), 201–205.

THUNELL, R.K. (1995), 'Taxonomy of leuconostocs', *J. Dairy Sci.* 78, 2514–2522.

TRÉPANIER, G., SIMARD, R.E. and LEE, B.H. (1991), 'Effect of added lactobacilli on composition and texture of Cheddar cheese during accelerated maturation', *J. Food Sci.* 56, 696–700.

TRÉPANIER, G., ABBOUDI, M.E., LEE, B.H. and SIMARD, R.E. (1992), 'Accelerated maturation of Cheddar cheese: microbiology of cheese supplemented with *Lactobacillus casei* subsp. *casei* L2A', *J. Food Sci.* 57, 345–349.

TROVATELLI, L.D. and SCHIESSER, A. (1987), 'Identification and significance of enterococci in hard cheese made from raw cow and sheep milk', *Milchwissenschaft* 42, 717–719.

TURNER, K.W. (1988), 'Some aspects of the microbiology of cheese ripening investigated using aseptic manufacturing techniques', PhD thesis, Massey University, Palmerston North, New Zealand.

TURNER, K.W., LAWRENCE, R.C. and LE LIEVRE, J. (1986), 'A microbiological specification for milk for aseptic cheesemaking', *NZ J. Dairy Sci. Technol.* 21, 249–254.

TZANETAKIS, N. and LITOPOULOU-TZANETAKI, E. (1989), 'Biochemical activities of *Pediococcus pentosaceus* isolates of dairy origin', *J. Dairy Sci.* 72, 859–863.

TZANETAKI, N. and LITOPOULOU-TZANETAKI, E. (1992), 'Changes in the numbers and kinds of lactic acid bacteria in Feta and Teleme, two Greek cheeses from ewe's milk', *J. Dairy Sci.* 75, 1389–1393.

VAFOPOULOU-MASTROJIANNAKI, A., LITOPOULOU-TZANETAKI, E. and TZANETAKIS, N. (1996), 'Esterase activities of cell-free extracts from "wild" strains of leuconostocs and heterofermentative lactobacilli isolates from traditional Greek cheese', *Lett. Appl. Microbiol.* 23(6), 367–370.

WALSH, E.M., MCSWEENEY, P.H.L. and FOX, P.F. (1996), 'Use of antibiotics to inhibit non-starter lactic acid bacteria in Cheddar cheese', *Int. Dairy J.* 6, 425–431.

WILLIAMS, A.G. and BANKS, J.M. (1997), 'Proteolytic and other hydrolytic enzyme activities in non-starter lactic acid bacteria (NSLAB) isolated from Cheddar cheese manufactured in the United Kingdom', *Int. Dairy J.* 7, 763–774.

WILLIAMS, A.G., WITHERS, S.E. and BANKS, J.M. (2000), 'Energy sources of non-starter lactic acid bacteria isolated from Cheddar cheese', *Int. Dairy J.* 10, 17–23.

ZARATE, V., BELDA, F., PEREZ, C. and CARDELL, E. (1997), 'Changes in the microbial flora of Tenerife goat's milk cheese during ripening', *Int. Dairy J.* 7, 635–641.

21

The production of smear cheeses

W. Bockelmann, BafM, Germany

21.1 Introduction: smear-ripened cheese varieties

A small proportion of the cheese varieties sold worldwide have a surface covered by a layer of yeasts and bacteria, e.g. Tilsit, Limburg, Romadour, Chaumes, and the acid-curd 'Harzer', or 'Handkäse' (Table 21.1). These aerobic microorganisms have a strong impact on the appearance, flavour and texture development of the cheeses, which usually leads to shorter ripening periods of several weeks rather than months. Smear cheeses are generally known for their intense sulphurous and ammoniacal smell (Reps, 1993).

Figure 21.1 illustrates several smear cheese varieties: left rear, soft Chaumes cheese with a bright orange surface which is tightly covered with a thin paper layer partly removed on this picture; left front, mature acid curd cheese (no quarg core) with a translucent light brown colour of rind and core and with a rubbery texture; right rear, semi-soft Tilsit cheese with a light reddish-brown surface and the typical irregular holes (size of cut area *ca.* 13 × 13 cm); right front, soft Limburg cheese with typical white streaks (*G. candidum*) on an orange background (yellow-pigmented *A. nicotianae* and/or *M. gubbeenense* predominant).

Apart from the influence of the physical and chemical parameters of the cheese milk, starter and non-starter lactic acid bacteria, these secondary cheese cultures contribute significantly to the complexity of cheese manufacture. Maintaining a high level of hygiene as well as a profound knowledge of the needs of a typical surface flora are essential during ripening because the cheese surfaces are exposed to an unsterile environment. Undesirable contaminating bacteria or moulds will grow immediately if the balance of the cheese microflora is disturbed (Bockelmann, 1999).

Table 21.1   Surface-ripened cheese varieties (adapted from Chapman and Sharpe, 1990, and Kammerlehner, 1993)

Cheese variety	Origin	Ripening period (months)
Soft		
Limburger	Belgium	<1
Romadour	Germany	<1
Chaumes	France	<1
Semi-soft		
Münster	France	1
Brick	USA	1–2
Monterey	USA	1–2
Saint Paulin	France	1–2
Taleggio	Italy	2
Havarti	Denmark	1–3
Tilsit	Germany	1–5
Bel Paesa	Italy	4–5
Hard		
Danbo	Denmark	1–2
Gruyère	France	4–12
Acid-curd		
Harzer Roller	Germany	<1

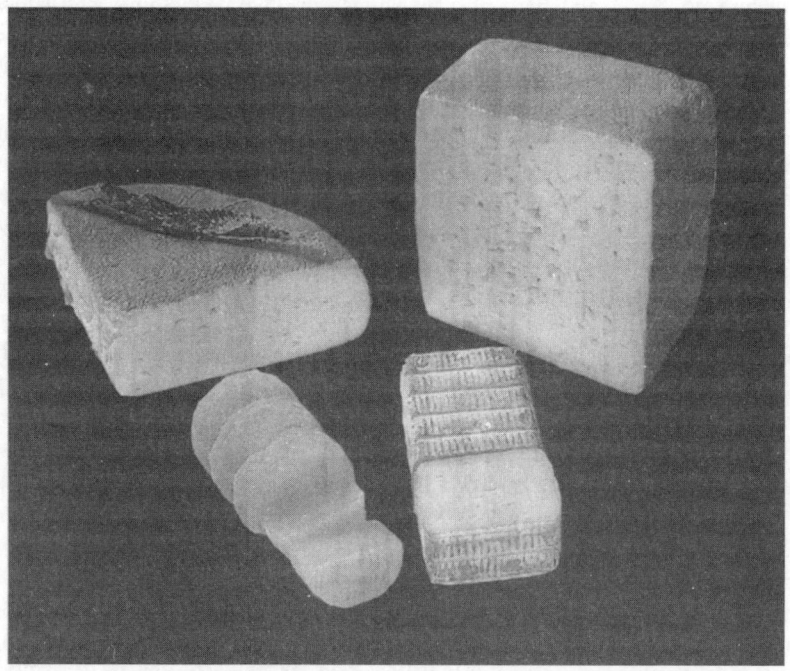

Fig. 21.1   Size and appearance of several smear cheese varieties.

In the present chapter special emphasis will be put on new developments in surface starter technology, a long neglected area. Contamination of smear cheeses with *Listeria monocytogenes* is still reported periodically, sometimes leading to food poisoning incidents and, consequently, to large economic losses for cheese manufacturers (Rudolf and Scherer, 2001). Most of the data presented on novel starters were obtained by studies on semi-soft Tilsit-like cheese (an EU-funded project). Some new results on new surface starters for soft cheeses and acid-curd cheeses that are presented here were obtained in two current projects funded by the German Federal Ministry of Economics and Labour (AiF projects).

21.2 Production and ripening

The annual production of cheese in the European Union exceeded 6 million tons in 1998. Probably due to their intense sulphurous smell, smear cheeses are not mass produced like Gouda or Cheddar cheese. Smear cheeses are traditionally produced on a small scale in a farmhouse environment in many European countries. Production is more industrialised in countries such as Denmark, France, Germany and The Netherlands; however, most cheese companies are still small or medium-sized enterprises.

Smear-ripened cheeses can be produced from any kind of rennet curd (Table 21.2). They can be divided into (semi-)soft (moisture 45–55%), semi-hard (moisture 45–50%) and hard cheeses (moisture 35–45%). Some well-known cheese varieties are listed in Table 21.1. In general, cheeses are salted by brining in ≥18% sodium chloride. Small soft cheeses such as Limburg and Romadour are brined for 1.5–4 h, the larger semi-soft and hard cheeses for approximately 24 h. An alternative traditional manual method is wiping small cheeses with cloths soaked in brines. A newer salting method is dry salting, where cheeses are sprayed with dry salt vapours, a method established for small soft smear cheeses.

After salting, the cheeses are smeared (brushed, wiped or sprayed) with salt water containing suitable yeasts and bacteria. Thus, apart from the influence of starter and non-starter lactic acid bacteria, cheese ripening is influenced by metabolic activities of the surface microflora (Bockelmann, 2002a). Typical ripening times are 2 weeks for the soft Limburg/Romadour varieties (200–500 g), 1–6 months for semi-soft Tilsit-type cheeses (2.5–3.5 kg), and 6–12 months for hard cheeses like Gruyère (>2.5 kg).

Quite different from all rennet-type cheeses are the 'sour milk' (acid-curd) cheeses which have a long tradition in Germany. They are produced from low-fat quarg (>30% dry mass), which is produced with *Streptococcus thermophilus* and *Lactobacillus delbrueckii* ssp. *bulgaricus*. Salting of acid-curd cheeses is performed by mixing quarg with ripening salts (NaCl, NaHCO$_3$, CaCO$_3$) to obtain the appropriate salinity and pH. Ripening of acid-curd cheese is usually restricted to 1–3 days in the factory, progressing during transport and cold storage in food markets over the shelf-life of 37–45 days after packaging (Table 21.2, Engel and Roesch, 1995).

Table 21.2 Ripening patterns of the major groups of smear-ripened cheeses; 'mature' cheese indicates condition at the time of packaging (data taken from various textbooks on dairy technology).

Semi-hard cheese	Semi-soft cheese	Acid-curd cheese
Pressed rennet curd, pH 5.6	Pressed rennet curd, pH 5.0	Quarg pH 3.7–4.1
Brining, 24 h, pH 5.1	Brining or dry salting, 1–4 h, pH 5.0–5.1	Mechanical mixing of curd/salt/'culture cheese' pressing, pH 5.2
	Low-temperature sweating, 20–22°C, >95% r.h.	High-temperature sweating, 30–33°C, >95% r.h.
→**First smearing** (addition of starters)	→**First spraying** (addition of starters)	**First spraying** (addition of starters)
Ripening, 13–15°C, 95–98% r.h.	Ripening, 13–15°C, 95–98% r.h.	Ripening, 13–15°C, 95–98% r.h., 1–3 days
Repeated smearing, ∼6 times during 6 weeks	Repeated smearing, ∼5 times during 2 weeks	
		Mature cheese (>2 days)
	Mature cheese (>2 weeks)	Extended ripening, 2 weeks for 'culture' cheese
Mature cheese (>4 weeks)		

21.2.1 Traditional ripening

Bacterial smear-ripened cheeses have a long tradition. Without knowledge of the bacterial nature of the surface flora, a large variety of smear cheeses was produced long before the year 1900 (Fox, 1993). When cheeses produced from raw milk – an important source of surface microorganisms – are exposed to air with a high relative humidity (>95%) they naturally tend to develop a smear layer on the surface, typically consisting of yeasts and bacteria. More than a century ago, Laxa (1899) already isolated and described yeasts and yellow-pigmented bacteria from the surface of smear cheeses.

Surface-ripening of smear cheeses begins with the growth of yeasts (e.g. *Debaryomyces hansenii*) which utilise lactate and increase the surface pH of the cheese (Busse, 1989; Eliskases-Lechner and Ginzinger, 1995b; Reps, 1993). When the pH increases above 6, *Brevibacterium linens*, other coryneform bacteria and staphylococci (micrococci) begin to grow and eventually cover the whole surface of the cheese (Fig. 21.2; Eliskases-Lechner and Ginzinger, 1995a; Bockelmann *et al.*, 1997c). Figure 21.2(a) shows typical 'coryneform bacteria', i.e. Gram-positive, aerobic, non-motile, irregularly shaped rods (club- or V-shaped) belonging to *Corynebacterium*, *Brevibacterium*, *Arthrobacter* and *Microbacterium*. The fissures seen in some cells indicate the post-fission

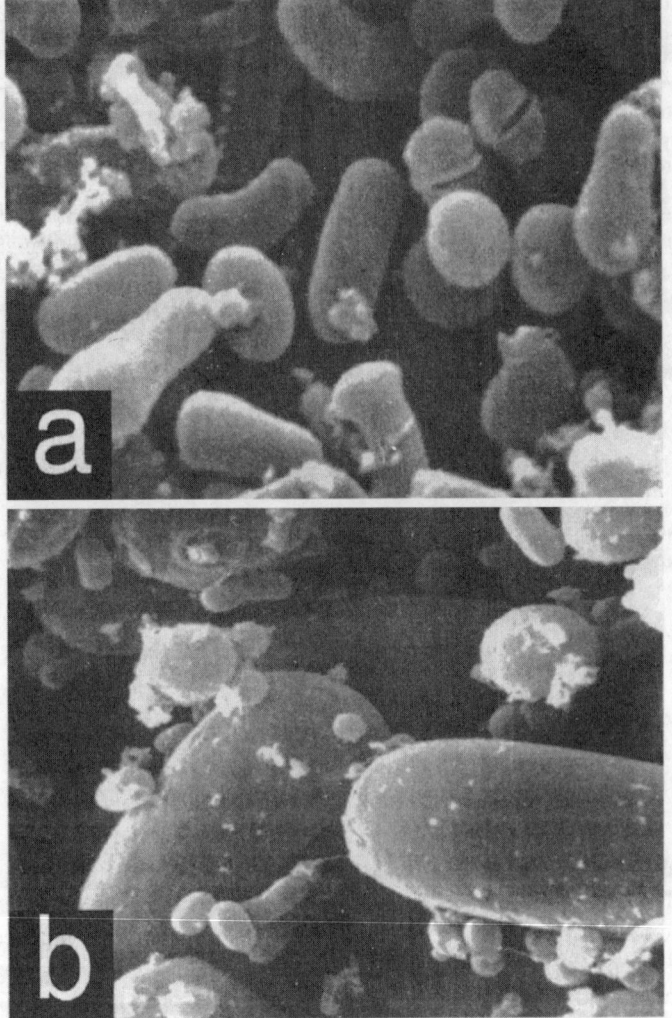

Fig. 21.2 Scanning electron micrograph of the surface of Romadour cheese (courtesy of H. Neve, Institute of Microbiology, Federal Dairy Research Centre, Kiel, Germany).

snapping of cells typical of 'coryneform bacteria' (magnification 10 000×). Figure 21.2(b) shows cylindrical *Geotrichum candidum* and globular *Debaryomyces hansenii* yeasts coexisting with coryneform bacteria and cocci, most likely *Staphylococcus equorum* or *S. xylosus* (magnification 5000×). The sources of the typical surface microorganisms are cheese milk, cheese brines, the air of ripening rooms, ripening pads and the human skin. Since the introduction of pasteurisation, which has considerably improved food safety, the cheese milk flora has less influence on the surface microflora of cheeses (Holsinger *et al.*, 1997). From starter companies, some yeasts and bacteria can be obtained to mimic the endogenous raw milk microflora (see Chapter 3).

Correct handling and storage of smear cheeses during ripening is essential. Ripening temperatures range from 14°C to 19°C, and the humidity should be at least 95%. Excessive ventilation should be avoided. In addition, repeated turning of cheeses and surface treatment by repeated smearing (brushing) are most important for ripening (Kammerlehner, 1995).

The smear is applied to the cheese using a rotating brush, which is wetted when moving through the smear liquid placed at the bottom of the machine. For soft cheeses spraying machines are used instead. The smear liquid is made up in water or whey containing ∼3% salt to mirror the salinity of the cheeses and is generally inoculated by commercially available surface starters (Bockelmann, 2002a). The recommendation is about 10^4 cfu/ml in the cheese milk, or 10^6 cfu/ml in the smear or 10^{11} cfu per 100 kg of cheese. However, cheese producers do not often rely on these cultures alone. Traditionally, mature cheeses are smeared (sprayed) before young cheeses in the same machine, which is called 'old–young' smearing because part of the 'old' flora from mature cheeses is retained in the smear liquid and thus is brushed (sprayed) subsequently onto the surface of green cheeses. For acid-curd cheeses a different old–young step is included with the same effect: a special batch of cheeses, ripened for 2 weeks instead of 2 days ('culture cheese'), is mixed with quarg and ripening salts (2–4% w/w) to initiate the ripening of the 'sour milk cheeses' (ripening 2 days, with further uncontrolled ripening in the packaged state during transport and marketing; Bockelmann, 2002b).

21.2.2   The surface microflora of commercial smear cheeses

Semi-soft cheeses

Due to their natural presence in cheese brines (Jaeger *et al.*, 2002), *D. hansenii* and cream or orange *S. equorum* are always found on semi-soft cheeses, with the highest cell counts in the first week of ripening. If commercial 'Micrococci-Preparations' (trade name) are used for smearing, *Staphylococcus xylosus* can also be detected on the cheese surface (Bockelmann and Hoppe-Seyler, 2001). A certain percentage of yellow-pigmented *Arthrobacter nicotianae* and *Microbacterium* sp. is detected, species with similar technological properties that can be reliably identified only by molecular methods (e.g. partial sequencing of the 16S rDNA or ARDRA; Hoppe-Seyler *et al.*, accepted for publication). Cream-coloured corynebacteria are most abundant in the surface flora. Unfortunately, classification of *Corynebacterium* spp. is difficult. A species frequently associated with smear cheeses is *C. casei* (Bockelmann, 1999). *Brevibacterium linens* is generally called the 'typical red smear bacterium' before all other species because of its bright orange pigments. It is one of the best studied cheese bacteria; the strong sulphur metabolism and the bacteriocins specific for *L. monocytogenes* have been studied in detail (Eppert *et al.*, 1997; Valdes-Stauber and Scherer, 1996). However, the cell counts of *B. linens* on the cheese surface are rather limited. Even with no *B. linens* detected on selective agars (<0.1% of the microflora) cheeses can be of normal appearance and flavour (Bockelmann *et al.*, 1997c).

Table 21.3   Surface cell counts of several types of smear cheeses

Surface microflora	Tilsit-type cheeses	Chaumes	Limburg/ Romadour	Acid-curd cheese
Yeasts (cfu/cm^2)	10^3–10^6	10^4–10^7	10^4–10^7	10^7–10^8
Smear bacteria (cfu/cm^2)	10^8–>10^9	10^8–>10^9	10^8–<10^9	10^8–>10^9
Corynebacterium spp.	50–90%	50–70%	10–>60%	20–90%
Arthrobacter, Microbacterium	0.1–5%	1–30%	2–>50%	n.d. (<0.1%)
Brevibacterium linens	0.1–15%	<1%	<1–15%	0.1–50%
Halomonas spp.	—	—	30–40%[a]	—
Staphylococcus spp.	0.1–5%	0.1–5%	<1%	1–40%
Micrococcus spp.	—	0.1–20%	—	—
Enterococcus spp.	<10^3	<10^5	<10^4	<10^6
Pseudomonas spp.	<10^2	<10^2	<10^3	<10^3
Coliform bacteria (titre)	<10^2	<10^5	<10^3	<10^5
Gram-negative rods (VRBD)	<10^5	<10^6	<10^4	<10^6

[a] Typical for one factory only; detected in all samples from 2000 and 2001.

A certain low level of contaminating bacteria (enterococci, enterobacteria) can always be expected on the surface of smear cheeses (Gianotti, 1999). Summarised results are shown in Table 21.3, for which red smear cheeses were analysed routinely over several years (1995–2002) with more than 20 samples for each cheese variety. Generally, cream-coloured colonies belonged to the species *C. casei*, yellow orange to two species, *Arthrobacter nicotianae* and *Microbacterium* sp. and orange colonies of irregular rods to *Brevibacterium linens*. Staphylococci (cream and orange colonies) were generally classified as *Staphylococcus equorum*. Sometimes *S. xylosus* and *S. saprophyticus* were identified. The latter species was quite commonly found on the surface of acid-cured cheeses. Identification was performed by ARDRA and the restriction patterns were compared to type strains of the species (Hoppe-Seyler *et al.*, accepted for publication).

Soft cheeses

The surface microflora of soft cheeses shows distinct differences (Table 21.3). The yeast flora consists of two predominant yeasts, *D. hansenii* and *Geotrichum candidum*. Apart from numerous cream-coloured coryneform bacteria (*Corynebacterium* spp.) a high percentage of yellow coryneform *Arthrobacter nicotianae* and *Microbacterium* sp. is observed (Table 21.3). Although usually at 20–50% of the flora (Limburg, Romadour), the percentage can be near 100% of total cell counts in some factories. *Brevibacterium linens* and *Staphylococcus* spp. show normal low cell counts as observed for semi-soft cheeses. A typical finding for the French Chaumes cheese over several years was orange *Micrococcus* species, microscopically being large diplococci (Bockelmann and Hoppe-Seyler, 2001). The presence of a high percentage of salt-tolerant, motile rods (*Halomonas* sp.) was typical for a single cheese producer, being always detected on cheeses over several years (Table 21.3). The degree of contamination with enterococci and enterobacteria is usually higher than for semi-soft cheeses.

Acid-curd cheeses
The different technology of production of acid-curd cheeses from quarg results in significant differences in the appearance, flavour and surface microflora (Table 21.3). A number of yeast species is found, *Kluyveromyces marxianus*, *Candida krusei*, *C. utilis*, *C. lipolytica* and *Trichosporon asahii* being frequently identified. Most common in many of Engel's analyses (Engel and Roesch, 1995) were *K. marxianus* and *C. krusei*. Since many *C. krusei* strains show a preference for lactic acid as C-source leading to fast deacidification of the acid curd, this species may be typical and important for smear development. *Trichosporon* species are unwanted contaminants because they are frequently related to human skin diseases in the scientific literature.

As for semi-soft cheeses, cream-coloured coryneform bacteria are predominant (Table 21.3). Yellow-pigmented *Arthrobacter* or *Microbacterium* species are rarely found in high cell numbers. The percentage of *B. linens* and *Staphylococcus* species of total cell counts is quite variable. A considerable amount of the *Staphylococus* counts can be caused by *S. saprophyticus*, an important contaminant of acid-curd cheeses (Bockelmann, 2002b).

21.2.3 Current problems during ripening
It is still general practice to use the mature smear layer of aged cheeses for the treatment of young cheeses by performing old–young smearing. The associated hygienic problems are obvious: saprophytic or pathogenic bacteria as well as moulds can become part of the house microflora and can persist over long periods of time by this in-house contamination cycle. A certain undetected low level of contamination with enterobacteria, pathogens such as *Listeria monocytogenes* and other contaminants can be assumed for traditionally old–young smeared cheeses. For reasons largely unknown, pathogens sometimes grow to high cell numbers, only then posing a risk for consumers. Not the pathogenicity but the common (transferable) multiple antibiotic resistances are matters of concern when enterobacteria and enterococci are contaminating the cheese surface (Teuber, 1999; Teuber and Perreten, 2000). Therefore old–young smearing is more and more criticised and efforts have been initiated to establish alternative methods, i.e. functional defined surface starter cultures, to meet the continuously increasing hygienic demands of European guidelines and regulations.

21.3 Developing ripening cultures

Trade in the so-called secondary cheese cultures is small compared with that in lactic starters for cheese and fermented milks. Therefore culture development is rather poor. Mainly, *Debaryomyces hansenii*, *Geotrichum candidum* and *B. linens* (*B. casei*) are used, and these are offered as smear cultures by all major starter companies (e.g. Chr. Hansen, Denmark; Danisco-Cultor, Germany; Degussa-Bioactives, Germany/France; Rhodia-food, France; Sacco srl, Italy). So-called 'Micrococci' preparations contain *Staphylococcus xylosus* or *S. carnosus*. One supplier offers *Microbacterium* sp. and mixed-strain combinations containing unspecified corynebacteria.

The range of cultures offered does not reflect the microflora of the different smear cheese varieties. The recommended doses for smear cultures are 5×10^{10} cfu per 1000 litres of cheese milk, or 10^6 cfu/ml in the smear liquid, or 10^{11} cfu per 100 kg cheese (data taken from starter suppliers' leaflets). However, cheese manufacturers seem to use lower concentrations for cost reasons (several German cheese manufacturers, personal communication). According to Bockelmann *et al.* (1997b) a defined surface culture should contain at least 10^7 cfu/ml to initiate smear development without using old–young smearing.

The functionality of some commercial culture strains seems to be questionable. In a Swiss study it was shown that the deacidification properties of commercially available yeasts were rather poor compared to natural isolates from various sources (Wyder and Puhan, 1999). *Brevibacterium linens* strains used in smear starters are often not found on mature cheese in significant numbers, without any negative effect on cheese quality (Bockelmann, 2002a). In one study in which 'Micrococci-preparations' (*S. xylosus*) were used to inoculate cheese brines, naturally occurring *S. equorum* were predominant in the brines after several weeks (Bockelmann and Hoppe-Seyler, 2001). Looking at the complex composition of a smear cheese microflora (Table 21.3), only a minor role of these commercial secondary cultures can be expected; the influence of an intact house microflora is still essential today. However, the use of fully functional smear cultures might be necessary for cheese factories in the future to meet the continuously increasing hygienic demands of European guidelines and regulations.

To define the requirements for a functional surface starter, essential components of the surface microflora have to be identified, and the role of the species detected has to be understood. The composition of the surface flora of commercial smear cheeses still depends on the specific house microflora of the cheese manufacturer. However, some general bacteriological similarities can be found for all smear cheese varieties. The bacterial surface flora consists mainly of so-called 'coryneform bacteria' which is not an accepted taxon but a useful descriptor for irregular, club- or V.-shaped rods belonging to the genera of smear bacteria *Corynebacterium*, *Brevibacterium*, *Arthrobacter* and *Microbacterium* (Bockelmann, 1999).

23.3.1   Classification
The taxonomy of smear bacteria is still undergoing frequent changes. Depending on the classification system used, many authors give different names for isolates,

e.g. for staphylococci. Until the mid-1970s, all clump-building, Gram-positive and catalase-positive cocci which did not metabolise glucose under anaerobic conditions were grouped into the genus *Micrococcus*. In contrast to staphylococci (e.g. *S. aureus*), micrococci were considered food grade and were described as typical smear bacteria. Later, differences such as the molecular architecture of cell walls, sensitivity of staphylococci to lysostaphin and furazolidon, resistance against bacitracin, and differences of the GC content were used to distinguish between the two genera. Therefore, part of micrococci are now grouped in the genus *Staphylococcus* (for references see Bockelmann, 1999). But still, the term 'micrococci' is used as a trade name to acknowledge the non-pathogenic, food-grade status of cultures. Food-grade staphylococci are of general importance for smear cheeses, true micrococci were only found on French Chaumes cheeses (Bockelmann, 2002a; Table 21.3).

A reliable identification can only be obtained by a combination of methods such as biochemical identification (e.g. API system), partial sequencing of 16S rDNA, amplified ribosomal DNA restriction analysis (ARDRA), and perhaps other methods. With only limited data available the early studies of Bockelmann *et al.* (1997b) described the use of *A. nicotianae* CA12 in a defined five-strain smear culture. According to new results obtained by ARDRA (Hoppe-Seyler *et al.*, accepted for publication) this strain might belong to a new *Microbacterium* species. This study also showed that all yellow-pigmented bacteria with coryneform morphology isolated from the surface of smear cheeses (*n* > 20) could be divided into two species, *A. nicotianae* and perhaps *M. gubbeenense*.

However, further taxonomic changes may be possible. Brennan *et al.* (2002) described three new species isolated from Irish farmhouse smear cheeses, *Microbacterium gubbeenense*, *Corynebacterium moorparkense* and *Corynebacterium casei* which are closely related (homology of 16S rDNA sequences >98%) to the known species *M. barkeri*, *C. variabile* and *C. ammoniagenes*. Since the type strains of the three latter species were not isolated from smear cheeses but from raw domestic sewage (MB: DSM-20145), food (CV: DSM-20132) and infant faeces (CA: DSM 20306), it is possible that the species isolated and described in many papers on the microflora of smear cheese will have to be renamed.

Molecular classification is time-consuming and can only be used for a small number of isolates. To obtain a fast, rough picture of a smear microflora the very rich 'modified milk agar' can be used for plating (i.e. plate-count agar containing additional casein hydrolysate, vitamins, sodium chloride and skim milk powder, Hoppe-Seyler *et al.*, 2000). By colony morphology (pigmentation) and microscopy (irregular rods, clumping cocci), cream-coloured colonies indicate the presence of *C. casei* (and other species), while orange colonies are most likely caused by *B. linens* and *Staphylococcus* sp. (e.g. *S. equorum*). Staphylococcal colonies are quite typical (larger diameter) and easy to distinguish from brevibacteria by microscopy. Most likely, yellow colonies can be classified as *Arthrobacter nicotianae* or *Microbacterium* sp.

At the moment only molecular analysis is able to distinguish between these two genera.

21.3.2   Screening of yeasts and bacteria

A mixed-strain surface ripening culture consisting of several species has to meet the following criteria:

- Fast growth on the cheese surface (i.e. fast deacidification)
- Development of typical smell and taste
- Prevention of bacterial and fungal contaminations.

Bacteria and yeasts isolated from the surface of smear cheese varieties can be screened to some degree in pure or mixed culture in the shake liquid milk model described by Bockelmann *et al.* (1997b). The most important property for yeasts (*D. hansenii*) is probably deacidification which can be studied easily in the model. A slight yeasty smell was the only contribution of *D. hansenii* to the volatile aroma in pure or mixed cultures. *C. casei* present in very high cell numbers on smear cheeses and staphylococci showed a neutral aroma in the model. In pure culture, *B. linens* (BL) possessed a fishy, ammoniacal smell for which the species is known. The yellow-pigmented *M. gubbeenense* (MG) and *A. nicotianae* (AN) showed a distinct urine-like smell. However, in mixed culture (BL+MG or BL+AN) a more or less typical smear cheese aroma was produced. A similar aromatic profile was obtained with pure cultures of *B. linens* supplemented with methionine (Bockelmann, 1999). Mixed cultures grew to cell counts two magnitudes higher than the pure cultures of both species.

   The nature of colour development was also studied in the liquid milk model. Mixed cultures of *B. linens* and *M. gubbeenense* liberated extracellular red-brown colour typical of semi-soft smear cheeses like Tilsit. The orange cell-bound pigments of *B. linens* did not seem to be responsible, since the spectrum of the pigments was different (Bockelmann *et al.*, 1997a). The addition of casein hydrolysate to pure cultures of *M. gubbeenense* also led to the liberation of red-brown pigments. Thus the proteolytic properties of the highly proteolytic *B. linens* are probably important for colour development on cheese.

   When *M. gubbeenense* was replaced by *A. nicotianae* in more recent studies, the same effects regarding aroma and colour development were observed. Colour development, however, seemed to be more pronounced when *A. nicotianae* was used (Bockelmann, unpublished results).

Small-scale cheese trials

For further screening of defined smear cultures a real cheese environment is necessary. A simple and fully functional setup for smallest-scale cheese trials was described by Bockelmann *et al.* (2000). A glass tank (e.g. a 50-litre aquarium), closed with a lid and equipped with a stainless steel grid for the cheeses, can be used for ripening. Sufficient humidity (>95%) can be provided either by a water reservoir at the bottom of the tank or by placing the tanks in climatic rooms with appropriate humidity, which is the better solution. With this setup many surface cultures can be tested in separate units at the same time without the risk of cross-contamination, and the generally too strong ventilation of climatic chambers or rooms can be avoided. Cheese ripening with defined surface cultures as described below was always performed in these ripening cells.

21.3.3   Defined cultures for smear cheeses
Cultures for semi-soft cheeses
After completion of an EU project (CT98-4220) in 2001 the minimum requirements for defined surface smear cultures for semi-soft Tilsit-like cheeses could be formulated. The composition of the culture used by Bockelmann *et al.* (1997b) was slightly modified (*S. sciuri* was replaced by *S. equorum*). Several strains of all species have been used successfully for numerous laboratory-scale cheese trials (unpublished results). In the following, strain names are not given since the general importance of the species is assumed.

One yeast species (*D. hansenii*) and *S. equorum* are essential for ripening to start. Their highest cell counts were always observed during the first week of ripening. Initially, both species were added to the smear cocktail which was used for smearing. Later it was shown that these microorganisms could be inoculated into the cheese brines instead (see the subsection headed 'Brine microflora' below). Together, *M. gubbeenense* or *A. nicotianae* and *B. linens* are essential for the development of aroma and colour. As stated before, the contribution of *B. linens* to colour development seems to be the enzymatic properties and not their orange pigments. *Microbacterium gubbeenense* or *A. nicotianae* reach highest cell numbers in the second week of ripening, while the cell counts of *B. linens* increase slowly over weeks. All three species are usually found at 1–5% of total cell counts but are essential for ripening nonetheless. *Corynebacterium casei* belongs to the group of cream-coloured coryneform bacteria which are important for ripening owing to their fast growth. Corynebacteria are predominant in all stages of ripening and can build over 90% of the surface flora (Bockelmann, 2002a).

Defined surface cultures were used successfully if 10^7–10^8 cfu/ml were present in the smear. Smearing with cultures was performed once at start of ripening, then cheeses were turned every second day and brushed with 3% salt water after 5–7 days which was repeated in the second week when the smear distribution was not uniform. Deacidification was comparable to that in old–young smeared control cheeses (Fig. 21.3). In the figure, batch 1 (mean of four cheeses, open circles) was smeared with smear bacteria of cheese origin (two strains of *B. linens*, two strains of *A. nicotianae*, one strain of *C. casei*, one strain of *S. equorum*). For batch 2 (mean of four cheeses, open squares), DSM and ATCC type strains of the species *B. linens*, *A. nicotianae*, *B. casei* and *S. equorum* were used in the five-species starter. The concentration in the smear liquid was >10^8 cfu/ml for each species. For both batches, the yeast

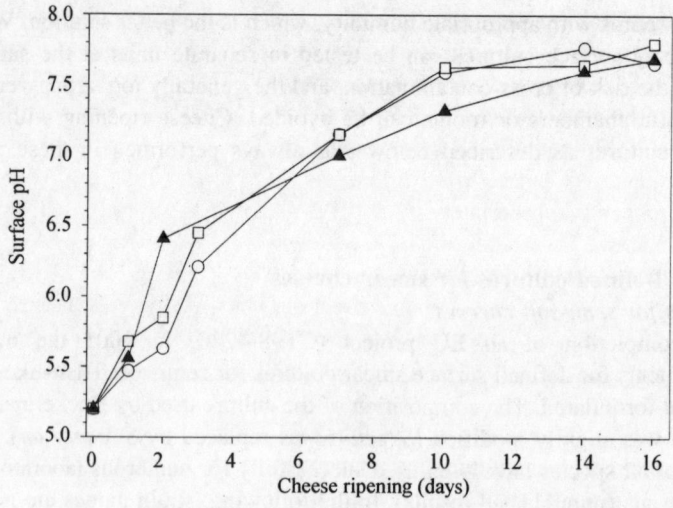

Fig. 21.3 Deacidification of the surface of smear-ripened cheeses.

Debaryomyces hansenii was used in the smear (10^7 cfu/ml). Cheeses of batch 3 (mean of four cheeses, filled triangles) were smeared with an old–young smear obtained from a local Tilsit cheese producer (total bacteria cell counts >10^{10} cfu/ml). Sterile brines were used for salting.

The bacterial composition of the experimental cheeses analysed over the ripening period of 6 weeks was quite similar to that of old–young smeared control cheeses (Table 21.4). In the table, Tilsit-like cheeses were smeared with *D. hansenii*, *B. linens*, *M. gubbeenense*, *C. casei* and *S. sciuri* (10^8 cfu/ml for each species). An old–young smear was obtained from a local Tilsit cheese producer. Similar results were obtained in later experiments, but with *S. sciuri* replaced by the more common *S. equorum* and with *D. hansenii* and *S. equorum* excluded from the smear but inoculated into the cheese brines instead (10^6 cfu/ml). Instead of the yellow-pigmented *Microbacterium gubbeenense*, yellow-pigmented *A. nicotianae* strains were used later. Both species occur on smear cheeses, and in

Table 21.4 Total surface cell counts of experimental cheeses

Surface cell counts (cfu/cm^2)	Defined surface starter			Old–young smeared 6 weeks
	1 week	2 weeks	6 weeks	
D. hansenii	9.1×10^6	6.9×10^5	3.9×10^5	2.9×10^5
Bacterial counts	1.7×10^9	8.1×10^8	2.6×10^9	3.3×10^9
C. ammoniagenes	76%	74%	90%	90%
M. barkeri	7.2%	12%	1%	2%
B. linens	3%	2%	1%	6%
S. sciuri	13.3%	12%	8%	2%

the experimental cheese trials they seemed to possess similar technological properties. By strain identification using pulsed field gel electrophoresis of bacteria isolated from the experimental cheese surfaces after 2 and 8 weeks of ripening (60 isolates), it was confirmed that the surface flora consisted of near 100% of the starter strains (Bockelmann *et al.*, submitted for publication).

After numerous cheese trials it can now be concluded that semi-soft cheese ripening proceeds appropriately if the pH is greater than 7 and the total bacterial counts are above 10^9 cfu/cm^2 after 7 days of ripening; the pH was measured with a flat surface electrode, and for sampling thin slices of 20–30 cm^2 were cut from the surface, 10 g of a slice homogenised in 90 ml of Ringer's solution being taken as 10^{-1} dilution (Hoppe-Seyler *et al.*, 2000).

Cultures for soft cheeses

Less information is available on the requirements for defined surface cultures for smeared soft cheeses. Culture development for these cheeses is currently being studied in a German project conducted at the Federal Dairy Research Centre, Kiel, Germany (AIF-FV 12780N, 2001–2003). The mature flora of smeared soft cheeses showed distinct differences from that of semi-soft cheeses (Table 21.3). A very high proportion of yellow-pigmented coryneform bacteria, *M. gubbeenense* as well as *A. nicotianae* (see above), and the presence of a second yeast species, *Geotrichum candidum*, are typical for the microflora of Limburg- and Romadour-like cheeses (Bockelmann, 2002b).

The appearance of the cheeses with a soft, white and dry layer of yeasts with streaks or spots of orange bacterial growth indicates the presence of *G. candidum* and smear bacteria (Fig. 21.1). Perhaps due to the growth of *G. candidum* covering large areas of the cheese, the bacterial cell counts on the cheese surface are lower than for Tilsit-type cheeses; 10^8 cfu/cm^2 of smear bacteria are usually found on commercial soft smear cheeses after 2 weeks of ripening when the cheeses are packaged (Bockelmann, 2002b). During this time commercial cheeses are old–young sprayed up to six times depending on the visible smear development (personal communication from several German cheese producers).

The deacidification of traditionally old–young sprayed soft cheeses by smear bacteria is quite different from that of semi-soft cheeses, showing a delay in the pH increase of 2–5 days. Then, deacidification proceeds rapidly and a surface pH of 7 is also achieved after one week as for semi-soft smear cheeses (Fig. 21.4). In the figure, for the five experimental cheese batches (filled symbols) the cheese milk was inoculated with *Geotrichum candidum* (10^2 cfu/ml). The cheese brines contained *Debaryomyces hansenii* and *Staphylococcus equorum* (10^6 cfu/ml). Cheeses were smeared with several combinations of *Arthrobacter nicotianae*, *Microbacterium gubbeenense*, *Brevibacterium linens* and *Halomonas variabilis* (10^7 cfu/ml in smear). The deacidification of commercial (old–young smeared) cheeses was measured in three German cheese plants (open symbols).

The use of a typical Tilsit surface culture for soft cheese ripening did not lead to typical deacidification, growth of smear bacteria, colour and aroma

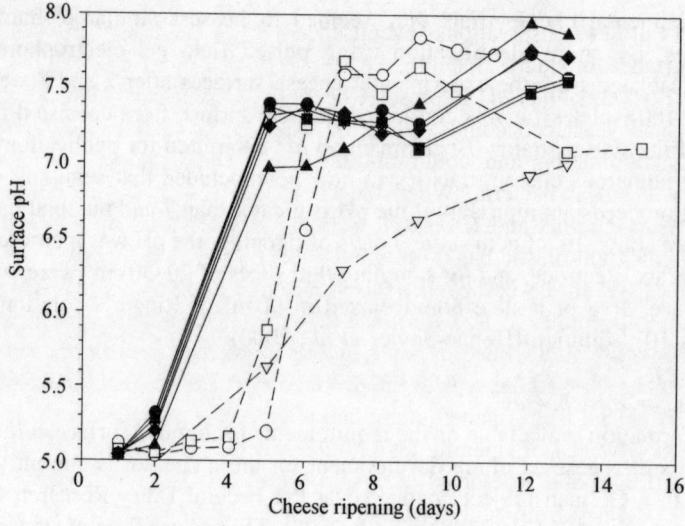

Fig. 21.4   Ripening of soft Limburg cheese.

development (Bockelmann, 2002b). The addition of *G. candidum* to the cheese milk (10^2–10^3 cfu/ml) in combination with a Tilsit starter led to a quite typical flavour. However, the appearance, smell and taste were further improved when the smear consisted of strains and species isolated from smeared soft cheeses (unpublished results, Table 21.3). Deacidification of the cheese surface by defined surface cultures lacked the delay of the commercial cheeses, the important high surface pH value of 7 being generally reached earlier (Fig. 21.4). At the moment pilot-scale cheese trials are being performed in cooperation with an industrial partner to test the suitability of the cultures in an industrial background.

Cultures for acid-curd cheese

Culture development is least developed for acid-curd cheeses, probably because of the limited local importance for some parts of Germany. A project on culture development for acid-curd cheeses was recently started (AIF-FV 13018, 2001–2003). It is quite difficult to maintain the high quality of acid-curd cheeses, since the production of the raw material (low-fat quarg) and the ripening of cheeses are performed independently by separate companies. In this process, microbiological ripening is already occurring when the quarg is transported to the cheese companies over many hours, often under conditions of insufficient cooling. The quarg is usually further stored at 10–15°C for a couple of days before the cheeses are produced from combined batches of different quarg producers. At this stage the quarg shows yeast cell counts of 10^5–10^7 cfu/g with a very aromatic smell (ester, alcohol, fruity, yeasty; Engel and Roesch, 1995).

Based on these observations several cheese trials were performed to assess the importance of quarg ripening, i.e. the presence of yeasts, for the whole process (Bockelmann *et al.*, in press). Cheeses produced from fresh quarg (total bacterial and yeast cell counts below 10^2 cfu/g) were quite sensitive towards fungal contamination and could not be ripened appropriately by spraying cheese with smear bacteria. When the cheese milk was inoculated with two yeasts (*K. marxianus* and *C. krusei*, >10^3 cfu/ml) and the quarg was ripened (stored in air-tight plastic bags) for about 7 days, no mould growth occurred on the cheeses within a week even if no smear was applied to the surface. The maximum cell counts of *K. marxianus* were observed during quarg ripening, while the cell counts of *C. krusei* increased during cheese ripening. The ripened quarg showed the typical intense aromatic profile described above and cheeses produced from ripened quarg had a quite typical appearance, taste and smell after 2 weeks of ripening and storage (Table 21.4). This confirmed the results of Engel and Roesch (1995) who found that these two species could always be isolated from acid-curd cheeses and should be essential for a typical cheese ripening.

Staphylococcus saprophyticus is a common undesirable contaminant on commercial acid-curd cheeses (Bockelmann *et al.*, 2002). Cheese trials revealed that the acid- and salt-tolerant *S. equorum* added to the ripened quarg together with ripening salts had a beneficial effect on cheese ripening, especially on the texture of experimental cheeses. Similar effects, the improvement of the texture of cheese, are claimed for commercial staphylococci (*S. xylosus*, *S. carnosus*) by starter companies. The ripening of cheeses was typical and reproducible when they were produced under the described conditions and with *B. linens* sprayed on the surface at the first day. The deacidification was faster compared to commercial acid-curd cheeses (Fig. 21.5: see below). The typical shrinking of the white quarg zone starting at the surface was already quite advanced after 5 days (ripening at >30°C and 15°C for 2 days, storage at 8°C for 3 days; Table 21.2, Fig. 21.6: see below). Studies concentrating on selecting appropriate surface smear cultures are currently being performed.

In Fig. 21.5, for the experimental cheese batches the milk was inoculated with *K. marxianus* and *C. krusei* at >10^3 cfu/ml. The quarg (dry mass 32%) was incubated in closed plastic bags at 16°C for 7 days before the quarg was mixed with salts and the cheeses were formed. The first data point of the curves resembles the quarg pH before the addition of ripening salts, the second the surface pH of the cheeses 12 h (24 h) after the addition of salts. *B. linens* was sprayed onto the surface after moulding (10^6 cfu/ml).

In Fig. 21.6, the quarg used for production was ripened with *K. marxianus* and *C. krusei* (added to the cheese milk) at 16°C for 7 days. Cheese ripening was performed at >30°C and 97% r.h. for 24 h, then after spraying with smear cultures the cheeses were incubated at 12°C and 80% r.h. for 24 h before being packed in foil and stored at 8°C. The photograph was taken after 3 days of storage. The speed of ripening, clearly seen by the shrinking of the quarg core, is comparable to that of commercial acid-curd cheeses which are old–young

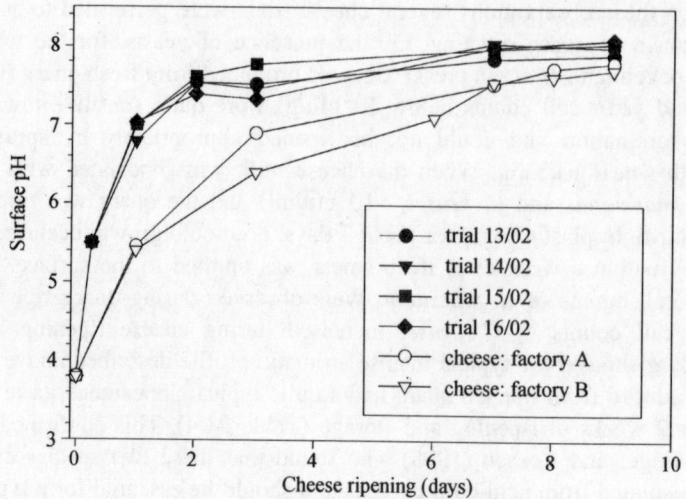

Fig. 21.5   Ripening of acid-curd cheese.

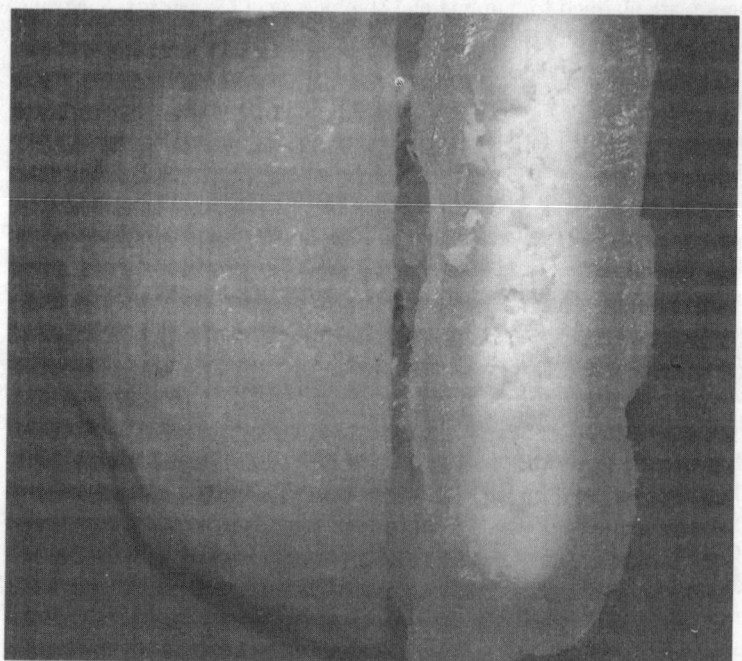

Fig. 21.6   Ripening of acid-curd cheese with defined cultures.

ripened. Contaminants (moulds, enterococci, enterobacteria) were below the detection limit (10^2 cfu/cm^2).

Brine microflora

Cheese brines which are not pasteurised regularly (semi-soft cheeses, e.g. Tilsit) develop a typical salt-tolerant microflora with a composition depending on the house microflora of the factory (Bockelmann, 2002a). Apart from many fungal and bacterial species which can be found at low cell counts (<10^2 cfu/ml), typical smear microorganisms can be detected at 10^4–10^6 cfu/ml in aged brines. Salt-tolerant yeasts (*D. hansenii*) and staphylococci (*S. equorum*) are usually predominant. Sometimes cheese brines can be contaminated with *Penicillium*, *Mucor* and other moulds. Since the surface of smear cheeses is not covered by any artificial means (wax, foil) after brining, it can be imagined that the brine microflora has a significant impact on the development of the surface microflora and product quality of smear cheeses. Obviously, no effect is present when dry salting is used, or for acid-curd cheese when quarg is mixed with solid ripening salts.

The control of the brine microflora is widely neglected. However, results of Jaeger *et al.* (2002) showed a clear mould-inhibiting effect of high concentrations of *D. hansenii* and *S. equorum* (>10^6 cfu/ml) during cheese ripening and a beneficial effect on deacidification in the first 2 days (Fig. 21.7). In the figure, four experimental cheeses were brined in the presence of *D. hansenii* and *S. equorum* (cell counts > 10^6 cfu/ml for each species ▲), and four control cheeses were salted in sterile brines (●). For the control cheeses a complete smear culture consisting of five species (see the start of Section 21.3.3) was used for smearing. Smearing of the other cheeses was performed with the three species *B. linens*, *C. casei* and *M. gubbeenense*. Deacidification of all cheeses proceeded as

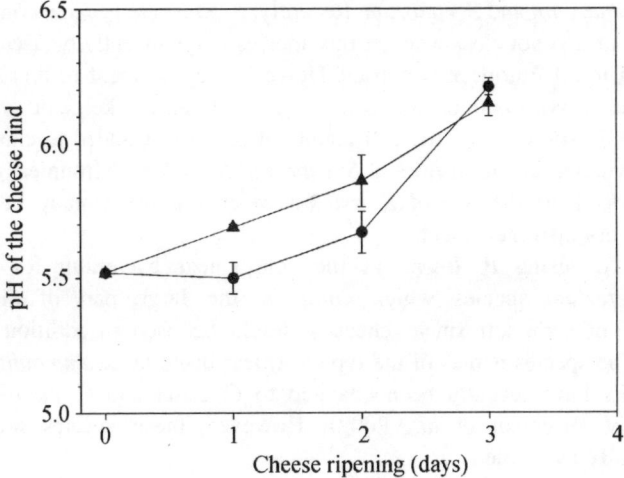

Fig. 21.7   Deacidification of the surface of Tilsit-type cheese.

shown in Fig. 21.3 after 3 days. Laboratory-scale cheese trials showed that both *D. hansenii* and *S. equorum* could be excluded from the smear culture if they were present in the brines without a negative effect.

21.4   Conclusions and future trends

There is no universal surface culture for all smear cheeses. The surface microflora of the three cheese types mentioned showed distinct differences. Results obtained so far showed that defined customised surface cultures can be used successfully for ripening instead of the described old–young processes. However, future studies will show whether the positive results obtained mainly on a laboratory scale can be transferred to industrial practice. A demonstration project funded by the EU starting at the end of 2002 will concentrate on establishing methods for the ripening of semi-soft Tilsit and related cheeses.

There is no doubt that the use of defined surface cultures will improve food safety by minimising microbial contamination. Microbial analysis of experimental cheeses produced on a laboratory scale showed that the cell counts for enterobacteria, enterococci, pathogenic or saprophytic staphylococci and pseudomonads were generally below the detection limit (unpublished data). With 'old–young' contamination cycles no longer present in factories, which stabilise any contamination occurring, it should be possible to reduce common microbial contaminants significantly. The question remains as to whether the aroma and appearance of these cheeses can be kept unchanged, a topic also studied in the projects mentioned above.

Several measures for improvement could be introduced immediately. Whenever brines are used for salting, the brine microflora should be actively controlled. Fresh brines should be inoculated with the naturally occurring species *D. hansenii* and *S. equorum*. Recently, *S. equorum* became commercially available but it is not clear whether this species may currently be used in cheese production in all European countries. However, replacement of this species by commercial *S. xylosus* does not seem to be practical. Bockelmann and Hoppe-Seyler (2001) showed that the cell counts of *S. xylosus* added to cheese brines dropped, whereas a natural flora of *S. equorum* from the environment developed over weeks. Thus the use of *S. xylosus* in cheese brines may be not only expensive but also inefficient.

Instead of using *B. linens* as the sole smear bacterium for smearing, *Corynebacterium* species which comprise the large part of the surface microflora of semi-soft smear cheeses should be used in addition for these cheeses. The species names of the typical smear bacteria *C. ammoniagenes* and *C. variabile* have recently been changed to *C. casei* and *C. mooreparkense*, respectively (Brennan *et al.*, 2002). However, these species are not yet commercially available.

The yellow-pigmented bacteria *A. nicotianae* and *M. gubbeenense* are of special importance for the ripening of soft cheeses, and should be used more widely for these products. Studies are currently under way to determine the typical percentage of the two species on the surface of the different smear cheeses. First results indicate a predominance of *M. gubbeenense*.

Even though of minor importance for the European cheese market, acid-curd cheeses can be very interesting foods for consumers who prefer calorie-reduced milk products. Acid-curd cheeses are traditionally produced from low-fat quarg and have very interesting sensory properties. At the moment, their wider distribution is probably prevented by their very traditional production, leading to an almost random surface microflora with unavoidable levels of fungal or bacterial contamination. First results of Bockelmann *et al.* (2002) indicate that culture development (yeasts and bacteria) may yield positive results in the near future to develop mild products which are microbiologically stable over the shelf-life of 7–8 weeks.

21.5 Sources of further information and advice

Apart from data presented in the scientific literature and textbooks on dairy microbiology and dairy processing, further information on culture development for smear cheeses is available on the web pages of European national research institutions in the agricultural sector. The use of defined surface smear cultures features prominently in the work of the Federal Dairy Research Centre, Kiel (Institute of Microbiology, http://www.bafm.de), the Netherlands Dairy Research Institute (http://www.nizo.nl) and the Institute of Food Science and Nutrition of the University of Zürich (Laboratory of Food Microbiology, http://www.mb.ilw.agrl.ethz.ch).

Last but not least, a view of the latest developments can be obtained from brochures or the corresponding web pages of the major starter culture companies (in alphabetical order: Chr. Hansen, Denmark; Danisco-Cultor (formerly Wisby), Germany; Degussa-Bioactives (formerly Sanofi or SKW), Germany; Rhodia-food (formerly Texel), France; Sacco srl, Italy). All companies are aware of the research going on in this area and some are partners in the R&D projects mentioned in this chapter. New cultures may soon be offered for smear cheese varieties.

21.6 References

BOCKELMANN, W. 1999, 'Secondary cheese cultures', in *Technology of Cheesemaking*, 1st edn, B.A. Law, ed., Sheffield Academic Press, Sheffield, pp. 132–162.

BOCKELMANN, W. 2002a, 'Development of defined surface starter cultures for the ripening of smear cheeses', *Int Dairy J*, 12(2–3), 123–131.

BOCKELMANN, W. 2002b, 'Kulturenentwicklung geschmierter Käse', *DMZ, Lebensmittelindustrie und Milchwirtschaft*, 3, 93–98.

BOCKELMANN, W. and HOPPE-SEYLER, T. 2001, 'The surface flora of bacterial smear-ripened cheeses from cow's and goat's milk', *Int Dairy J*, 11, 1–8.

BOCKELMANN, W., FUEHR, C., MARTIN, D. and HELLER, K.J. 1997a, 'Color development by Red-Smear surface bacteria', *Kieler Milchwirtschaftliche Forschungsberichte*, 49(4), 285–292.

BOCKELMANN, W., HOPPE-SEYLER, T., KRUSCH, U., HOFFMANN, W. and HELLER, K.J. 1997b, 'The microflora of Tilsit cheese. Part 2. Development of a surface smear starter culture', *Nahrung*, 41(4), 213–218.

BOCKELMANN, W., KRUSCH, U., ENGEL, G., KLIJN, N., SMIT, G. and HELLER, K.J. 1997c, 'The microflora of Tilsit cheese. Part 1. Variability of the smear flora', *Nahrung*, 41, 208–212.

BOCKELMANN, W., HOPPE-SEYLER, T., JAEGER, B. and HELLER, K.J. 2000, 'Small scale cheese ripening of bacterial smear cheeses', *Milchwissenschaft*, 55(11), 621–624.

BOCKELMANN, W., WILLEMS, P., JAEGER, B., HOPPE-SEYLER, T., ENGEL, G. and HELLER, K.J. (2002), 'Reifung von Harzer Kaese', *Kieler Milchwirtschaftliche Forschungsberichte*, 54, 317–335.

BRENNAN, N.M., WARD, A.C., BERESFORD, T.P., FOX, P.F., GOODFELLOW, M. and COGAN, T.M. 2002, 'Biodiversity of the bacterial flora on the surface of a smear cheese', *Appl Environ Microbiol*, 68(2), 820–830.

BUSSE, M. 1989, 'Die Oberflächenflora von geschmiertem Käse', *Milchw Berichte*, 99, 137–141.

CHAPMAN, H.R. and SHARPE, M.E. 1990, 'Microbiology of cheese', in *Dairy Microbiology: The Microbiology of Milk Products*, 2nd edn, Vol. 2, R. K. Robinson, ed., Elsevier Applied Science, London, pp. 203–289.

ELISKASES-LECHNER, F. and GINZINGER, W. 1995a, 'The bacterial flora of surface-ripened cheeses with special regard to coryneforms', *Lait*, 75(6), 571–583.

ELISKASES-LECHNER, F. and GINZINGER, W. 1995b, 'The yeast flora of surface-ripened cheeses', *Milchwissenschaft*, 50(8), 458–462.

ENGEL, G. and ROESCH, N. 1995, 'Development of yeasts during production and ripening of Harzer cheese (yellow cheese type)', *Kieler Milchwirtschaftliche Forschungsberichte*, 47(2), 97–112.

EPPERT, I., VALDES-STAUBER, N., GOTZ, H., BUSSE, M. and SCHERER, S. 1997, 'Growth reduction of *Listeria* spp. caused by undefined industrial red smear cheese cultures and bacteriocin-producing *Brevibacterium linens* as evaluated *in situ* on soft cheese', *Appl Environ Microbiol*, 63(12), 4812–4817.

FOX, P.F. 1993, 'Cheese: an overview', in *Cheese: Chemistry, Physics and Microbiology*, 2nd edn, Vol. 2, P.F. Fox, ed., Chapman & Hall, London, pp. 1–36.

GIANOTTI, S.M. 1999, *Microbiology and Biochemistry of the Enterobacteriaceae Flora of the Surface of Typical Swiss Cheeses*, ETH Zürich.

HOLSINGER, V.H., RAJKOWSKI, K.T. and STABEL, J.R. 1997, 'Milk pasteurisation and safety: a brief history and update', *Rev Sci Tech Oie*, 16, 441–451.

HOPPE-SEYLER, T., JAEGER, B., BOCKELMANN, W. and HELLER, K.J. 2000, 'Quantification and identification of microorganisms from the surface of smear cheeses', *Kieler Milchwirtschaftliche Forschungsberichte*, 52(4), 294–305.

JAEGER, B., HOPPE-SEYLER, T., BOCKELMANN, W. and HELLER, K. J. (2002), 'The influence of the brine microflora on the ripening of smear cheeses', *Milchwissenschaft*, 57(11/12), 645–648.

KAMMERLEHNER, J. 1993, 'Käsesorten', *DMZ*, 22, 624–632.

KAMMERLEHNER, J. 1995, 'Cheese with smear rind', *Dtsch Milchwirtsch*, 46(19), 1084–1086.

LAXA, O. 1899, 'Bakteriologische Studien über die Reifung von zwei Arten Backsteinkäse', *Centr Bl Bakter Parasitenk*, 5, 755–762.

REPS, A. 1993, 'Bacterial surface-ripened cheeses', in *Cheese: Chemistry, Physics and Microbiology*, 2nd edn, Vol. 2, P.F. Fox, ed., Chapman & Hall, London, pp. 137–172.

RUDOLF, M. and SCHERER, S. 2001, 'High incidence of *Listeria monocytogenes* in European red smear cheese', *Int J Food Microbiol*, 63(1–2), 91–98.

TEUBER, M. 1999, 'Spread of antibiotic resistance with food-borne pathogens', *Cell Mol Life Sci*, 56, 755–763.

TEUBER, M. and PERRETEN, V. 2000, 'Role of milk and meat products as vehicles for antibiotic-resistant bacteria', *Acta Vet Scand*, 75–87.

VALDES-STAUBER, N. and SCHERER, S. 1996, 'Nucleotide sequence and taxonomical distribution of the bacteriocin gene *lin* cloned from *Brevibacterium linens* M18', *Appl Environ Microbiol*, 62(4), 1283–1286.

WYDER, M.-T. and PUHAN, Z. 1999, 'Investigation of the yeast flora in smear ripened cheeses', *Milchwissenschaft*, 54(6), 330–333.

22

Flavour formation in cheese

W. J. M. Engels, J. E. T. van Hylckama Vlieg and G. Smit, NIZO Food Research, The Netherlands

22.1   Introduction

Micro-organisms play a number of major beneficial roles in the food industry. They are used to transform organic matter in foods, e.g. in fermented beverages, milk, meat and vegetables, and thereby they contribute to the preservation of food, but also to flavour and texture. Fermented milk products play an important if not dominant role in any discussion on food fermentations, which is no surprise in view of the size of the world's annual consumption, more than 15 billion kilograms (Kosikowski and Mistry, 1997). A variety of lactic acid bacteria and other micro-organisms are used in the production of a wide range of fermented dairy products. The main purpose of their use is to ensure a proper preservation of the fermented product. The rapid conversion of lactose, present in milk, into lactic acid is the most important feature of lactic acid bacteria in this respect. The resulting reduction of pH, a concomitant lowering of the redox potential and the absence of lactose inhibit growth of undesired bacteria in the dairy product, e.g. cheese.

In addition to the production of lactic acid, organisms used in fermented dairy products also determine flavour of the product. Milk is a rather bland product with regard to its flavour. This means that in fermented dairy products, the flavour compounds are nearly all generated during the fermentation and ripening of the product. Flavour development in fermented dairy products is a complex and, in the case of cheese ripening, slow process involving chemical and biochemical conversions of milk components (Engels and Visser, 1996; Engels *et al.*, 1997). Lactic acid bacteria (LAB), e.g. *Lactococcus lactis, Lactobacillus* species, *Streptococcus thermophilus* and *Leuconostoc mesenteroides*, form the main microflora in dairy products and are essential for the biochemical conversions that determine the specific flavour. However, additional cultures are also used, such as *Propionibacterium* in the case of Swiss-type and Maasdammer-type cheeses, and various aerobic cultures, e.g. *Brevibacterium*, *Arthrobacter*, *Staphylococcus*, *Penicillium* and *Debaromyces*, for surface-ripened cheeses (Bockelmann, 2002; Molimard and Spinnler, 1996). As well as these starter organisms, endogenous milk enzymes, added enzymes (rennet) and mesophilic lactobacilli can also play a role. The latter, originating from the milk environment, might grow in the dairy products and thereby be a source of enzyme activities leading to the formation of flavours. Flavour compounds are formed by three processes: the conversions of lactose and citrate (glycolysis and/or pyruvate metabolism), fat (lipolysis), and caseins (proteolysis).

Although lactose is mainly converted to lactate by LAB, a fraction of the intermediate pyruvate can alternatively be converted to various flavour compounds such as diacetyl, acetoin, acetaldehyde or acetic acid, some of which contribute to typical yoghurt flavours. Lipolysis results in the formation of free fatty acids, which are precursors of flavour compounds such as methyl ketones, alcohols, lactones and esters (Molimard and Spinnler, 1996; Gallois and Langlois, 1990). Lipolysis is mainly due to mould activity, and much less to LAB activity (Molimard and Spinnler, 1996; Gripon, 1987). Fat hydrolysis is particularly important in soft cheeses like Camembert and blue cheeses.

The degradation of milk proteins is the major biochemical pathway for flavour formation in hard-type and semi-hard-type cheeses (van Kranenburg *et al.*, 2002; Engels, 1997). The activities of rennet enzymes, the cell-envelope proteinase and the peptidases from LAB yield small peptides and free amino acids from casein. These small peptides and amino acids are responsible for the important background flavour in a matured cheese, e.g. savoury, brothy and salty. However, the actual cheesy flavour is formed by amino-acid-converting enzymes and is superimposed on that basic flavour (Engels and Visser, 1994). This further conversion of amino acids yields various alcohols, aldehydes, acids, esters and sulphur compounds, facilitating specific flavour developments.

This chapter focuses on the main pathways involved in flavour formation from amino acids. The mechanisms of conversion of amino acids to volatile flavour compounds will be discussed in detail with examples of how fundamental knowledge of the flavour production pathways can be used to improve the flavour of a given cheese. The chapter summarises various aspects which have been reviewed by van Kranenburg, Smit, Yvon and their respective colleagues.

22.2   Amino acid conversion

22.2.1   Introduction

The volatile aroma components of various cheeses have received a great deal of attention and a large number of volatiles have been detected in individual types of cheese. Various methods have been applied for extraction of the volatiles from WSF (water soluble fraction) and subsequent gas-chromatographic analysis of the compounds. Banks *et al.* (1992) used steam distillation and gas chromatography–mass spectrometry (GC–MS) for extraction and identification of volatile compounds from Cheddar cheese. The use of high-vacuum distillation, combined with gas-chromatographic analysis, has also been reported (Gallois and Langlois, 1990; Moio *et al.*, 1993). Headspace techniques (Bosset and Gauch, 1993; Wood *et al.*, 1994; Yang and Min, 1994) are used frequently nowadays. These methods measure all the volatile compounds while only a small fraction of volatiles are odour-active. In order to identify the odour-important compounds in cheese, analytical methods that combine gas chromatography and olfactometry have been developed (Acree *et al.*, 1984; Taylor *et al.*, 2000; Engels *et al.*, 2001). Some of the potent odorants result from lactose fermentation or citrate degradation and from lipolysis, while many other compounds result from amino acid conversion, mainly degradation of branched-chain and aromatic amino acids and methionine. In Table 22.1 typical examples of volatile compounds in various types of ripened cheese are shown. The volatiles can be divided in six major groups: fatty acids, esters, aldehydes, alcohols, ketones and sulphur compounds. Most of these compounds are present in all types of cheeses, though their concentrations show distinct differences.

Table 22.1 Major groups of volatile compounds formed during cheese ripening (after Engels, 1997)

Compounds	Typical examples	Cheese type where especially found
Fatty acids	Acetic acid	Gruyère, Parmesan, Camembert
	Propionic acid	Emmental, Maasdam
	Butyric acid	Gruyère, Parmesan, Camembert
Esters	Ethyl butanoate	Gruyère, Parmesan
	Ethyl decanoate	Roquefort
Aldehydes	3-Methyl-butanal	Proosdij, Parmesan
	2-Methyl-butanal	Parmesan
	Benzaldehyde	Comté
Alcohols	1-Butanol	Gruyère, Parmesan, Maasdam
	3-Methyl-1-butanol	Edam, Maasdam, Parmesan
	Phenylethanol	Camembert
Ketones	2-Heptanone	Roquefort, Camembert
	2-Nonanone	Roquefort, Camembert
	2-Butanone	Edam
Sulphur compounds	Dimethyldisulphide	Limburger, Cheddar, Gouda
	Methional	Cheddar, Emmental
Various components	Phenol	Limburger
	Limonene	Fontina
	δ-Decalactone	Emmental
	4-Hydroxy-2,5-dimethyl-3(2H)-furanone	Emmental

It is important to realise that there is not a single compound or class of compounds which is responsible for the full flavour of cheese. The flavour is indisputably due to the presence of numerous components as already mentioned. Most of these compounds originate from lactose and the casein and fat fractions of the milk and are formed by the enzymatic action of the starter cultures used. Furthermore, chemical conversions of intermediate compounds occur concomitantly.

22.2.2   Amino acid biosynthesis and requirements

Flavour formation from amino acids by LAB depends on a very complex network of reactions, and many factors may contribute to the balance of various flavour compounds. In general, the main processes are:

• Generation and uptake of amino acids, i.e. formation of the intracellular pool of amino acids
• Conversion of amino acids
• Regulation of these pathways.

Lactococci have a limited capacity for biosynthesis of amino acids, which explains their complex nutritional requirements. They require essential amino acids for growth, and the number of essential amino acids is strain-dependent (Andersen and Elliker, 1953; Reiter and Oram, 1962; Chopin, 1993; Jensen and Hammer, 1993; Ayad et al., 1999). Most dairy Lactococcus strains need glutamate, valine, methionine, histidine, serine, leucine and isoleucine. Typically, industrial L. lactis ssp. cremoris strains require more amino acids for growth than dairy and non-dairy wild strains (Ayad et al., 1999). Wild L. lactis ssp. cremoris and ssp. lactis strains generally require fewer than three amino acids. The absence of some amino acid biosynthethic pathways in dairy lactococci might be a consequence of their adaptation to dairy products, since amino acids are readily available by the proteolysis of caseins, and as a result amino acid auxotrophy will not have a negative influence on cell growth. Strains isolated from natural niches are usually not associated with a rich environment such as milk, which makes them more dependent on their own synthesis of amino acids compared to industrial strains.

Since the concentrations of free amino acids and peptides are very low in milk, the starter cultures depend heavily for growth in milk on their proteolytic systems. The degradation of milk proteins (caseins) yields peptides and free amino acids, which can subsequently be taken up by the cells (Kunji et al., 1996; Christensen et al., 1999). Proteolysis is initiated by a single cell-wall-bound extracellular proteinase (Prt), which can be either chromosomally or plasmid-encoded (Exterkate et al., 1993). While most dairy LAB strains contain such an extracellular proteinase, several do not and these strains are mainly dependent on other strains in the starter culture for the production of peptides and amino acids. Such dependency of strains is rather common in starter cultures, and it is expected that, in order to be able to develop stable starter cultures, knowledge of the population dynamics between strains is essential (Ayad *et al.*, 2001a).

Peptide and amino acid transport systems have been studied extensively in lactococci, but far less is known for other LAB such as lactobacilli (for a review, see Kunji *et al.*, 1996). Peptide uptake occurs via oligopeptide transport systems and di-/tri-peptide transporters. The oligopeptide transporter is an ABC transporter capable of transporting peptides ranging in size from four to 18 amino acids (Detmers *et al.*, 1998). Also various amino acid transport systems have been identified with a high specificity for structurally similar amino acids (Konings *et al.*, 1989).

Following uptake, the peptides are degraded intracellularly by a variety of peptidases, which have been extensively studied in both lactococci and lactobacilli (reviews by Kunji *et al.*, 1996; Christensen *et al.*, 1999). These peptidases can be divided into endopeptidases, aminopeptidases, di-/tri-peptidases, and proline-specific peptidases. The specialised peptidases in LAB for hydrolysis of Pro-containing peptides have been postulated to be important for the degradation of casein-derived peptides, since these are known to have a high proline content.

The balance between the formation of peptides and their subsequent degradation into free amino acids is of particular importance for the taste of cheeses, since accumulation of peptides might lead to a bitter off-flavour (Stadhouders *et al.*, 1983; Visser *et al.*, 1983; Smit *et al.*, 1996, 1998). Various bitter-tasting peptides have been identified and especially these peptides should be degraded rapidly in order to prevent bitterness (Stadhouders *et al.*, 1983; Visser *et al.*, 1983; Smit *et al.*, 1998). Specific cultures have been selected with high bitter-tasting-peptide degrading abilities (Smit *et al.*, 1998) and such cultures are nowadays frequently used in the preparation of various types of cheese.

22.3 Amino acid catabolism

Amino acids are the precursors of various volatile cheese flavour compounds that have been identified in cheese (Engels *et al.*, 1996, 1997, Yvon *et al.*, 1997; Yvon and Rijnen, 2001). They can be converted in many different ways by enzymes such as transaminases (aminotransferases), decarboxylases, deaminases and lyases (Fig. 22.1). Transamination of amino acids results in the formation of α-keto acids that can be converted into aldehydes by decarboxylation and, subsequently, into alcohols by reduction or into carboxylic acids by oxidation (Yvon and Rijnen, 2001; Engels *et al.*, 2000; Christensen *et al.*, 1999). Many of these components are odour-active and contribute to the overall flavour of the dairy product. Moreover, other reactions may occur, e.g. by hydrogenase activity towards α-keto acids resulting in the formation of hydroxy-acids, which hardly contribute to the flavour. Aromatic amino acids, branched-chain amino acids and methionine are the most relevant substrates for cheese flavour development.

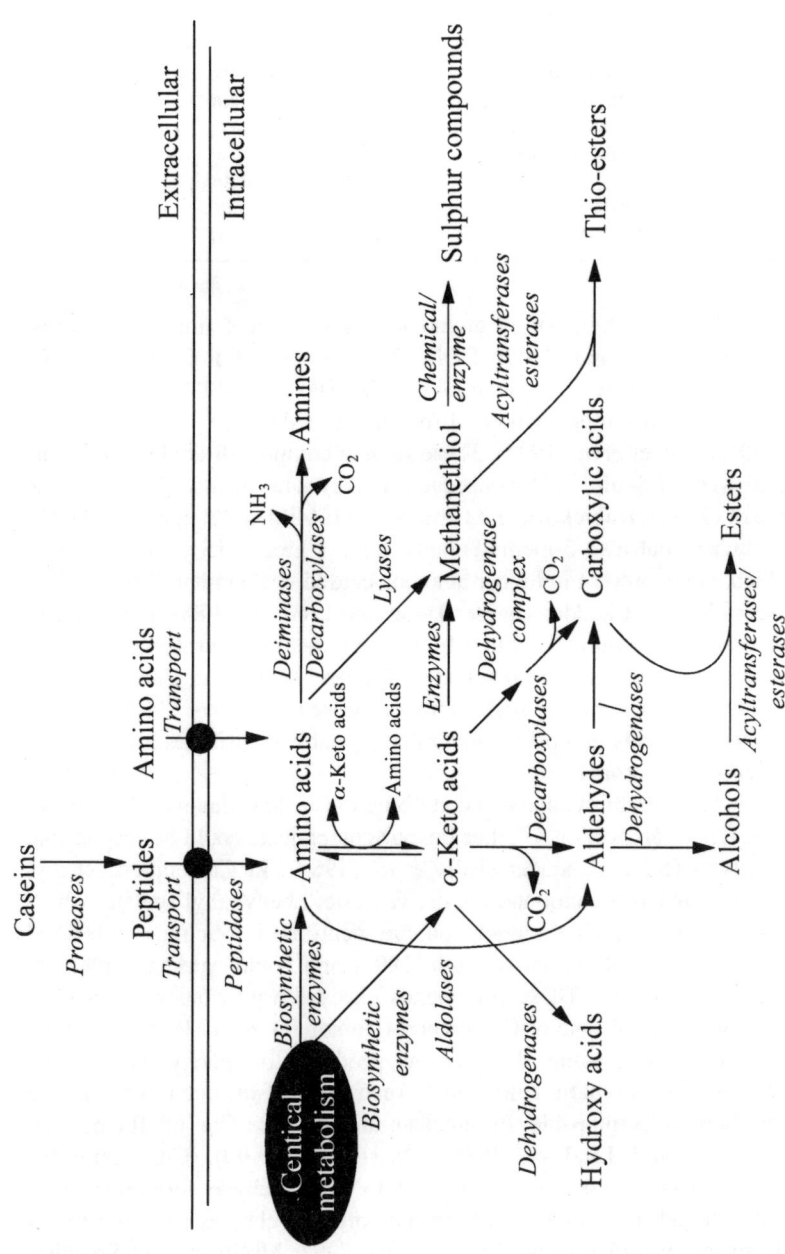

Fig. 22.1 Pathways of amino acid conversion leading to flavour compounds.

Table 22.2   Examples of products formed by breakdown of amino acids during cheese ripening

Amino acid	Volatile product	Flavour
Leu	3-Methyl-1-butanol	Fresh cheese, fruity
Ile	2-Methylbutanal	Malty, chocolate
Met	Methanethiol	Onion, cheese
Phe	Phenylacetaldehyde	Rose
Tyr	Phenol	Phenol, medicinal
Thr	Acetaldehyde	'Green', yoghurt
Val	2-Methylpropanal	Malty, chocolate

Compounds from catabolism of amino acids also include ammonia, amines, phenols and sulphur compounds. In Table 22.2, examples of amino acid-derived cheese volatiles are given. Methanethiol but also DMDS and DMTS contribute to the desirable garlic/sulphury note of the cheeses (Manning, 1974; Yvon and Rijnen, 2001; Weimer *et al.*, 1999). These sulphur compounds are highly odour-active and very volatile, and consequently they are mainly found in the headspace of cheese (Kubickova and Grosch, 1997; Milo and Reineccius, 1997). 2-Methylbutanal, but also 3-methylbutanal, have a green malty/chocolate-like odour which, when present in higher amounts caused unclean-harsh and dulling flavour sensations in Cheddar cheese (Dunn and Lindsay, 1985). However, in low concentrations the odour becomes fruity and rather pleasant. Isovaleric acid, derived from leucine, is more prevalent in Camembert than in Cheddar but it was also found in other cheeses such as Swiss cheese (Bosset *et al.*, 1993). It has a rancid, cheesy, sweaty and putrid odour that probably contributes highly to the very ripened-cheese aroma.

Esters, such as ethylbutyrate, also contribute to Cheddar flavour, although an excess of esters in proportion to other flavour components could be responsible for the fruity defect of Cheddar (Bills *et al.*, 1965). In Camembert, phenyl acetaldehyde, 2-phenylethanol and the derived ester phenylethyl acetate, which all result from phenylalanine degradation, are identified in fractions with floral rose-like odour (Kubickova and Grosch, 1997) and could cause the pleasant floral note of this cheese. These compounds have been previously assumed to cause the pleasant floral note of Camembert (Dumont *et al.*, 1974; Roger *et al.*, 1988). However, the same degradation products of phenylalanine and metabolites of other aromatic amino acids such as p-cresol, indole and skatole were identified as responsible for unclean-utensil, rose-like off-flavours in Cheddar (Dunn and Lindsay, 1985, Christensen, 1999). Conversion of tryptophan or phenylalanine can also lead to benzaldehyde formation. This compound is found in various hard-type and soft-type cheeses and contributes positively to the overall flavour (Engels *et al.*, 1997; Molimard and Spinnler, 1996). Many of the reactions can also occur under cheese conditions and are highly dependent on the strain used (Gao *et al.*, 1997). LAB strains may vary greatly in their capacity to metabolise amino acids, depending on the enzymes they possess and express. In the following sections, degradation of individual amino acids and the enzymes involved is described.

22.4 Methionine catabolism

The decomposition products of methionine are of crucial importance for cheese flavour development. The catabolism of methionine by starter organisms has been reported, and especially methanethiol, dimethyldisulphide and dimethyltri-sulphide contribute significantly to cheese flavour (Dias and Weimer, 1998a; Urbach, 1995; Engels, 1997). In fact, a Gouda cheese-like flavour can be generated by incubation of methionine with cell extracts of *L. lactis* (Engels and Visser, 1996). Smear-ripened cheeses, such as Tilsit, Danbo, Limburger and Appenzeller, host a rather wide range of micro-organisms on their surface. These micro-organisms, primarily bacteria (such as *Brevibacterium linens* and staphylococci) and yeasts, are responsible for a relatively high production of volatile sulphur-containing flavour compounds in these cheese types. Conversion of methionine by LAB can occur via an aminotransferase-initiated pathway by branched-chain or aromatic aminotransferases, or via an α,γ-elimination of methionine by the lyase activities of cystathionine β-lyase (CBL) and cysta-thionine γ-lyase (CGL) (Fig. 22.2) (Alting *et al.*, 1995; Bruinenberg *et al.*, 1997; Dias and Weimer, 1998a, 1998b; Engels *et al.*, 2000; Gao *et al.*, 1998; Gao and Steele, 1998; Rijnen *et al.*, 1999; Yvon *et al.*, 1997, Fernández *et al.*, 2000, 2002). In *B. linens* methionine γ-lyase (MGL) plays a central role (Dias and Weimer, 1998b). Aminotransferase activity results in the formation of 4-methylthio-2-

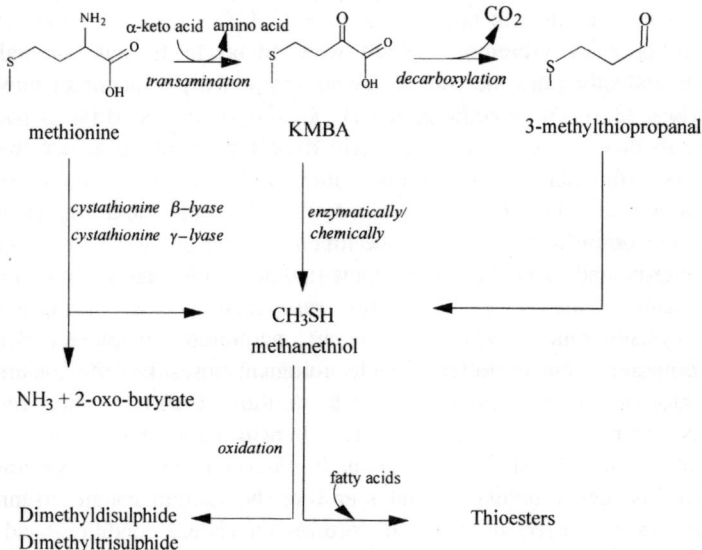

Fig. 22.2 Pathways of conversion of methionine to volatile sulphur compounds.

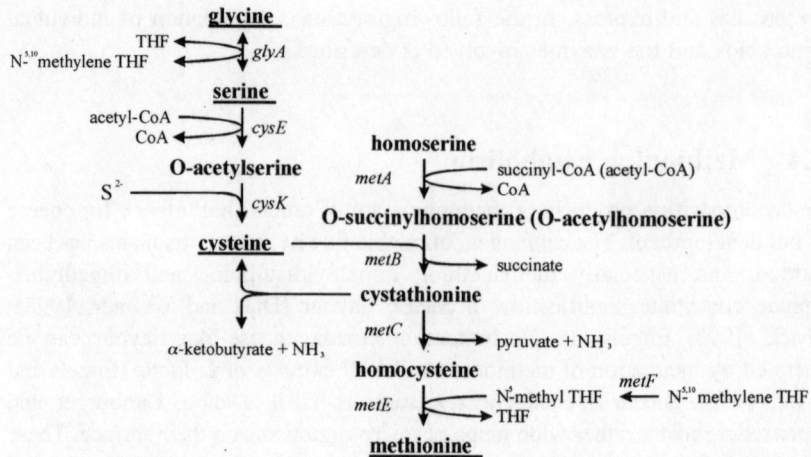

Fig. 22.3   Cysteine and methionine biosynsthesis pathways (van Kranenburg *et al.*, 2002).

ketobutyric acid (KMBA) which can be converted to methanethiol, probably via a thiamine pyrophosphate (TTP)-dependent decarboxylase that produces 3-methylthiopropanal (methional), and subsequent breakdown (Engels *et al.*, 2000).

Although cystathionine lyases are active under cheese-ripening conditions (Alting *et al.*, 1995; Ayad *et al.*, 1999; Smacchi and Gobbetti, 1998), their activity towards methionine could not be detected using ^{13}C nuclear magnetic resonance (Gao *et al.*, 1998). With this technique, only the aminotransferase-initiated pathway was observed, suggesting that this pathway is most prominent in methionine catabolism to produce methanethiol. On the other hand, strains that overproduce cystathionine β-lyase were found to be able to degrade methionine, indicating the potential of this enzyme in the production of sulphury flavours (Fig. 22.3). The specificity of CBL (Alting *et al.*, 1995) is a particular advantage in this respect, since one might expect that only sulphury flavour components will increase in strains with high activity. In the case of overproduction of other less specific enzymes such as transaminases more pathways will be influenced at the same time.

Biosynthesis and degradation of some amino acids are strongly linked pathways as illustrated in Fig. 22.3 for some amino acids. During cheese ripening, cystathionine β-lyase can convert methionine to various volatile flavour compounds, but in bacteria its physiological function is the conversion of cystathionine to homocysteine, which is the penultimate step in the biosynthesis of methionine (Fig. 22.3). This indicates that AACEs are in fact involved in the biosynthesis of amino acids. It is well known that biosynthesis of amino acids is highly regulated, and therefore the growth conditions of the starter cultures may affect their flavour-forming capacities.

For instance, in *L. lactis* the gene coding for cystathionine β-lyase (*metC*) is clustered together with a gene coding for cysteine synthase (*cysK*) (Fernández *et*

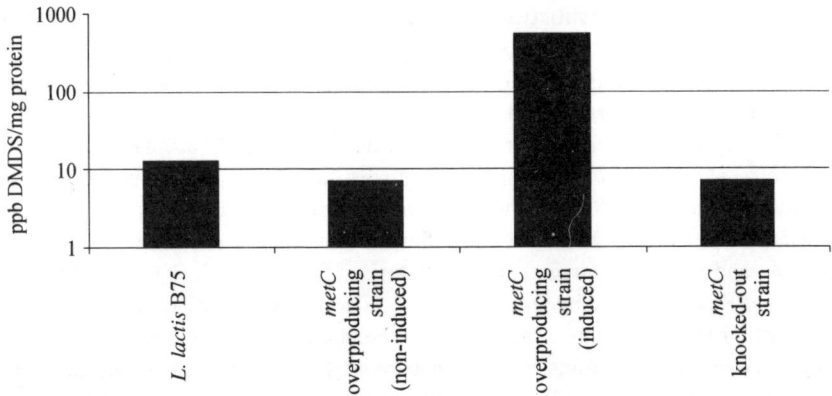

Fig. 22.4   Role of *metC* in production of sulphur flavours from methionine (DMDS = dimethyldisulphide).

al., 2000), thus genetically linking the methionine and cysteine biosynthesis pathways (Fig. 22.4). The expression of the *metC–cysK* gene cluster is strongly influenced by the amounts of methionine and cysteine in the culture medium (Fernández *et al.*, 2002). High concentrations of these amino acids completely abolish transcription and result in *L. lactis* cells almost deficient of cystathionine β-lyase activity. These regulatory aspects are probably very important in the control of flavour-forming enzymes in starter cultures and adjunct cultures.

22.5   Branched-chain and aromatic amino acid conversion

Amino acid transamination is a key step in the amino acid conversion to aroma compounds by cheese micro-organisms. In LAB, catabolism of aromatic amino acids (ArAAs), of branched-chain amino acids (BrAAs) and, at least in part, of methionine is initiated by a transamination reaction. It was demonstrated in lactococci (Gao *et al.*, 1997, 1998; Yvon *et al.*, 1997), in mesophilic lactobacilli such as *Lb. paracasei, Lb. casei, Lb. plantarum* and *Lb. rhamnosus* (Gummalla and Broadbent, 1996; Tammam *et al.*, 2000) and also in thermophilic lactobacilli such as *Lb. helveticus, Lb. delbrueckii lactis, Lb. delbrueckii bulgaricus, Streptococcus thermophilus* or *Propionibacterium freudenreicheii* (Gummalla and Broadbent, 1999; Thierry and Maillard, 2002) that an α-keto acid is used as amino group acceptor in transamination.

Amino acid transamination is catalysed by aminotransferases which are pyridoxal-S′-phosphate-dependent enzymes and are widely distributed in micro-organisms. Transamination results in the formation of α-keto acids while the α-keto acid acceptor is transformed to the corresponding amino acid, e.g. glutamate in the case of α-ketoglutarate. Aminotransferases are more or less specific for one group of amino acids (e.g. ArAAs, BcAAs) but often have broad, overlapping substrate specificities (Yvon and Rijnen, 2001). Transaminations are physiologically very important because they play a crucial role in the biosynthesis as well as the catabolism of amino acids (Engels *et al.*, 2000; Yvon and Rijnen, 2001).

Despite their importance in amino acid conversion to aroma compounds, aminotransferases of cheese micro-organisms have been poorly studied. ArAA aminotransferases of *B. linens* were partially purified several years ago (Lee and Desmazeaud, 1985). More recently the aminotransferases active on ArAAs, BcAAs and Met were purified and characterised from *L. lactis* (Yvon *et al.*, 1997; Gao and Steele 1998; Engels *et al.*, 2000). The aromatic aminotransferases can convert aromatic amino acids, but also leucine and methionine, while the branched-chain aminotransferases can convert the branched-chain amino acids leucine, isoleucine and valine, but also methionine, cysteine and phenylalanine (Yvon *et al.*, 1997; Engels *et al.*, 2000). The physiological role of these aminotransferases in bacterial metabolism is to catalyse the last step in the biosynthesis of branched-chain or aromatic amino acids. Optimal pH for activity is around pH 7.5–8 and optimal temperature 35–50°C (Yvon *et al.*, 1997; Engels *et al.*, 2000). The enzymes are still active under cheese ripening conditions (low pH and temperature, high salt). Expression of the *bcaT* gene is repressed by high concentrations of branched-chain amino acids or methionine (Yvon *et al.*, 2000). This illustrates that the selection of culture conditions can strongly influence the flavour-forming capacities of *L. lactis*.

Yvon and co-workers (1998) demonstrated that the amount of α-keto acids, functioning as co-substrate, is very important for high amino acid conversion rates. Overproduction of the transaminases alone did not lead to a strong increase in amino acid conversion without a simultaneous addition of keto acids as co-substrate (Yvon *et al.*, 1998). The introduction of a glutamate dehydrogenase gene, the dehydrogenase catalysing glutamate conversion to α-keto glutamate, from *Peptostreptococcus* in *L. lactis* resulted in a similar effect (Rijnen *et al.*, 2000). However, whether this activity also results in a strong increase in the desired flavour components remains to be determined. Recently, experiments were performed during which α-ketoglutarate was added to cheeses. The results suggested a positive effect on formation of cheese flavour compounds (Rijnen *et al.*, 1999; Banks *et al.*, 2001). Ayad *et al.* (2001b) found that also the presence of enzymes required for subsequent conversions of α-keto acids might be of crucial importance (see below). α-Keto acids resulting from amino acid transamination are further degraded to various compounds either by enzymatic reactions or by chemical reactions. Hydroxy acids, carbolic acids and aldehydes are resulting products. Moreover, KMBA, the methionine α-keto acid, can be degraded to methanethiol. Phenylpyruvic acid resulting from phenylalanine transamination is chemically converted to benzaldehyde in the presence of oxygen and manganese (Nierop Groot and De Bont, 1999). All these compounds, except hydroxy acids, are major aroma compounds.

The reactions and the enzymes involved in further degradation of α-keto acids have been only partially elucidated. Both conversion to aldehydes or alcohols and conversion to carboxylic acids seem of importance. Formation of 3-methylbutanal and 3-methylbutanol by *L. lactis* can take place by enzymatic decarboxylation (followed by a reduction step in the case of the alcohol) of the α-keto acid from leucine, α-keto isocaproic acid (Smit, B.A. *et al.*, 2002, submitted). Production of carboxylic acids probably proceeds via a process of oxidative decarboxylation (Yvon and Rijnen, 2001). Conversion of KMBA by decarboxylation was already mentioned in the previous section. Several enzymes can thus be considered as being involved in degradation of amino acids, but also in biosynthesis, and α-keto acids are key intermediates.

22.6   Conversion of other amino acids

Threonine catabolism by LAB is initiated by threonine aldolase (serine hydroxymethyltransferase), an enzyme widely distributed in LAB. Threonine aldolase converts threonine to aceetaldehyde and glycine (Lees and Jago, 1976; Marshall and Cole, 1983). Aceetaldehyde is an important flavour compound of yoghurt, but also of cheese, butter and buttermilk (Ott *et al.*, 2000).

Two pathways for the catabolism of arginine have been described. The most common pathway for the catabolism of arginine in LAB is via the arginine deiminase (ADI) pathway (Cunin *et al.*, 1986; Konings *et al.*, 1995). This pathway results in the conversion of arginine into ammonia and ornithine and CO_2. Glutamic acid catabolism in LAB proceeds via transamination (to α-ketoglutarate) followed by decarboxylation or takes place directly by decarboxylation. In the latter case, γ-aminobutyrate (GABA) is the resulting product. Certain *Streptococcus thermophilus* strains present in starter cultures for, e.g., Parmesan-type cheese show high glutamate decarboxylase activity, resulting in excessive CO_2 production (Zoon and Allersma, 1996). Histamine production from histidine in fermented foods is of importance for health and safety concerns. In *Lactobacillus* histamine production could occur by histidine decarboxylases (Voight and Eitenmiller, 1978).

For the above-mentioned processes to take place, availability of free amino acids is of course essential. This requires a balanced proteolysis in cheese as well as (probably) lysis of starter cells to some extent (Visser, 1993). In contrast to the activity of peptidases (see above), where lysis generally enhances the activity, it probably depends on the type of enzyme (system) whether lysis will improve the activity or not. For instance, enzymes which require co-factors or co-substrates (e.g., PLP, NAD, NADP) might be negatively affected by lysis of the cells. The delicate balance, which is needed for the whole set of enzymes involved in flavour formation, will probably be affected by lysis (Smit, G. *et al.*, 2002).

The diversity observed in amino-acid-converting capacities of various strains, but also in lysis behaviour, implies that by targeted selection of starter bacteria the formation of desirable flavours can be influenced. A similar strain dependency is also found for enzyme activities which result in the formation of undesired flavour compounds. This indicates that a strong potential for starter improvement exists. In the next section examples will be given of optimisation of flavour of dairy products by rational selection of strains.

22.7   Natural biodiversity and tailor-made starter cultures

Amino-acid-converting abilities of LAB are linked to the ability to synthesise amino acids. Lactococci used in dairy fermentations are known for their limited capacity for biosynthesis of amino acids, which explains their complex nutritional requirements. As described above, they require several amino acids for growth, and the number of essential amino acids is strain-dependent (Andersen and Elliker, 1953; Reiter and Oram, 1962; Chopin, 1993; Jensen and Hammer, 1993; Ayad *et al.*, 1999). Most dairy *Lactococcus* strains need glutamate, valine, methionine, histidine, serine, leucine and isoleucine. Industrial *L. lactis* ssp. *cremoris* strains require more different amino acids for growth than so-called wild lactococcal strains (Ayad *et al.*, 1999). The latter are more dependent on their own biosynthesis of amino acids.

The growth requirement for specific amino acids can result either from the absence of functional specific biosynthetic genes or from specific regulatory mechanisms (Chopin, 1993). For example, the existence of defects in biosynthesis of histidine and branched-chain amino acids has been established in *L. lactis* strains resulting from accumulated mutations and deletions within the genes coding for the biosynthetic enzymes (Delorme *et al.*, 1993; Godon *et al.*, 1993; Bolotin *et al.*, 2001). The involvement of regulatory mechanisms in amino acid requirements has also been demonstrated in *L. lactis*. For instance, the biosynthesis of the amino acids of the glutamate family (Glu, Gln, Arg and Pro) is dependent on the synthesis of glutamate itself which, in turn, can be affected by the ammonium ion concentration in the medium.

Interestingly, lactococci isolated from natural niches (wild strains) were found not only to have a larger potential in amino acid production, but concomitantly also to be able to produce rather unusual flavour components. This natural biodiversity could offer new possibilities when explored and applied in practice. Recently, it was demonstrated that the absence of parts of the flavour-forming pathways in individual strains can be complemented by using defined strain combinations (Ayad *et al.*, 2001b). For instance, the combination of artisanal lactococcal strain *L. lactis* B1157 and industrial lactococcal strain SK110 in milk resulted in a very strong chocolate-like flavour, due to high levels of 3-methyl butanal. In SK110, a highly proteolytic strain, the complete pathway from casein via leucine to 3-methyl butanal cannot proceed due to the lack of a decarboxylating enzyme in this strain (Fig. 22.5a). B1157 is a non-proteolytic strain and therefore unable to produce enough free amino acids that can serve as substrate for the subsequent transamination and decarboxylation steps (Fig. 22.5b). However, when B1157 and SK110 are incubated together, the strains complement each other with regard to their

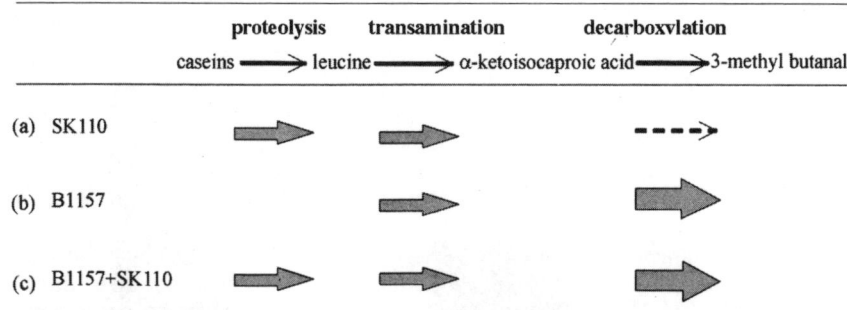

	proteolysis	transamination	decarboxvlation
	caseins ⟶ leucine ⟶		α-ketoisocaproic acid ⟶ 3-methyl butanal

(a) SK110

(b) B1157

(c) B1157+SK110

Fig. 22.5   Pathway of leucine comversion by individual and combined lactococcal strains (after Ayad *et al.*, 2001b).

enzyme activities, resulting in a high production of the chocolate flavour component 3-methyl butanal (Fig. 22.5c).

The use of a selected mesophilic *L. lactis* strain with high activity to form 3-methyl butanal to improve the taste of Proosdij cheese is another example of the application of fundamental knowledge on flavour-forming abilities for the optimisation of flavour. Proosdij cheese is a Gouda-type cheese, prepared with a mesophilic starter culture in combination with a thermophilic adjunct culture. This cheese has a flavour profile with characteristics between Gouda and Parmesan cheese. One of the key flavours in the cheese is 3-methyl butanal (Neeter *et al.*, 1996; Engels *et al.*, 1997). The selected *L. lactis* strain (B851) was used in combination with the regular cultures (mesophilic starter Bos and thermophilic culture S1138) used for this type of cheese. The cheeses made with and without the selected strain were analysed for the production of 3-methyl butanal by headspace gas chromatography (Ayad *et al.*, 2001a) and graded by an expert panel (Ayad *et al.*, 2001b). It was found that the use of the selected adjunct strain in cheese resulted in an increase in both the key-flavour production (Fig. 22.6(b)) and the intensity of the Proosdij cheese flavour (Fig. 22.6(a)).

22.8   Future trends

Knowledge of the amino-acid-converting enzymes is currently expanding rapidly. Whole genome sequences of various lactic acid bacteria are becoming available, e.g. *L. lactis* (Bolotin *et al.*, 2001) and *L. plantarum* (Kleerebezem *et al.*, 2003) genomes, which will expand our knowledge of flavour-forming pathways and mechanisms in different bacteria even faster. Combined with the understanding of the microbial physiology of flavour formation and the use of genomics tools, it will soon allow prediction of the flavour-forming capacity of various lactic acid bacteria. This will make the rational design of improved tailor-made industrial cultures with attractive flavour-forming properties possible and lead to the design of probes for high-throughput screening and strain selection in the future.

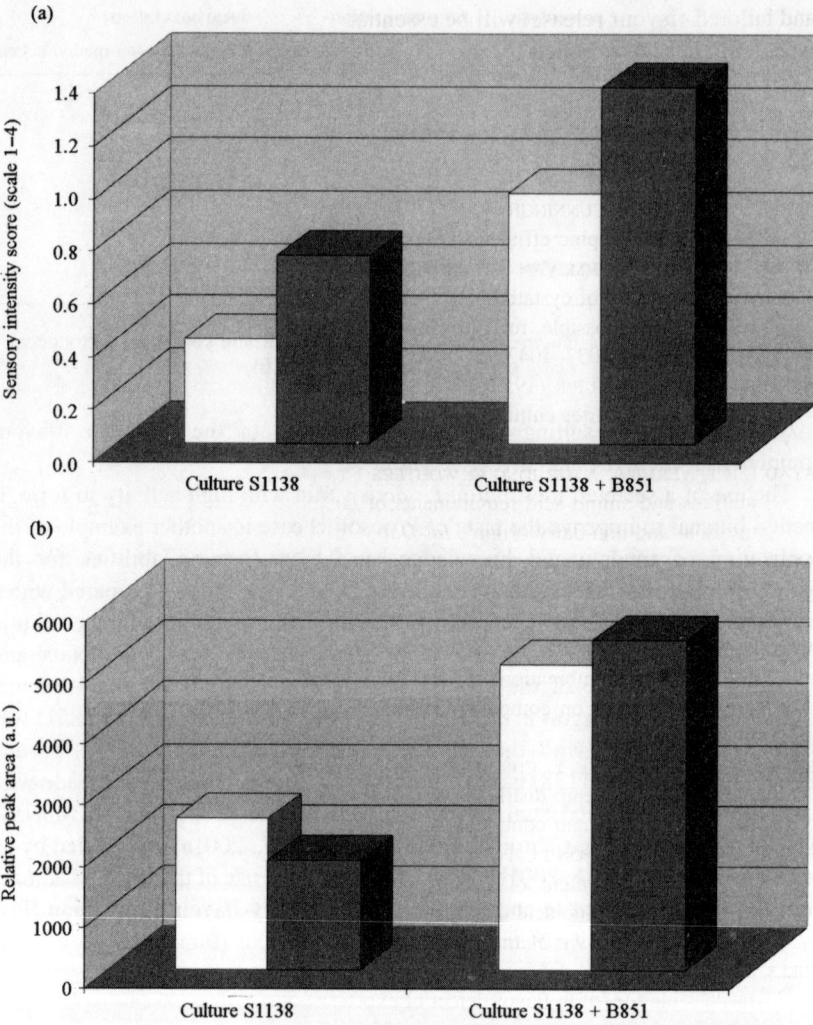

Fig. 22.6 Intensity of Proosdij cheese flavour (A) and relative amount of 3-methyl butanal (B) after 6 weeks' (open bars) and 3 months' (filled bars) ripening. Culture S1138: cheese made with starter Bos and adjunct culture S1138. Culture S1138: cheese made with starter Bos and adjunct culture S1138 and selected *L. lactis* strain B851.

New developments in the analysis of formation of flavours in fermented food products can be of great help for product development. By knowing the key flavours and their release patterns we can define more precisely the criteria for a successful product. An exciting perspective is the development of multifunctional starter cultures that combine excellent flavour-forming characteristics with a health-promoting effect such as the production of vitamins (Smid *et al.*, 2001). A multidisciplinary approach including key flavour component analysis, directed screening for flavour-producing starter organisms, and tailored-flavour release, will be essential to accelerate development of these types of enhanced products.

22.9   References

ACREE T E, BARNARD J, CUNNINGHAM D G (1984), 'A procedure for the sensory analysis of gas chromatographic effluents', *Food Chem,* 14, 273–286.

ALTING A C, ENGELS W J M, VAN SCHALKWIJK S, EXTERKATE F A (1995), 'Purification and characterization of cystathionine β-lyase from *Lactococcus lactis* subsp. *cremoris* B78 and its possible role in flavour development in cheese', *App Environ Microbiol,* 61, 4037–4042.

ANDERSEN A W, ELLIKER P R (1953), 'The nutritional requirements of lactic streptococci isolated from starter cultures. I. Growth in a synthetic medium', *J Dairy Sci,* 36, 161–167.

AYAD E H E, VERHEUL A, DE JONG C, WOUTERS J T M, SMIT G (1999), 'Flavour forming abilities and amino acid requirements of *Lactococcus lactis* strains isolated from artisanal and non-dairy origin', *Int Dairy J,* 9, 725–735.

AYAD E H E, VERHEUL A, WOUTERS J T M, SMIT G (2001a), 'Population dynamics of lactococci from industrial, artisanal and non-dairy origins in defined strain starters for Gouda-type cheese', *Int Dairy J,* 11, 51–61.

AYAD E H E, VERHEUL A, ENGELS W J M, WOUTERS J T M, SMIT G (2001b), 'Enhanced flavour formation by combination of selected lactococci from industrial and artisanal origin with focus on completion of a metabolic pathway', *J Appl Microbiol,* 90, 59–67.

BANKS J M, BRECHANY E Y, CHRISTIE W W, HUNTER E A, MUIR D D (1992), 'Volatile components in steam distillates of Cheddar cheese as indicator indices of cheese maturity, flavour and odour', *Food Res Int,* 25, 365–373.

BANKS J M, YVON M, GRIPON J C, FUENTE M A D L, BRECHANY E Y, WILLIAMS A G, MUIR D D (2001), 'Enhancement of amino acid catabolism in cheddar cheese using α-ketoglutarate, amino acid degradation in relation to volatile compounds and other aroma character', *Int Dairy J,* 11, 235–243.

BILLS D D, MORGAN M E, LIBBEY L M, DAY E A (1965), 'Identification of compounds responsible for fruity flavor defect of experimental Cheddar cheeses', *J Dairy Sci,* 48, 1168–1173.

BOCKELMANN W (2002), 'Development of defined surface starter cultures for the ripening of smear cheeses', *Int Dairy J,* 12, 133–140.

BOLOTIN A, WINCKER P, MAUGER S, JAILLON O, MALARME K, WEISSENBACH J, EHRLICH S D, SOROKIN A (2001), 'The complete genome sequence of the lactic acid bacterium *Lactococcus lactis* ssp. *lactis* IL1403', *Genome Res,* 11, 731–753.

BOSSET J O, GAUCH R (1993), 'Comparison of the volatile flavour compounds of six European "AOC" cheeses by using a new dynamic headspace GC-MS method', *Int Dairy J,* 3, 359–377.

BOSSET J O, COLLOMB M, SIEBER R (1993),'The aroma composition of Swiss Gruyère cheese. IV. The acidic volatile components and their changes in content during ripening', *Lebensm Wiss u-Technol,* 26, 581–592.

BRUINENBERG P G, DE ROO G, LIMSOWTIN G K Y (1997), 'Purification and characterization of cystathionine γ-lyase from *Lactococcus lactis* subsp. *cremoris* SK11: possible role in flavour compound formation during cheese maturation', *Appl Environ Microbiol*, 63, 561–566.

CHOPIN A (1993), 'Organization and regulation of genes from amino acid biosynthesis in lactic acid bacteria', *FEMS Microbiol Rev*, 12, 21–38.

CHRISTENSEN J E, DUDLEY E G, PEDERSON J A, STEELE J L (1999), 'Peptidases and amino acid catabolism in lactic acid bacteria', *Antonie van Leeuwenhoek*, 76, 217–246.

CUNIN R, GLANSDORFF N, PIÉRARD A, STALON V (1986), 'Biosynthesis and metabolism of arginine in bacteria', *Microbiol Rev*, 50, 314–352.

DELORME C, GODON J J, EHRLICH S D, RENAULT P (1993), 'Gene inactivation in *Lactococcuss lacis*: histidine biosynthesis', *J Bacteriol*, 175, 4391–4399.

DETMERS F J M, KUNJI E R S, LANFERMEIJER F C, POOLMAN B, KONINGS W N (1998), 'Kinetics and specificity of peptide uptake by the oligopeptide transport system of *Lactococcus lactis*', *Biochem*, 37, 16671–16679.

DIAS B, WEIMER B (1998a), 'Conversion of methionine to thiols by lactococci, lactobacilli, and brevibacteria', *Appl Environ Microbiol*, 64, 3320–3326.

DIAS B, WEIMER B (1998b), 'Purification and characterization of L-methionine γ-lyase from *Brevibacterium linens* BL2', *Appl Environ Microbiol*, 64, 3327–3331.

DUMONT J P, ROGER S, ADDA J (1974), 'Etude des composé volatils neutres présents dans les fromages à pâte molle et croûte lavée', *Lait*, 54, 31–43.

DUNN H C, LINDSAY R C (1985) 'Evaluation of the role of microbial strecker-derived aroma compounds in unclean-type flavors of Cheddar cheese', *J Dairy Sci*, 68, 2859–2874.

ENGELS W J M (1997), 'Volatile and non-volatile compounds in ripened cheese: Their formation and contribution to flavour', Ph.D. thesis, Wageningen, The Netherlands, Wageningen Agricultural University.

ENGELS W J M, VISSER S (1994), 'Isolation and comparative characterization of components that contribute to the flavour of different types of cheese', *Neth Milk Dairy J*, 48, 127–140.

ENGELS W J M, VISSER S (1996), 'Development of cheese flavour from peptides and amino acids by cell-free extracts of *Lactococcus lactis* subsp. *cremoris* B78 and its possible role in flavour development in cheese', *Neth Milk Dairy J*, 50, 3–17.

ENGELS W J M, DEKKER R, DE JONG C, NEETER R, VISSER S (1997), 'A comparative study of volatile compounds in the water-soluble fraction of various types of ripened cheese', *Int Dairy J*, 7, 255–263.

ENGELS W J M, ALTING A C, ARNTZ M M T G, GRUPPEN J, VORAGEN A G J, SMIT G, VISSER S (2000), 'Partial purification and characterization of two aminotransferases from *Lactococcus lactis* subsp. *cremoris* B78 involved in catabolism of methionine and branched-chain amino acids', *Int Dairy J*, 10, 443–452.

ENGELS W J M, BOELRIJK A, VAN HYLCKAMA VLIEG J E T, SMIT G (2001), 'New developments in flavour research for innovations in fermented food production', *Innov Food Technol*, 11, 62–65.

EXTERKATE F A, ALTING A C, BRUINENBERG P G (1993), 'Diversity of cell envelope proteinase specificity among strains of *Lactococcus lactis* and its relationship to charge characteristics of the substrate binding region', *Appl Environ Microbiol*, 59, 3640–3647.

FERNÁNDEZ M, VAN DOESBURG W, RUTTEN G A, MARUGG J D, ALTING A C, VAN KRANENBURG R, KUIPERS O P (2000), 'Molecular and functional analyses of the *metC* gene of *Lactococcus lactis*, encoding cystathionine β-lyase', *Appl Environ Microbiol*, 66, 42–48.

FERNÁNDEZ M, KLEEREBEZEM M, KUIPERS O P, SIEZEN R J, VAN KRANENBURG R (2002), 'Regulation of the *metCcysK* operon involved in sulfur metabolism in *Lactococcus lactis*', *J Bacteriol*, 184, 82–90.

GALLOIS A, LANGLOIS D (1990), 'New results in the volatile odorous compounds of French cheeses', *Lait*, 70, 89–106.

GAO S, STEELE J L (1998), 'Purification and characterization of oligomeric species of an aromatic amino acid aminotransferase from *Lactococcus lactis* subsp. *lactis* S3', *J Food Biochem*, 22, 197–211.

GAO S, OH D H, BROADBENT J R, JOHNSON M E, WEIMER B C, STEELE J L (1997), 'Aromatic amino acid catabolism by lactococci', *Lait*, 77, 371–381.

GAO S, MOOBERRY E S, STEELE J L (1998), 'Use of 13C nuclear magnetic resonance and gas chromatography to examine methionine catabolism by lactococci', *Appl Environ Microbiol*, 64, 4670–4675.

GODON J J, DELORME C, BARDOWSKI J, CHOPIN M C, EHRLICH S D, RENAULT P (1993), 'Gene inactivation in *Lactococcus lactis*: branched-chain amino acid biosynthesis', *J Bacteriol*, 175, 4383–4390.

GRIPON J C (1987), 'Mould-ripened cheeses', in Fox P F, *Cheese: Chemistry, Physics and Microbiology*, vol 1, London, Elsevier Applied Science Publishers, 121–149.

GUMMALLA S, BROADBENT J R (1999), 'Tryptophan catabolism by *Lactobacillus casei* and *Lactobacillus helveticus* cheese flavor adjuncts', *J Dairy Sci*, 82, 2070–2077.

JENSEN P R, HAMMER K (1993), 'Minimal requirements for exponential growth of *Lactococcus lactis*', *Appl Environ Microbiol*, 59, 4363–4366.

KLEEREBEZEM M, BOEKHORST J, VAN KRANENBURG R, MOLENAAR D, KUIPERS O P, LEER R, TARCHINI R, PETERS S A, SANDBRINK H M, FIERS M W E J, STIEKEMA W, KLEIN LANKHORST R M, BRON P A, HOFFER S M, NIEROP GROOT M N, KERKHOVEN R, DE VRIES M, URSING B, DE VOS W M, SIEZEN R J (2003), 'Complete genome sequence of *Lactobacillus plantarum* WCFS1', *Proc Natl Acad Sci USA*, in press.

KONINGS W N, POOLMAN B, DRIESSEN A J M (1989), 'Bioenergetics and solute transport in lactococci', *CRC Crit Rev Microbiol*, 16, 419–476.

KONINGS W N, LOLKEMA J S AND POOLMAN B (1995), 'The generation of metabolic energy by solute transport', *Arch Microbiol*, 164, 235–242.

KOSIKOWSKI F V, MISTRY V V (1997), 'History and origins', in Kosikowski F V, *Cheese and Fermented Milk Foods, Vol. 1, Origins and Principles*, Westport, CT, Kosikowski LLC, 1–17.

KUBICKOVA J AND GROSCH W (1997), 'Evaluation of potent odorants of Camembert cheese by dilution and concentration techniques', *Int Dairy J*, 7, 65–70.

KUNJI E R S, MIERAU I, HAGTING A, POOLMAN B, KONINGS W N (1996) 'The proteolytic systems of lactic acid bacteria', *Antonie van Leeuwenhoek*, 70, 187–221.

LEE C-W, DESMAZEAUD M J (1985), 'Utilization of aromatic amino acids as nitrogen sources in *Brevibacterium linens*: an inducible aromatic amino acid aminotransferase', *Arch Microbiol*, 140, 331–337.

LEES G J, JAGO G R (1976), 'Formation of acetaldehyde from threonine by lactic acid bacteria', *J Dairy Res*, 43, 75–83.

MANNING D J (1974), 'Sulphur compounds in relation to Cheddar cheese flavour', *J Dairy Res*, 41, 81–87.

MARSHALL V M, COLE W M (1983), 'Threonine aldolase and alcohol dehydrogenase activities in *Lactobacillus bulgaricus* and *Lactobacillus acidophilus* and their contribution to flavour production in fermented milks', *J Dairy Res*, 50, 375–379.

MILO C, REINECCIUS G A (1997), 'Identification and quantification of potent odorants in regular-fat and low-fat mild Cheddar cheese', *J Agric Food Chem*, 45, 3590–3594.

MOIO L, DEKIMPE J, ÉTIÉVANT P X, ADDEO F (1993), 'Volatile flavour compounds of water buffalo Mozzarella cheese', *Ital J Food Sci*, 5, 57–68.

MOLIMARD P, SPINNLER H E (1996), 'Compounds involved in the flavour of surface mold-ripened cheeses: origins and properties', *J Dairy Sci*, 79, 169–184.

NEETER R, DE JONG C, TEISMAN H G J, ELLEN G (1996), 'Determination of volatile compounds in cheese using dynamic headspace techniques', in Taylor A J, Mottram D S, *Flavour Science: Recent Developments*, London, Royal Society of Chemistry, Burlington House, 293–296.

NIEROP GROOT M N, DE BONT J A (1999), 'Involvement of manganese in conversion of phenylalanine to benzaldehyde by lactic acid bacteria', *Appl Environ Microbiol*, 65, 5590–5593.

OTT A, HUGI A, BAUMGARTNER M, CHAINTREAU A (2000), 'Sensory investigation of yogurt flavor perception: mutual influence of volatiles and acidity', *J Agric Food Chem*, 48, 441–450.

REITER B, ORAM J D (1962), 'Nutritional studies on cheese starters. I. Vitamin and amino acid requirements of single starter strains', *J Dairy Res*, 29, 63–77.

RIJNEN L, BONNEAU S, YVON M (1999), 'Genetic characterization of the major lactococcal aromatic aminotransferase and its involvement in conversion of amino acids to aroma compounds', *Appl Environ Microbiol*, 65, 4873–4880.

RIJNEN L, COURTIN P, GRIPON J C, YVON M (2000), 'Expression of a heterologous glutamate dehydrogenase gene in *Lactococcus lactis* highly improves the conversion of amino acids to aroma compounds', *Appl Environ Microbiol*, 66, 1354–1359.

ROGER S, DEGAS C, GRIPON J C (1988), 'Production of phenyl ethyl alcohol and its esters during ripening of traditional Camembert', *Food Chem*, 28, 1–12.

SMACCHI E, GOBBETTI M (1998), 'Purification and characterization of cystathionine γ-lyase from *Lactobacillus fermentum* DT41', *FEMS Microbiol Lett*, 166, 197–202.

SMID E J, STARRENBURG M J C, MIERAU I, SYBESMA W, HUGEHOLZ J (2001), 'Increase of folate levels in fermented foods', *Innov Food Technol*, 10, 13–15.

SMIT B A, ENGELS W J M, WOUTERS J T M, SMIT G (2002), 'Diversity of L-leucine catabolism in various micro-organisms involved in cheese-ripening and identification of the bottleneck in 3-methylbutanal formation', submitted for publication.

SMIT G, KRUYSWIJK Z, WEERKAMP A H, DE JONG C, NEETER R (1996), 'Screening for and control of debittering properties of cheese cultures', in Taylor A J, Mottram D S, *Flavour Science: Recent Developments*, London, Royal Society of Chemistry, Burlington House, 25–31.

SMIT G, KRUYSWIJK Z, VAN BOVEN A (1998), 'Control of debittering activity of cheese starters', *Austr J Dairy Technol*, 53, 113.

SMIT G, VAN HYLCKAMA VLIEG J E T, SMIT B A, AYAD E H E, ENGELS W J M (2002), 'Fermentative formation of flavour compounds by lactic acid bacteria', *Austr J Dairy Technol*, 57, 61–68.

STADHOUDERS J, HUP G, EXTERKATE F A, VISSER S (1983), 'Bitter formation in cheese. 1. Mechanism of the formation of the bitter flavour defect in cheese', *Neth Milk Dairy J*, 37, 157–167.

TAMMAM J D, WILLIAMS A G, NOBLE J, LLOYD D (2000), 'Amino acid fermentation in non-starter *Lactobacillus* spp. isolated from Cheddar cheese', *Lett Appl Microbiol*, 30, 370–374.

TAYLOR A J, LINFORTH R S T, HARVEY B A, BLAKE A (2000), 'Atmospheric pressure chemical ionisation mass spectrometry for in vivo analysis of volatile flavour release', *Food*

Chem, 71, 327–338.

THIERRY A, MAILLARD M B, (2002), 'Production of cheese flavour compounds derived from amino acid catabolism by *Propionibacterium freudenreichii*', *Lait*, 82, 17–32.

URBACH G (1995), 'Contribution of lactic acid bacteria to flavour compound formation in dairy products', *Int Dairy J*, 5, 877–903.

VAN KRANENBURG R, KLEEREBEZEM M, VAN HYLCKAMA VLIEG J E T, URSING B M, BOEKHORST J, SMIT B A, AYAD E H E, SMIT G, SIEZEN R J (2002), 'Flavour formation from amino acids: predictions from genome sequence analysis', *Int Dairy J*, 12, 111–121.

VISSER S (1993), 'Proteolytic enzymes and their relation to cheese ripening and flavor: an overview', *J Dairy Sci*, 76, 329–350.

VISSER S, SLANGEN C J, HUP G, STADHOUDERS J (1983), 'Bitter flavour in cheese. 3. Comparative gel-chromatographic analysis of hydrophobic peptide fractions from twelve Gouda-type cheeses and identification of bitter peptides isolated from a cheese made with *Streptococcus cremoris* HP', *Neth Milk Dairy J*, 37, 181–192.

VOIGHT M N, EITENMILLER R R (1978), 'Role of histidine and tyrosine decarboxylases and mono- and diamine oxidases in amine build-up in cheese', *J Food Prot*, 41, 182–186.

WEIMER B, SEEFELDT K, DIAS B (1999), 'Sulfur metabolism in bacteria associated with cheese', *Antonie van Leeuwenhoek*, 76, 247–261.

WOOD A F, ASTON J W, DOUGLAS G K (1994), 'A cold-trap method for the collection and determination of headspace compounds from cheese', *Austr J Dairy Technol*, 49, 42–47.

YANG W T, MIN D B (1994), 'Dynamic headspace analyses of volatile compounds of Cheddar and Swiss cheese during ripening', *J Food Sci*, 59, 1309–1312.

YVON M, RIJNEN L (2001), 'Cheese flavour formation by amino acid catabolism', *Int Dairy J*, 11, 185–201.

YVON M, THIROUIN S, RIJNEN L, FROMENTIER D, GRIPON J C (1997), 'An aminotransferase from *Lactococcus lactis* initiates conversion of amino acids to cheese flavour compounds', *Appl Environ Microbiol*, 63, 414–419.

YVON M, BERTHELOT S, GRIPON J C (1998), 'Adding α-ketoglutarate to semi-hard cheese curd highly enhances the conversion of amino acids to aroma compounds', *Int Dairy J*, 8, 889–898.

YVON M, CHAMBELLON E, BOLOTIN A, ROUDOT-ALGARON F (2000), 'Characterization and role of the branched-chain aminotransferase (BcaT) isolated from *Lactococcus lactis* subsp. *cremoris* NCDO 763', *Appl Environ Microbiol*, 66, 571–577.

ZOON P, ALLERSMA D (1996), 'Eye and crack formation in cheese by carbon dioxide from decarboxylation of glutamic acid', *Neth Milk Dairy J*, 50, 309–318.

Part IV

Appendix

23

Improving the nutritional quality of milk

D. I. Givens and K. J. Shingfield, The University of Reading, UK

23.1 Introduction

Milk is a food of outstanding interest, not least because it was designed to be a complete food for young growing animals. The role of bovine milk in the human diet as a source of fat, amino acids and other nutrients, including calcium, has been recognised for centuries. Milk is a complex colloid consisting of globules of milk fat suspended in an aqueous solution comprised of lactose, proteins (primarily caseins), mineral salts and water-soluble vitamins. Typical milk from Holstein/ Friesians contains about 40, 36 and 45 g/kg of fat, protein and lactose respectively, with an energy content of 2.8 MJ/kg. However, these values vary considerably between different breeds and in response to variations in nutrient supply.

Milk proteins are of high nutritional quality with a biological value and net protein utilisation approaching 100%. As a result, recent research has been directed towards maintaining or enhancing milk protein content and examining factors that control the secretion of casein proteins that are of particular importance with respect to cheese making. In addition, there has been considerable interest in the relationship between milk fat consumption and human health.

There is now a general consensus that the consumption of foods rich in saturated fatty acids (SFA) is associated with an increased risk of cardiovascular disease and the development of insulin resistance and dyslipidaemia (Vessby *et al.*, 2001). Higher intakes of *trans* fatty acids are also thought to be associated with increased cardiovascular risk (Willet *et al.*, 1993), whilst more recent studies have clearly demonstrated the important and positive role of *cis*-monounsaturates (*cis*-MUFA) and long chain n-3 polyunsaturates (n-3 PUFA) in the human diet.

Notably, a recent comprehensive study across 14 Western European countries (Hulsof *et al.*, 1999) identified that milk and dairy products contribute up to 40, 58 and 72% of total fat, SFA and *trans* fatty acid intake, although these values vary considerably between individual countries. However, it is important to recognise that the functionality of *trans* fatty acids from milk and dairy products remains unclear, and it is possible that some may be beneficial. In view of the potential benefits, there has been intense interest in manipulating milk fatty acid composition with the overall aim of improving the long-term health of the population. One of the major strategies has been to simultaneously reduce the proportion of $C_{12:0}$ to $C_{16:0}$ and increase those of MUFA and n-3 PUFA.

Lactose is a disaccharide normally readily digestible, but some individuals lose the ability to produce intestinal lactase as children or later in life and develop lactose intolerance, a condition that causes bloat, pain and diarrhoea. The incidence of lactose intolerance is particularly high in non-white races. Manipulation of milk lactose content is extremely limited and is therefore not considered in more detail.

Milk composition can be manipulated by nutritional means or utilising natural genetic variation. Genetic improvement can be attained through exploitation of between- (cross-breeding) or within- (selection) breed variation, while recent advances in genetic engineering offer the promise of changes not previously possible using traditional nutritional and genetic approaches (Karatzas and Turner, 1997). Nutrition can be used to manipulate milk fat content and composition, but concentrations of protein are much less responsive (Sutton, 1989), and therefore genetic selection represents a more effective long-term strategy for enhancing milk protein content.

23.2   Factors affecting milk protein content

Protein is the most valuable milk constituent and is influenced by nutritional, physiological and genetic factors (Erasmus *et al.*, 2001). Milk protein constitutes about 95% of total milk nitrogen, and is comprised of caseins (α, β, κ and γ), whey proteins (β-lactoglobulin and α-lactalbumin), serum albumin and immunoglobulins. Even though whey proteins are of high nutritional value, only the casein fraction is important to cheese makers. Casein accounts for between 76 and 86% of total milk protein (DePeters and Cant, 1992) and is essentially independent of nutrition and stage of lactation (Coulon *et al.*, 1998). Non-protein nitrogen fractions (urea, peptides, amino acids, creatinine and purine metabolites) appear in milk as a result of diffusion from the peripheral circulation, while milk proteins, other than serum albumin and immuno-globulins, are synthesised in mammary epithelial cells from amino acid precursors.

Milk protein content is dependent on both breed and stage of lactation, as well as nutrition. Breeds that produce milk with a high fat content also have higher protein concentrations, but the ratio of protein to fat is lower for Channel

Island breeds compared with the Ayrshire, Holstein or Friesian. In addition to changes during lactation, milk protein content is also affected by parity and progressively decreases in animals above three years old, such that across five successive lactations a 4% reduction can be expected (Erasmus *et al.*, 2001). Changes in protein content across lactations are also associated with a decline in the proportion of casein in total milk protein, but there is little consensus on the extent of decrease that can be expected.

23.2.1   Effects of energy intake

Nutrition also affects milk protein content. It is well established that energy intake is the most important dietary attribute influencing milk protein content. Across a wide range of diets, an increase in one MJ of metabolisable energy (ME) intake has been estimated to stimulate 0.2–0.3% increases in milk protein content (Spörndly, 1989). Coulon and Remond (1991) estimated that in early and mid-lactation cows an additional MJ of ME intake could be expected to result in respective 0.04 and 0.08 g/kg increases in milk protein content. However, these changes do not appear to be accompanied by improvements in the proportion of casein in total milk protein (Coulon *et al.*, 1998).

While the relationship between energy intake and milk protein synthesis is widely accepted, it is clear that this holds true only when increases in energy are derived from carbohydrates and protein. Feeding fat supplements generally results in a 1–4 g/kg depression in milk protein content (Spörndly, 1989; Sutton, 1989; DePeters and Cant, 1992). In practice, increases in energy intake can be achieved with concentrate supplements or replacing grass silage with forages of higher intake potential and/or energy content. Increases in concentrate supplementation generally increase milk protein content but responses are unpredictable and vary between -0.06 to 0.82 g/kg per kg concentrate DM intake (Shingfield, unpublished data).

23.2.2   Effects of type of forage

The intake and milk production potential of maize silage is higher than grass silage (e.g. Fitzgerald and Murphy, 1999). Replacing grass with maize silage consistently increases milk protein content, even when maize silage contains relatively low amounts of starch (Phipps *et al.*, 2000). It is a popular perception that these improvements are related to higher intakes of energy and the amount of starch available for absorption from the small intestine but this explanation ignores the changes in rumen fermentation and post-absorptive metabolic and endocrine status (Reynolds *et al.*, 1997). Furthermore, post-ruminal infusions of maize or wheat starch have not stimulated appreciable increases in milk protein content (Reynolds *et al.*, 2001). Feeding maize silage would be expected to increase the amount of amino acids available for absorption, since microbial protein synthesis is essentially a function of organic matter intake (Shingfield, 2000) and is energetically more efficient for maize than grass silage based diets

(Givens and Rulquin, 2002), and ruminal propionate production is also enhanced (Fitzgerald and Murphy, 1999). It appears that at least part of the increase in milk protein content associated with feeding maize silage may be explained by improvements in amino acid and gluconeogenic precursor supply.

23.2.3   Amino acid supply

Numerous studies have shown that arterial essential amino acid concentrations and milk protein synthesis increase in response to abomasal infusions of casein (e.g. Hanigan et al., 2001) leading to the general conclusion that the amino acid composition of protein entering the duodenum is the single most important nutritional factor influencing milk protein content (Erasmus et al., 2001). Enhancing arterial amino acid concentrations underpins nutritional strategies for enhancing milk protein content by promoting increases in amino acid availability to the mammary gland and/or improving the supply of essential amino acid that limits milk protein synthesis. As a result there has been considerable interest in replacing protein supplements of relatively high degradability with less degradable sources to increase the flow of amino acids entering the duodenum. Often, the improvements in milk protein yield are realised through increases in milk yield, rather than milk protein content.

Research has been directed towards determining the relative deficiencies of individual amino acids in order to identify the most appropriate protein supplements for various diets. Post-ruminal infusions have implicated lysine and methionine as first and second limiting for milk and milk protein synthesis in most diets. In cases where maize and maize by-products provide the majority of rumen undegraded protein, lysine appears to be first limiting, but for maize based diets supplemented with animal or vegetable proteins, methionine is thought to be first limiting (Polan et al., 1991, Schwab et al., 1992). For grass silage based diets histidine (Kim et al., 1999; Vanhatalo et al., 1999), rather than leucine (Huhtanen et al., 2002), methionine or lysine (Varvikko et al., 1999) appears first limiting. Even when post-ruminal infusions of single amino acids have stimulated increases in milk protein, responses are generally confined to an increase in yield rather than concentration.

23.3   Factors affecting milk fat content

In contrast to milk protein, nutrition can be used to effect substantial changes in milk fat content and milk fatty acid composition.

23.3.1   Milk fat synthesis

Milk fat is comprised of a complex mixture of lipids, most of which are present as triacylglycerides (about 98%), in addition to small amounts of di- and monoacylglycerides, phospholipids, cholesterol and non-esterified fatty acids

(Christie, 1995). Fatty acids secreted in milk originate from two sources, direct incorporation from the peripheral circulation and *de novo* synthesis in the mammary gland. *De novo* synthesis accounts for all $C_{4:0}$ to $C_{12:0}$, most of the $C_{14:0}$ and about half of $C_{16:0}$ secreted in milk, while all C_{18} and longer chained fatty acids are derived entirely from circulating blood lipids (Hawke and Taylor, 1995). A distinctive feature of the bovine mammary gland is the ability to release fatty acids from the synthetase complex at various stages, resulting in the secretion of a wide range of short and medium chain fatty acids.

Due to extensive metabolism of dietary unsaturated fatty acids in the rumen, $C_{18:0}$ is, under normal conditions, the predominant long chain fatty acid available for absorption. However, *cis*-9 $C_{18:1}$ output in milk exceeds uptake due to the activity of stearoyl Co A (Δ-9) desaturase in mammary secretory cells (Kinsella, 1972). The introduction of the *cis*-9 double bond is thought to occur as a means of ensuring milk fluidity necessary for efficient ejection from the mammary gland (Grummer, 1991). Conversion of $C_{18:0}$ to *cis*-9 $C_{18:1}$ is the predominant precursor:product of the Δ-9 desaturase, and about 40% of $C_{18:0}$ taken up by the gland is desaturated (Chilliard *et al.*, 2000). In addition to $C_{18:0}$, both $C_{14:0}$ and $C_{16:0}$ are also converted, whilst more recent studies have shown that *trans*-11 $C_{18:1}$ (Griinari *et al.*, 2000) and *trans*-7 $C_{18:1}$ (Corl *et al.*, 2002; Piperova *et al.*, 2002) are desaturated to *cis*-9, *trans*-11 $C_{18:2}$ and *trans*-7, *cis*-9 $C_{18:2}$, respectively.

23.3.2   Lipid metabolism in the rumen

It is well established that ruminant lipids contain much higher levels of SFA relative to ingested dietary lipids as a result of extensive biohydrogenation in the rumen. Data from both *in vitro* and *in vivo* studies have allowed the major biohydrogenation pathways to be elucidated (Harfoot and Hazlewood, 1988; Fig. 23.1). Metabolism of $C_{18:3}$ (n-3) proceeds via isomerisation to a $C_{18:3}$ conjugate (*cis*-9, *trans*-11, *cis*-15), followed by sequential reduction of double bonds to *trans*-11, *cis*-15 $C_{18:2}$, *trans*-11 $C_{18:1}$ (trans vaccenic acid, TVA) and $C_{18:0}$. Biohydrogenation of $C_{18:2}$ (n-6) involves an initial isomerisation to *cis*-9, *trans*-11 $C_{18:2}$ (conjugated linoleic acid, CLA) and successive reduction to form *trans*-11 $C_{18:1}$ and $C_{18:0}$. The final reduction is considered to be rate limiting, such that *trans* $C_{18:1}$ can accumulate in the rumen (Griinari and Bauman, 1999). Bacteria that convert *trans* $C_{18:1}$ fatty acids to $C_{18:0}$ are also thought to metabolise $C_{18:1}$ (n-9). Biohydrogenation of unsaturated fatty acids is extensive, and under normal conditions about 80% (range 70–95) of $C_{18:2}$ (n-6) and 92% (range 85–100%) of $C_{18:3}$ (n-3) are metabolised in the rumen (Doreau and Ferlay, 1994).

23.3.3   Altering milk fat content

Breed has a marked effect on milk fat, and concentrations are between 19 and 30% higher for Jerseys than Holstein dairy cows (Drackley *et al.*, 2001; White *et al.*,

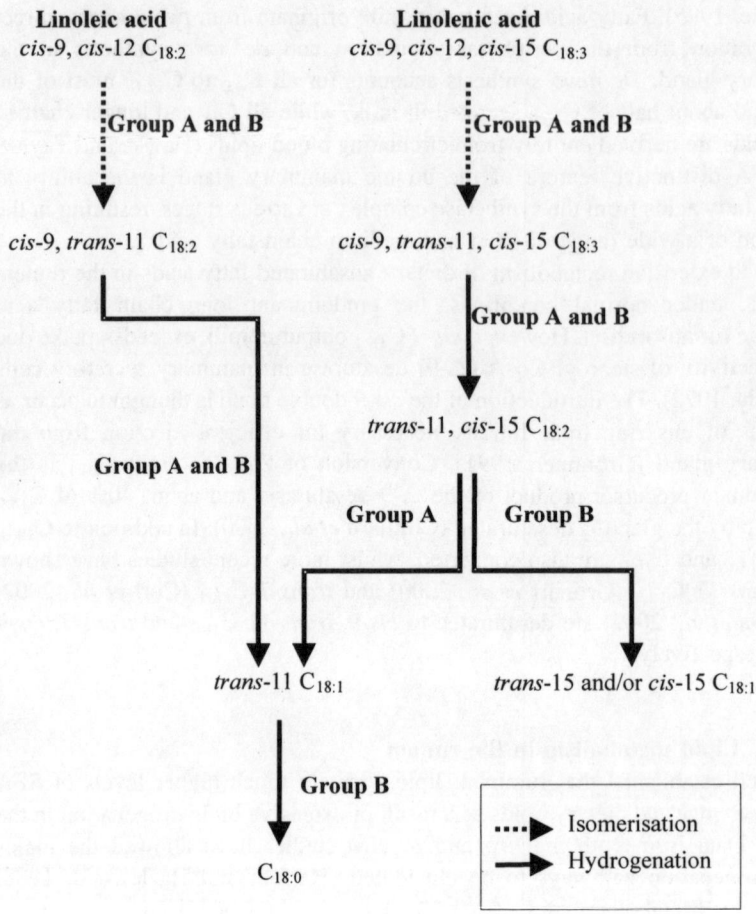

Note: Group A and B refer to different rumen bacteria capable of biohydrogenation characterised according to Kemp and Lander (1984).

Fig. 23.1 Major metabolic pathways of ruminal biohydrogenation of polyunsaturated fatty acids (adapted from Harfoot and Hazlewood, 1988).

2001). Milk fat content is also dependent on the stage of lactation, and changes in much the same manner as milk protein content. Nutrition represents the most effective means of manipulating milk fat content (e.g. Palmquist *et al.*, 1993). Under normal conditions, increases in concentrate supplements have little impact on milk fat content (Table 23.1), until the proportion of forage decreases to below 50% of dietary dry matter (Thomas and Martin, 1988) or concentrates contain relatively high levels of polyunsaturated fatty acids (Griinari *et al.*, 1998). Decreases in milk fat content typically occur within a few days after changes in the diet and can occur in the absence of alterations in the secretion of milk or other milk constituents. During milk fat depression, secretion of all fatty acids is reduced, the extent of which is greater for those synthesised *de novo* (Bauman and Griinari, 2001).

Table 23.1 Typical milk production responses to increases in concentrate supplementation

Basal forage	Range in supplement offered (kg/day)	Milk yield (kg/day)	Milk protein[a] content (g/kg)	output (g/day)	Milk fat content (g/kg)	output (g/day)	Reference
Grass silage	3–6	1.6	0.30	61.0	0.23	70.3	Sutton et al. (1994)
Grass silage	2–4	0.61	0.50	25.5	0.39	31.1	Agnew et al. (1996)
Grass silage	4–6	1.12	0.35	37.7	-0.71	29.4	
Grass silage	6–8	0.59	0.82	34.3	-1.00	0.63	
Grass silage	2–8	0.77	0.56	32.4	-0.42	20.6	
Grass silage	2–4	1.93	0.06	55.2	1.32	94.3	Keady and Murphy (1997)
Grass silage	4–6	1.11	0.58	38.2	0.46	46.8	
Grass silage	2–6	1.52	0.26	46.7	0.89	70.6	
Grass silage	4–6	0.82	0.12	29.4	0.06	35.3	Fitzgerald and Murphy (1999)
Grass silage	6–8	0.95	0.42	36.8	-0.53	21.1	
Grass silage	4–8	0.89	0.28	33.3	-0.25	27.8	
Maize silage	4–6	0.41	0.65	29.4	-0.24	17.7	Fitzgerald and Murphy (1999)
Maize silage	6–8	0.47	0.35	23.5	0.94	47.1	
Maize silage	4–8	0.44	0.50	26.5	0.35	32.4	

Mean response per kg concentrate DM intake[a]

[a] Responses calculated as the difference between treatment controls and supplemented diets and expressing the response on a kg concentrate DM intake basis.

Feeding high starch concentrate supplements are generally thought to be associated with milk fat depression (e.g. Keady *et al.*, 1999), but replacing starch with fibre has in some cases also decreased milk fat content (e.g. Huhtanen *et al.*, 1995). Even though the impact of changes in concentrate energy source on milk fat are often unpredictable, switching cereals for soluble carbohydrates, and replacing starch for digestible fibre has been suggested as an effective strategy for alleviating milk fat depression on low forage diets (Sutton, 1989).

Lipid supplements are generally used to increase dietary energy content, but have variable effects on milk fat content that are dependent on inclusion rate, degree of unsaturation and physical form (Sutton, 1989). Fish oil consistently depresses milk fat content, irrespective of the basal diet (Table 23.2). A number of theories have been proposed to explain dietary induced milk fat depression, that attribute the lowered milk fat secretion to (i) reductions in acetate and butyrate production in the rumen limiting mammary *de novo* fatty acid synthesis, (ii) increased production of propionate and glucose causing increased insulin secretion resulting in absorbed fatty acids being partitioned towards adipose at the expense of the mammary gland or (iii) direct inhibition by *trans* fatty acids produced during ruminal biohydrogenation of dietary unsaturated fatty acids. None of these theories offer a universal explanation for this phenomenon, but the *trans* fatty acid hypothesis is currently thought to be the most robust (Bauman and Griinari, 2001). Recent work has established that post-ruminal infusions of *trans*-10, *cis*-12 CLA, but not *cis*-9, *trans*-11 CLA, inhibit milk fat synthesis (Fig. 23.2), in a dose dependent manner (e.g. Baumgard *et al.*, 2000; Peterson *et al.*, 2002).

23.3.4   Altering milk fatty acid composition

In addition to the effects on milk fat content, milk fat concentrations of $C_{16:1}$, $C_{18:1}$ and CLA are higher, and that of $C_{6:0}$, $C_{8:0}$, $C_{10:0}$, $C_{12:0}$ and $C_{14:0}$ are lower for Holstein than Jersey dairy cows (White *et al.*, 2001). Higher levels of $C_{16:1}$, $C_{18:1}$ and CLA are consistent with the view that the activity of Δ^9-desaturase is higher in Holstein mammary tissue (Beaulieu and Palmquist, 1995), while the higher concentrations of short and medium chain fatty acids suggest a greater proportion of Jersey milk fat is synthesised *de novo*. Stage of lactation also affects the proportion of fatty acids derived from *de novo* synthesis with concentrations of short and medium chain fatty acids being lower in early lactation.

Use of dietary lipid supplements is the most common nutritional means for manipulating milk fatty acid composition. However, both the type and source of dietary fat affect the magnitude of changes that can be achieved (Table 23.3). Supplements of plant oils or oilseeds reduce short and medium chain but increase long-chain fatty acids in milk, resulting in an overall shift towards $C_{18:0}$ at the expense of $C_{16:0}$ (Mansbridge and Blake, 1997) due to decreased *de novo* synthesis and/or reduced mammary uptake of absorbed $C_{16:0}$. Reductions in milk unsaturated fatty acid content are characterised by small increases in the

Table 23.2 Typical milk production responses to dietary lipid supplements

Lipid	Basal forage	Inclusion (g/kg DM)	Milk yield (kg/day)	Milk protein content (g/kg)	Milk protein output (g/day)	Milk fat content (g/kg)	Milk fat output (g/day)	Reference
				Mean response[a]				
Fish oil	Grass silage	16	0.4	-3.0	-35	-10.9	-167	Offer et al. (1999)
Fish oil	Grass silage	31	3.2	-3.8	7	-15.0	-250	Keady et al. (2000)
Fish oil	Grass/maize silage	37	-4.5	-2.4	-198	-10.0	-358	Ahnadi et al. (2002)
Fish oil	Maize silage	17	1.5	-0.9	16	-13.3	-300	Chilliard and Doreau (1997)
Linseed oil	Grass silage	16	1.8	-1.1	41	-0.8	69	Offer et al. (1999)
Rapeseed oil	Maize silage	35	-1.9	-1.7	-112	0.0	-56	Jenkins (1998)
Rapeseed oil	Maize silage	33	0.8	-0.7	3	-2.8	-80	Loor et al. (2002)
Soyabean oil	Maize silage	35	0.4	-0.1	10	-6.7	-189	Jenkins et al. (1996)
Sunflower oil	Maize silage	37	-0.8	-1.2	-59	-3.0	-104	Kalscheur et al. (1997)
Tallow	Maize silage	40	-4.2	0.9	-101	-3.0	-253	Onetti et al. (2001)

[a] Responses calculated as the difference between treatment controls and lipid supplemented diets.

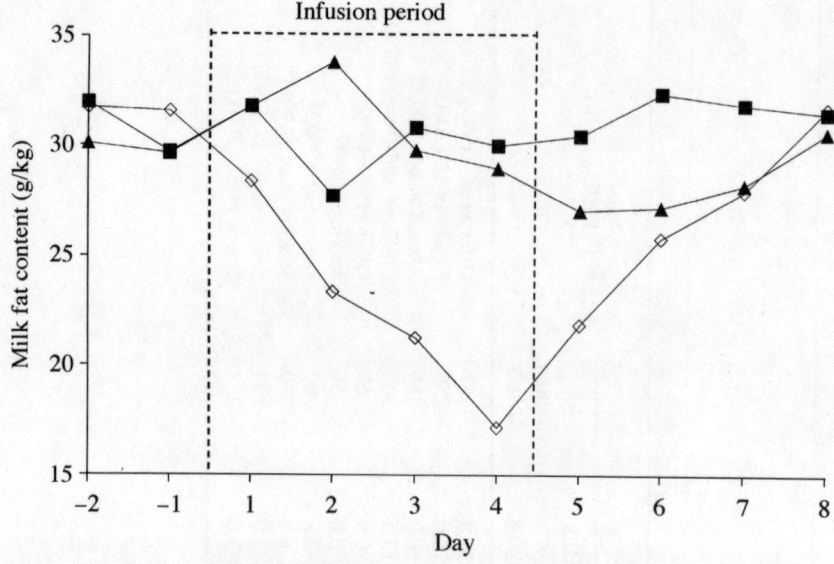

Fig. 23.2   Effect of abomasal infusions (10g/day) of control (), *cis*-9, *trans*-11 CLA (_) and *trans*-10, *cis*-12 CLA (—) on milk fat content (data derived from Baumgard *et al.*, 2000).

concentration of the predominant fatty acid in lipid supplements. In all cases, feeding plant oils increases milk fat $C_{18:0}$, *cis*-9 $C_{18:1}$ and *trans* $C_{18:1}$ content due to extensive ruminal metabolism of long chain fatty acids, leading to an increase in the supply of biohydrogenation intermediates and $C_{18:0}$ to the mammary gland.

It is notable that PUFA are not synthesised in any appreciable quantities in ruminant tissues and therefore concentrations in milk are primarily dependent on the amount leaving the rumen. As a result, oils rich in $C_{18:2}$ n-6 and $C_{18:3}$ n-3 have been used with the aim of increasing the concentrations of these PUFA in milk fat. In addition, much work has been carried out with the aim of increasing the concentrations of the long chain n-3 PUFA eicosapentaenoic (EPA, $C_{20:5}$ n-3) and docosahexaenoic (DHA, $C_{22:6}$ n-3) acids in milk. This has normally involved feeding fish oil supplements rich in EPA and DHA. However, the transfer efficiency into milk of EPA and DHA is low due to extensive biohydrogenation in the rumen and transportation in phospholipid and cholesterol ester fractions of plasma that are poorly utilised by the mammary gland (Rymer *et al.*, 2003).

A number of technologies have been developed to protect lipids from ruminal metabolism to reduce biohydrogenation and minimise the negative effects of dietary fat on animal performance. The approaches used include encapsulating oils and oilseeds within a formaldehyde casein complex, producing calcium salts of non-esterified fatty acids or generating fatty acyl amides. Even though these products are often only partially protected from ruminal metabolism, they are

Table 23.3 Typical milk fatty acid responses to dietary lipid supplements

Lipid	Mean response[a]										Reference
	$C_{14:0}$	$C_{16:0}$	$C_{18:0}$	cis-9 $C_{18:1}$	trans $C_{18:1}$	$C_{18:2}$	$C_{18:3}$	SAT	MUFA	PUFA	
Rapeseed oil	-0.03	-0.20	0.55	0.39	0.30	-0.09	0.11	-0.07	0.30	-0.04	DePeters et al. (2001)
Rapeseed oil	-0.19	-0.33	0.51	0.67	2.00	-0.04	0.60	-0.18	0.60	0.15	Loor et al. (2002)
Soyabean oil	-0.29	-0.28	0.45	0.23	4.61	0.33	–	-0.19	0.53	0.33	Jenkins et al. (1996)
Sunflower oil[b]	-0.32	-0.32	0.14	0.27	3.07	-0.05	-0.24	-0.22	0.53	0.12	Kalscheur et al. (1997)
Sunflower oil	-0.23	-0.26	0.15	0.11	2.79	0.07	-0.21	-0.17	0.36	0.21	Kalscheur et al. (1997)
Linseed oil	-0.11	-0.15	0.27	0.26	0.94	-0.14	0.17	-0.07	0.23	-0.06	Offer et al. (1999)
Fish oil	0.04	-0.01	-0.45	-0.25	8.08	0.24	0.03	-0.09	0.24	0.29	Offer et al. (1999)
Fish oil	0.30	0.35	-0.77	-0.73	2.19	0.39	0.07	-0.05	-0.10	2.17	Shingfield et al., in press
Tallow	–	0.06	0.04	0.22	0.19	-0.37	-0.37	-0.06	0.19	-0.36	Onetti et al. (2001)
Protected lipids											
Butylsoyamide[c]	-0.06	-0.05	0.04	-0.04	0.61	0.74	–	-0.04	0.01	0.74	Jenkins et al. (1996)
Canolamide[d]	-0.24	-0.33	0.76	0.74	0.93	0.04	0.40	-0.16	0.55	0.08	Loor et al. (2002)
Ca-salts of rapeseed oil	-0.24	-0.37	0.31	0.76	–	0.10	-0.20	-0.23	0.69	0.07	Chouinard et al. (1998)
Ca-salts of soyabean oil	-0.31	-0.37	0.35	0.73	–	0.23	-0.20	-0.23	0.63	0.19	Chouinard et al. (1998)
Ca-salts of linseed oil	-0.26	-0.37	0.34	0.54	–	0.36	0.40	-0.21	0.46	0.36	Chouinard et al. (1998)
Fish oil[e]	–	0.00	-0.36	-0.29	2.34	0.33	0.19	-0.10	0.19	0.45	Lacasse et al. (2002)
Soyabean/fish oil[f,g]	-0.04	-0.27	-0.73	-0.29	2.34	1.39	1.00	-0.29	0.14	1.78	Gulati et al. (2003)
Soyabean/fish oil fh	-0.03	-0.25	-0.79	-0.44	3.15	0.69	0.33	-0.31	0.18	1.45	Gulati et al. (2003)
Rapeseed/soyabean oil[f]	-0.26	-0.35	-0.13	0.51	-0.14	5.50	2.00	-0.25	0.44	4.21	Ashes et al. (2000)

[a] Responses calculated as proportionate differences between treatment controls and lipid supplemented diets.
[b] Sunflower oil rich in cis-9 $C_{18:1}$.
[c] Prepared by reacting soyabean oil with butylamine
[d] Prepared by reacting rapeseed oil with ethanolamide.
[e] Encapsulated fish oil in a glutaraldehyde-treated protein matrix.
[f] Lipids encapsulated in a matrix of rumen-inert protein.
[g] Fish oil rich in $C_{22:6}$ (n-3).
[h] Fish oil rich in $C_{20:5}$ (n-3).

more effective in changing milk fatty acid composition compared with parent oils (Table 23.3). The apparent transfer of $C_{18:2}$ n-6 and $C_{18:3}$ n-3 have been increased from less than 0.05 to 0.35 and 0.42, respectively, in response to formaldehyde protected lipids (Grummer, 1991), but these changes can be too extreme, and result in a dramatic increase in the incidence of spontaneous oxidation and off-flavours.

23.3.5   Conjugated linoleic acid

Conjugated linoleic acid (CLA) is a generic term used to describe a mixture of geometric and positional isomers of $C_{18:2}$ in which the double bonds are conjugated rather than methylene interrupted . There is now increasing evidence that CLA exhibits anti-carcinogenic properties and may also improve immune function (see review of Williams, 2000). Dairy products are the major source of CLA in the human diet, primarily as the c9, t11 isomer (Lawson *et al.*, 2001) that is also responsible for the anti-carcinogenic effects in animal models. In view of these benefits, there has been considerable interest in understanding the mechanism that controls CLA synthesis in the dairy cow, with the overall aim of producing CLA enriched milk.

CLA is formed as an intermediate of $C_{18:2}$, c9, c12 biohydrogenation in the rumen that is subsequently reduced to *trans*-11 $C_{18:1}$ (TVA), an intermediate also generated during the biohydrogenation of $C_{18:3}$ n-3 (Fig. 23.1) Since the final reduction of *trans* $C_{18:1}$ is normally the rate limiting step in the biohydrogenation of unsaturated C18 fatty acids, *trans* $C_{18:1}$ can accumulate and leave the rumen. The ratio of CLA to *trans* $C_{18:1}$ in rumen fluid of around 1:40 (Griinari and Bauman, 1999) is much higher than milk fat (1:3) leading to the suggestion that a large proportion of CLA secreted in milk is produced by the mammary gland. Furthermore, diets rich in C18:3 (n-3) but low in C18:2 (n-6) have substantially increased milk fat *cis*-9, *trans*-11 CLA concentrations, even though this isomer is not produced during ruminal metabolism of C18:3 (n-3). Further studies have established that *cis*-9, *trans*-11 CLA is formed from TVA via Δ-9 desaturase in the mammary gland (Griinari *et al.*, 2000) and endogenous conversion can account for up to 90% of the CLA in milk. Endogenous conversion also occurs in human tissues (Adlof *et al.*, 2000) and therefore the occurrence of TVA in milk fat may also be beneficial.

23.4   Future trends

The overall nutritional value of milk as a food is not in doubt but there are concerns regarding the intake of certain fatty acids derived from milk and dairy products. At the same time there is considerable interest in fatty acids and lipids unique to milk fat including CLA, branched chain fatty acids and sphingolipids that may afford very considerable benefits in disease prevention. These may well explain the positive effects of milk fat consumption in several long-term epidemiological studies. Both milk fat content and fatty acid composition can be modified by various means, nutritional being the most effective. Even in the absence of more definitive data, certain positive changes could be implemented at the present time. However, for this to happen there must be a market driver to provide producers a financial incentive to deliver modified milk. Major progress in this area is unlikely until the dairy industry embraces these potential opportunities.

23.5 References

ADLOF, R.O., DUVAL, S. and EMKEN, E.A. (2000) Biosynthesis of conjugated linoleic acid in humans. *Lipids* **35**: 131–135.

AGNEW, K.W., MAYNE, C.S. and DOHERTY, J.G. (1996) An examination of the effect of method and level of concentrate feeding on milk production in dairy cows offered a grass silage-based diet. *Animal Science* 1996 **63**: 21–31.

AHNADI, C.E., BESWICK, N., DELBECCHI, L., KENNELLY, J.J. and LACASSE, P. (2002) Addition of fish oil to diets for dairy cows. II. Effects on milk fat and gene expression of mammary lipogenic enzymes. *Journal of Dairy Research,* **69**: 521–531.

ASHES, J.R., GULATI, S.K., KITESSA, S.M., FLECK, E. and SCOTT, T.W. (2000) *Utilisation of rumen protected n-3 fatty acids by ruminants.* In: Recent Advances in Animal Nutrition (P. C. Garnsworthy and J. Wiseman, eds). Nottingham University Press, Nottingham, 2000. pp 129–140.

BAUMAN, D. E. and GRIINARI, J. M. (2001) Regulation and nutritional manipulation of milk fat: low-fat milk syndrome. *Livestock Production Science,* **70**: 15–29.

BAUMGARD, L. H., CORL, B. A., DWYER, D. A., SAEBO, A. and BAUMAN, D. E. 2000 Identification of the conjugated linoleic acid isomer that inhibits milk fat synthesis. *American Journal of Physiology,* **278**: R179–R184.

BEAULIEU, A. D. and PALMQUIST, D. L. (1995) Differential effects of high fat diets on fatty acid composition in milk of Jersey and Holstein cows. *Journal of Dairy Science.* **78**: 1336–1344.

CHILLIARD, Y. and DOREAU, M. (1997) Influence of supplementary fish oil and rumen-protected methionine on milk yield and composition in dairy cows. *Journal of Dairy Research* **64**: 173–179.

CHILLIARD, Y., FERLAY, A., MANSBRIDGE, R. M. and DOREAU, M. (2000) Ruminant milk fat plasticity: nutritional control of saturated, polyunsaturated, trans and conjugated fatty acids. *Annales de Zootechnie* **49**: 181–205.

CHOUINARD, P.Y., GIRARD, V. and BRISSON, G.J. (1998) Fatty acid profile and physical properties of milk fat from cows fed calcium salts of fatty acids with varying unsaturation. *Journal of Dairy Science* **81**: 471–481.

CHRISTIE, W. W. (1995) *Composition and structure of milk lipids.* In: Advanced Dairy Chemistry Volume 2: Lipids. (P. F. Fox, ed.). Chapman and Hall, London. pp. 1–36.

CORL, B. A., BAUMGARD, L. H., GRIINARI, J. M., DELMONTE, P., MOREHOUSE, K. M., YURAWECZC, M. P. and BAUMAN, D. E. (2002) *Trans-7, cis-9 CLA is synthesized endogenously by delta 9-desaturase in dairy cows. *Lipids* **37**: 681–688.

COULON, J. B. and REMOND, B. (1991) Variations in milk output and milk protein-content in response to the level of energy supply to the dairy-cow – a review. *Livestock*

Production Science **29**: 31–47.

COULON, J. B., HURTAUD, C., REMOND, B. and VÉRITÉ, R. (1998) Factors contributing to variation in the proportion of casein in cows' milk true protein: a review of recent INRA experiments. *Journal of Dairy Research* **65**: 375–387.

DEPETERS, E. J., GERMAN, J. B., TAYLOR, S.J., ESSEX, S.T. and PEREZ-MONTI, H. (2001) Fatty acid and triglyceride composition of milk fat from lactating Holstein cows in response to supplemental canola oil. *Journal of Dairy Science* **84**: 929–936.

DEPETERS, E. J. and CANT, J. P. (1992) Nutritional factors influencing the nitrogen composition of bovine milk: a review. *Journal of Dairy Science* **75**: 2043–2070.

DRACKLEY, J. K., BEAULIEU, A. D. and ELLIOTT, J. P. (2001) Responses of milk fat composition to dietary fat or nonstructural carbohydrates in Holstein and Jersey cows. *Journal of Dairy Science* **84**: 1231–1237.

ERASMUS, L. J., HERMANSEN, J. E. and RULQUIN, H. (2001) Nutritional and management factors affecting milk protein content and composition. *International Dairy Federation Bulletin* **366**: 49–61.

FITZGERALD, J.J. and MURPHY, J.J. (1999) A comparison of low starch maize silage and grass silage and the effect of concentrate supplementation of the forages or inclusion of maize grain with the maize silage on milk production by dairy cows. *Livestock Production Science* **57**: 95–111.

GIVENS, D. I. and RULQUIN, H. (2002) Utilisation of protein from silage-based diets. *Proceedings of the Eighth International Silage Conference*, September 11–13th, Auchincriuve, Scotland, UK, pp. 268–282.

GRIINARI, J. M. and BAUMAN, D. E. (1999) Biosynthesis of conjugated linoleic acid and its incorporation into meat and milk in ruminants. In: *Advances in conjugated linoleic acid research. Vol. 1* (M. P. Yurawecz, M. M. Mossoba, J. K. G. Kramer, M. W. Pariza, and G. Nelson, eds). AOCS Press, pp. 180–200.

GRIINARI, J. M., DWYER, D. A., MCGUIRE, M. A., BAUMAN, D. E., PALMQUIST, D. L. and NURMELA, K. V. V. (1998) Trans-octadecenoic acids and milk fat depression in lactating dairy cows. *Journal of Dairy Science* **81**: 1251–1261.

GRIINARI, J. M., CORL, B. A., LACY, S. H., CHOUINARD, P. Y., NURMELA, K. V. V. and BAUMAN, D. E. (2000) Conjugated linoleic acid is synthesized endogenously in lactating dairy cows by delta 9–Desaturase. *Journal of Nutrition* **130**: 2285–2291.

GRUMMER, R. R. (1991) Effect of feed on the composition of milk fat. *Journal of Dairy Science* **74**: 3244–3257.

GULATI, S.K., MCGRATH, S., WYNN, P.C. and SCOTT, T.W. (2003) Preliminary results on the relative incorporation of docosahexaenoic and eicosapentaenoic acids into cows milk from two types of rumen protected fish oil. *International Dairy Journal* **13**: 339–343.

HANIGAN, M. D., BEQUETTE, B. J., CROMPTON, L. A. and FRANCE, J. (2001) Modeling mammary amino acid metabolism. *Livestock Production Science* **70**: 63–78.

HARFOOT, C. G. and HAZELWOOD, G. P. (1988) Lipid Metabolism in the Rumen. In: *The Rumen Microbial Ecosystem*, (ed. P. N. Hobson). Elsevier Science, London, UK, pp. 285–322.

HAWKE, T. W. and TAYLOR, J. C. (1995) Influence of nutritional factors on the yield, composition and physical properties of milk fat. In: *Advanced Dairy Chemistry Volume 2: Lipids*. (P. F. Fox, ed.). Chapman and Hall, London. pp. 37–88.

HUHTANEN, P., JAAKKOLA, S. and SAARISALO, E. (1995) The effects of concentrate energy-source on the milk-production of dairy-cows given a grass silage-based diet. *Animal Science* **60**: 31–40.

HUHTANEN, P., VANHATALO, A. and VARVIKKO, T. (2002) Effects of abomasal infusions of histidine, glucose, and leucine on milk production and plasma metabolites of dairy cows fed grass silage diets. Journal of Dairy Science 85: 204–216.

HULSOF, K.F.A.M., VAN ERP-BAART, M.A., ANTTOLAINEN, M., BECKER, W., CHURCH, S.M., COUET, C., HERMANN-KUNZ, E., KESTELOOT, H., LETH, T., MARTINS, I., MOREIRAS, O., MOSCHANDREAS, J., PIZZOFERATO, L., RIMESTAD, A.H., THORGEIRSDOTTIR, H., VAN AMELSVOORT, J.M.M., ARO, A., KAFATOS, A.G., LANZMANN-PETITORY, D. and VAN POPPEL, G. (1999) Intake of fatty acids in Western Europe with emphasis on trans fatty acids: The TRANSFAIR study. European Journal of Clinical Nutrition 53: 143–157.

JENKINS, T.C. (1998) Fatty acid composition of milk from Holstein cows fed oleamide or canola oil. Journal of Dairy Science 81: 794–800.

JENKINS, T.C., BATEMAN, H.G. and BLOCK, S.M. (1996) Butylsoyamide increases unsaturation of fatty acids in plasma and milk of lactating dairy cows. Journal of Dairy Science 79: 585–590.

KALSCHEUR, K.F., TETER, B.B., PIPEROVA, L.S. and ERDMAN, R.A. (1997) Effect of fat source on duodenal flow of trans-C18:1 fatty acids and milk fat production in dairy cows. Journal of Dairy Science 80: 2115–2126.

KARATZAS, C. N. and TURNER, J. D. (1997) Toward altering milk composition by genetic manipulation: Current status and challenges. Journal of Dairy Science 80: 2225–2232.

KEADY, T.W.J. and MURPHY, J.J. (1997) The effects of treating low dry matter herbage with a bacterial inoculant or formic acid on the intake and performance of lactating dairy cattle. Animal Science 1997 64: 25–36.

KEADY, T. W. J., MAYNE, C. S., FITZPATRICK, D. A. and MARSDEN, M. (1999) The effects of energy source and level of digestible undegradable protein in concentrates on silage intake and performance of lactating dairy cows offered a range of grass silages. Animal Science 68: 763–777.

KEADY, T.W.J., MAYNE, C.S. and FITZPATRICK, D.A. (2000) Effects of supplementation of dairy cattle with fish oil on silage intake, milk yield and milk composition. Journal of Dairy Research 67: 137–153.

KIM, C. H., CHOUNG; J. J. and CHAMBERLAIN, D. G. (1999) Determination of the first-limiting amino acid for milk production in dairy cows consuming a diet of grass silage and cereal-based supplement containing feather meal. Journal of Science Food and Agriculture 79: 1703–1708.

KINSELLA, J. E. (1972) Stearyl CoA as a precursor of oleic acid and glycerolipids in mammary microsomes from lactating bovine: possible regulatory step in milk triglyceride synthesis. Lipids 7: 349–355.

LACASSE, P., KENNELLY, J.K., DELBECCHI, L. and AHNADI, C.E. (2002) Addition of protected and unprotected fish oil to diets for dairy cows. 1. Effects on the yield, composition and taste of milk. Journal of Dairy Research 69: 511–520.

LAWSON, R. E., MOSS, A. R. and GIVENS, D. I. (2001) The role of dairy products in supplying conjugated linoleic acid to man's diet: a review. Nutrition Research Reviews 14: 153–172.

LOOR, J.J., HERBEIN, J.H. and JENKINS, T.C. (2002) Nutrient digestion, biohydrogenation, and fatty acid profiles in blood plasma and milk fat from lactating Holstein cows fed canola oil or canolamide, Animal Feed Science and Technology 97: 65–82.

OFFER N.W., MARSDEN M., DIXON J., SPEAKE B.K. and THACKER, F.E. (1999) Effect of dietary fat supplements on levels of n-3 poly-unsaturated fatty acids, trans acids and conjugated linoleic acid in bovine milk. *Animal Science* **69**: 613–625.

ONETTI, S.G., SHAVER, R.D., MCGUIRE, M.A. and GRUMMER, R.R. (2001) Effect of type and level of dietary fat on rumen fermentation and performance of dairy cows fed corn silage-based diets. *Journal of Dairy Science* **84**: 2751–2759.

PALMQUIST, D. L., BEAULIEU, A. D. and BARBANO, D. M. (1993) Feed and animal factors influencing milk fat composition. *Journal of Dairy Science* **76**: 1753–1771.

PETERSON, D. G., BAUMGARD, L. H. and BAUMAN, D. E. (2002) Short communication: Milk fat response to low doses of *trans*-10, *cis*-12 conjugated linoleic acid (CLA). *Journal of Dairy Science* **85**: 1764–1766.

PHIPPS, R. H., SUTTON, J. D., BEEVER, D. E. AND. JONES, A. K. (2000) The effect of crop maturity on the nutritional value of maize silage for lactating dairy cows 3. Food intake and milk production. *Animal Science* 2000 **71**: 401–409.

PIPEROVA L.S., SAMPUGNA, L., TETER, B.B., KALSCHEUR, K.F., YURAWECZ, M.P., KU, Y., MOREHOUSE, K.M. and ERDMAN, R.A. (2002) Duodenal and milk *trans* octadecanoic acid and conjugated linoleic acid (CLA) isomers indicate that postabsorptive synthesis is the predominant source of *cis*-9–containing CLA in lactating dairy cows. *Journal of Nutrition* **132**: 1235–1241.

POLAN, C. E., CUMMINS, K. A. SNIFFEN, C. J. MUSCATO, T. V.. VICIANI, J. L CROOKER, B. A. CLARK, J. H. JOHNSON, D. G. OTTERBY, D. E. GUILLAUME, B. MILLER, . L. D VARGA, G. A. MURRAY, R. A. and PEIRCE-SANDNER S. B. (1991) Responses of dairy cows to supplemental rumen protected forms of methionine and lysine. *Journal of Dairy Science* **74**: 2997–3013.

REYNOLDS, C. K., SUTTON, J. D. and BEEVER, D. E. (1997) Effects of feeding starch to dairy cattle on nutrient availability and production. In: *Recent Advances in Animal Nutrition 1997.* (P. C. Garnsworthy and J. Wiseman, eds) Nottingham University Press, Nottingham. pp. 105–134.

REYNOLDS, C.K., CAMMELL, S.B., HUMPHRIES, D.J., BEEVER, D.E., SUTTON, J.D. and NEWBOLD, J.R. (2001) Effects of post-ruminal starch infusion on milk production and energy metabolism in dairy cows. *Journal of Dairy Science* **84**: 2250–2259.

RYMER, C., GIVENS, D.I. and WAHLE, K. W. J. (2003) Dietary strategies for increasing docosahexaenoic acid (DHA) and eicosapentaenoic acid (EPA) concentrations in bovine milk: a review *Nutrition Research Reviews* **73**: 9R–25R.

SCHWAB, C. G., BOZAK, C. K., WHITEHOUSE, N. L. and MESBAH, M. M. A. (1992) Amino acid limitation and flow to duodenum at four stages of lactation. 1. Sequence of lysine and methionine limitation. *Journal of Dairy Science* **75**: 3486–3502.

SHINGFIELD, K. J. (2000) Estimation of microbial protein supply in ruminant animals based on renal and mammary purine metabolite excretion. A review. *Journal of Animal and Feed Sciences* **9**: 169–212.

SHINGFIELD, K.J., AHVENJÄRVI, S., TOIVONEN, V., ÄRÖLÄ, A., NURMELA, K. V. V., HUHTANEN, P. and GRIINARI, J.M. (in press) Fish oil inhibits the biohydrogenation of fatty acids causing an increase in milk trans fatty acid and conjugated linoleic acid content. *Animal Science* (in press).

SPÖRNDLY, E. (1989) Effects of diet on milk composition and yield of dairy cows with special emphasis on milk protein content. *Swedish Journal of Agricultural Research* **19**: 99–106.

SUTTON, J. D. (1989) Altering milk composition by feeding. *Journal of Dairy Science* **72**: 2801–2814.

SUTTON, J.D., ASTON, K., BEEVER, D.E. and FISHER, W.J. (1994) Milk production from grass silage diets: the relative importance of the amounts of energy and crude protein in the concentrates. *Animal Production* **59**: 327–334.

THOMAS, P. C. and MARTIN, P. A. (1988) The influence of nutrient balance on milk yield and composition. In: *Nutrition and Lactation in the Dairy Cow.* (P. C. Garnsworthy, ed.). Buttersworth, London. pp. 97–118.

TOCHER, D. R., LEAVER, M. J. and HODGSON, P. A. (1998) Recent advances in biochemistry and molecular biology of fatty acyl desaturases. *Progress in Lipid Research* **37**: 73–117.

VANHATALO, A., HUHTANEN, P., TOIVONEN, V. and VARVIKKO. T. (1999) Response of dairy cows fed grass silage diets to abomasal infusions of histidine alone or in combinations with methionine and lysine. *Journal of Dairy Science* **82**: 2674– 2685.

VARVIKKO, T., VANHATALO, A., JALAVA, T. and HUHTANEN, P. (1999) Lactation and metabolic responses to graded abomasal doses of methionine and lysine in cows fed grass silage diets. *Journal of Dairy Science* **82**: 2659–2673.

VESSBY, B., UUSITUPA, M., HERMANSEN, K., RICCARDI, G., RIVALLESE, A.A., TAPSELL, L.C., NALSEN, C., BERGLUND, L., LOUHERANTA, A., RASSMUSSEN, B.M., CALVERT, G.D., MAFFETONE, A., PEDERSON, E., GUSTAFSSON, I.-B. and STORLIEN, L.H. (2001) Substituting dietary saturated for monounsaturated fat impairs insulin sensitivity in healthy men and women. *Diabetologia* **44**: 312–319.

WHITE, S.L., BERTRAND, J.A. WADE, M.R. WASHBURN, S.P. GREEN, J.T. and JENKINS, T.C. (2001) Comparison of fatty acid content of milk from Jersey and Holstein cows consuming pasture or a total mixed ration. *Journal of Dairy Science* **84**: 2295– 2301.

WILLET, W.C., STAMPFER, M.J., MANSON, J.E., COLIDITZ, G.A., SPEIZER, F.E., ROSNER, B. A., SAMPSON, L.A. and HENNEKENS, C.H. (1993) Intake of *trans* fatty acids and risk of coronary heart disease among women. *Lancet* **341**: 581–585.

WILLIAMS, C. M. (2000) Dietary fatty acids and human health. *Annales de Zootechnie* **49**: 165–180.

Index